POINT OF HONOR

POINT

OF HONOR

BY *M. R. Kadish*

RANDOM HOUSE · NEW YORK

Copyright, 1951, by M. R. Kadish

FIRST PRINTING

ALL RIGHTS RESERVED
UNDER INTERNATIONAL AND PAN-AMERICAN COPYRIGHT
CONVENTIONS. PUBLISHED IN NEW YORK BY RANDOM
HOUSE, INC., AND SIMULTANEOUSLY IN TORONTO, CANADA,
BY RANDOM HOUSE OF CANADA, LIMITED.

MANUFACTURED IN THE UNITED STATES OF AMERICA
BY KINGSPORT PRESS, INC., KINGSPORT, TENNESSEE
A.B.

To Ruth

POINT OF HONOR

I

~~~~~~

THAT night Captain Fuller had guests. Captain Crown, glass in hand, round cheeks shining in the candlelight, sang for the party a song they'd never heard before. Even the cannoneers outside could hear the high tenor voice.

> Oh, they're shifting father's grave to build a sewer,
> They're shifting it regardless of expense,
> They're shifting his remains
> To put in ten-inch drains
> To carry off the crap from residents . . .

Crown stopped the song's lilt short and grinned hugely at the company. His plump shoulders shook with glee. They were in the palm of his hand, they were.

"Come on, Cap'n, come on," pleaded Grostock. "Jesus!"

"I forget what comes next," said Crown.

"Come on, you Headquarters bastard, give," said Fuller.

Crown took another swallow and began precisely at the next note.

3

"Gor' Blimey," he sang.

> Now father in his life was not a quitter,
> And I don't suppose he'll be a quitter now,
> But up and down the streets
> He'll haunt those latrine seats
> And never let the bastards crap in peace.

The S-3 chuckled happily. His bald head gleamed in the candlelight. Everybody was happy waiting for Captain Crown, who slammed his empty glass upon the little table.

> Cracky, won't there be some constipation,
> Won't those sad-assed toffs shout and rave,
> But they'll get what they deserve
> For having the bloody nerve
> To screw around with a British workman's grave.

Crown drew the last words out lugubriously. It was almost like singing as he used to do once in the small night club downtown, the stage all his, feeling the oily perspiration on his skin once again, doing as he liked with the little bastards in the audience. "*Finito*," he said. "That's the way I remember it." He flipped the large red bottle directly to his lips and swallowed.

"Write it down," said Fuller in his heavy voice and reached for paper. Crown waved him aside. "C'mon," said Fuller, ingratiating, in the manner few men and no women ever resisted, "write it down." But Crown could resist. Crown waved him aside. "Some other time."

"What's Gor' Blimey?" Grostock wanted to know.

Crown beamed at them all and ignored little Grostock. "Got it from a couple of Limey officers," Crown said. "Got the bottle the same time. Took the bastards," he said savagely. Oh, he wasn't drunk. It took a lot more than

4

this piss to make momma's little boy Dickie drunk. But he felt fine, fine. The stuff made him himself again.

"Hey, what's Gor' Blimey?"

Grostock was bouncing up and down with excitement. "Why, you ignorant, dumb bastard!" said Crown, grinning widely so that his even white teeth gleamed at Grostock.

"Huh?" said Grostock, as though Crown had punched him in the stomach. "Huh?" Then he became all serious. "You shouldn' oughta say that," protested Grostock. "You shouldn' oughta say that."

"You're an ignorant, dumb bastard," said Crown.

Fuller and the S-3 were laughing. Crown joined them. Everyone was laughing at Grostock.

"Don't let him get away with that," said Fuller to Grostock. He put an arm around Grostock's shoulders and laughed, and with the other hand poured himself another drink. It was Dickie Crown's party, all right, all right.

"I am not a ignorant, dumb bastard," said Grostock. A worried frown was spread upon his face. "I admit I'm ignorant. But I ain't dumb, am I, Cap'n Fuller? I'm a damn good Exec, ain't I?"

Everybody laughed louder. It was preposterously funny. Captain Crown led the laughter.

"Sure you know the Exec business," said Fuller seriously. "Never mind that Headquarters knucklehead. Have another drink."

"Screw you, Fuller," said Crown, glancing quickly and savagely with his soft, brown eyes from one to the other. He looked at his bottle. It was only half empty. "Sure," he said, "have another drink of the stuff. You can't be choosy, boys, you can't be choosy. Only the 4-Fs can be choosy."

"If I take another drink o' that piss you picked up, I am

5

a ignorant, dumb bastard," Grostock had grumbled. He brightened when everybody laughed. Then he laughed too; then he took a long gulp.

Captain Crown was equal to, better than, anyone. Captain Crown was kingly, a dispenser of favors and of frowns. "You're drinkin' it, bub. You're drinkin' my piss." He got up on his feet. Joyously, he sloughed responsibility off his shoulders. "Hey," he said. "Shut up. I got a toast." He kept them waiting while with care and precision, so that not a drop spilled, he refilled their glasses.

"I got a toast," he said, raising his tumbler. "To everything," he said. "Screw it. Screw the shipyard workers at a hundred a week, and all that tail back home going to bed with the 4-Fs. Screw the 4-Fs too. Crap on the Wops, the Frogs and the Dutchmen, not to mention the Limeys. Crap on the crap we eat. Crap on the bastards who got us here. Crap on everything!"

Grostock laughed admiringly. Crown was grinning from ear to ear. Crown was the life of the party.

About this time the word passed around. The darkness never stopped the word. It was passed to the men who listened with envious insight to the noise given off by the black shadow of the C.P. tent. The word went that there was a tent set up. That for two candy bars, or perhaps fifty lire, a man could do it. The word said it was cheap at twice the price. Only the officers inside never heard the word.

The sergeant said, "Look, we'll make an arrangement. Half of those who want to go, go first and then relieve the other half."

The corporal with the Kraut accent thought it was a good system.

Dan MacCarthy was bewildered. "Pady," he protested, "you going too?" Someone hee-hawed.

Before Dan's eyes they were choosing up sides. They were milling around within the howitzer split trails and deciding who would go first.

"Look, Dan," Pady Padrone whispered urgently. "You damn well better get in on this. At least put on an act. If you don't want to do anything, nobody has to know."

Dan fingered his horn-rim spectacles; behind their lenses blinked his child-round eyes. "Dan says count him in," Dan heard Pady say. He looked vaguely at his friend.

But it was all true and all real, every bit of craziness. He made as if to square his plump, round shoulders. For some reason he could not fathom, it was always the incredible which you had no choice but to believe. Dimly, he remembered his priest, and stared hard at the shadows of the cannoneers.

"C'mon," said Pady. Pady and he were on the same shift. They were walking. Pady caught his foot in something and cursed without humor. Pady wasn't Pady. Even his voice sounded heavier, and in some way blurred. Pady's cockeyed grace and lightness were all gone. Dan was perfectly willing to learn from experience, but every man in the shabby night looked like a shabby ghost. Suddenly Dan was horrified.

"Pady," he said, "you can't get on line." The old earnestness and desperation rose in his gorge. "My God, Pady!" He didn't know what to say. "It's cruel. It's beastly." But his voice sounded artificial in his own ears. He pressed on

7

harder. "It's cruel. I mean it, honest, I mean it. It's against human nature," he found himself insisting. "Men and women weren't made to treat one another like that."

Pady laughed and walked faster. Dan chased after him on his short legs.

"There has to be respect," pleaded Dan.

"Sure," said Pady, Pady with the long, delicate fingers and elfin face. "Respect for my balls."

There was a small line forming, and the line grew toward the low silhouette of the pup tent and a man entered the tent. Dan saw Pady's figure get on the line. He knew every member of that line. He knew them by the way they moved, by the back of their necks and the width of their shoulders. They jostled one another.

But he would jostle no one for this. True, he could never explain so that it didn't sound ridiculous. Nevertheless, shoulder and flank, he would never press against other men for this. There should be love. How hard and fast his heart pumped! There should be tenderness.

But he would watch. He had to know in which direction the world turned while his heart pounded and he felt that old, terrible longing for a love he had never known. Dan moved closer to the line. But it must be sacred, not hateful or sinful.

"Come on, Dan, get in front o' me," Tomlinson said and laughed like hell.

Dan's voice creaked when he said, "I'll take my own place." For, after all, Pady's advice was worth taking, Dan told himself with enormous bitterness. Thank God, Tomlinson ignored him now. In fact none of the guys paid any attention to him. A few of them, he saw, were pushing.

The only talk happened when those being pushed told those who pushed to cut it out.

For a moment Dan couldn't recall what he was sticking around for. A flare of red light and an enormous crash blasted over the field. The guns had fired. So what?

Weren't those Holloway's high shoulders? "Our guns just fired," said Dan.

Holloway was brusque and angry. "Get on back to the end of the line," he ordered.

Holloway thought he wanted to inch in. Why should Holloway think that of him? Dan demanded it of himself in a grievous anger. Was he like that? Was he the man to stand on a line with ten other men with ten more coming after? Dan had never been in a tent that way before. He'd never laid a woman before.

All the restlessness and vagueness of Dan's desires grew together suddenly, focused, burned. The rebellion in him quickened. It rose up in one urgent overflow. That once before he died, that once before he became like the Survey men who had died the other day, that once, only once, he might seize a woman's buttocks and feel her yield! How little that was, how every bastard had it, and not he! How this sweetness he'd never had stabbed him now! Dan clenched his fists, and in the shielding darkness one tear touched his cheek.

But maybe she was young, maybe she was pretty, maybe she'd been sold to someone who had taken her out to make a good profit. Why did he have to feel pity, why did he have to have knowledge? The pity drove a hot wind into Dan's head.

Light flickered on the horizon and a rolling noise followed. Someone was catching it. A vague balloon drifted over the line of men. He used to play with balloons like that once. When it descended, someone struck it up again. It was a game. A few of the fellows were laughing. He turned his head to look for the laughers.

Balloon, hell. Someone had blown up a rubber. Dan laughed.

He'd known all along that eventually he would stand at the end of the line, moving slowly to an end, watching others fall in behind. His round childish face wrinkled in torment. He had leaped toward justice praying it might be there solid on the other side when he landed, and this was where he had come down. His eyes narrowed, his eyelids trembled. It was as though there were some sudden glare in the dark and he were looking into it. Now, submerged, sunken in this waste, this murkiness, Dan felt his spirit shrink and turn upon itself to escape its own scrutiny, become two tight little balls burning behind the pupils of his eyes.

Comparatively few were ahead of him by this time. They moved fast. On her and off, he remarked to himself, like rabbits. Did he want that? He made a coarse sound in his mind. That and more, and he rubbed the admission into himself. Now damn you, you men ahead, move, let's get going. Urgently, he pressed against the man in front.

"Don't get yer balls in an uproar." The man had fury in his voice.

Dan giggled. He noticed that two men in particular seemed to be in charge. They were questioning the people on line, scurrying busily about. Cronin and Jablowsky, the battery's self-anointed funny men. Dan was faintly surprised.

Cronin approached him. "Ya got a rubber? Ya gotta be sure and have a rubber."

Dan reached into a pocket of his combat jacket. There was nothing there. Oh, Christ!

Cronin laughed and handed him the little brown envelope. "Use this and never say I never gave ya nothing."

He was nearly there now. Only a few men were ahead. What was that scuffling noise in the tent? Fascinated, he listened for it again. A high-pitched voice said, "*Ancora!*" Dan's mind emptied and drained of everything but what was in that tent. His mouth was open. His flesh crawled. Someone inside said, "Oh." Dan's tight brain pushed and shoved its way into the tent.

Jablowsky came, his long grin shadowed by the night. "Got yer candy bars?" he demanded. "She likes candy bars. Two of 'em."

Dan didn't hear.

"I said 've ya got candy bars. What the hell's a'matter with ya?" Then he began to chuckle.

Dan spoke up with an effort. "Haven't any." He was listening.

Jablowsky laughed maliciously. "No candy bars, no tail."

The words were fearful. He must have showed it. Jablowsky laughed even louder.

"Okay," said Jablowsky at last. "Fifty lire if you got no candy."

Dan's panic quieted. He fumbled with some paper currency, shoved it at Jablowsky. "Le' me alone," he mumbled. It was his turn next. His. What, was Jablowsky still there? He turned ferociously upon him.

"Take it easy," said Jablowsky in a fat, stroking voice. "Take it easy."

11

Dan's head trembled, his thin neck felt weak. He heard Jablowsky tell him in his ear with mock secrecy that it was his turn now. His. End of the line, step off, end of the line.

"What'n hell ya waitin' for?" asked Jablowsky.

Dan stepped off. Hands and knees on the ground, pawing at the dangling tent flap, his breath heavy, coming in spasms, his turning brain asked him who this Dan was on all fours, this tent crawler. He found himself carrying himself in, in, all his body in. The glare was in his eyes now, hotter, fiercer than ever. Outside, the tent flap dropped down again when Dan reached out his arms.

The beam of a flashlight struck into his eyes. He saw the round ball of light turn slowly upward and illuminate the face of its owner.

A whisper said, "Take it easy, boy, take it easy."

"Chase," he whispered thickly. "What the hell are you doing here? Where's the girl?"

Chase's grin became obscene. His eyes creased with appreciation, glittered with it. Then he shut off his light. In the blank darkness he said, "Keep yer mouth shut, Dan."

The soft sibilance came to Dan again. "There just ain't no girl. Me an' Cronin an' Jablowsky made it all up." Dan scuffled in the blankets. "Good, ain't it?" Chase asked, laughing gently.

Dan's fever shook him. He couldn't help his soft groan.

"Good," urged Chase. "Do it again. Ya got the idea."

He heard a falsetto voice plead "*Ancora*," and then a low, cheerful, deadly chuckle. Hoax. The whole damn thing was a hoax. Dan couldn't accept it, he wouldn't.

"You shouldn't have done it," Dan said.

The quiet laugh jeered him.

Then it seemed to Dan that the shame in his heart

brimmed over, gushed over himself, the tent, the world, and all the people in it, in one great and foul wave, fouling everything. All this, all of it, led to an empty tent, to an empty sin. It was almost funny.

Dan said, "I won't give the game away." He could not possibly give away that there was only defeat at the end of the line and shame, that all the fearful waiting would find the tent empty. Dan thought that he would like to cry, but he was too tired. Get out. Only leave. He started to move off the way he'd come.

"Not that way, ya dope. Go out the other way."

He crawled over Chase and entered into the lean night. Red flicker snapped again over the mountains. Dan stood erect upon his feet and watched the next man enter. Several men had jostled him out of their way when he felt a hand upon his shoulder. "Well, Dan, did you get screwed?" asked the owner of the hand.

Dan turned around to face Padrone. The way Padrone had said it, there was no bitterness anywhere around the question. There was only a kind of amusement, and Dan, knowing that Padrone had also been taken in, for one quick moment hated him profoundly. Then Dan's resentment fell back into his weariness.

"Yeah, Pady, I got screwed, all right."

Right and left, right and left.

DAN and Pady, restless, wishing they could sleep, were seated on one of the trails of Number One gun engaged in staring at the night when they heard men coming. With nothing in particular in mind they looked in the direction from which the sudden noises came.

13

"Where's the whore?" they heard.

Voices milled around them. One made a flat statement. "We been gettin' a runaround."

"Whore?" asked Padrone grinning.

"You heard us."

Dan said, "There isn't any." The figures in front of him seemed to tighten. "Don't give us none of that crap." They surrounded Dan and Pady. Their rising voices were sharp, angry and wrong, dead wrong.

"It's true," said Dan. These sharp voices were cutting away that fragment which was left of the solid earth. "There really isn't any."

"I suppose the whole damn battery got on line for the fun of it."

"No kiddin'," confirmed the clear high tones of Padrone. "It's just a practical joke."

"A joke. Ha ha."

"If ya know what's good fer ya, cut the clowning. We got a gutful of it."

"Honest, a few guys had nothing to do tonight so they rigged up a tent and made believe there was a whore inside. We all got stuck. Truth," said Pady.

"Look," said another of the accosters quietly, "the other guys at least tol' us about it, even if their directions were fouled up. We got as much right to a whore as you an' we're gonna get what's comin' to us if we have to beat it outa ya."

"Oh, hell," burst out Padrone, "they told you jerks that because they wanted you stuck too. Cool off. Look, there's Holloway. Ask him."

Holloway was their sergeant. His awkward figure strode toward them with its long arms dangling and its head thrust forward on a skinny neck, a man of length—length of jaw, length of bone, large-headed, unmistakable even in the darkness. He walked into the clump of men.

"Tell those fellows, Sergeant," said Dan. "Tell 'em there's no whore." For Holloway was solid and would bear witness. It was Holloway who had organized them in shifts for the sake of the tent.

Holloway stood there, his big hands bulging in his pockets.

"Tell 'em, Sergeant," said Dan.

Quietly, Holloway looked at Dan and then at the others. "Dan's right, boys," his dry voice said, "no soap. No whore," and chuckled.

"You in on the runaround too, Holloway?" Dan recognized the demanding voice of Number Four's section chief.

"Where the hell are ya, Jones?" said Holloway.

"Right here," said Jones, and a heavy figure pushed a way forward.

"Yep," said Holloway, "guess I am. Only there's not a damn thing to be in on. Not a damn thing because Dan and Pady went and told you the truth." His dry voice suddenly rose, turned brittle, penetrating. "You're a bunch of damn fools. Go on back."

Dan saw the Number Four men tense forward, but there was nothing they could do about it.

"Okay," said their section chief. "Okay. Maybe we're wrong and maybe we're not. I think maybe you and your boys are just screwin' us. We'll find out and when we do maybe we'll know what to do."

One by one the men of the fourth gun section turned and left.

"You know," said Holloway afterwards, "they never

will believe there was no damn whore in the tent. The sad bastards," he added, admiringly.

They're better off, it occurred to Dan.

It took the short, slight man six hours of the intensest effort to make the return trip down from the Observation Post. They were hours which even in this month of October made the creeping sweat smart his temple and smart underneath the sparse colorless beard, which made the pale blue eyes go vague and the straight lips quiver. When finally in the darkness the man made out the shape of the Command Post tent his muscles were shiveringly taut and loose by turns. Lieutenant David Evans had been delighted when they relieved him from his mountainside. He had shuddered with pleasure at the thought of a shave and a sponge bath in the C.P. where he stayed with Captain Fuller. Now, in the late evening, all he wanted was light and a place to sit down. He heard:

> They'll get what they deserve,
> For having the bloody nerve . . .

What in blazes? Evans worked his way through the blackout curtains. Hogarth the S-3, Fuller, Crown and Grostock. Evans blinked at the bottle on the table between his cot and Fuller's.

> To screw around with a British workman's grave.

Evans asked himself what he was doing here. The candles winked at him.

"Well, for Chris' sake, look who's here!" "Hey, come on in, come on in." "Have a drink." Evans grinned and threw off his steel hat. These, then, were the men who had that other night let him sit around unawares on a mountainside with a German patrol.

The other night, screened by a network of branches and a few surviving leaves, he had seen Mt. Porcchia and Mt. Trocchio break with their backs the white tumbling mists which filled the valley and curled around their wide bases, and he had examined the white mist billows for the path of Route Six, for the minute and meaningful curves in the land, the broken shapes of San Vittore, of San Pietro, for all the town wreckage of war. Then the field telephone had rung.

"Switchboard, sir. Shouldn't be calling you about something I overheard, but nobody got in touch with you, they mus've forgotten, and I thought you'd want to know about it. A Kraut patrol came up the road nearby us. Our fellows and some infantry broke 'em up. We think they're wandering around in the woods now."

"What time was this?" Now it was midnight.

"About eight."

Eventually the assistant S-3 had called and told Evans. They had forgotten him for four hours; they had recalled his life as an afterthought. Evans took their drink and swallowed it.

> Sambo was a lazy old coon
> He never worked in the afternoon . . .

Crown's musical voice led the festivities. Except perhaps for Hogarth, they were all half drunk. Evans was intensely weary. The candle six inches in front of his nose almost hypnotized him.

> Too goddamned lazy was he . . .

17

Fuller had his hand on Evans' shoulder now. If he meant nothing to these people, they meant nothing to him. Recriminations weren't worth the bother. But why didn't they go home? The drink sifted the remaining strength from Evans' muscles. He felt giddy and loose-tongued and disgusted and all too capable of talking.

"How you feelin', Dave old boy?" Fuller was asking him.

"Fine." Surely they weren't going to apologize for the O.P. business. Evans winced.

Fuller's handsome face was grave and masculine. His hand weighed a ton on Evans' aching shoulder. His forehead crinkled with man-to-man earnestness.

"I've got bad news for you, Dave."

Evans sighed with relief. At least he would be spared soul baring with a bunch of drunks. But bad news? Fuller's pause reeked drunken drama. Evans felt as though he were on a movie screen.

"Your Survey crew got it, Dave. That's why we called you down."

They were all staring at him. The small tent seemed to swell with the heat of the gasoline stove. Perspiration, sentiment, gasoline stink and liquor made Evans' stomach turn.

Evans reached for a cigarette. "Schlummer, too?" He inhaled deeply. This was, of course, serious. It was unfortunate he was so tired.

"Schlummer and every man jack except Cajusik, who was with you, old boy." The memory of these men had been preserved for two days, then, in alcohol. "Don't take it too hard, Dave old man," Fuller told him.

"We'll get ya another Survey section," said Grostock,

who paused, furrowed his brow as though wrestling with a problem of enormous difficulty, and added, "A stinkin' mine got 'em all. A stinkin' mine!"

"They were good men," said Fuller.

"They were all pushin' together a lousy jeep," said Grostock.

Crown's fat face was leaning down over Evans. "You got to expect that kind of thing," he said. "Ain' it?" he grinned. Crown's beautiful fat face gloated over living. When he turned away from it, there was Fuller, handsome, reeking manly sympathy.

"How 'bout a drink?" said Evans, striking out for time. For they were crowding around him now once again, all except Major Hogarth, the S-3. The Major sat back with a faint smile and a drink. But Evans knew by now that the faint smile of this good brain meant nothing but disuse of faculties, waiting, the hum of the engine.

"T.s." Crown was saying. "Plain t.s. Like I say, we got to expect this kind of thing. . . ."

Evans swallowed his drink. The S-3, then, was simply intelligent. Did he himself have the will, the mind, to drive off, for example, Crown? Could he assume the Colonel's force, the domination that was not entirely a matter of rank, which pressed the buttons in the S-3's life, which drove Crown wild, which, with its self-evident sanity—he must admit it—compelled him also?

Evans turned to Crown. "Tell me," he said, "why I should expect the Survey crew to get blown to hell, why I should expect things like it, what right you have to say t.s.?" The hate in Evans' own voice surprised him.

Crown stopped in the middle of the swallow.

"Yeah," said Grostock with sudden vehemence, "why?"

while Andy Fuller laughed and said, "Give 'em hell, Davie!" Nobody heard the hate in Evans' voice, then. Nobody except Crown, whose red lips twisted.

"But ask one thing at a time," said Major Hogarth.

Thank you, S-3. Evans was dizzy but cool and he recognized good advice when he heard it. Underneath his coolness he would not care to venture. "Tell me," he said to Crown, "why I should expect the Survey crew to get knocked off?" That was it. Simple. Just for Crown. And maybe for himself, too, because Evans hated the cry "t.s." so much that the very thought of it might drag him to the heat underneath his coolness.

Crown's red lips writhed in disdain and Evans saw him fling a quick look at the others to see how he ought to take Evans, but the others were waiting for an answer, too. He fixed on Evans and began to laugh at him. "I've heard some crap-headed questions before," he jeered, made a motion to the rest of the company to show that this was the most crap-headed question of them all. Evans bore his stare.

"S'not crap," said Grostock. "Nobody oughta hafta die."

Evans was dizzy and cool and fantastically well controlled. "You talk as though you thought you were in the goddamned infantry, Captain," he said, throwing a bone to the hound of military courtesy, he was so fantastically well controlled. "You talk as though you thought you were a screwin' hero, Captain," he said, rubbing it in. He made his voice hard to punch Crown in his fat guts. "What in hell do you mean we've got to expect it? A stupid accident killed the men. Probably there'll be more empty accidents like that. But you and everyone here damn well expects to keep living. Admit those guys were the losers. Admit it—and that it was tough, by God, damn tough."

The fat guts started toward him, the liquid obscenity rolling from its lips fascinating Evans.

"Easy," said the S-3 to Crown. "He's right."

Veritas vincit omnia, with a little help from Fire Direction Center. Happily, Evans grinned at Crown stalled by popular opinion.

"Hey," Grostock was chortling, Evans' buddy of Battery B, "you sure shut ol' Cap'n Crown up. Hey, Cap'n, you ain't gonna be mad, huh?" Fuller was enjoying it too—Dandy Andy Fuller, loyal and true, Evans' own battery commander, slapping him on the back. Where was all the sorrow of a minute ago? Suddenly, Evans writhed in scorn and fatigue.

"We're not in the infantry," he could hear the S-3 considering, "but we're in the war, you know. Course the odds aren't as great as those against the infantryman. But haven't you ever thought, Evans, of the chances which really are against you? Of the war you're in?"

This push-button major, this walking dispersion curve . . . Evans had almost forgotten about him. He would let daylight into him too, into all of them. In this way perhaps he would get rid of them. The tiredness squeezed.

"I'll tell you something, Major," he said, for the sake of the aching tiredness. "We didn't find the war in the southern part of Italy. Not the war that gripes us worst. In the southern part of Italy we just picked up accessories. Howitzers, Observation Posts, casualties and high persons in authority. Just like a man picks up the syph, Major. The sores come after a time. But it's the sickness in us that's the terrible thing, the sickness we don't understand . . ."

"I sometimes think of the chances against me," said the calculating major. "You're off the ball."

"Crazy as a bedbug," grinned Crown, coming into victory again.

Evans shrugged. Crown was probably right. But Evans was only trying in his tiredness to reach for the truth. The only door that slammed tight shut and protected the really tired man was the truth. But how did he get on the right side of such a door? Evans was fantastically well controlled and infinitely tired and he mustered all his strength to reach for the truth.

Evans said it flatly. "As for the Survey crew, I knew them only casually. I've known a lot of men in the Army that way, including my best friends. So far as I'm concerned they've been transferred to another unit."

And that did it. That slammed the door upon them all. Fuller removed the heavy weight of his arm from Evans' shoulders. Poor Grostock, stuck upon surprise, no longer approved the prowess of his fellow B Battery officer. Sarcasm widened the S-3's faint smile. It was true that Crown beamed triumphantly; but Crown, too, was on the other side of the door now. Why, then, didn't they leave and let him sleep?

Instead Crown teetered upon his heels there in front of Evans on the other side of the door. "But, Lieutenant," he was saying softly, "you should definitely know your men more than casually. Because, you know, Lieutenant, you're responsible for your men," Crown was saying from the softness of his smile.

So Evans hadn't blocked them off after all. How could he do it, and how could he hold off the Colonel's myth sprung from the mouth of Crown? His weariness, unhindered, would fight them for him. Evans stared at Crown.

"I have no responsibility," said Evans, listening to himself. "I have no power to choose, and I wash my hands. I do what is forced from me. What business have I with responsibility?"

He could hear Fuller gritting in his ear, "You knucklehead!"

But now Evans felt free, light-headed but wonderfully free. He had really touched them. He could tell off the whole crew of them because his mind was attentive to the way things were. With but one more effort of his mind, he could shake them off.

"We," he told them, "make our stinking little choices scared witless. In ignorance. They run out of our hands. We pretend to know what to expect of them but who are we kidding? You leaders," he told them, feeling the revulsion in his stomach, "you responsible men," with the anger bursting in his chest, "you men of decision," he climaxed it, driving it home—"screw you, oh, screw every one of you, you fearful bastards, you liars, and for God's sake get out of here and let me get some sleep."

Someone hit him hard on the jaw.

MAJOR HOGARTH, the S-3, waited for the pupils of his eyes to expand and catch what light the moon afforded, so that he could return to Fire Direction and relieve the assistant S-3. But he did not expect anything much would be doing tonight.

He chuckled. Back in the tent Evans was flat on his back. Fuller and Crown were trying to lug him onto his cot. Crown was jeering and wouldn't leave. Fuller and Grostock

23

were cursing Crown and Evans alternately. It was a shame to go. But the S-3 could see enough now. He braced himself and stepped into the dark, war-twisted field and the tortuous three hundred yards back to Fire Direction Center.

Tomorrow the battalion displaced forward.

2

THE man with the silver leaves upon his shoulders stood five foot seven in his stocking feet and his shoulders seemed almost as broad.

Roughly, Lt. Colonel Colouris called Fuller. "That's your area over there. You're sure you can get into it?" He was pushing fifty hard and wore glasses.

"Yes, sir," said Captain Fuller, knowing very well his men were good and that nothing could go wrong with Andy Fuller. But Colouris considered him and his neatly fitting trench coat with a skepticism none of his officers could fully appease.

"Yes, sir," said Fuller again, "I'm sure we can do it."

Colouris surveyed again the muddy, open area assigned to him for his battalion of howitzers and probed for the tenth time the arrangements he'd made for displacement forward: That the guns would move in from Route Six beginning at dusk. That they would move into their predetermined positions at irregular intervals one by one and be ready to fire before daybreak. That his battery commanders knew all that.

"All right," said Colouris, "we'll try it now."

Fuller ordered a corporal to run down beyond the bend in the road and fetch the prime mover. The small group of officers sensed the rain pat their steel helmets as they waited.

The trouble was mud and mines. Colouris wanted to force his sight through the covering topsoil, to find a bottom to the field which would support fifteen-ton howitzers, to search out the Teller mines which, despite all the exertions of the engineers, must still underlie the area into which he must move three firing batteries. But muddy and desolate, holed and rutted, flat under a wet sky, the field admitted nothing. Suspiciously, Colouris raised his head to examine Mt. Rotondo. What was beyond it? Or beyond Longo over there?

"I hope," said Captain Crown with solemn earnestness, "Headquarters area is free of the damned things."

Colouris glanced at Crown's girlish face and thick bull neck. Headquarters area was minor. The important thing was the firing battery, since you could fight a war without a Headquarters Battery, if necessary, but you needed guns, eight-inch howitzers, precisely laid and safe. These were the investments he must safeguard in this, the second expedition of his life against the German.

"Goddamn it, where's your Mack?" Colouris said to Fuller. Colouris' problem was to make the field talk.

Baker Battery's prime mover sloshed heavily up Route Six. Colouris could hear it roar. The double wheels churned the mud and crushed the hard rock underneath. This was the machine that pulled his howitzers and carried their ammunition. Colonel Colouris regarded it moodily as it approached. The machine had another use now.

The driver in his cab looked down at the road ten feet below and smiled tightly at Captain Fuller stepping out into the road to wave him down. He slowed the Mack so that it came to a halt a few feet beyond the Captain and spattered him.

Fuller ignored the mud upon his trousers. "Tomlinson," he called up, "I've got a job for you. You don't have to do it if you don't want to. I want you to drive in there between the white tapes and I want you to keep on going until they lead you out to the road again. That's all. Do you understand?"

In his high place, Tomlinson looked down upon his captain, kept his thin features quiet, and slowly nodded his head.

"The lanes between the tapes should be safe. They've been swept. But maybe not. We figure a truck this big will set off mines set for the heavy pieces. We want to make sure it's safe for the guns, get it?"

"Yeah."

"Remember, you don't have to do it. I can get someone else."

"Ah'll be safe in this baby."

Fuller stepped back and rejoined his colonel and with him watched the vehicle maneuver, heard its gears grind as the driver double clutched, saw the mass of it lurch heavily forward. Fuller braced his shoulders with pride. The prime mover's steel heart roared at the sky. Its front wheels dipped into the rut at the field's edge.

Tomlinson sat high above them all in the driver's seat. His right foot was steady against the accelerator, his left foot delicately touched the clutch pedal. His hands, hard and careful on the steering wheel, felt the contours of the land and the massive rear wheels breaking through them. Tomlinson could feel all the softness and all the slipping. He was going in, all the way into a Wop field so early Monday morning; and going in in low gear. His lips methodically formed the outlines of all the obscene words he knew. Slowly he nosed the prime mover forward.

"Good man, Tomlinson," said Captain Fuller in his deep voice to his colonel. Tomlinson was *his* man. When the Colonel had stated his plan for testing the field, Fuller had plucked Tomlinson directly from the firing battery.

Macks were easier to replace than howitzers, considered the Colonel, and you could get along if you lost one, but they were valuable pieces of equipment, integral to the economy of the battalion. The close-shaven blue skin on the Colonel's jaw tightened. The drizzle obscured the steel-rimmed regulation glasses he favored, and he pulled them from his face. The economy of the battalion was his business; the prime mover treading down the mud flat and roaring as it moved bore within its straining guts a portion of his mind.

"Glad to, Captain," Tomlinson had told Fuller. "Ah'm getting tired of screwin' around."

A soft spot. The wheels churned and Tomlinson could sense the rear of his vehicle drift leftwards toward the white line of tape which marked the limit of safety. Now his foot barely touched the accelerator. He leaned out of the cab and stared at the wheel and the tape. Just enough pressure and no more. He laughed softly. Nevertheless the wheel slid in its slow revolving closer to the tape.

Colouris thought there was no use to shout and upset the man. But watch it, boy, watch it.

Tomlinson dared not stop because then he might not be able to get up enough traction to start again. Besides, he never stopped. He fought back. His eyes distended and stared feral. Now the great tire touched the tape.

"Christ," muttered Crown. It touched and passed beyond the tape.

"Get it out of there, Tomlinson," bellowed Fuller.

Tomlinson grinned and pressed one short jab upon the accelerator. The wheel tore a section of the tape, but the Mack lunged forward and into the mine-cleared path again. One short jab. Tomlinson laughed. He could see the fat little Captain Crown take off his helmet and wipe his forehead. Tomlinson giggled and leaned forward over his old whore of a Mack and nursed her forward.

The Mack was picking up a little speed, Colouris noted. The rear wheels threw large gobs of mud high and back. The Mack was beyond the spot where Number Three howitzer would be placed, and it looked as though the Mack might well make it. Colouris glanced quickly and pridefully at his officers. The Mack was nosing by Number Four's position now.

Colouris drew back the corners of his wide mouth in a grin. Focusing on the Mack, he'd almost taken himself in. Actually there was no significant gamble here at all and, happily, no heroics whatever, not the shred of a heroic. For Colonel Colouris couldn't lose. Either the Mack got through, as seemed likely, and proved that Baker Battery's howitzers were probably safe, or it did not—whereupon, coolly and correctly, Colouris would point out the broken

Mack to the engineer commander and exact more work upon the field, further assurance for his guns, precaution after precaution in the face of the future.

The Mack swung around in the wide circle the tape prescribed. The driver was heading her into the home stretch now. Colouris had just begun to turn away when he saw the rear end of the Mack lift up violently half a foot and a cloud of muck and smoke rise higher than the truck and then the truck settle oddly squat in the mud.

"Christ!" said Fuller.

Very good, the Colonel said to himself. Now he would capitalize on his losses. He only hoped that the boy in the driver's seat was all right. Apparently. Very wearily, the driver was climbing from his perch. "Damn shame, Colonel," said Fuller when Colouris had finished his inspection of the damage. Fuller was a valuable officer, but a bit obtuse.

"Fuller," he said, "get that truck pulled out of your area and over to Ordnance immediately."

Barring shells or possible mortars, then, the howitzers should enter unscathed. In the free, competitive market of the war, upon his own initiative and in an unorthodox fashion, he had enforced the best possible deal for his battalion. Colouris' grin was very broad and happy.

To the battery commanders clustered around him he said, "We pull out tonight as planned," and led his party to the waiting jeeps.

THE four eight-inch howitzers of Battery B sat at last each behind its Mack prime mover under the fragmentary trees, and blotched the side road which led to Route Six and beyond. Holloway asked himself where in hell the tractor was. Except for the tractor they were ready to move. He glanced at his wrist watch. 1630 hours it told him in Army language. That meant half past four in the afternoon. They were scheduled to get out of here in an hour. Where the hell was the tractor?

"Sergeant Holloway!" Evans calling. Holloway had almost forgotten the skinny little officer with the pale eyes and adenoids. Now what?

"Here, sir."

Evans' helmet looked too big for him. His pistol belt sagged. "Sergeant, have you seen the cat?"

"I was about to ask you, Lieutenant. We're bound to need it when we pull in."

"You stay here with the guns."

Holloway watched Evans' trench-coated figure proceed down the road with short, rapid steps, its head stuck oddly forward. If the officer wanted to chase after the tractor, that was fine with Holloway. That left Holloway on his own again. Wryly he surveyed his crew scattered over the back of the Mack, perched on the closed trails of the howitzers, like bugs on a junk heap. Half of them had their steel helmets off.

"Truth is truth." Holloway figured it must be Grossberg talking. "Useta knock 'em down like flies on the road. Three or four Ayrabs in their long sheets jus' stood there lookin' at 'im, not makin' a move even to see maybe they could do somethin'."

Oran and Africa. Holloway recalled it very clearly, despite the months between.

"Dumb sonsuvbitches. Ain't they the dumb sonsuvbitches?" Borman. Holloway smiled. He knew them all.

31

"No!" Round-faced, bespectacled Dan MacCarthy, waving his hands over an eight-inch shell. "Just uneducated. Nobody ever gave them a chance. The French exploited 'em. We took pot shots at 'em when they got too close. Nobody's got the right to say a word against 'em."

"Ahhh."

In the distance Holloway could hear the dumb pounding of the guns, the whistle of distant shells which as yet had never been more than a whistle at someone else's station. This remembering Africa could go on and on. Dan would go on trying to convince everyone of God knows what because he was such an innocent damn fool kid. The rain would go on raining. Evans would go on looking for the tractor. Route Six would continue sitting up there on the ledge while he waited on and on. What in Christ for? Holloway was amused.

Padrone, long-nosed, elfin, roused him. "Hey, Holloway, how 'bout you? You for or against the Ayrabs?" Padrone was another damn fool kid.

"I'm not for 'em and I'm not against 'em," said Holloway, grinning at the whole crew of them perched on the piles of ammunition, on the gun, on the gun trails. "They're none of my business."

It was funny the way Dan exploded. Holloway, of course, had expected it. "That's where you're wrong, Sergeant. We're sitting on this damn gun because of the way the Ayrabs live and people treat 'em. Things like that. That's the real reason you're here, and it *is* your business."

"Nuts, Dan," said Holloway quietly. Dan talked like a book. "That's only the reason you'd like to have us here for. Mostly we got into the Army because Roosevelt and his boys worked it out that way. Not that I've got anything against the sonuvabitch for it—probably he got screwed into it too." Holloway's voice turned dry. "You know, Dan, some day maybe you're going to finish Sunday school and find out there never has to be a real reason for anything at all."

"Fr'instance," said Padrone with mock woe, "take the Army. Did you ever find a sensible reason for anything as long as you've been in it? Anybody. I dare ya!"

A mist of injustices seemed to rise up and cloud Borman's eyes. "You ain't kiddin'," he affirmed with infinite emphasis. "You sure as hell ain't kiddin'."

Then Dan MacCarthy drew himself up to his five and a half feet of height. "But," said Dan MacCarthy . . .

THEY saw this shell explode. In the midst of their talk they heard the arched cry of the shell and then one hundred yards away in the field they had just left they saw the billowing mud rise up and heard the flat caromph. It was their first. They looked at one another.

There they were, stuck up fifteen feet in the air on the back of a Mack. "Jesus," yelled Borman. And they moved. They slung themselves over the sides of the truck. They ran.

"Make for the goddamn Exec house!" That was Holloway yelling. Twenty yards away was the thick-walled white house Grostock, the Exec, had occupied. They made for it. They let their carbines bang against their ribs. They damned their carbines. They made for the Exec house. And now the long scream came at them again and they were running their asses off, falling in the mud, getting up and falling, and then, oh my God, they were in the white walls

33

of the Exec house, the blast of the explosion smash in their ears!

Holloway felt his pulse banging in his temple. Who of his section had made the Exec house? Padrone, Ehrlich, Borman, MacCarthy . . . Roll call. Ca-romph! Not many. He mastered himself and went to the window which faced the road. Some of his men were under the truck, some of them in the mud beside the road. The other gun sections took the same kind of cover. There was nothing he could do for them.

He saw the others on the floor huddled in the corners of the room. He asked, "Everybody okay?" Holloway repeated his question. Yeah, yeah, everybody's all right. Then it was quiet. Lines of strain tensed through the quiet. In the quiet there were four white empty walls and an old chair.

"Damn," said Padrone, "I never would've believed it."

Nobody asked what Padrone would never have believed.

"I mean," said Padrone, "a guy could get hurt." Padrone started to laugh, but then he stopped.

Only Ehrlich took up the laughter, Ehrlich the short, foreign gunner corporal with dirty blond hair. Ehrlich had a very loud, unfunny laugh. "Shut up," said Borman. It disturbed their listening.

They heard what they were listening for. It hadn't been a mistake, after all. It was the long cry of a shell coming in again. Holloway sat down fast. Borman's cheek muscles quivered. Ca-romph. Accent on the second syllable. But these white walls were surely strong. Ca-romph again. But the roof might fall in. Dan MacCarthy remembered how heaven fell down upon the chickens in the story his aunt used to tell him. How they all ran! Ca-romph.

34

But this was serious. Someone wanted to kill Padrone. And Dan. They looked at one another and grinned. They felt foolish.

"Oh, the goddamn lousy Cherman Army," Ehrlich was saying, "it shoots good, eh?" He had been in that Army once. Maybe he should tell them to stop? Ehrlich laughed raucously.

Borman's muscles were so tight they were ready to snap. "You lousy Kraut," he said to Ehrlich.

That struck Ehrlich even funnier. His mouth was still open when the shell struck the base of the stone wall outside.

The chalk dust and powder smoke filled their eyes, their mouths, their nostrils. Their chests rang like bells. There was a booming in their heads, and they could hardly see. They could hardly see even the white walls in the shimmer of this sudden fog, and then slowly the dust began to settle and there they were, each one of them, and the four white walls and the little broken chair. Borman looked around him slowly. All these people, they were crazy. What were they doing here? What was he doing here? The four walls seemed to close about him.

Holloway saw Borman get up. Holloway wondered vaguely, with his chest still vibrating like a struck drum, what big Borman was getting up for with his lip stuck out like a child's. Big Borman was making for the door. Big Borman was shrieking. What was the idea?

Borman wanted to break the rules, then! The rules were to stay where you were because even if it was bad here, it was worse outside. Christ! Holloway lunged. He hit Borman in the knees. Then Borman was underneath him, and he was shaking Borman's heavy shoulders so that Borman's head banged against the floor with the shaking, and he didn't stop shaking him until Borman stopped yelling and looked at him inquiringly. Then Holloway got to his feet.

"You goddamn fools," he shouted. "Those bastards don't know what they're shootin' at any more than we do. Nobody's going anywhere. Get that? Nobody's going anywhere until I say it's okay."

Ca-romph outside. Again? To hell with it. They couldn't get closer than the one before this. Things might hold together, after all. Holloway felt like laughing.

But the howitzer! He had forgotten the howitzer and the men outside. Quickly, he moved to the window space. "The gun's all right, Sergeant"—it sounded like Ehrlich talking—"I look already." The howitzer seemed all right, all right. Ehrlich? Holloway turned abruptly. Ehrlich was grinning at him with his blue eyes. The little sonuvabitch Ehrlich.

Holloway looked again. There were the four howitzers lined neatly along the road. He could even pick up some men prone in the ruts. Ca-romph outside. Holloway winced, but continued watching. Nothing seemed touched. He couldn't even see the bursts. Of course that was because the bursts were coming in the field behind and to the right of the house, while his window faced the road and the guns. Holloway chuckled.

He had been right, after all. The bastards really didn't know what they were shooting at. They were tossing their rounds into the field where the guns had been. An hour late. Snafu, in German.

"What's so goddamn funny?" Ehrlich. Holloway had been laughing out loud and the others were staring at him.

"The screwed-up German Army, Ehrlich," he said.

"Your German Army." He explained it to them. They didn't believe him, except Ehrlich. He had to explain that the concentration was in the field and that the round that had hit their house was short, a snafu itself.

"In fact," he said, "the guns on the road are better off than we are." Very deliberately, he looked at Ehrlich when he said that.

"We ran in the wrong direction," said Holloway broadcasting his error. "But it's a good strong house. Their shorts can't hurt us."

THERE were no more explosions for five minutes. "Sergeant," Dan MacCarthy was asking, peering helplessly through his thick glasses, "shouldn't we all get out of here while we have the chance?"

Ca-romph outside.

"He takes it back," said Padrone. The bastards were still out to kill *them*—but they didn't know how. Padrone laughed to Dan and Dan answered. The absurdity impressed Padrone.

Holloway noted the time on his wrist watch. Quietly he glanced up at Ehrlich, held his glance for a moment and then took in the others. Holloway was very matter of fact. "Number One gun," he said, "is scheduled to pull out in three minutes. Lieutenant Evans is not here." He smiled. "He's out looking for a tractor. Ehrlich, you know where the new gun position is. You take over Number One. I'll send the other pieces on and come up with the last gun section."

Reasons be damned. The point was to get the lead out of your ass. He had nothing against Evans. Holloway smiled.

37

"Nothing to worry about," he said. "Their heavy fire is over. The poor suckers are harassing an empty field."

"Not," said Padrone, "so long as we're in it."

"Then let's go," answered Holloway.

They left the house in a bunch and dashed with their shoulders cringing against the blow which never came. There they were at the Mack. The other men in the section were sitting up in their hiding place. Slowly the realization emerged and tickled them also: nothing had touched them.

"I'll be damned," said Padrone. Everybody wanted to stand there and watch the rounds go off in the field.

"All right," yelled Holloway. "Mount up!"

Maybe mounting up and getting out wasn't such a bad idea.

Holloway watched Number One gun, his gun, roar up the incline to Route Six. The enemy shell seemed to scream directly over the gun before it exploded in the field. Holloway grinned. This, at least, he could handle. So far so good.

Then he went to the other chiefs of section and told them his idea. Staff Sergeant Holloway, senior section chief, would take the responsibility.

WHERE the devil was Hannigan, the tractor driver? Lieutenant Evans didn't like leaving the guns out of sight. The guns depended upon him.

"Do you good to get a little more experience with the men," Fuller had said to him this morning. "Sorry about last night," Fuller had said later when Evans, waiting him out, simply nodded his head to the transfer, "but you brought it on yourself." Evans had had to admit it—drunk or tired he became an oratorical ass. Then with reciprocal apologies he and the man who'd struck him cut whatever slight relation had ever tied them.

Now Evans was out looking for a tractor. He pushed his head forward and took his fast short steps through the perpetual slight rain and listened to the splat, splat of his thick-soled shoes in the everlasting mud. The only thing to do was to go to where they kept the tractor posted and see what was up, because you had to have a tractor or you might never get your guns into position.

"Hannigan, is that you?" He propelled the words out.

"Yeah, sir."

"Where the hell have you been? Where's the cat?"

"Stuck in the mud. I been trying to get it out."

"Go on back to the guns, damn it."

Dialogue in limbo. Nevertheless he would have to check on that tractor. And he hated to leave the guns out of sight.

Evans splashed along the muddy road. He broke into a slow trot, watching the darkness seep up slowly from the mud. If he could work out a way of getting that damn tractor out of whatever it was in, then, it occurred to him, he should never have sent the tractor driver back. Blunder Number One. He would undoubtedly have to return for the man. But Evans had reached the spur of road down which fifty yards or so the tractor sat, and determined to see for himself.

He'd sunk to his hips in the mud. He could feel the chill, damp stuff seep through the tops of his combat shoes, pour between the laces, soak his trousers. Luckily he was near the road's embankment and could seize a projecting branch for support, dragging his right foot from the sea of loose excrement, then the other. On more solid earth, he regarded himself. The weather struck him in the face in a wet wrath. Tentatively, carefully, groping his way, he advanced along the side of the embankment. Twigs scratched at his face.

He wouldn't be stopped. Though it was pretty nearly the hour for him to start the guns on their way, he had to find out about that tractor. There was a limit to the futility even he would put up with.

Then the tractor, impassive, gray-colored, proper to the wind and the cold rain, squatted over its treads in the mud. Evans knew there was nothing he could ever do about it but find help somewhere and it was getting late, damn late. Evans braced himself. He would go to the engineers nearby. The night kept coming on.

Soon the guns must move.

The brilliantly lighted C.P. of the engineers, their cots, their stoves, their strong, unanxious voices, talk of chow and the dryness, these insulted him. He wished to God he were in the engineers.

The guns would have to wait for the tractor.

Certainly, they'd be glad to do anything they could. Get Sergeant so-and-so. The Sergeant would go back with him and see what could be done. The Sergeant was expert in this sort of thing. While Evans waited, would he care for anything to eat?

No. Time was passing. Hurry, please. He got up and walked about and kept swallowing all the time. It was time for the guns to pull out even now. For God's sake, what unearthly business was this of his?

No, thank you, he'd wait where he was, only please make it fast. Holloway would be waiting now, also, wondering where in blazes . . . Waiting quietly, no doubt, with a small, quiet core of contempt. But not only the big, gangly man. The mass of the battalion waited on Evans, and Evans squirmed under the weight and the dropping of the minutes made his mind stagger. He told himself the reaction was preposterous since he couldn't help himself.

Thank God, here was this Sergeant so-and-so, the expert. Together they left the light for the outside darkness and Sergeant so-and-so drove. Evans sat beside the driver and listened to the rain batter the peep's canvas roof.

Evans should be with his guns. What was he doing here?

The Sergeant said, "If anything can be done, Lieutenant, we'll send a cat up as soon as one's available, so don't worry about it."

What else could he have expected of the engineers on a night like this? He should have remained with the guns.

"Then there's no help available now in any case?"

"Right. They're all out on the road. Everybody, everybody in the whole screwing war has got himself stuck tonight."

Oh, for heaven's sake, make him drive you back to the guns!

But maybe, maybe the bitter Sergeant would have an idea if he saw the tractor? Maybe there would be help? Keep a cool, competent head. They were at the spur, anyway.

The Sergeant led him out of the vehicle's shelter. They strained with their eyes after the beam of the Sergeant's flashlight. Flashlights in a blackout were against the rules. Screw the rules. There, there in the dim circle of the light bulked the abandoned lump of steel which plagued Evans so, the hateful, miserable, indifferent lump of inert steel. The Sergeant cut his light.

"Sorry, Lieutenant. We can't do a damn thing about that mess until morning."

Evans nodded. You began to do something; then nothing

could be done. You started for something, you went and you went and you never, never got there. Pretty soon you forgot where you were going.

"Okay, Sergeant," he said. "Go on back to your outfit."

Why keep the poor bastard out in the rain? Evans headed back for his guns. He had failed. He had done nothing about the cat and he had kept the guns waiting. Fuller would have to send someone else after the tractor. Evans had failed and admitted it. Walking toward the guns was almost walking home.

Then he peered at his wrist watch and shuddered. It was late, late, late! And here he was merely strolling along. How long had he been wandering around? The guns were waiting for *him*. Had he forgotten? What a bitter, bitter fool he was! He himself had sent back the expert sergeant who could have driven him. Evans cursed himself and meant it.

He began to run. It was late and he was dreaming and he could never make it in time because he was hideously late for the appointment he dared not miss and certainly he must be dreaming. He ran faster.

But he should be able to make out Number Four howitzer by now. It must be darker than he thought. The guns had to be there, of course. Still no Number Four? There must be some mistake. They must have bunched the guns up at the head of the road. It couldn't be there weren't any guns. What would he say if there weren't any? How could he ever answer for a battery of howitzers? What would he do? He broke into a wild run. His pistol holster slapped unheeded against his thigh. The cold air cut his wheezing lungs. Faster. Please God, let them be there. At least that.

Evans stopped dead. Someone in this infernal night kept

pulling the world away from him. In the place where the guns had stood, where the men had flung themselves wearily upon the Macks—friendly men, his men—was nothing, nothing, nothing at all. What was he going to do in the rain and in the darkness alone and quite cut off? He began to run back and forth, looking for somebody.

"Hey," he screamed. No one. Only the spattering of the rain against his steel helmet, the whistle of his own loud breathing, the fist of the night squeezing him. At last he stood quietly in the middle of the road. Someone had taken the guns away and left no word behind.

Had he been afraid that night on Observation Post when finally they told him there had been a patrol of Germans on the loose for hours and he in their path? But indignation sustained him then. Now he had no indignation. Also, now he had no phone wire to waken him and tell him of the danger and say how the neglect had all been a mistake. Now he was cut off. His own folly had cut him off. He himself had stove the bottom of the world. And this was worse than fear, this black and absolute vacuum.

What was he going to do? Words aside, what was he going to do? His arms dropped limp and weak with help-lessness to his sides.

Not much later, just after he had thought to make the long trek back to the engineer outfit, slowly making its way down the blankness of the road, a shadow came making noise, and the shadow became a peep.

Reality was! Evans got in front of it. He waved his arms violently. "Stop," he yelled. Strangely, it halted before him. There was an "it" after all to halt before him. Tears rolled down Evans' cheeks.

"Lieutenant Evans?" asked the driver.

His name. "Yes, yes," said Evans hoarsely, "let me in!" As though he were thirsty and a great stream flowed through the vehicle.

"Captain Fuller sent me to look for you," said the driver.

And seated in the vehicle beside the little driver, Evans moved in midstream with the current, as a part of the current, while the weighty stream distended his personality and made it full again—and then plump with fear. "Christ, man! Where in hell are the guns?"

The driver looked at Evans curiously and turned the vehicle north on Route Six. "Oh, the guns, Lieutenant? I saw them up there before I got sent back. They were trying to get in."

Evans didn't notice the water splashing on the bottom of the peep; he didn't notice his soaked feet nor the chill nor the attempts of the driver to talk with him a little. In silence they drove up Route Six. He was through for the night. The guns had arrived. They had never really needed him, and he had nothing to answer for, nothing, and never would. He merely had to follow along. He was through for the night, let them say what they liked. He was himself again.

They drove to where the gun positions lay hidden in the darkness, and only the clank of steel and a distraught voice rose fitfully above the dark vibrations of the motor.

"Lieutenant Evans!" It was Captain Fuller, loud, peremptory and angry.

"Here," announced Evans. Home again. He left the peep and went to his commander.

"Where's the cat Holloway says you went after?" Fuller's voice was strained and rough and anxious. Evans smiled, past master of anxiety, but *past*, thank God. Evans told him what had happened. Looking back, Evans perceived that he had only done what he could, and that the bungling hadn't mattered after all.

"Oh, for Chris' sakes," said Fuller. "You knucklehead. Why in hell didn't you go back to the engineers and steal a cat if you had to? Who needs you here? Number Four can't get in, damn it. We got to have a cat and you come straight from the engineers without one."

Screw you, Fuller, screw you most fervently and to hell with you.

"Now," said Fuller, "I want you to get into your peep and I don't want you to come back until you have a tractor behind you and for Chris' sakes don't screw up again."

Evans wasn't through, then, after all.

THE imperative voices careened through the darkness. The muck plagued their feet and they wondered what lay beneath the muck. Down from their places on the prime mover the men learned again what earth was. They dug holes in it for hiding. They felt it against their skins; their ears were full of it, their nostrils stuffed with it. They were intimate with crowbar, cable and the twisted skeins of camouflage nets. Their helmets pressed heavily upon their heads; they threw them off. They threw down raincoats which rain had long since permeated. Into their clothes the wetness soaked, into their bodies, carrying cold. And, except for a sky flicked red at odd moments with cannon lightning, there were shadows only in all the world.

Two miles back, with the wind curling around the peep's windshield and ripping at his hollow-cheeked face with rain, Evans searched along the edges of Route Six for some sign, any sign, of engineers. He would spend the remainder of his night hunting the tractor; and, if he read correctly the blunt symbolism of events, other nights and other days in the fervent pursuit of an equal irrelevance. Now he picked up a house of sorts from which shivered a counter-to-order ray of light.

Elsewhere, the men who took care of the wire had got themselves lost. They had strung their black threads from phone to phone, spinning the web of communications. Two men alone—and where the hell was the Command Post? They knew that the past stretched out behind them because they held the palpable end of it in their hands. As for the future, they were undecided, and chose a direction because they had to rip off with their pliers the rubber coating of the thin wire and stick the wire's end into the proper little hole and tighten down the screw upon it. Their carbines, carried inverted upon their backs, caught the brush as they pushed through and held them back. The slippery earth made them fall, cursing. Where in hell were they? They kept getting lost.

"Hold it," said Evans and entered the house two miles back. No, they told him, but there's a construction outfit down the road on the left a mile or two or three—or is there? He had resumed his place in the complexity of disorganized warfare. However insanely, his life tied in again. It was only Dandy Andy angry who had tied the knot, and God knew the knot was snarled and hardly clean. But Evans felt better now, paying his clear reverence to the insanity of which he was a part and which, insanity or no, sustained him.

And the men of the ammunition crews slaved in the black with two-hundred-pound masses. They slipped steel bars through the eye plugs of the projectiles. One man at each end, borne deeper into slime by what they carried, heads twisted to the side, each small muscle suffering for it, lugged shells to guns, dropped them splashing, returned, and began again. "Screw it," they cried, "screw it, screw it!" They meant that heaven, earth, wind, rain and howitzers somehow should be sat upon and fouled, as they themselves were—that in simple justice, some impersonal power should stick into it all and make it squirm as they squirmed who always and always got the screwing.

Evans found his engineers. Sleep had tired of hanging upon his eyes. Aware and wide-eyed he waited for the tractor they'd promised him. He was paying his debt to Fuller and beyond him to the Colonel and beyond the Colonel to things as they were, with all the force of his meager competence. Well, he could skip Fuller. But if the Colonel, that egregious individualist, that highly competent fool who disarmed you with his sudden laughter and entirely illegitimate kindliness, leaving you no protection against the thrust of his will, if this Colonel found Evans' offering inadequate, then Evans would override him with agreement! Humiliation and rock bottom would, if necessary, serve.

When finally the tractor came, Evans smiled with pleasure. "Driver," he said, "follow me. There's a gun in the mud. We need you."

Fuller, in the C.P. tent, abstracted, weary, crawling fully clothed into his bed roll, looked up at Evans. "Tractor? Oh, yes. We got Number Four in a couple of hours ago. Send the cat home." Then Fuller finished getting into his bed roll and looked at him blearily. "Almost forgot. Colonel was down here. Said something about assigning you to the Air O.P. for a tour of duty next week."

The Colonel knew, then, and had judged. Evans could be dispensed with. It was to be expected.

But who, he wondered vaguely, had sent the guns ahead in the first place? Holloway, probably. Holloway had done the job. Holloway and the Colonel. Evans shrugged and sent the tractor back. For the time being, he would sleep.

3

THE field telephone's metallic tones jarred the sentry at Number One piece. When he lifted the receiver from the box it was almost as much to stop the jarring as to answer.

"Number One, Private Grossberg." His tongue was heavy with the disuse of hours and the remaining fatigue of yesterday's occupation of position.

"Grossberg, this is Lieutenant Grostock. Get this. We're gonna have a harassin' mission for your piece in a few minutes. Wake up the guys an' tell Sergeant Holloway to call quick."

"Yes, sir," said Grossberg, and replaced the receiver.

His gun section had an agreement. Nobody was going to run around yelling "Fire Mission" in the middle of the night. Instead, a few men would be assigned each day for any night fire mission that might come up. The other fellows could sleep that way. Of course, if there were danger of brass coming, with its yelps about four men on a rammer staff and that kind of crap, the sentry would awaken everyone. At one in the morning, however, brass never showed up. Brass was asleep.

It occurred to Grossberg as he prepared to act upon the agreement that he was going to have company very soon. With that comfort soothing the back of his mind he hastened his steps toward Holloway's hogan.

Soon Holloway heard Grossberg's voice intrude softly, insistently, upon him. "Hey, Sarge, wake up, fer Chris' sake. Fire mission. Y'wake? Fire mission, Sarge . . ." and Holloway felt something pulling his leg; he grunted acknowledgment. "Call up Lieutenant Grostock, don' ferget," said the voice, and the tugging left him. Holloway gathered his wits together.

And Grossberg, with increasing glee, wandered abroad rousing the others. He found Padrone pretending not to hear him, but Grossberg wouldn't be tricked. He forced Padrone out of his burrow of sleep. Tomlinson, however—returned from his Mack driving of a day ago—barely needed waking. He pushed Grossberg's shoving hand impatiently from his leg. Corporal Ehrlich, who cursed the awakener in sleepy, guttural German, began immediately, in the midst of the haze of his sleep, to drag his shoes on.

Grossberg lumbered back to the howitzer, his mission accomplished. He was gloating to himself over how his night watch had been broken, and he was grinning to himself over how the others had hated to get up. Screw, those were his sentiments. He was up, wasn't he? Why shouldn't they be? The bastards could keep him company now, they could. He noticed that he could see slightly better than before. The fog which consumed the earth had shifted so that a few rags of moonlight swathed the outlines of things. Grossberg appreciated that. The light was a good sign, he felt. If it weren't so damn chilly, it wouldn't be a bad night.

When Grossberg reached the howitzer he discovered Holloway already at the phone and, pleased with a human voice, sat himself down to wait. He made no effort to understand what his sergeant might be saying to Lieutenant Grostock. The ringing had set him upon the road of events; now he was waiting for it to lead him somewhere. One by one his comrades joined him.

Their disordered, uncovered hair caught in the drifts of fog. Their shirttails hung limply over their trousers. They were that way because they'd had no time to dress completely before the mission and because here it made no difference to them how they dressed, here where it was dark and no brass bothered—and where they didn't give a damn.

Holloway could see the disconsolate shapes of his four men slouch awkwardly in waiting, too bemused with the wisps of their sleep to ask him any questions or to bitch.

"Okay, guys," Holloway said softly because the fog demanded softness. "We've got a harassing mission. We've got to harass the bastards. We send 'em five rounds in the next hour at irregular intervals. Then we can go to sleep again—if nothing else turns up, as it usually does."

Padrone awoke sufficiently to remark, "I think we're gettin' harassed more than the Krauts." But no one paid him the honor of comment. His rueful voice scratched on their fatigue.

"As I was saying," said Holloway quietly, "we fire five rounds spread out during the hour after the Lieutenant gives the commands for the first one. We now have six or seven minutes before we shoot, so it will be easy for the five of us to handle it."

51

"Ya, ya," said Ehrlich, "we know all about it," and he removed the canvas cover from the gun sight, prepared without talk.

Holloway picked up the phone again. "We're ready for the commands, Lieutenant." He seemed to confide in the phone, he spoke so quietly. For he found that the abnormal quiet was a kind of force which held him back, which made it harder to use his competence.

Commands came to him in Grostock's intense, battered English, spoken as if Grostock's life depended on it. "Number One adjust, shell H.E." Holloway repeated the commands after him slowly. His mouth still felt the coating of sleep.

Slowly, heavily, the four others stirred themselves to action. Holloway could see them, so many heavy, clumsy ghosts drifting through the fog and moving with earth-bound feet in the mud. Holloway saw all the old familiar motions. Grossberg pushing a projectile upon its tray . . . Ehrlich, bent over the out-jutting sight while he moved the tube of the howitzer in a horizontal plane, seeking to catch with cross hairs the dim red light on the aiming stake one hundred yards away . . . Padrone's slight form raising the dark tube to address its muzzle at the single, sudden rift of light in the smeared-out sky . . . All of it seemed to Holloway part of the sleep he had just left so reluctantly. Only the sharp, occasional blatance of metal on metal severed the world he stood in from sleep—that and the damp, insistent cold of the night air.

"All right, fellers," said Holloway, "we've got three minutes before loading up." But what was a man to do with three minutes? Go on and wait, the same you did with three minutes anywhere. Holloway felt that you did what you had to do and that was all there was to it. He remained at his post to await the word from Grostock.

The others clustered together, shivered, and kept the silence and the foggy peace. Not even the sound of a distant gun came to break through the darkness as they sought to recover for their minds the close-fitting sheaf of sleep. Still, sleep was lost. Irretrievably. There was preserved only remembrance of the touch of it, a sulky nostaglia for it. They hated to find themselves awake, who were committed to wakefulness in a dark hour.

The word came. "Load up," said Holloway, speaking clear and flat now, dreams to hell.

Ehrlich and Tomlinson grasped the handles of the ammunition tray and with tightened muscles bore the weight of the shell to the howitzer's open breech. With a quick, throwing-off motion Holloway left his phone and seized with Grossberg the long rammer staff, which they heaved against the back plate of the shell. Using all their strength they forced the projectile deeply into the tube's chamber so that the soft copper band around it was grooved by the tempered steel lands. Deftly, while Padrone was elevating the tube, eyes fixed on quadrant, Holloway went on to place the powder charge and slam the breech block shut.

They were ready. Holloway saw that Padrone had picked up the end of the lanyard while the others crouched. Holloway returned to the phone and informed Grostock that the piece was ready to fire. In a moment, because they had accepted, because they had arisen in the silent heart of the night, and worked, it would be—

"FIRE."

An intense light seared the fog wreaths, the masking slope, bushes, trees, the rough and twisted land, the men,

53

all the latent, unswathed content of the night, with ghost red—and then flashed out, in a minute fraction of a second, dropped everything from existence—with a mass of sound which was more terrible than the light because it was a power which shook cannoneers from their teeth to their heels, which made their chests buzz like struck drums, which devoured their strength and in exchange gave them a long high note for their ears and also an acrid stink for their nostrils, stink which penetrated through their nostrils into the back of their heads and forward into the front of their heads, to their eyes—which held in them still, open or closed, the red glare.

"On the way," said Holloway into the phone with his own blast-hollowed voice foreign in his ears.

NEVERTHELESS, they were used to all this, and promptly forgot firing as they gathered together to wait for the next round's proper time. But the firing had worked its change. It had cast sleep from their minds and left them with no replacement. They were at loose ends. They were left wanting something or other.

"I bet," said Padrone desperately after a few minutes, "I bet we sure bothered the Krauts."

"Yeah," said Grossberg eagerly, "I bet we blowed 'em ta hell."

That topic was exhausted. Grossberg began a soft whistle. It was a slight, fuzzy line of sound lost in the fog, but Tomlinson told him to can the whistle. Grossberg did, because he felt he had the best of the bargain—with them keeping his night watch with him.

"Say," Padrone exclaimed. "What we need is some music!"

"Maybe you would like a brass band with trumpets?" inquired Ehrlich.

"No, I'm serious. The wire crew's got a battery radio. Why don't I go over an' borrow it for us?" Padrone was eager. "How about it, Sarge? We can keep it low so nobody'll hear it."

"Sure," said Grossberg, "sure. Why should we suffer when we don' hafta?"

"Okay," said Holloway, "so long as we keep it low I don't see how it would hurt."

Then Tomlinson wanted to know of Padrone, "What yuh waitin' fer?" in his easy, drawled manner. He felt friendly. It surprised him how friendly he felt toward the little Wop. When Padrone left for the radio it seemed to all of them that they had something set up between themselves and the night. They were owners, possessors, with a stake in time.

"Well, fellers," said Holloway with a surprising catch of pleasure in his voice, "this shouldn't be bad at all, eh?"

A cause for worry occurred to Grossberg. "Say," he asked, "what kinda music ya think we're gonna get so late?"

"Cherman music," judged Corporal Ehrlich.

"Ya think maybe it could be swing? Ya think maybe the Krauts'll play swing?" The sudden idea filled Grossberg with anticipation. "Gee, swing," he said, and the idea filled him to overflowing.

"Yer a craphead if'n yuh expec' a goddamn thing," said Tomlinson suddenly and softly.

Ehrlich grinned at him in the darkness. The grin showed in his voice. "You want hilly-billy music, Tom? Not from the Chermans you don't get that."

Holloway intervened quickly. Ehrlich and the southern boy played with one another badly. "So long as it's music," Holloway said. He thought he had better change the subject. "Do you guys know 'Lili Marlene'? It's a good tune. How does it go again, Ehrlich?"

Ehrlich hummed and Holloway listened quietly, watching Ehrlich's dim shadow. There was something questionable and resistant about this chunky man humming under the camouflage net beside Holloway. Holloway couldn't quite figure the man out, except to know that he was the best damn gunner corporal he had ever seen. And Holloway wanted to figure the man out. Ever since they'd run into the Wop house together that time the Krauts overshot, he'd wanted to understand what the man was driving after —and failed.

Ehrlich hummed in his harsh voice and before he knew what he was doing the melody grew into some strong and unidentifiable meaning and it was too late to halt. A small wind blew the notes through the rustling camouflage net and into the night sky. Ehrlich raised his voice and added words. "Lili Marlene," his comrades heard, and then a blank which was German. It helped that the words were German and they could not understand them except to know that there was some very much wanted woman in the song. The vague and poignant dream in each man suffered no distraction that way. "Lili Marlene . . ." They heard the sorrowful not-having, the wistful desire. The quavering, rough voice held as much of Ehrlich's desolation as of their own, and yet it was a desolation somehow sweetened. They listened silently, each man secluded in the slight fog, wanting, wanting, remembering what was never experienced and longing for it.

"Hey, shut up. Someone'll think we're Krauts an' shoot the hell out of us!"

Padrone had returned. They could make out the rectangular bulk of the radio under his arm. Holloway laughed.

"Yah, I shut up," said Ehrlich bitterly. "It's a lousy Cherman song. Why in hell should I sing it?"

Padrone deposited the radio on a tarpaulin sufficiently far from the left trail so that concussion would not burst the tubes. His friends were joining him when they heard Holloway.

"We better get the second round off before we start playing around."

There was no denying it and no one thought of denying it. They turned around and returned to the gun. They were disgusted because it meant dropping "Lili Marlene" and because the Padrone's gift waited, but they returned. The metal surfaces seemed oddly repellent as they touched them, but they touched them. That was all there was to it.

Corporal Ehrlich, formerly of the German Army, made doubly sure that the gun's deflection was correct. Against those who had cast him out, he strained with all the power in his eyes that the reading on the gun sight, illumined by the white glow of the night-lighting device, might be precise. That whatever it was they were shooting at might be irrevocably blasted, torn to shreds. As he had been torn to shreds.

When the great blast came again, it threw off with the

57

shell the tight ball of hatred in Ehrlich. With a calmer, re-hardened mind, he hastened to join his comrades who had gathered around the radio.

"Go on, Pady," urged Grossberg. "Get somethin'."

Padrone crouched beside the radio delicately fingering the dials. A sputter of foreign language burst out first and Padrone quickly spun away. "Jesus," he said disgustedly. Then he discerned an English-speaking voice. "Here's something," he cried. All five men listened without knowing what they wanted to hear but hoping it would be whatever it was they wanted.

"What's the sonuvabitch talkin' about?" Tomlinson demanded, sensing an affront in the broad a's, the over-mellifluous talk issuing from the little wooden box. It made Grossberg giggle to hear it.

"Shh," warned Ehrlich, "it's news. Listen a minute."

The voice described great aerial thrusts, promised invasion of France, found confidence in the valor of the Allied arms.

"Say, does he mean us?" asked Padrone. But they were listening.

It was talking of the Asiatic campaigns, of the mounting tide of Allied power which would surely and inevitably obliterate the Nazi tyranny from the face of the earth. The first, more than familiar notes of the Fifth declared the speech over.

"And not a stink'n word about Italy," commented Padrone. "You'd think we weren't even in the war."

"We don' count nothin'," said Grossberg softly.

"Five forgotten men," half laughed Padrone. "Usually

at least they talk about artillery duels on the Italian front."

Who remembered Pady Padrone on a fire mission at night, in stinking Italy? Most of them wouldn't even know what a harassing mission was. The thought made him angry.

Padrone hunted for music, searched the wave lengths for something which would be with them, not different from them. He found static, and scattered words abruptly cut off by his turning dial. He reached through Italy, Germany and France hunting connections with the sensitive feelers of his little box; while Grossberg felt his hopes die and thought he'd have to return to Italy, and even Holloway, self-contained, impassive, felt forlorn. But Padrone was working for them all. He knew it. He was their representative in search of a world, and he didn't mind the sarcastic cracks pulled at his expense because he knew they were encouraging him that way and meant to cheer him on.

Grossberg began to pound him on the back. "Ya got it now, ya got it now, leave it alone." Grossberg's mind was suddenly lit with interest. "Chris', don' move it." There was a touch of awe in his voice as he spoke because he was hearing music now, real music, and had never expected to.

It was a rhythmic, swirling blast of jazz. It was tinny and it was loud and it was outdated. But it was fast. It shook the small radio until Holloway stepped over silently and turned it down; then they heard the ecstatic pulsing of the rhythms even sharper and clearer, because their ears could catch the night wind while the music played, and because the twitching, jarring drums, horns, pianos splattered against the fog loudly instead of going through it.

Grossberg was swaying in time. He placed his clenched hands behind his neck and performed a little bump with his behind. The others could see enough to laugh. "Hot stuff," said Padrone, gleeful. Tomlinson's eyes contracted in the dark. Ehrlich said "Hah" to Padrone and stamped heavily with his foot, disregarding the thick mud.

It was a hard music, a jagged music dancing on broken glass. It chucked restraint into a tin can and clamped over it a tin cover. Its accelerating beat punched the cloudy, noxious world to pulp. It was frantic. It stamped and tossed itself about and brayed through a tin horn.

Grossberg's mind turned clear and white. A faint sweat glossed his fat puffy cheeks and he breathed heavily. This was what he wanted. It put him outside himself. It put him on a dance floor in Poughkeepsie, shaking with the rhythm while someone yelled, "Go on, fat boy. Swing it!" Again the harsh light blared out in the dark, and Grossberg had hold of life.

He spread the rhythm through the moist air, pushing it along with his fat figure, jerking and swaying it through the night. He made Holloway clap his hands in glee, Tomlinson catch the beat and nod his head to it in quick little jerks. Soon Ehrlich stamped his foot, slapped his heavy boot into the mud, slap-slapping it in time while Padrone asked for a dance in elaborate pantomime. Grossberg didn't have to know he held the center of the stage. He'd absorbed the stage. An infinite smile settled upon his features. He was a receiver of oracles. He let the nervous drums strike their beat into his body and shivered. He let those drums bounce him about, pluck his nerves, wring the sweat out upon his temples, lubricate his great, thick arms and legs with the smooth sweat.

They were nowhere in sight of Italy. They'd abandoned sunny Italy in the middle of the night. They'd abandoned the world and didn't give it a second thought. They just let the wind come down from Cassino to ruffle their hair, entangle and disentangle the fog wisps round their waists. Swing it. The husk of earth and heaven discarded, they had a rhythm left.

"Go on, fer Chris' sake, Grossy, go on. Give, boy!"

But the jazz hit the end of the line. The long, off-pitch note of the saxophone screeched like a brake; and Grossberg shivered and relaxed, sighing, into himself.

Holloway rose suddenly from the steel trail he'd been sitting on the while he beat out time. "Jesus Christ, fellers," he exclaimed, "I almost forgot. We better get another round off fast or Grostock will wonder what in hell happened to us."

He raised a general laugh. "Screw Grostock," said Ehrlich. "We do our job. We finish the screwin' mission for him."

"Well," said Padrone, "if he wanted the rounds out uneven he's sure as hell gettin' what he wanted."

Dazedly, Grossberg, with remembrance of the jazz ringing in his head, went to his place. Shaking his buttocks a little in time to the remembered music—which made Padrone roar until Holloway told him to shut up and get busy—Grossberg obediently went about his work.

They sent another projectile churning with the noise of half a dozen freight cars toward the interdicted crossroad. They didn't know it was an interdicted crossroad because Grostock had been too sleepy to explain—and they wouldn't have cared much had they known. The fact was that they had to get the round out; reasons were in the great shadow of a fact as simple as this one.

WHEN the men found their ways back to the radio they heard it broadcast a more sentimental tune. It kept saying, *You'd be so nice to come home to*, and Padrone said, "Ain't it the truth?" Whereupon they all laughed. . . . *by the fire*.

"You know," said Padrone, breaking in again upon the listening, "that last number we heard, that fast one, was real corn. Funny we got such a kick out of it. Shows . . ."

"Shut up, Pady," said Tomlinson, "an' listen."

So Padrone held his musicology in check and the five of them perched close together upon the gun trail for the warmth and for the comfort, while the radio imported sentiment and the atmosphere of movie houses—and unheard-of gorgeous women on the screen, singing that you, *you* would be so nice to come home to.

Only Ehrlich regarded the little mechanism somberly because of its product. The metallic raptures of the last music had helped him against the sweetness of "Lili Marlene." Now here she was again, American version, more innocuous, yet still the same something "to come home to," which he could never meet again—which was impossible, barred by exile, mocked by war, and which his friends, who had no sense of the impossible, longed for nonetheless. He sniffed contemptuously, but held his peace.

"Gawd," said Grossberg wistfully, "I betcha that dame singin' has a wunnerful ass. . . ."

Nobody laughed.

The sensuous, pleading voice came to its final notes. *To come home to and love*, it sang.

"That's a purty song," drawled Tomlinson. "We're kinda lucky on this here radio tonight." Tomlinson felt more at ease than he had in a long, long time. He stretched himself lazily on the hard steel of the trail and looked with

62

wide-open eyes at the in-gathering fog above his head and around him.

"That Limey's here again," said Padrone. Over the radio came the same voice which, with its ignoring of them, had offended them before. Padrone bore the voice a special grudge, would have killed it conveniently with a flick of his wrist but that Holloway warned he might not be able to get anything better. "You think that's good?" demanded Padrone sarcastically, but he sat down again. The few words prevented them from catching the announcement, but they didn't need to. Holloway stirred, pleasantly surprised by the stringed introduction.

"Hey, Ehrlich," he said, "it's 'Lili Marlene' again." Holloway knew some of the words. *Underneath the lamp post, by the barracks gate* . . . He wished he knew them all. Something in the sugared, doleful melody touched him. Even though he had always gone it alone with no woman waiting for him by the barracks gate, wandering pretty much as he pleased, pleased to face circumstance with his own indifferent competence, even so, something in it touched him.

Ehrlich had heard. "Yah," he grunted, "the Cherman song . . ."

The words turned out to be English this time. They were having good luck all right; the men were sure of it. They listened carefully for the words. They wished to remember them. Even Ehrlich listened. But something was wrong. That couldn't be it. Those words couldn't fit what they knew the song was. Slowly, grievously, disappointment stole upon them. Tomlinson shook his head to clear it. Something was wrong. Holloway's mouth twisted as he gathered what it was and Padrone said, "I'll be damned."

Then Ehrlich began to chuckle, quietly, because the baritone was singing with a plaintiveness that went just a little too far.

And Lili Marlene's boy friend will never see Marlene,
And Lili Marlene's boy friend will never see Marlene . . .

Lugubriously it told how she might wait forever at the barracks gate and under the lamp light because her boy friend had fallen miserably in Russia or frozen in Italy, how his pack would no longer be either light or heavy when he thought of Lili Marlene, since he would never think of her.

They listened in utter silence, and when the voice had finished Tomlinson rose and switched off the radio. Then there was silence except for the low sounds of Ehrlich's chuckle. Grossberg was the first to speak.

"Now what's the screwin' idea a that?" he wanted to know.

"Well," said Holloway after a moment's angry thought, "I suppose they think it's propaganda. I suppose we're supposed to go around singing the new words. But," he added, "I don't think it's right."

"It stinks," said Padrone bitterly. Was this a use for music? "They shouldn't 've killed a good song that way. It was a damn good song. Why couldn't the bastards leave it alone out of the war?"

Tomlinson had stretched himself again upon the trail. Staring straight up, he said, "Ah'm with ya there, Pady. Krauts an' songs is different."

Ehrlich's chuckle had died; he was too incredulous to chuckle. "Chesus," he exploded. It seemed to him suddenly that he hardly knew his comrades. Were they so far gone in other worlds as that? But it invalidated *his* world, that

64

so easily, for a song, they discarded war and the long, over-bearing murder of the Nazi. For a song . . . His life, what he knew, what was cut into his bone, was less than a song. "Chesus," he said.

"What you guys doin' here anyway?" He asked it in sheer awe.

"I dunno," answered Padrone.

He and the others were looking at Ehrlich's short, broad figure and it seemed as unfamiliar to them as their figures did to him. Who was he to talk like that?

"Aw, come on," said Padrone, trying to bridge the gap with friendliness. "A song's a song, even a Kraut song. You're a German yourself."

"I cannot belief it," said Ehrlich. Awe still gripped him. "A song of the Cherman Army which you shoot at, and you feel bad because . . . I cannot belief it."

"You might as well believe it," said Holloway roughly. A man had a right to his opinion, Holloway thought, and if the little foreigner disagreed, that was no reason for him to jump the rails. Nothing was certain, anyway—except that Ehrlich was being nasty in a way Holloway especially hated.

"Screw yuh, Kraut," said Tomlinson in his soft, tense voice.

Suddenly the awe left Ehrlich. It left him wanting to fight. He restrained his voice with effort; it vibrated and shook against the ties of the effort. "Chesus." This was the time for him to speak and he found it so hard to speak, in chains to a foreign language, with his passion rocking him so.

"Yah." He half whispered. "I'm a Kraut. A Chewish Kraut, yah? Also I was once in the Cherman Army like

I told you, and I'm the one that hates them. Me. You don't. It takes a Kraut, yah?" He laughed. Bitterness filled him completely. "I can't be sentimental fools like you. Over Lili Marlene's boy friend! You, you," he pointed around him, "all of you—dumb kids! You don't know what it's all about and you don't want to know. Me, I am kicked out from the Cherman Army. My father is killed, my brother. So maybe I don't care if they sing good songs. They got good armies too, yah? They kill good too, you think maybe? Sure, sure, once I like their songs, I like to sing them." The tearful, sentimental tunes, the nostalgia and the good feeling—he had liked them very much. "But not any more. Now I learn. Now they make me smart. I kill them with anything if I can, with guns, with words. But you got sentiment. Fools, fools, in the middle of the war, fools . . ." Ehrlich choked over his passion.

"Tell me," he asked, "please tell me. Why you take all this?" He had swept his arms around him, at the fog, at the gun, at everything in sight. "Why you stand it?"

Holloway's voice hit the darkness viciously. "That's enough out of you, Ehrlich," he said, but Ehrlich, hearing no answer to his question, took breath to go on. Tomlinson intruded in a deadly, insistent tone which Ehrlich recognized.

"Who yuh callin' fools, Kraut?"

Ehrlich glared at the figure of Tomlinson rising from its prone position on the trail. "You make a mistake, Tomlinson," he said. "You mix me maybe with Dan. Don't do it." Ehrlich looked away from him to the others. "I call everybody here fools because you are. You, Pady, you think maybe Lili Marlene is such a nice girl? You are too delicate to hear a song hurt, yah? Soft in the head, you are.

66

Sergeant Holloway, who knows how to do everything, you, maybe, I think, are the worst fool of all because you don't care about nothing . . . Nothing."

Tomlinson was waiting him out, rigid upon his feet.

"Grossberg, you are a Chew from Poughkeepsie and all you think about is shakin' your ass." His voice was vivid with contempt.

"I don't know why we take this," said Holloway. To hell with what made Ehrlich go! Ehrlich, the little foreigner, was dead wrong about him, dead wrong, by God. But what was right? The question spurred his anger.

"And Tomlinson . . ." began Ehrlich.

"We all don' need t'take it, Sarge," said Tomlinson.

He launched himself upon Ehrlich, but Ehrlich was waiting and eager. The two men clasped one another in their arms and Ehrlich tried to break Tomlinson's ribs against his own deep chest while Tomlinson pounded him hard in the kidneys. Within the confines of the trails they made a squashing, liquid noise as they rolled about, and the others heard only that sound and the heavy-taken breath.

Suddenly, Holloway, realizing consequences, awoke from his own fury. He, Padrone and Grossberg, managed to drag the wrestlers apart. He was very grim when he spoke. "Ehrlich," he said, containing himself, "if you ever sound off like this again I'll have you busted out of Corporal. I don't care how good you are at the gun sight. You, Tomlinson, maybe you had reason this time. But, sure as hell, I'll get you out of my section if I catch you fighting with any of our guys again. Now pull yourselves together. We got another round to send out."

Ehrlich shrugged and trudged to his gun sight. Holloway was of course right. They had work to do and there had to be order. Ehrlich watched for the cross hairs to sever the red light.

But he had not told them everything. Let Holloway be careful. It was not only the German Army Ehrlich fought. It was them, God in heaven, them—these men around him, these mortal enemies and only friends of Ehrlich. And Ehrlich stood alone and ready for them and stronger than they were, stronger than all the men who rejected him from continent to continent!

"FIRE!"

The blast of the gun, the long howling of the projectile as it hurled head on toward the invisible enemy, failed this time to discharge the low-pitched, nagging anger from him. That stayed.

Eli, eli? Hell, no, not for Sigmund Ehrlich.

There was instead the wonderful, wonderful pleasure of clasping Tomlinson's undernourished body and feeling its ribs bend and the back give.

WHEN the round was gone and the work finished the five men did not cluster together around the radio. They made a few hesitating steps to do so, stopped and turned their backs on one another. Before, they had drawn together and hurt had come of it for them; now they were a little afraid of what each might inflict. For each man had become questionable to the other, become a variable suddenly and profoundly independent, freighted with suspect possibilities, dangerous. They were embarrassed, mortally embarrassed, although they had no need to say to themselves that it was so; and they eyed one another's forms covertly. Nevertheless they hoped that someone would make a break and prove that everything was really all right so that they could warm themselves again in society. Because outside one another, alone in the fog, they became too conscious of the chill in the air and it was very hard to be a man. No one turned on the radio.

Padrone wasn't used to feeling as broken off from his friends as he felt now. It went counter to his proper nature to have it happen. He tried to draw a sort of pleasure from the softness of the fog. He drew pleasure easily from most things. He tried to draw ease from the unusual, absolute quiet. But this time he couldn't make it. His foot would reach the threshold of the achievement and then, hesitating, embarrassed, draw back. It wouldn't do. It was stupid. The whole thing was stupid.

"Aw, fellers," he said, "don't ya think we're makin' more of a fuss over Lili Marlene than the bitch is worth?"

"Yer damn well told," seconded Grossberg, relieved by a way out opening before him.

"Why don' ya put on somethin' on the radio, Pady?" Grossberg added. "What the hell!"

"Roger," said Padrone, and if his speaking had a flat quality in his own ears, he reached down for the radio none-theless. When he had switched it on, the first thing they heard was a woman. She was a soft, insinuating woman. She made Grossberg prick his ears up and gathered even sullen Holloway's attention.

"Axis Sally," said Padrone, stating a fact. "First we get Lili, then we get Sally. From one whore to another."

Sally was prattling over a list of war prisoners. Except for Holloway, the men listened intently because usually they liked the music Sally played for them, and enjoyed the titillation which came of listening to a voice which they knew hated them. Sally wanted them to come and surrender, join those who were out of the whole sad mess. She oozed false sympathy out of the loudspeaker. She commiserated with her poor American friends.

Holloway listened with half his mind; the other half was wrathful. Ehrlich had missed the truth about him, about the others. Of this he was furiously aware. It was a slander which must be answered. But how? Holloway didn't know, and his anger swelled against Ehrlich, against the bitch on the radio with her blabbing, against himself for not knowing, for having no defense. He could not bear to be defenseless. He did care, he insisted to himself, he did care, about many things if he could recall them. About being fair; about being strong; about being any number of clear and simple things which made a man a man. But somehow, in the waste of the fog, in the middle of the night, these were not enough.

What was enough? Holloway despised to ask himself such questions. They left him vulnerable. They were a foreigner's questions.

Sally was still going on. "Tell me, boys," she said confidingly, "why do you go on suffering day after day and night after night? What's the point? What makes you do it? You're not fighting for anything, you know, except for the Jews. Don't you get tired of it? Wouldn't you like to be at the soda fountain with your girls?"

"Shut that bitch off, damn it." It was Holloway, wrathful. "Shut it off, I tell you." He took a step toward the radio.

Padrone shut it off.

Corporal Ehrlich laughed when he spoke. "What's the

matter, Sergeant Holloway, she insults you? She makes you feel small? Don't worry, I make no speeches."

Holloway looked absent-mindedly at Ehrlich. For a moment he wasn't thinking of what Ehrlich meant. Sally had disgusted him. When she paralleled his mind he had felt like throwing up, that was all. How did Sally and Ehrlich fit in? He wondered for a moment.

Coldly, he regarded Ehrlich. "I think, Ehrlich," he said, "maybe I should finish up the job Tomlinson started. Maybe I will some day. But until I decide what I want to do about you, Ehrlich, stay on your own goddamn side of the line." Slowly he turned his back on Ehrlich. "Now, you guys," he told them all, and for a moment it seemed to Holloway as though he'd begun to answer Ehrlich, "let's get off that last round."

Grossberg, Samson-like in Philistia, at the mill with *goyim*, including Ehrlich, joined Holloway at the rammer staff and rammed the shell in tight. Weariness be damned. Cold be damned. Arguments be damned. Padrone watched the bubble on his quadrant and, turning the elevating hand wheel, delicate fingered, careful, saw the bubble slide gently between the two red lines. So that the range might be correct. Tomlinson, anger or no anger, hope or no hope, threw in the charge of powder behind the shell and hurled the breech block shut with a resolute, singing clang. And Ehrlich forgot how far he was from his comrades and they from him as he checked his instrument's deflection.

"FIRE," said Holloway.

The last round of Number One gun's harassing mission went outward over the Italian plain.

4

"THE trouble," said Colonel Colouris to his S-3 in a stone house near Mignano, "the trouble with the big brass—they fear action." He sat down on a wooden box and stared at the tin hat in his hands. A while ago he had been at Group Headquarters trying to discover when the battalion could move forward. Nobody knew. But he and Colonel Grey—full Colonel Grey—had talked the matter over.

"How not to win a war," said Colonel Colouris to his S-3, who could be depended upon to listen intelligently. "Sit. Fritter away men and materials. Never make a significant decision because the consequences may be politically inexpedient.

"Sometimes," said Colonel Colouris, after a moment, pulling back the corners of his mouth, "sometimes, Hogarth, I think we'll be here forever."

Hogarth, the S-3, glanced around the stove-warmed Fire Direction Center he controlled, every map and every graph and every instrument and man adequate to its proper function, and shrugged his shoulders. The Colonel had a perpetual bee up his ass. Not him. They'd only been here about two weeks, anyway. And suffered no losses.

"The goddamned war," bitched the Colonel, in his calm but rasping voice, "is a bureaucrat's war, and the bureaucrats can't be expected to see that we ourselves really do have to beat the German. They're in politics and business be damned."

He and Colonel Grey had bitched that way together and Colouris enjoyed repeating what he felt so strongly. But suddenly it seemed to Colouris as though their complaints had acquired a sharper meaning, and he looked up slowly at the S-3 as that meaning forced itself upon him.

"Do you know, Hogarth," he said gently, "centralization and politics, big organization, big society—they're leaving us no room for enterprise. They're giving us no choice anywhere, in war or in peace, but to fuddle with their forms and their delays. And there's not a damn thing I can do about it!"

Hogarth glanced up quickly at the sudden passion in the Colonel's voice, but Colouris recovered quickly, stared coldly at Hogarth and offered him his bony jaw to turn the note of hurt into cold anger and conviction. There must be no doubt who was battalion commander.

"When in blazes," he said in Hogarth's face, "does Evans go up in that Cub?" Colouris was here now to listen in on the way Evans handled a fire mission from the air (if, that is, Evans succeeded in finding a target), not for fruitless yapping. Colouris smiled slowly. Why, indeed, should he trouble himself over failures beyond his scope? Actually, he had a good deal to be pleased with right now. A good deal.

"You see anything yet?" the pilot was yelling back.

Loud, so that Jordan, the pilot, could hear over the propeller's roar, Evans yelled, "No. Do you?"

Jordan shook his head to the negative and sharply banked the single-engined, canvas-covered plane. Perhaps, Evans speculated, Jordan underneath that quick efficiency, that matter-of-fact craziness, also felt the unease which gnawed at Evans in a Piper Cub on display before the silent enemy? Nevertheless, it wasn't the possibility of small-arms fire which disturbed Evans now. It was the thirty-five hundred feet of altitude which protected them from such fire. There were enemy planes in the region. They would like you sitting up high, top speed eighty miles an hour with a favorable wind.

Evans swallowed high and peered intently through the plastic windows while the cold air swept in through the cracks and his stomach turned with the drop and sweep of the plane. Occasionally he raised his field glasses to examine some point several miles away in the German-held land. That was what he was up there for. Not to gape at thin air for enemy planes, not to twist his neck. That was for the pilot, who conveyed him back and forth, back and forth along the edge of the front line and sometimes beyond it, for this tight, cold hour of observation.

He could see the front flung forward, miles of it writhing along the narrow Rapido over which he hovered. He could see that fast, cold stream, the Rapido, patches of it silver in the sun, break from the Garigliano, crawl northwest and enter Cassino and, within blotched banks, lose itself. He could see mountains in the distance, too, mountains hump-backed to the east on the Garigliano's farther side and nearer, northward, the white-topped cone of Monte Cassino, dominating. He saw Cassino itself, hinge of the German battle line nailed down by Monastery Hill, smeared and blurred by bombardment, a town only by the insane inference of conventional geography. Beyond the Rapido's deviousness the Liri Valley, gateway to Rome, possession of the enemy, lay before him prostrate and wreathed in occasional mists.

That was the naked body of the war underneath the plane. Evans could see it. It inhabited the banks of the Rapido and hid its head in disintegrating Cassino. Had he thought once that the war had an issue? Anti-Fascism, perhaps? Under aerial observations, war shed issues. War was Fact, Thing-in-Itself, Existence sheer beyond argument; it spoke from the Rapido and beyond. "I AM THAT I AM" it declared to you. "I AM MY OWN JUSTIFICATION—and if you don't believe Me, consider the frightened little field-gray men waiting for your possible volleys in the hills or, if you will, consider yourself." The argument was hardly valid, but who could argue with a God? Evans had suffered his scabs and boils.

Back and forth along the river. Jordan turned his head profile to Evans, raised a disgusted eyebrow and shrugged his boredom. Poor hunting. Jordan was searching for targets more single-mindedly than Evans. Evans lived through a second of intense hostility. How could he observe when no one watched the air for him? Evans glanced around him quickly. No. No little black specks in the sky growing larger, thank God.

Evans blinked and felt the tension and the emptiness curl within his heart. Also, his feet were cold. But he was on a mission, he told himself, paying the unending price of an admission ticket to somebody else's world, because it was

75

worse outside. He would try not to complain. There were no bureaus set up to receive complaints. And good Lord, it wasn't his first mission!

HE HEARD the repetitious tympane. Bang. Bang. Rhythmless. Bang. German ack-ack! At them! Where was it, where? Jordan flung the plane into a desperate wing-over. Where? Were they close? But the air was clean. No multiplying black puffs corrupted it.

What the hell? questioned Jordan silently, and looked back to see whether Evans had seen anything. No, though he was stretching his neck enough in the effort. Here it came again. Jordan banked steeply and examined the ground below him.

There, on their own side of the river, the shells of the enemy turned into little black mushrooms. Evans pounded him excitedly on the back. Yes, yes, Jordan had seen it too. Evans shouted in his ear, "See if we can find where they're shooting from." Goddamn it, of course. Evans didn't have to tell him that. In slow sweeps they circled over the cascading explosives below, searching for the source of them.

Evans first picked up the quick, betraying flashes. "Near San Giorgio in the hills," he yelled. "There they go again." Jordan confirmed him with a nod. Enemy artillery. Plenty of it.

Evans fumbled with the accordion-folded map. Jerkily, he glanced out the window and back at the map, comparing. The trick was to get the co-ordinates right, get the first round close and fast. He scribbled rapid numbers on the margin of his map, picked up his little microphone and radioed Group Headquarters.

76

"Enemy guns, six of them, co-ordinates 674–493," he announced.

They assigned him to his own battalion for the mission. He talked to his outfit now, repeated the co-ordinates. "Request speed," he told them.

Finally: "Number One is ready."

"Fire Number One," shouted Evans.

"On the way," they told him.

And Evans was in the war. Wait now, while the great shell rides its parabola toward the target . . . Five seconds . . . Ten . . . Better begin watching for it, don't want to waste the round . . . Fifteen seconds . . . Twenty . . . "Splash," Fire Direction warns over the receiver. That meant the round was about to strike. Don't miss the big debut! And now that swelling cloud of black smoke, that must be it. Sure! Jordan was nodding, he'd seen it too, where their shell had burst. In relation to the projectile's lines of flight, the burst must have been about two hundred yards left and two hundred over the target area's center.

Evans spoke into the microphone. "Two hundred left, four hundred over. Fire when ready." He sat back. For a moment he closed his eyes. He had the mission in hand now. He was part of the war now. What though he floated over the lines? To hell with exposure. His skill was part of other skills, meshed with them, yes, even directing them. This was dominion. This must be what Jordan felt when he guided his Cub to a safe landing in high winds.

"Two hundred left, four hundred over. Fire when ready." Evans' sensing came in, clear and nervous over the Fire

77

Direction loud speaker. Colouris nodded slightly. So far so good.

The problem of judging his officers and allocating them weighed heavily upon his attention. For example, he suspected Evans' nerve. That's why he sat here listening now. Not that he believed Evans a coward, in the ordinary sense. But he suspected that the mainspring might be broken, the man incapable of aggressive action. There were, on the other hand, some cowards quite capable of aggressive action.

"On the way," said Hogarth into the microphone for Evans' benefit. The Fire Direction crew, Colouris noted, operated with ease and sureness.

That the man was fundamentally incapable of action—what else but that could Crown's strange tale of Evans' behavior at Fuller's party mean? Evans thought decisions preposterous because he was preparing to avoid making them. That kind of cynicism was simply a contemptible excuse. The fiasco of the loss of Evans' own guns gave further confirmation. Evans should never have been commissioned. So, at least, it seemed. It followed that the thing to do with Evans was put him where he could be carried around, where he could do his job almost automatically, a strictly limited job which yet required some degree of guts and discrimination. Besides, air observation had to be done and he could easily spare Evans from the battalion.

"Splash," said Hogarth to Evans.

Colouris leaned forward. Now for Evans' sensing. The damn fool. Evans was clearing his throat with the microphone button pressed! But here it was—"One hundred right, two hundred short," said Evans somewhere over the

Rapido. Nervous as hell, but he hadn't jumped his bracket. Colouris nodded his approval.

Hogarth reported that Evans had fired a couple of pretty good missions before this one. It looked as though Colouris had made Evans mesh. Not only Evans. Evans was trivial. He had made all his officers mesh in this battalion of his. Not entirely, perhaps—Crown found it necessary to drink and Fuller to shine shoes to a high polish, and they would bear watching. But on the whole this was a damn good battalion, and his battalion, and war was a problem in efficiency and in will which Colouris was determined to crack wherever it confronted him. Colouris thrust his jaw at Hogarth sitting near the radio and frowned down his own pleasure.

"On the way," said Hogarth.

Colouris still had room for enterprise and action, by the Lord Harry. Matters were not so bad at all.

"Splash," said Hogarth.

Colonel Grey had a bad heart. After Colouris and he had talked a while, Colouris noted the dejection softening his superior's features.

"Well," Colonel Grey had told him, "I may soon be leaving the Group. No choice."

Colouris had expressed emphatic concern. He approved of Grey as an experienced soldier. Grey approved of him. Another commander might restrict him as Grey never had. But Grey had shrugged and regarded him curiously.

"Would you like to take over?"

"Five zero left," said Evans. "One hundred over. Fire for effect." Really very well handled.

Colouris turned over the memory of that question. He felt the impact of it even now. A Group command and a full colonelcy were unusual for a National Guard officer such as he was. Colouris smiled to himself. He had made his face impassive and hard as Grey's had become. "If it comes to it, yes." A flat statement. Colonelcy or no, Colouris would ask for nothing. But matters were not so bad at all.

"Two battery volleys," said Hogarth to Evans. "Wait."

Eight hundred pounds of high explosive would now be dumped upon the German by this battalion Colouris had shaped. He smiled faintly at Hogarth and the men at work with him. He would hate to leave his battalion. But he had to admit that making the decision would be pleasant. As a full Colonel he might even decide to stay in the Army when the war ended. The wife and younger children could join him wherever he was.

"On the way," said Hogarth, keen and happy at his microphone.

Would the command ever really be offered him? Colouris tightened his mouth. Grey's question was at best a straw in the wind. Straws broke. He'd been daydreaming like a child, or worse—like an army politician. Colouris shook his head to clear it of such dreams.

"Splash."

The fact was only the ineffectuals spent themselves bitching and dreaming of a promotion. Events escaped them. In consequence they sought rank to assure themselves of the contrary. He had seen officers like that. But as for him, promotion and honor would come, when they came and if they came, because of clear superiority. He would never seek them—they would be tagged onto him in his passage. Colouris tensed now to hear what happened to his battalion's fire. Action mattered, made up manhood. Events had handles which a cunning, vigorous man could grasp if only in his heart he were man enough to want to.

"All rounds in target area!" Evans yelled it through the loudspeaker. "Wait." Good shooting, Evans boy! Colouris smiled his delight as he waited. "There's a big column of smoke," Evans was yelling, "a big column of smoke coming out of the target area," and it struck Colouris that that was the strangest cry of pleasure he had ever heard.

Colouris laughed to Hogarth and Hogarth grinned like a Cheshire cat.

Even Evans knew now what it was like to do a job and win. Did Colouris need proof that he was right—that action rightly handled made the man and never substitutes, never dreams? Listen to Evans gloating a few thousand feet in the air over the Rapido—to Evans, of all people in the battalion!

"Suggest zone fire," Evans was saying to Hogarth.

"Give him all the fire he wants," ordered Colouris.

But shortly after the mission had ended, Hogarth tried to contact the plane for a routine job and no one answered him. He looked up questioningly. Colouris smiled and motioned Hogarth away from the phone for which Hogarth had reached. Trouble was a battalion commander's business.

JORDAN seemed to surrender altitude as they moved rearwards. Evans could see the darker spots which, for all their camouflage, marked the guns of his battalion to the accustomed eye. The cannoneers were resting now, no doubt. His fire mission had been sloughed off into their past. That was that.

81

Evans became passive to the motion of the plane. He submitted to its wide swings, its slow descent. It appeared to him that his strength had somehow ebbed and, indifferently, he submitted to whatever he might incur. End of mission. What could be next? He answered himself. Another mission, another keying up of oneself. Repetition after repetition of War's slipshod proof of His rightness, a proof in the nature of things always unanswerable and always unacceptable, always ending in the small shower of disgust Evans felt raining upon his spirit now.

Look at Jordan in front there, friendlier than ever, indicating strenuously where he wished Evans' attention directed.

"Out there," Jordan said, "I'm goin' to make a dash out to the front. You see what you can make out of that armored vehicle."

Jordan, he observed, with calm incredulity, wanted more. His taste for change and action would never be sated until they wore down his physical energies. Then he would collapse into petulance and streak for home regardless of the mission. It had happened that way once before. It would be an economical action too, since at the point he made for the airstrip Jordan would have reached the level where returns on his energy minimized. But, in the meanwhile, the world would present itself ordinary and highly negotiable, a place wherein he could make his way. Jordan's strength, then, amounted to the insight that everything was too commonplace to be significant and, therefore, nothing worthy of his concern. But Evans' own strength?

Evans was filled with self-disgust.

Abruptly, he realized they were less than five hundred feet up and flying at the Rapido, and that this was the im-port of what Jordan had said about the armored vehicle. Christ!

"Hey, Jordan," he shouted, "where the hell do you think you're going?"

"You wanted to see the tank, didn't you? Couldn't tell for sure all the way up there what the hell it was."

Evans contracted his body and followed Jordan's pointing finger. Since his neck was out anyway, Evans might as well look. "Nuts," said Evans. "It's too close to our troops. We can't fire it. Let's get out of here."

Jordan nodded his head but circled around back again, clearly involved in one of his spasms of curiosity. There wasn't a damn thing Evans could do without making a chicken fool of himself in the kid's eyes. Evans remembered the airstrip, the pyramidal tent with the warm stove where he could read a book or write an undisturbed letter. An infantryman erect in his shallow trench waved to him. He returned the salutation. But this was impossible!

"You goddamn fool, Jordan!"

Long dotted lines of silver streaked by the wing tip. "Jordan," he screamed, "tracers!" Evans' muscles tightened against the coming blow, the piercing, ripping stream of machine gun bullets—rip, rip through his buttocks, his genitals.

Jordan spun the Cub violently around, banked, twisted, flung it steeply diving. The searching tracers followed. Evans pushed against the seat in front of him to make the plane go faster. Panic, and nothing for him to do!

What was Jordan saying, why did he turn that way? "Jordan, what's the matter?" Jordan's lips formed words Evans couldn't hear. Then he saw just the edge of the red stain on Jordan's leg.

Yet Jordan was straightening the plane, inclining its head, and reaching with it for the protecting earth. Evans patted him helplessly on the shoulder. Evans said, "Take it easy, Ralph. Make it, Jordan." Evans heard a ripping, crashing noise behind him. Face distorted, figure twisted, his body reached for impossible safety . . .

Then they were flying level with the earth behind a rise of ground. The wheels were touching the pitted clearing, the plane bouncing. Evans couldn't believe it. Oh, the good man Jordan, skillful Jordan. A little while longer, one last effort . . . They were rolling crazily along the ground, the motor dead.

Evans sat for a second quite still until he remembered his pilot. He seized the white scarf from Jordan's neck while the boy's head slumped suddenly forward. He flung open the side of the cockpit. With stiff, reluctant legs he stumbled out of the plane onto the field. He reached inside the plane, put gentle arms around Jordan's waist and carried him out and laid him down upon the soft earth. There was the wound above the knee, spouting blood in heavy spasms, and the leg all awry. He tried to use Jordan's scarf as a tourniquet.

The infantrymen who ran up to the plane found Evans on the ground beside the pilot, holding desperately to the red silk rag. Two of them with Medical brassards upon their arms took up Jordan.

And then the first tide of sorrow rolled upon Evans for Jordan, for himself, for all the poor universes obliterated from dead men's heads.

"Don't worry, Lieutenant," someone said to Evans, "we'll take care of him."

Don't worry. Evans almost burst into a laugh. Why

there was no need to worry now, weren't they safe? Hadn't they landed? The mission over? And this fellow says not to worry. What a joke. Suddenly Evans couldn't restrain the riot of mirth and sorrow in his chest.

GOING home now to his battalion, southward, in a peep, leaving the front, the plane which squatted behind the hill, and Jordan with a hole in his leg—events, Evans felt, were over for him. He'd been pummeled sufficiently to earn his keep. He surrendered his body to the peep's motion as he had before to the plane's. But this time there was release and quiet for him. There was a kind of peace. If a spectacle marched before him, he would watch it. If it rose inside him, he would observe it there. And if he became weary with too much of it, sleep. No one would interfere.

"Pretty rough, wasn't it, Lieutenant?" The stranger driver asked it to show his sympathy. Answer him.

"Yes."

Let the batteries adjust, let the tracers flow by, he was out of it. He asked for no reasons, he wanted to explore no further. This small tree they were passing, for all its scarred bark, stretched its members flat against the sky. That was somehow consoling. The road his vehicle traveled, pot-holed and blasted as it was, lengthened in a sane direction toward rest.

For Jordan, that common-sense man with the crazy streak, had saved both their lives. He'd simply accepted the bullet ripping him and he'd held on, seeing that what he had to do required that he hold on. After Evans had rested he would go and see Jordan in the hospital and watch the lively eyes make nothing of the whole affair. But that was after he'd rested. Now he felt soothed, almost consecrated, and very weary too. His head nodded. He fell off into sleep as the little vehicle surged its splashy way down Route Six.

But the driver caught him up. "Hey, Lieutenant, there's someone waving at you—in that command car coming toward us." Evans opened his eyes. Colonel Colouris' head protruded beyond the side of the windshield and his outstretched hand waved.

Colonel Colouris, the man who'd ordered him here. Evans had no rancor toward the quiet man in the front seat of the command car. He would want to know what had happened. He'd expect to hear all about it, how Jordan was making out and the rest of it. Only Evans didn't feel too much like talking. Still, he gathered himself together and, when his vehicle stopped at the edge of the road, stepped out and greeted his colonel.

"I heard what happened, Evans. We needn't waste time going over it." The large eyes of the man were troubled.

"Yes, sir," said Evans gravely, "we were shot down." What mattered was not the event, but the common plight of man, of Evans and Ralph Jordan beside the downed Cub. Evans could see this clearly now. How long had he known it? How long had he known to sorrow gravely for the thing that dies and recognize his membership in the community of the dying? It seemed to Evans that there was no beginning to the knowledge, that it was a great fact, perpetually alive inside him—and it seemed strange to him that he had first sensed the knowledge as he tightened the silken tourniquet around Ralph Jordan's leg.

Calmly, the Colonel asked, "How's the plane?"

A simple matter-of-fact question. "The plane? Some

holes in it, I suppose." Now they could marvel together at his and Jordan's luck, at the humanity of man and the incredibility of his fortune. Oh, the words were pompous, but Evans knew what he meant.

"You suppose! Goddamn it man, I could guess that much myself."

Evans' eyes widened.

"Is it too badly damaged to fly out of there?" the Colonel gritted at him.

Evans looked at his colonel with awe.

"What's the matter with you?" Sharp, demanding words.

Evans blinked. "Not a damn thing, Colonel. Lieutenant Jordan was hit. Did you know that, too, Colonel?" The nails on Evans' fingers dug into the palms of his hands.

Colouris looked at him, his lips twisted slightly. Who, Evans wanted to know, was Colonel Colouris? "Yes," said the Colonel. "I know about it. Get out of the way," and nodded sharply to his driver.

The command car lurched forward. Its spinning wheels spattered Evans with mud. He touched a wet spot on his cheek. His quiet was dead now. Had the world been warm one minute previous? It was cold now, icy, it made him shiver in the marrow of his bones.

He hadn't left the war at all. What in hell's name had made him think otherwise? The Colonel was entirely right. May God damn Colonel Colouris.

IN THE raw winter, frontwards, Colonel Colouris' command car rode steadily. Colonel Colouris was worried. He speculated whether if the plane were not too badly damaged the other pilot might not be able to fly it out. If it flew in, it should be able to fly out. It wasn't too easy to replace a Cub. The 794th might easily be hampered in its observed fire, of which you could not get enough. Well, if it were humanly possible, he'd see they got the plane out of there.

"Looks like Evans had a rough time," offered Colouris' S-2 from the rear seat of the command car. Colouris frowned. He'd forgotten the S-2 was back there. That was Colouris' major fault, not making sufficient use of his staff officers.

After all, the Air O.P. was the S-2's responsibility. "What do you think, Captain, do you think he's up to finishing his tour of duty with the Air O.P.?"

"Well, sir, it's hard to say offhand . . ."

Colouris nodded. It was. You could never predict how the fellow would react. Of course Colouris had asked about the plane! He could do nothing about Jordan, but he could do a great deal about the plane. The Colonel shook his head in annoyance. What was he supposed to do, offer his shoulder to be cried upon?

But if Colouris hadn't pulled out fast at the moment he did, Evans might have left him no choice but court-martial. Sentimentalists were very rash. It might be best to leave him to himself for the time being. There was, after all, no point in losing a competent observer in addition to a pilot.

By God, the worst of it was not Evans but Jordan! The chances were Jordan would never return to the battalion. Colouris would be stuck with some inexperienced kid pilot fresh from the States. Colouris glared angrily at his driver as they lurched into a shell hole.

Well, Keller, the other pilot, ought to have arrived at

the plane by the time Colouris did. Perhaps Keller would be able to fly the damned thing out of there. Not an easy assignment, but that couldn't be helped. He'd find out what Keller had in him at the same time . . . Two birds with one stone. Well, this was about as far as he could drive. Colouris consulted his map for the small cross which marked the Cub's location. Get out and walk now.

"Pull up to the side of the road under that tree, driver. I'll be back. Let's go, Captain."

Colouris trudged grim and exasperated through the mud. The captain piled out of the rear of the command car and followed his silent colonel.

These idiots, Colouris was reflecting, probably thought command of a battalion was easy. People like Evans. They knew nothing of the thousand and one worries which beset him. My God, did he want Jordan to get himself hit? Or, for that matter, to be chasing around up here in the muck and cold, hunting a lousy Cub?

"Goddamn it, stop lagging," he said to the Captain.

His years were beginning to wear upon him, considered the Colonel, after another fifteen minutes of hard walking. He was having difficulty maintaining the pace. Deliberately he broke into a slow trot. A man could always do more than he thought he could. Look at his S-2, fifteen years younger than himself, gasping beside him.

Contempt twisted the Colonel's mouth. The man had no hardness in him. Breathing heavily between his teeth, the Colonel plodded on. Only soft people to work with. Where in hell were the unyielding men, the men with the pride to drive themselves further through the mud, through senti-ment, to whatever end they took upon themselves to reach?

There were never many of them, he supposed. His lungs were whistling. The icy air burned them. Strength was the thing.

That jelly-spirited Evans!

At last. In the shadow of a low hill Colouris welcomed the sight of the downed plane. There were four or five figures fidgeting around it. Could Keller be among them, examining the plane? Yes, that was Keller's short, stocky figure. The Colonel slowed to a walk in order not to breathe too heavily when he spoke to Keller. He glanced at the Captain beside him and allowed himself to enjoy the irritated respect of the wheezing staff officer. Men only respected competence and force, except for a few confirmed fools.

Keller stood erect and saluted; Colouris returned the salute negligently. The few curious infantrymen continued unperturbed their inspection of the plane.

"Well?" Colouris demanded.

"A few holes in the wings and fuselage, Colonel. The radio's shot to hell. But so far as I can see she should fly."

Colouris glanced at the Cub. Surprising they both got out of it alive, all right. "Will you chance it, Keller?"

For answer Keller reached into the cabin and turned on the ignition. Walking around to the front, he seized the upper blade of the propeller with both hands, and, putting all his weight behind the effort, dragged down hard and sharp. The engine sputtered, caught, roared out loud in the cold air. Keller walked back to the Colonel. "All ready, sir."

Colouris grinned happily.

Keller climbed into the plane. Pushing forward with both feet against the brake pedals, he inched the throttle forward until the small craft shivered with the pull. Colouris could see him in the cockpit looking quite indifferent.

Suddenly, released and free, no longer shivering, the Cub darted down the short level stretch toward the tree line. With worried eyes Colouris watched it bound up, and, failing, strike with its wheels the field again. It seemed to him almost as though he were watching the Mack once more, watching it move toward the silent earth on the other side of the tapes, and waiting. Only this time he had confidence. He knew Keller would make it.

The Cub's light, soaring body cleared the trees and turned quickly rearwards toward her native airstrip. Colouris watched the plane grow small. He turned to his captain. "This," he said, grinning, "is the way to win a war."

There was no question but that the battalion would fulfill its missions. Colouris wished he could give that confidence to every man in the battalion.

5

HE WOULD write in German both because in English he was almost an illiterate and because, since the battery officers could not read German, some stranger would have to censor his mail. A stranger was more impersonal, official. Corporal Sigmund Ehrlich stared vacantly at the canvas walls of his pup tent rattling slightly in the wind.

Dear Alfred, he wrote. *I have not written to you in a long time because I have been very busy with affairs the censor who reads this will not let me describe. This makes me unhappy because I have never lost my interest in military affairs, and I remember how you and I before America entered the war used to find such angry pleasure following the German campaign in Russia.*

Ehrlich contemplated his paragraph and heard the voices of the others on the other side of the canvas.

Ah, my distant friend, he finally wrote, *I am lying now. I do not care any longer about military affairs, perhaps because I am too much in them. You will not believe it—in so much*

*foolishness here I become foolish myself—but slowly I am be-
coming a psychologist. That is unbelievable, do you not think,
Alfred, for me who have such an incredible lack of talent here
that it is a very old story?*

*I am thinking through why all these strange people in my
section are dangerous to me and to you, too. It is this, Alfred:
the Nazi thinks enough of inferiors like us to commit murder,
which is, after all, a great compliment from one point of view;
but these people I am among, they really know we are inferiors;
they really believe it so that they ignore us or "kid" (there is no
such word in German) us or maybe give us another chance to be
like them! With their magnificent innocence they actually know
before any proof how much better they are than you. That is
what their "kidding" means when they "kid" us, Alfred. You
must never believe that you may join them simply by taking
out citizenship papers and wearing their uniform. They are
protected against you by the tolerance of which they are so very
proud.*

*You will wonder how I live with them; you will say to
yourself what a ridiculous minority of one I surely am. Alfred,
I live by giving them more than they give me. It is not hard.
They are not really strong. I have learned to make hard jokes as
they do; I show I am not intimidated and that they are not
"kidding" me; if necessary, I fight. I show that I am on to them,
as I am. Now, of course, you are wondering how many people
I have managed to offend with my tactless tongue, and I will
admit that they are many. Among them—I tell the truth about
my folly—is my Sergeant Holloway. Sgt. Holloway I find so
carefully fair, so superior, indifferent and ignorant all at once
that if I could manage to live with him in peace then the
millennium would have come, and I should be a 100% American.*

How I ramble! Listen, I will tell you one important thing. Though I am more and more by myself and talk these days to almost no one, I have accomplished one very great achievement. You will be foolish to laugh. But it is that I have made myself disliked for myself alone! You are laughing now. But I have destroyed a great lie about myself as you have not. You are a Jew; Grossberg in my section is also a Jew. You are both disliked for that reason. But me, I am not confused with a delusion. I am a German refugee, a gunner corporal, a strange fellow they have to watch. Padrone calls me Herr Ehrlich. The least of them, the stupid, the ignorant Borman, the dirt over whom Holloway walks—when in his stupid way Borman is angry with me, he calls me "Kraut." And because he is the least of them that is the dearest triumph of all. So, then, since these things they say about me are more or less true, I have won an identity, Alfred. Are you laughing now? I have beaten Herr Hitler.

Now I shall dig my slit trench a little deeper. I hope that you will write to me and that you will remember me to Hansi on Riverside Drive. Perhaps I will write to her also.

TOMLINSON yawned, sat up, and shook his head. After a moment of blank staring at the darkness Tomlinson said, "Guess I'll go git some chow." He pulled on his shoes and laced them. He pulled back the canvas flap which kept rain out, so that the dim light of the ending day sifted through and made Borman blink; so that a current of moist, cold air circulated through the small dugout and perturbed Borman vaguely. "Comin'?" Tomlinson asked in his neutral way, but waited for no answer. Instead he lifted his weight out onto the flat field and stood erect, mess kit in hand. Borman could see his legs like pillars planted in the mud before Tomlinson sloshed off.

Borman, left alone, glanced vacantly at the patch of bleak light where the flap still hung back and watched occasional gray drops of snow silhouette against it. When he put his head through the opening of the tent he saw not fifteen yards from the gun, blackened and split, tumbled helter skelter, the five-gallon gas cans exploded by this afternoon's gunfire. To boost himself up, he placed his hands upon the ground at each side of the hole which the shelter halves protected from the rain. He squeezed the cold, wet earth between his fingers; and his fingers remembered, the back of his neck remembered, the roots of hair upon his head remembered the dead M.P. with his mouth open and his eyes unblinking flesh here beside this very tent when this afternoon's gunfire ceased. The screw of memory whirled at the back of Borman's neck and caught the flesh and dug and caught the spinal nerve and Borman wanted to shout out loud.

He remembered the idiotic screaming of the shells, and a man screaming. He remembered the mine-crammed promises of the ugly, ugly mud; and the blood-caked mattress covers of the Survey crew neatly in line a month ago. He remembered the unanswerable contempt of Sergeant Holloway, and the laughter he hardly ever understood. He remembered that this was a country where a man's bowels twisted and his knees got numb with the squatting—a country where his skin crawled and he yearned for a crap and couldn't and thought that the next shift of his legs would set off the mine the Kraut had left for him. He remembered that he was quite alone and lost in a flat spot among the mountains.

It occurred to him that the others would throw at him again the long screamings with the crash at the end, that again the earth would boil from underneath, that again the weight of strangers would sit upon his shoulders; and he thought how high the mountains were and that he could never see beyond them. The sum of his life stunned Borman.

It picked him up and flung him desperate and wondering from the dugout's opening. He couldn't believe it. He protested to think that he should walk out there in that cold gray, erect; that this vulnerable skin of his, before he could even shout how stinking the deal was, out there in one sudden second should part and spill his guts upon the mud—Borman clasped his arms about himself. He screamed in his heart. He would stay here, where he was safe, where the earth was friendly and warmed by his body, where the blankets, the tin hat, the soiled comic book, the knapsack belonged to no one but himself.

A while later he realized how hungry he was, but thought of the long deadly walk to the kitchen between two white tapes under a wide-open sky, and told himself, screw the chow. But poor, poor Randolph Borman would surely starve here. Would those bastards, would those sonsuv-bitches ever bring him food? Never. They would let him starve and laugh and howl as he starved. He thought about their laughter for a while and then decided that he would show them. How he would love to show them all. The tent flap had dropped. He tore it open. But the wind curled in and chilled the sweat upon his cheek and froze the anger in him.

He wouldn't go out. He would never go out, not out there. The others were crazy to go out, they were stupid, stupid bastards. And Borman was hungry. Gentle little sobs shook his massive chest. Why, they had trapped him. And it was all unbelievable. He couldn't imagine why anyone should want to trap Randolph Borman.

He heard Tomlinson returning.

Tomlinson examined the black square of his dugout's entrance. Where was Borman? He hadn't seen Borman at chow and Borman never missed chow. What was that funny crying sound? "Yuh in there, Borman?" he called. The funny noise quieted.

"Borman," he called gently, "that you in there?"

Borman heard his drawl. Borman, sucking in his breath, whispered harshly, "Yeah." But then all at once the words flew up at Borman from himself, bitterly, loudly, condemning his past, his present, his future. "Yeah, it's me, Borman."

"Well, ah'll be damned," said Tomlinson to the opening. "Don' yuh think maybe yuh might be wantin' some chow?" asked Tomlinson, gently prodding the man in the hole.

Originally he'd bunked with him merely because Borman was silent and dumb, almost like no one; and Borman would dig when Tomlinson hated to touch a shovel.

"No, screw you. Le' me alone."

"Yuh big lump o' crap," said Tomlinson. "Sick?"

Borman's voice turned to a wail. "No. Le'me alone."

"If you ain't sick," said Tomlinson gravely, his eyes lit with interest, "how come yuh ain't eatin'? Gittin' a bang out a stayin' in that li'l ol' hole?"

"Yeah, I like it, ya hear? I like it. Go 'way an' le' me alone."

"Ah think," said Tomlinson "yuh don't like it at all. Ah think yore lyin' to me, Borman. Yuh know what more ah'm thinkin', Randy ol' ass-hole buddy?" Tomlinson chuckled. "Ah think yore too damn scared t'come out."

Borman's bitterness became a scream. "I'm not scared, I tell ya. I'm not scared, you bastard."

No doubt now, no doubt at all. Borman, the big lug with the big, diggin' muscles, scared! The grin spread around

Tomlinson's mouth. "Hey, fellers," he called out, "come heah an' see somethin' worth seein'." Three or four cannoneers came rattling their mess gear.

Ehrlich came out of his tent. Tomlinson saw him. They stared steadily at one another. "You care t' know somethin', Corporal?" said Tomlinson. "Borman's scared. What yuh think o' that, Corporal?" But his face was quiet as he watched Ehrlich come toward them.

"Yah?" said Ehrlich.

"Yuh sure said a mouthful, Corp'ral," said Tomlinson, and turned quickly upon his toes to face Borman's hole. "Hey, Randy," he shouted into it, raw-voice, "Corp'ral Ehrlich here thinks yer too chicken t'come out. Yuh gonna let him git away with that? Come on outa there an' show 'im." Slowly he winked at Ehrlich.

What Borman shouted, they couldn't make out. They heard sobs.

"I be damned," ejaculated Ehrlich. Borman! Slowly Ehrlich began to grin. He ignored Tomlinson and all the other little men watching him. Borman! A vast and amused contempt for Borman, for all of them, came over Ehrlich. Did Tomlinson expect him to back away? "Hey, Borman," he shouted. "Whatcha 'fraid for?"

Fury rose in Borman's breast; fury and pain made him stutter. "Oh you l-lousy b-bastard, I ain't scared, I ain't . . ."

Ehrlich laughed. "He sure as hell is," said Ehrlich. He, too, could kid.

Tomlinson stood by chuckling. Borman's heavy sobs rose louder from the dugout. Someone said, "Cut it out."

"Hey, Borman," said Ehrlich. "Come out an' say hello to the boys," and slapped his hand against his thigh.

"Oh," said Borman in his hole, "oh." He reached out his beefy arms in the blackness and shook them.

"Borman, you lousy bastard you, you yeller?" Ehrlich, hands upon his hips, stuck his chin out, screamed down into the hole, shouting laughter.

They heard a roaring in the earth. They heard a scuffling in the dugout and a howl. They drew back. Ehrlich's blue eyes wavered, admitted doubt. Tomlinson poised upon the balls of his feet. In the faded light they saw Borman's fleshy hand stretched out of the ground to grip the earth, and then the other, while the roaring loudened. Borman's face, wrath-struck, appeared.

"Jesus Christ, fellers, run!"

Borman's thick chest heaved up out of the earth, but no one ran except for the man who'd shouted. Instead, they watched Borman scramble clumsily to his feet. They saw the open mouth. The thick rage tumbling from it appalled them. Borman stretched out his arms and then fear seized them by the scruffs of their necks and hurled them apart.

"Borman's gone nuts." The cry blazoned across the gray murk hovering over the field. "Borman's gone nuts." One man scampered for his carbine.

In the Executive position, Captain Fuller and Lieutenant Grostock heard the call and looked at one another, then dropped the cards they held. They heard someone half falling down the stairs and saw Cronin's livid face. "Come quick, Captain. Come quick. Borman's crazy."

Fuller, bareheaded and buckling on his .45 as he ran, followed Cronin in his dash into the open. "There he is," said Cronin, and he pointed to where Borman hulked over the ground his tormentors had fled. Fuller's mouth set as he

heard the long groan and roar issue from the big man's chest.

"You men," he said brusquely to several of the cannoneers who had run up to him, "put down those damned carbines and grab 'im," while his own hand gripped his automatic's butt. "Let's go."

Borman saw his quiet, bunched comrades come toward him. He saw them break up and some of them pass behind him. He saw their clenched fists and reaching arms. His mouth closed in awe. What was the matter with them? They seized him by the arms, they held him by the waist, they piled upon him and he could not shake them off. No matter how hard he flexed his muscles, he could not shake them off.

Tears, unperceived, coursed down over the mud that caked Borman's face. He, Borman, held down, head in the mud, frail, defeated, cried.

Fuller, watching his man, felt a sudden burst of sorrow. "Holloway," he said wearily, "see that he gets to the Medics."

They took Borman. They stood him upon his feet, still gripping him. They pushed and pulled him so that he had to walk over the ruts, through the muck which held he did not know what snares, under an unpredictable sky. They made him stand straight in the night where enemies assailed and where there were no comforters. And all the while he sobbed. He, Borman, poor lousy Borman with his mouthful of mud and his headful of wonder.

CAPTAIN FULLER slammed his cards down. A while ago he'd called up Doc Barnes and told him the boys were

bringing Borman down to him, told Doc the story. Now he'd had enough of cards. He looked angrily at Grostock.

"Damn it," he said, sweeping Grostock into his confidence with his anger, "this is the best firing battery in the battalion. That's no bull. I know it is. What the hell is the matter with it?"

Grostock, seated at the card game they'd resumed in the Exec position after Borman blew up, didn't know.

Grostock said placatingly and fiercely, "There ain't a damn thing wrong, Andy. It's the best goddamn battery there is."

Fuller stared at the space over Grostock's shoulder for a moment. "Haven't I taken care of the men?" he demanded. "Don't I take care of you?"

"You sure as hell do, Andy," said Grostock. "There ain't nobody with a legitimate bitch in the whole goddamn outfit."

"You got any ideas what more we can do? Any kind of ideas about anything. Come on. Let's have it." Fuller was bitter. But he meant it. "Come on. Speak up."

Grostock had no ideas.

"Then what got into Borman? And what the blazes come over Dave Evans? We used to get along okay. Now I got to punch him in the jaw, the knucklehead."

"Ya had to," said Grostock. "Why take the jerk to heart? You couldn' let 'im talk that way in front of Crown. Jeez, it was even for his own good."

"Sure, sure," Fuller said, his forehead all wrinkled with earnestness. "But why does he go off like that in the first place? Okay, he had a couple of drinks. So what?"

"Search me," said Grostock mildly.

Fuller paid no attention. "Borman, the big slob, has to go and blow his top now. Christ."

Fuller, tight mouthed, glared. On top of everything below him and everything on top, Borman! In fact, since the last position nothing, just about, seemed to work for him like it was supposed to. Okay, okay. He'd done his job as a battery commander should, tried to keep up morale, confidence. He'd continue. But somewhere there was an unfairness. He was getting damned fed up.

When the phone rang, Fuller grabbed at the receiver. "Yes!" He nearly shouted it. "Yes, this is Captain Fuller." Pause. "Tell 'im I'll be there." He slammed the receiver in place. "The Colonel," he said, "wants all battery commanders immediately."

Fuller put on his pistol belt and helmet. He'd come, all right. He knew his job. But by God he was sore clean through and through. Somehow, some way, somebody had been kidding him. He thought it might be the Colonel. He didn't know. He didn't even know how he had been kidded. But he was fed up, fed up. Fuller swung out of the Exec hole without a word.

Now Colonel Colouris was talking at them. Fuller sat there in the Colonel's stone C.P., and the Colonel with black rings under his eyes big enough for a week's drunk was telling them all his score.

"Gentlemen," the old bastard was saying, "we're getting the go-ahead. We're moving. You all know the area." Sure Fuller knew it. Colouris showed it to them yesterday. You had to watch where you spat or you'd hit a Limey dogface in the eye. "We hit it tomorrow just after dusk."

"I talked Group Headquarters into it," said the Colonel, and his face was twisted and happy and set like a rock.

"They need heavy stuff to smash these points around Cassino." He pointed out the points on the map. They were little white houses with walls a yard thick. "Anything that close to front-line elements has to get accurate fire. I told Colonel Grey that meant howitzers up close with concrete-piercing fuses, and that meant us."

The Colonel grinned. "At first they didn't want to risk more than one gun. Risk! I convinced 'em we might as well have the whole battalion available for any target of opportunity; that it's hard to do much damage to dispersed artillery. Surprise hell out of the Krauts, eh?"

Fuller saw that all the audience was with the Colonel, that the Colonel had them all with him, had them all feeling big. Then the Colonel clamped down. "Tomorrow morning," he said, all stern and suddenly cold, "you gentlemen will meet me here at seven for final reconnaissance. Each of the firing battery commanders will have available one Mack truck. I have in mind, of course, the same check we worked when we came into our present position. I see no reason why it shouldn't work again."

Neither did Fuller. The Colonel had paused, but this wasn't the end. The Colonel was looking them all over slowly, and Fuller observed an unpleasant curiosity in the midst of the man's coldness.

"When you pull into position the day after tomorrow," said the Colonel, "I want you prepared, unless you hear otherwise from me, to carry through any fire mission regardless of enemy reaction. It is entirely likely that between now and then I'll be able to arrange final co-ordination with the British infantry in the vicinity of the strong points we're firing. That will mean they will be set to take immediate advantage of our shoot. Of course I realize we have always chased the men to cover at the first sign of enemy fire. That is no longer economical. The shoot will not be discontinued."

"Christ, Colonel," burst out Fuller. "That's kind of rough." He would like to have said a lot more. Fuller burned with resentment. This was *his* battery the bastard was talking about. He could also feel the other battery commanders behind him as he prepared for the worst.

"Agreed," said the Colonel and then talked right over him, louder and louder. "Every officer the battalion can spare will be sent out on observation duty for that day. The Air O.P. will arrange to have a plane constantly in the air. Group will lend us observers, and will alert all artillery observers in the area. We should pick up the first sign of counter-battery action. And we will be prepared to hit back. Only one of our batteries will fire at a time; the others will be held in readiness to protect it, if necessary, with their fire. Given foresight and preparation, gentlemen, any circumstance can be beaten. Any circumstance, get it?"

Fuller believed for a moment that the Colonel would reach out and grip him and each one of them there. The Colonel shoved his hands into his pockets. "Major Hogarth's departure comes at a bad time," he said. "I hated to lose him. One doesn't ordinarily lose one's S-3 as a casualty." Fuller thought he heard uncertainty loosen the taut voice, but quickly the voice stretched hard and tight again, spat out its words at Fuller, at all of them sitting there in the small room blinking at the Colonel. "Nevertheless, the battalion will displace forward. Captain Berelli and I will handle the Fire Direction end. I want excuses from no one. That, gentlemen, is all."

It couldn't have been uncertainty, Fuller decided. The Colonel had everything figured too well. There was no doubt in Fuller's mind but that the Colonel would carry through the plan he'd thrown at them. Otherwise he never would have mentioned it. There was no doubt in Fuller's mind that he himself would carry through upon his own level what the Colonel would carry through upon his. Even the intent to expose Baker battery as the Colonel planned had become part of the normal order of things.

Only somehow the Colonel was kidding him and he didn't know how or where or why. Only . . . Fuller grinned broadly. Hogarth, the casualty! Hogarth had gotten himself a case of syph and every officer in the goddamn battalion knew it. Thinking of it now made Fuller's anger wonderfully gleeful.

CAPTAIN BARNES asked Holloway what he was waiting for. "Glad to have you around, Sergeant," he said. "But there's nothing you can do about your man." Doctor Barnes, whom nobody could ever get to call Captain, poured Holloway another drink.

Holloway gazed gravely at the unshaven little man sitting there with his feet outstretched patting his little belly, and ignored the man's remark. "What are you going to do about Borman?"

For the last half hour, ever since Doc had come out of the small room where Borman was now, and sent back the guards Holloway had posted, Doc had been amusing himself dodging that issue. Why? But Holloway played the game and waited patiently. It wasn't, after all, a very amusing game. Doc would tire.

Doc sat back and contemplated Holloway cheerfully for a moment. Then he pulled his legs back underneath the chair.

"I've been waiting," said Doc, "for Fuller or Grostock to show up. Apparently, they're not coming. Apparently, they think that what happens to Borman now is my responsibility and not theirs."

Holloway sat forward. Finally.

"Of course, that's ridiculous. The science of medicine merely suggests the event most likely to happen under given conditions and offers prescriptions in case you decide to avoid or live with it. If most doctors weren't schoolmarms at heart, they would realize as much and avoid inflicting their local prejudices upon their browbeaten patients by telling them what they ought to want."

Nuts. As Doc saw it, every man was in the Army except himself. That made him a bad man to deal with. That meant that you had to sit here listening to that crap because you were in the Army and knew it. Holloway moved impatiently.

"Quiet," said Doc. "Now it follows that I am in no position to realize either Fuller's or Grostock's or for that matter your expectations. I can't tell you what is to be done with Borman because I can't prescribe what you ought to want. Are you with me, Sergeant?"

"No," said Holloway flatly. "Something has to be done about Borman and you know it." Not that Holloway gave a damn what it was, by God. But, remembering Borman on the Army cot in the other room and the absolute amazement in his little pig's eyes, he knew that something had to be done and that he had to find out what it was.

Doc was staring curiously at him. What was underneath

the little man's big words, Holloway wondered. "You had better follow me, Sergeant. It turns out that you are all the military authority I have available. In consequence, I'll give you what I think to be the facts about Borman and you must tell me what to do . . . You see, you are, in a way, his nearest of kin."

"Doc," said Holloway, "I've had enough kidding. Cut it out."

Doc Barnes jumped suddenly to his feet. "This is no kidding," he said. "Or if it is, it's the most serious kidding anyone ever kidded. How in hell's name am I to tell them what to do with Borman? No, Sergeant. You make the decision. It's yours. I'll tell you what the score is, but I want nothing to do with your addition. Nothing, get me?"

But Doc was sincere. Doc almost yelled what he said. Doc wanted him to make a decision!

"Why pick on me?" said Holloway.

"Because," snapped Doc, his mild manner all gone now, "because Borman's in your section. You helped him along into his present stew. Because I can't get anyone else to pick on. Because suddenly I'm sick of being a goddamn moral camouflage net garnished with an M.D. degree. Your boy Borman's sitting there waiting. Well, face up to it. He's your boy. He's also Fuller's and the Colonel's, but he's yours too, and you're here and I'm putting it to you. Will you or won't you make a choice?"

Will you, won't you, won't you, will you, join the dance. Holloway laughed.

Doc sat down abruptly. "It is also significant," he ground out, "that I can get away talking like this only with a sergeant, as you have probably observed. Nevertheless, Holloway, I mean what I say. I act as camouflage for no one in this Borman business. You can choose as well as the next. How about it?"

A while ago, Holloway told himself, he never would have believed this possible. A while ago he would have been a staff sergeant. Suddenly, he was nearest of kin. Holloway grinned faintly. To the fouled-up Borman. Well, tomorrow he would think himself crazy and this man also. But tonight with this screwball doctor he could play games.

"All right," said Holloway. "We'll see. Let's hear the score. Only make it simple with no more crap about medicine."

Doc Barnes sank back. Holloway saw an element of sorrow in his eyes. "Have another drink," said Doc. They had another drink. He felt an annoying affection for Doc Barnes.

"It's really not especially complicated," said the Doc quietly. "As I see it, Borman's a simple man. Borman's a normal man. That's his trouble.

"Borman, I gather, spent his life in a small-town grocery store. I gather he's fond of his sister and dogs. He's dull, but by no means an imbecile. And he cannot, no matter how much you explain it to him, understand why he must be subject to mines, shells, and, if you will forgive me, Holloway, you. Not that he doesn't have roughly appropriate verbal responses. If you ask him, he'll tell you there's a war on and we've got to lick the Krauts and the Japs. But those are only words. The Krauts and the Japs have no connection with his present experience. That present experience seems incomprehensible and insane to him."

Was this what Holloway had to make a decision about? "Christ," he said, "Borman's not the only one."

Doc shrugged. "I'm leaving it up to you," he said. "The point is, if you will, that some people are too sane for the world and they go mad. Borman is one of those.

"All right," said Doc suddenly. "You get the picture. I can send him back and call it 'battle fatigue.' He might get out of the war. He might not. Or I can return him to the outfit. If he returns, he'll probably keep going for a while. This whole business has frightened the boy. You'll get some use out of him. But eventually he's going to blow up. And when he does, he's finished. Completely finished." Doc paused, and said quietly, "What do you want me to do with your man Borman?"

"I see," said Holloway. "You want to decide whether I should have you send a perfectly sane sonuvabitch back for 'battle fatigue' simply because he hasn't the guts to take it and beat it."

Doc Barnes grinned sarcastically. The friendliness seemed to dry out of him. "That's one way of putting it. Only remember that he doesn't have what you call the guts and that you can't talk it into him."

"You want me to decide whether to make one big exception of this big turd Borman. You're willing to save anything, aren't you Doc?"

"Forget me," said Doc. "I don't have anything either to save or throw away."

Holloway laughed and enjoyed the way the Doc drew back. He laughed because this was the greatest joke in all the goddamned army and he hadn't the faintest idea why he was in it except that the whole damn world had screwed itself up and he might as well do the same.

"Next time, Doc," he said, "when you have a decision

to make, don't call me in on it. Let me alone. That's fair
warning. Because next time I'll tell you and your doctoring
to go screw themselves." Holloway smiled happily at Doc.
"But now, Doc, so far as I'm concerned, you can send the
sad sonuvabitch home."

6

BAKER BATTERY'S howitzers are emplaced at twenty-yard intervals, deep in the bank of the narrow dirt road which the Executive officer of Battery B walks with an aiming circle over his shoulder. The earth shows raw around the new gun positions. Shells and powder cases are dumped around them. Only the camouflage nets rudely draped over the guns make the gesture of concealment. Some of the cannoneers have put up shelter halves, but most sleep rolled in their blankets upon a level patch. Grostock curses the banging of the British twenty-five-pounders a little further down the road, which breaks the rest of his men. They have important work to do soon.

Grostock is going from gun section to gun section. "Let the men rest," he tells each section chief. "Improve the position later," he grumbles at them. He hates to tell them that. If you are an Executive, you know that a battery's position should be neat and camouflaged. Also, it should have deep slit trenches and fox holes. Grostock's heavy eyebrows stay together with fatigue and irritation. All night long he has worked with his gun crews. Only at dawn has he been able to report to Fire Direction, battery laid and ready to fire.

Grostock looks angrily over his right shoulder and notices again how flat it is out there. Between the battery and the enemy are only a few broken trees, a narrow river and, they tell him, some infantry. The battery sits exposed to almost anyone who cares to look. The knowledge that the slit trenches should be a lot deeper gnaws at Grostock. But let 'em rest, let 'em rest a little bit because you had to shoot especially straight and accurate today. Captain Andy had told him. The Colonel had just told Captain Andy.

Captain Andrew Fuller stands around the kitchen truck with a cup of coffee in his hand. He is very intent. He is trying hard to explain the situation to his men when they straggle up for coffee. It has always been his deliberate policy to keep the men aware of the score but now as he watches these weary, soiled, unshaven strangers, his cannoneers, line up for breakfast, Andrew Fuller feels that it is uncommonly imperative that he give them the score and that he can never explain enough, no matter how long he stays here at the truck under the camouflage net gruffly waylaying them.

He has even rigged up a situation map upon a map board and leaned it against the kitchen truck's left rear wheel. He calls one bleary audience to the board, and then another. He doesn't mind repeating himself.

"You see," he explains to them, "we're here to knock out the Kraut strong points. Fire Direction has assigned our battery these points." He looks at them earnestly, to see that he holds his audience. "Here. Here. Here," he says, pointing to little squares marked in upon the map. "We have a battalion observer with the infantry now. That's Captain Harolds, the S-2. When he's in position we'll start adjusting on the points in our sector. Charlie Battery's already firing. Hear 'em?" They heard.

"We've got to be accurate," he pleads with them. "Our forward elements are right up close to those damned houses. That's why we have to be up close now. So we can reduce dispersion. Get it? One wrong round may hit our own men."

"This is unusual," and they had to get it, they had to understand. "This is close-up support with the heaviest artillery on the front except for the two-forties." Men are unpredictable. They keep themselves to themselves. You never know when you have them. He simply has to explain to them. He scowls and tries to take them into his confidence, tries to enter theirs, with his heavy scowl. "This is so goddamn important," he tells them, "that we're to keep on firing no matter what happens. No matter what happens, we finish the mission. Get it?"

They had to get it, all of them exchanging glances; they had to understand that the Colonel said today was more important than their lives, that the war said so, and not Andrew Fuller.

Everything is new with the sun upon it. The sun through the camouflage net makes blurry patterns on everybody's O.D.'s when they stand still long enough. This is their first morning together, this place and Pfc. Pady Padrone. Padrone looks curiously around while Fuller talks. Look at that gray old hill in front of him making like it was a mountain.

If the cold air bothers him as he half listens, it isn't just because he's chilly, because he isn't; he has his combat jacket zippered up to his neck and his dirty hands in his pockets. The air smells too fresh. It seems to be meaning things he can't make out. A funny kind of opening-out smell it is, hinting of something he can't pick up, but there all right. He can almost pick it up, too—but just when it seems to say what it wants to say, Whoosh the wind swirls in and it's just a fresh stink again.

This, as Mama would say, is what comes of getting yourself overtired.

"FIRE MISSION, GODDAMN IT GET THE LEAD OUTA YOUR ASS!"

The enormous tube lifts its head so slow and certain that there is nothing can hold it down; it is like the sun cruising along the sky in the middle of the day.

"FIRE!"

Quick flame flaring at the muzzle, the live steel animal lunging back in recoil, the small licking smoke at the tube's end, distinct smell and flavor of explosion—Holloway feels as though he has lived in the presence of this all his life.

Phone to ear, Holloway chuckles. "Lieutenant Grostock wants us to be sure and keep four men on the rammer staff." Hoots.

Number One gun is adjusting on its target. The other guns silently mimic the movements of its tube. Holloway eases into a kind of peace. Now he lives compact within the space of action. He can eye the present the way he saw a small snake eye a bird's nest once before the war. He coils his body tight and wary for the future and drops fatigue out of account.

"FIRE!" Padrone pulls the lanyard. Three seconds later

his chest still buzzes. Sometimes for no reason the concussion shakes you and makes you vibrate like a tight string; other times it passes you by.

Dan MacCarthy shudders with his need for sleep. Little waves of fatigue wash over him and recede, leaving him light minded and staring. His two hours of sleep are not enough. He needs sleep. Yet the gun, the rammer staff he pushes at with the others, the other men themselves, are preternaturally clear to him. And he isn't sleepy. Ideas and images jerk through his mind like small bright fish darting; when he catches one it dissolves. His hands do his work for him.

"FIRE!"

Standing beyond the reach of the tube's recoil, he can see the shell as it rises out of the tube and hear its whistle as the whistle whirs into the dim blue sky to vanish on the other side of the hill. He stands and waits for the next command. He finds himself vacuous and irritating, reaches for meanings but can't find them. This, he tells himself, is one day in the dark night of his soul. He blinks. He wishes he could go to sleep and come home again to himself.

"FIRE!"

But they become aware of a line of sound screaming crossways to the line of their own gun's projectile and this surprises them. Their eyes open wide. They have all simply stopped short. They are listening to the loudening sound and it isn't winter or daylight or Italy as they listen, but one pure sound. Some drop flat. The immense crash they hear shakes them as their own gun never had.

"About two hundred yards ahead of us up on the hill," Holloway reports into his phone while the echo dies. They are all looking to him. They remember the Captain's explanations. Nobody wants to believe the German shell because this time they cannot hide. "Okay, guys," Holloway says. "What the hell are you standing around for? Load 'er up!"

They load up. But they move quickly now. They glance over their shoulders as they work. The mission had better be important, or—or what?

"Screw it," yells Grossberg, "screw it," having managed to disbelieve the German shell. "If this takes me home I'm willin'." He heaves his full weight against the rammer.

"Yah," yells Cronin, "yah!" jeering at nothing Holloway could see.

"All right," Holloway says tightly, "don't get yourself in an uproar. That one may only have been a stray."

Holloway listens intently at his phone and amuses himself watching Ehrlich blinking at them with his mouth slightly open.

"FIRE!" He has shouted Grostock's command. Number One gun smashes out together with the others of the battery, and the field shakes.

But Holloway now decides that the German round was more than a stray. Because another is coming in. They hear it distinctly. Nine men between the split trails bend at the waist and drop. Not Padrone. Pady has the lanyard in his hand. Erect but for his hunched shoulders, he fixes his eyes on Holloway and feels the long incoming screech tear down upon him. He is waiting for Holloway's hand to drop in the signal to fire.

He can't hear Holloway yell "Fire" because the Kraut round goes off that very moment and it is the heart of the world splitting apart. He can even see that red heart flash into existence on the other side of the road behind Holloway. But he also sees Holloway's hand come dropping down and pulls the lanyard. Roar blares out next to him so that Pady can hardly tell the two explosions apart and it is one prolonged ear-racking bellow which makes him stagger and his mind grovel.

It's okay, though. Dan MacCarthy thanks the Lord. There is Holloway talking into the phone very hard about how they were bracketed, and Pady seems all right and no one seems hurt.

"Hey, Grossy," Pady says with his voice all cracked, "are you still willin'?"

"Heh," says Grossberg.

Carefully, carefully, Ehrlich brings back the cross hairs to the aiming stake. He hasn't slept in two nights, but he is gleeful with a mad, frightened, sappy kind of glee. His eyes burn as he stares through the panoramic sight.

"Drop flat, you guys," says Holloway quietly but so that his voice penetrated the exaggerated, sun spattered silence. "Nobody stand up except when we're loading the piece. On your bellies or in the slit trenches. That's it. As soon as you've finished your job get down there."

"Not you, Pady," he says, and there is a grave apology in his voice. "I need you to fire the piece. You see, Pady, I have to stay in contact with Grostock, so I have to stay here by the phone."

Pady knows it as well as Holloway. He'd forgotten for the moment only. He also knows there is nothing to be done about it and when there is nothing to be done about something, he, Pady Padrone, always does it. Slowly Pady rises to his feet and takes the lanyard. His mouth quivers and he waits.

"Goddamn it, Ehrlich, goddamn it, man, get away from

that screwin' gun sight," grits Holloway. He needs Ehrlich too. He needs all of them. He must conserve them all. Everyone must be conserved.

Holloway wonders vaguely how the other gun crews are making out.

The next enemy round explodes one hundred yards to the front and left of Holloway's gun. Very soon now, very soon he knows that the Krauts will be firing for effect. He tells Grostock so over the phone. Grostock interrupts him. "Fire," commands Grostock. "Fire," orders Holloway.

"Oh, fer Chris' sake, Cap'n," Grostock pleads over the phone in the Exec house, "they got my guns bracketed. Cut out the screwin' mission fer a minute, fer Chris' sake, what d'you think is goin' t' happen?" He pounds with his free hand on the table.

Berelli, the Assistant S-3, doesn't answer. "Hey!" Grostock yells over the phone, and turns his contorted face to Andy Fuller. Fuller stares at the ground.

"Listen, Grostock," says a hard, insistent, new voice in Grostock's ear. The goddamn Colonel! "The mission will continue. I want you to tell this to your men. We're hurting them. That's why they're firing back. And there's an attack scheduled when we're finished. An attack, get it? Our infantry are following up on the wreckage we're making. Tell the men that. Tell them Group has spotted the enemy artillery firing at you and that there's a mission on the way to silence them now. Able and Charlie Batteries are firing it. Tell them that, and for God's sake tell them to hit the ground when they hear the counterbattery and to fire between the Kraut volleys."

Fuller sees Grostock, frantic-faced, seize the phone to the

guns and hears Grostock's teeth grit as he clamps down upon himself and hears him talk into the phone hard and fast telling the men what the Colonel said.

Fuller says, "I'm going down to them," and walks out.

Holloway makes out Fuller's figure leaving the Exec house and moving on the run to Number Four gun.

Holloway tells the men what Grostock has told him. He has them all flat on the ground around him. He yells it at them as he kneels at the phone pole, and their faces look up at him timid and awed and hoping. Holloway has never seen his men this way before.

Tomlinson's curses roll hot and liquid from his tongue. He rolls over on his side. He pulls a crushed cigarette package from his pocket and puts a crushed cigarette to his lips. He curses it and forgets to light it; then remembers that he may not light it here anyway, and hates.

Holloway calls out the quadrant setting. "Load 'er up," he yells. "Load 'er up while we've got the chance."

"To hell with the screwin' mission," someone yells, and breaks for a shallow trench. Holloway finds he doesn't want to know who ran for the trench. He helps where the men need help. Besides, the sky is filling with sound now and there's only a second or two before the German barrage will strike at him!

"FIRE!" he screams at Padrone; and Padrone yanks at the lanyard with all his strength and dives for the ground while the howitzer hurls its shell into the dropping wall of steel and slides back in one smooth and rapid motion.

Panting, his chest resounding from the gun crash, fearful, proud, defiant, above all fearful, Holloway tries to force his way into the torn sod between the trails. He can hear Dan MacCarthy scream.

All around Baker Battery's four howitzers the broken earth suddenly blooms with the fire of the enemy. Concussion and concussion tremble the ground against which the men press. Bodies of noise roll down among them, among the guns, rolling behind them, in front of them. Shell fragments whang against the trails, against the tube, bury themselves in the earth. The men pull themselves into themselves; they want to hide in themselves; they close their eyes. They hear above explosion only the screaming in their hearts.

For five seconds this lasts. Then it stops. Quiet is a large, open hand which comes out from the continent of smoke drifting over them, and stops it.

OPEN-MOUTHED, Grostock holds the Fire Direction phone to one side of his head and the direct line to the howitzers at the other.

The Exec room is hazy with the lung-biting powder smoke. The recorder corporal crouches against the wall with his pad on his knee and blinks palely at Grostock.

Grostock tries again. "Quadrant 362," he says into the gun phone.

Nobody answers.

"Wait," he says into the Fire Direction phone. "Barrage must'a blew my lines to the guns." He puts down the phone while it yammers at him. He is cut off from his guns.

But they are his guns! Rage bubbles in his spirit, and then jets through his mind. Why isn't Evans here? Why did Evans have to be on that Air O.P. at a time like this? But the recorder is here. The recorder sits stupid-faced before him.

"Look," he growls at the recorder. "Look," he repeats

in his great anxiety. "You go on up to that window with the Fire Direction phone. I'm gonna be standin' as close to the guns as I can get so as I can also hear you. You're gonna call off the screwin' Fire Direction commands t'me, an' I'm gonna call 'm to the guns.

"Fer Chris' sake, get the hell off yer ass," he yells at the recorder, and in an ecstasy of worry makes for the middle of the field from which he had originally laid the guns. The section chiefs should be able to hear him from there; and if the recorder yells loud enough, Grostock can hear the recorder.

Because Grostock is never, never, never gonna be parted from his screwin' guns, like Evans was. Ya hear him, anybody?

Someone yells, "Medics!" The cry penetrates the chests of every man.

"Quadrant 362!" bawls Grostock from the center of his field. The powder burning high and bright in the field below him scorches his cheek.

"Medics to Number Three!"

"Three Six Two!" yell the chiefs of section confirming that they have it right.

"For Chris' sakes someone get the Medics!"

Captain Fuller at Number Four sees the two battery aid men running past him on the little road.

"Fire when ready!" screams Grostock.

Long ago there had been laughter and a drink and a woman looking at Fuller's shoulders underneath the Captain's bars. Now they are trying to load up Number Four. The men are milling about in the space between the trails and one of them holding one side of the tray with the shell stumbles. Fuller tries to help.

"For God's sake, Captain, we can handle it ourselves!"

The sergeant yells at him. Is this his battery, Fuller wonders? Once he knew these men and guns were his to do with as seemed best. Now he sees that the battery has pushed him off and all his claims. He can no longer deny that he has no battery.

In Fire Direction Captain Berelli, the assistant S-3, is busy on the phone instructing Grostock's recorder. Colouris himself has taken over the control of Able and Charlie Batteries' counter-battery fire against the enemy guns assaulting Baker Battery. He has just received the observer's sensing.

"Able and Charlie, six rounds!" the Colonel orders. That means his guns will now fire at his command forty-eight two-hundred-pound projectiles.

He moves Baker Battery against the German infantry. The Germans counter with artillery against Baker. But Colouris keeps Baker going and counters with Able and Charlie against the Kraut artillery. All the parts of his organization work together and the logic of foresight unfolds. "I want those rounds out fast as they can fire 'em," he grits at Able and Charlie computers.

Colouris' eyes glisten behind their steel-rimmed glasses. He sits at the nerve of events.

There is a quivering smile upon Pady's lips.

"Fire," says Holloway. Pady fires.

Snubbing him, aiming at the empty sky, the tube blasts and shakes Padrone, and then he hears the other howitzers fire out of rhythm.

Even now the sky is blue with a fuzzy white veil over it, he notes. Padrone drops to the ground. The cold has a lonesome sting. Pady is awfully weary. They should stop playing this monotonous game.

But now he hears it, now he can't help hear the sound of all the pianos ever made, dropped by all the moving men ever born, down from the sky over them; and his muscles go rigid so that they hurt and he forgets everything and in his pure agony, waits.

He would like to go home.

Ehrlich also awaits the initial downrush of the shells.

Deliberately he raises his head above the shallow slit trench he has dug. No one is here. No one. Wherever he can see, every man has left the earth, leaving behind a spattering of trees, a few howitzers, and a few quivering sacks of clothing here and there in part exposed above the ground.

They are hiding. Ehrlich wants to die. He burns with contempt; he bares his teeth, because no one can see him. Who tells him he must live? He defies, he accuses. He hears the snarl of the writhing shells. The passion flares in him. Come on! Kill him! Now! Oh, how desperately he would like to die!

The shells snatch at his throat. He pulls his head down and buries his forehead in the fresh earth. The detonating shells crumble pieces of earth from the sides of the trench into his ears, the fine fuzz of earth films his face. He knows that he might die here in his grave and he presses his cheek against its shaken bottom. He tastes the earth.

With the sudden silence, Grostock raises his head. He looks for the guns and only for the guns. The guns are still there. Smoke wreathes in and out among them, but they are planted firmly in their places and an occasional cannoneer rises tentatively.

They haven't hurt his guns after all. Grostock chokes

123

on the war smoke, but realizes it isn't easy to hurt eight-inch howitzers. The realization is a sudden view of mountains. Grostock grins innocently and happily.

Then his eyebrows form a single, intense line. There is business still in hand.

He hears, "Able and Charlie are firing for effect! Able and Charlie are firing for effect!" The recorder is yelling it at him.

Grostock relays the message. "Able and Charlie are firing for effect!" Mother of God, let them shoot straight. Grostock crosses himself.

"Medics!"

But there is a chance. Able and Charlie are firing for effect.

"Medics!" Again. Who is it this time?

They have helpers in the world, allies.

"Quadrant 372," shouts Grostock.

They run to the guns to load them. They stumble over one another. They want to get it over with.

It occurs to them they might succeed in doing so.

Two enemy rounds come in. They go wide. "Hey, Dan," says Pady holding his lanyard and seeing Dan MacCarthy's double chins in a hole a few feet away. "Did I ever tell you the one about little Audrey and how she screwed her Grandma? Well, little Audrey . . ."

"Fire the goddamn piece," yells Holloway.

Boom. Ehrlich laughs. For once they all laugh with him. They can hardly see for laughing and their insides hurt.

Grostock surveys his howitzers gleefully. "Fire Direction," he shouts to his men, "Fire Direction says Able and Charlie are shootin' the crap out of 'em!" He can't make out from the scattered shouts whether they're hooting or cheering. Grostock sighs with pride.

But the fire mission isn't over. They'll be shooting from now to doomsday, Holloway conjectures. He feels the strain in his stomach muscles as he and Grossberg jerk a projectile-loaded tray to the mouth of the howitzer.

"Where the hell did Cronin go?" Holloway yells. This is Cronin's job, and it occurs to Holloway that he has been doing it ever since the first Kraut fire for effect when the lines were shot out and Grostock started yelling from the field. Holloway feels fatigue break over him and dissolve his muscles. Why is he doing this? For the screwed-up Cronin? He is very bitter against Cronin. Why are they all doing this? Because they have a job. Screw the job, by God. He isn't getting this one off for any lousy job. They could stick their stripes. What in Christ's name ever made him think it was enough to do a job simply because it was your job? The job had a good deal to do with it!

His knees are shaky, his stomach hollow. Grostock calls fire? Okay. "Fire," says Holloway.

"CEASE FIRE, END OF MISSION!"

Arbitrary, causeless, out of the clouding heavens, the command has come and cut them short. They are back where they started. The wind has swept the smoke remnants off their road, their guns, themselves. The howitzers squat immobile as ever under their nets. These are men with nothing to show for their past except a shell here and there. Only the present exists.

"Pinch me," says Padrone.

Holloway shrugs this sudden present off. "First thing," his thick tongue says, "dig your holes deeper." He takes no chances.

Even Dan MacCarthy digs, and Dan is exhausted. He

125

leans his weight upon the shovel but the blunt end of it merely scratches on the intractable earth. He wrestles with his shovel and will not let it go. Dan looks helplessly around him.

"Where the hell is Cronin?" he hears Holloway yell. Holloway has to worry about everyone else as well as himself. Dan is dimly incredulous. He thinks it is right that even when your muscles hurt you think of others, and he wishes he could manage it.

"Anyone seen Cronin?" Holloway yells bitterly.

Dan hasn't seen him. He looks at Holloway stupidly and shakes his head. Cronin's one of the fellows who pulled the false whore gag on him. Cronin and this tough earth, he hates them both.

"Here he is," says somebody. "Cronin's dead."

MacCarthy stares at the earth. His eyes distend. The smile flares upon his face and the more he tries to deny it the wider it becomes. He goes off to shock the hellishness out of himself with the sight of Cronin dead.

Holloway has seen Cronin's huddled corpse. He has no trace of feeling and refuses to bite his own gut for it. He is much too weary for that. And yet were Cronin living, Holloway knows he would have worked to spare the foul-mouthed Irishman as he would work to spare the others. Were Cronin alive, he would have needed Cronin. What on earth for, he doesn't know.

"You guys get on back to your digging," he tells the men. His voice rasps at them. They leave staring back at Cronin. Cronin is a mess.

Holloway watches impassively while they carry off the mess. He needs to live compactly and hard as his father and brothers did; and at the same time he needs more, to conserve men, to stand with the sonsuvbitches, these timid, foolish, profane, childish men of his, these comrades, in the midst of this Italian winter and all its shelling. Holloway is surprised at himself.

He shrugs and postpones his private little riddle indefinitely. In the meanwhile, there is Dan MacCarthy returned to his shovel. Holloway shakes his head slowly and smiles with disgust and amusement. Nothing, he decides, ever teaches that kid anything.

"Look, Dan," says Holloway. "Watch me and for Chri's sakes remember how it's done." Wearily he takes Dan's shovel from his hands.

Grostock the Exec reports to Fire Direction. "One man dead at Number One gun," he tells them. "Two hurt at Number Two, two at Number Three. Four okay." There is a note of awe in his voice. The howitzers? They wanna know about the howitzers? He'll tell 'em about his howitzers! "The howitzers are perfectly okay, Cap'n, perfectly. We can shoot whenever you wan' us." That told 'im!

COLONEL COLOURIS came down to the guns with his chin thrust out and his heart ablaze with the victory of the well-calculated risk. His battalion had done more damage to the German today than in its entire history. The general himself had congratulated Colonel Grey, and Colonel Grey had shifted the credit to Colouris where, by God, it belonged. He himself had immediately sent the word, both of the general's congratulations and the battalion's complete success to the firing batteries with the instructions that every man jack was to be notified. Colonel Colouris was proud of his men.

At Captain Fuller's Command Post, as Colouris picked his way down the slight ravine in which the tent was placed, the Colonel carefully put his widely grinning mouth in order. Once before, just before they had moved into their first firing position, he'd joined a bunch of his officers for a few drinks. Before they knew it they were singing and he in his out-of-tune voice was singing a song of the last war when he had been a corporal and green. They had been startled, then they had been incredulous, then they had grinned like hell. This would never happen again.

Fuller jumped from his cot. "Colonel . . ." Colouris noted that Fuller's hair was disheveled and the mud thick on his boots. Fuller had had plenty of time to put himself in order. This was extraordinary. He waved Fuller down.

"How are your men?" Colouris demanded. Fuller didn't seem to understand. "Your men. How did they take it?— the counter-battery—the news I sent down." Colouris spat the words out.

"The slit trenches weren't deep enough," said Fuller.

That. Of course. Colouris grinned inside. The man's inveterate sense of property was injured. He felt that Colouris' order had resulted in injury to part of his battery property. Fuller regarded the battery he ran as an extension of his personality. That was a good thing. Colouris could afford to indulge such bitterness.

"Yes," said Colouris, "but had we spent time digging trenches along with everything else, the men would have been too knocked out to do the first-rate job they did."

"A man was killed," said Fuller.

"A hell of a lot of the Germans were killed," said Colouris. Fuller was a bit obtuse—which was, up to a point, a good thing, since obtuseness made him hold on harder.

Colouris grinned. Clearly, Fuller didn't know what to say now. This was the point to catch him. Colouris let his grin lapse.

"Why in hell aren't you down with your men?" Colouris smashed the words into him. "Goddamn it, man, get to your feet!"

Slowly, Colouris looked over this battery commander standing at attention. "Evans," said Colouris, "doesn't understand discipline. He thinks that discipline is spit, polish, injustice and saluting. Quite properly, he despises it." Colouris drew his chin in. He made his hard, sudden voice transfix Fuller. "Have you looked to your men since the counter-battery?" Fuller opened his mouth to answer. "There's the heart of discipline," said Colouris. "Get out of that goddamn pose. We're going down to your guns. What in blazes do you think I came for?" He left Fuller scrambling for his helmet and pistol belt.

Colouris walked quick and frowning through the now thoroughly churned mud between the white tapes where there were supposedly no mines, and reflected that Fuller should have used his moment alone to grab the phone and warn the gun sections of their coming.

Colouris heard a yell. "Hey, here they come!" He suppressed his amusement. He suppressed his pleasure over the neatness with which he had seen through Dandy Andy. Resolutely he put from his mind the thought of the battalion's great success, the thought which tickled him and made him want to jump for pleasure or at least grin like an idiot. He had implied to Fuller that what they were to do now was the rock bottom of real discipline. It was. Because if in the most peripheral detail, regardless of the reason, laxity set in, then, like an acid, that laxity would eat at a battalion until the battalion rotted in its most essential functions.

"Soldier, where's your helmet?" Grimly. But the enormous confidence within him made his eyes gleam.

There must be no such thing as abnormal circumstances. And when they came the commander must do everything in his power to deny the fact. "Captain, these men's tents are poorly camouflaged." Said so the men would hear. But of course there had been barely enough time to camouflage them. This man slumped over, staring at the ground. "Sergeant," you said, "why isn't this man standing at attention?" You examined the bore of the piece. You pointed out that an aiming stake was down. "Sergeant," you said, "those fuse boxes are not protected adequately." You would give Lieutenant Grostock hell later, and do it through Fuller.

Normality above all, normality of state and of function in a universe of menace, change and dissolution: to secure it was the object of the responsible man both in war and in peace. Normality and the atmosphere of confidence—these must be secured no matter how many sensitivities you troubled. The Colonel's eyes were large and severe. Here now was Number One gun where the man had been killed. But death itself was normal.

"Sergeant Holloway, sir." This tall, lank man reporting, Colouris remembered, was the man who'd sent the guns forward on his own initiative. The face was set and calm and hostile. You respected him.

And you examined his gun with special care. You checked his net, and the way the stacks of projectiles had been hidden, and the powder cases protected. You took quick, hard glances at the men. You noted with pleasure that for the most part there were no signs of sentimentality and de-composition. You couldn't help your lips twisting in a tight grin of appreciation.

"Sergeant, your tube's in poor shape. Clean it."

"We've been firing, sir." You recognize that this was no excuse but counterattack. Nevertheless, the tube was in bad shape.

"Tell your Executive officer you need time out. He'll get it for you." You stuck your jaw at him. You brooked no answers.

The Sergeant, of course, said nothing. He stared back hard and motionless. But what he thought was clear. Then you clinched it. You waited a moment. Then deliberately and harshly, with your lips pulled back in a half grin, you showed him that you were not only a bastard but in the same army too.

"Screw you too, Sergeant."

You gave them a legend. That was discipline.

Fuller accompanied Colouris to his peep. Did Fuller get it? But of course it wasn't necessary that Fuller get the point in so many words. Quizzically, Colouris regarded his officer.

"Colonel," said Fuller in that heavy voice of his as they walked, "I'd like Lieutenant Evans back with the battery."

Colouris would be damned. "Why?"

Fuller looked straight ahead as he walked. "We were in a bad way without an assistant Exec today, sir. We had to use the recorder. Could have ruined the whole mission."

Colouris nodded. Fuller had felt the force of the point, then. The chief value of the sense of ownership Colouris perceived to be not economic but moral. See how it made a man of Dandy Andy, made him look out for his own in the teeth of his superior. Colouris believed in private property, by God. "Very well," he said, as he entered his peep, returned Fuller's salute and drove off chuckling softly with his deep pleasure at this most wonderful of all days.

Frowning deeply, Fuller watched the peep recede. In the very heart of him he hated the man's guts. It consoled Fuller somewhat in the impotence of his rage to think that he had been able to trick Colouris into giving up Evans.

SNOWFLAKES rotated slowly in the still air. They touched tree limbs, Route Six, guns and the cheeks of cannoneers with a light and equal stroke, and then quietly transmuted to wetness.

Padrone, standing within the trails of Number One gun with his friend Dan, watched a flake die upon his wrist and another come in silence. He liked to watch the small flakes falling. He liked the smooth way they sifted by the guns. They didn't give a damn about guns. Nothing bothered them. They didn't even know there was a war on.

"Some snow," said Padrone.

Dan, staring into the thickening grayness, didn't answer.

"Aw, snap out of it, Dan," Padrone pleaded. "You can't help Cronin.

"Come on," said Padrone, but he sensed how remote Dan was from him. What, he asked, was the use. Dan would have to come out of it by himself. Padrone shook his head and watched the snowflakes touch the steel trail of the howitzer and dissolve on contact. No fuss. No memories. They came and they went and no one made a fuss about it.

Padrone sighed. "You should forget it, Dan," he said softly.

Grossberg passed. "Hi, Grossy." Grossy was preoccupied. Tomlinson, tight, burning up about something, turned away from Pady. The sky had opened up this morning and left a mess of Cronin. But what good did it do, Pady wanted to know, what good did it do to knock your brains out for it?

Now came Ehrlich, counting his projectiles and his white bags and his green bags. He had been pretty much left alone of late. Only Pady talked much to him. "Lo, Herr Ehrlich." Sometimes Dan talked to him too. That was all.

Ehrlich looked up slowly from his counting, nodded. Dan looked right through him. "What's the matter with him?" asked Ehrlich. Pady saw that Ehrlich's eyes were like the ends of two red beets stuck in his head. Pady shrugged his shoulders.

"Hey, Dan—how you doing?" Dan turned his back on Ehrlich. Ehrlich put away his pencil and his pad and walked over to them. He had a funny little grin which made Pady uncomfortable.

"Cronin?" he asked Pady. Pady nodded.

"Hey," said Ehrlich, with his funny little grin, "you think maybe we should call the Chaplain?"

"Ha, ha," said Padrone. Just like the ends of two red beets, Padrone decided, but stuck in a plate of dough— that was Ehrlich's pan.

Slowly Ehrlich regarded Dan. "Who do you think you are?" he asked Dan. "Who gives you a right to make poses here by the howitzer?"

"Hey!" protested Pady.

"Sure," said Ehrlich, "sure. Don't I know what bothers Social Consciousness over here? What'sa matter, Social Consciousness, you turn around now? Good, good. You mad with me maybe?"

"Cut it out," said Pady.

133

"Shut up!" There was a bitterness in Ehrlich's voice which Padrone had never heard unsheathed before.

"Yah," said Ehrlich, "I tell you what's the matter, Dan. You find out maybe your poses are foolish. You find out now nobody has any dignity any more, maybe not even yourself, no? You want instead a man should have a funeral with a coffin and hands folded and maybe nice, crying women to show he is a man. But a lot of insides in a mattress cover, and nobody giving a good goddamn, not even yourself—this offends you maybe? Sure!"

"For Chris' sakes, what in hell's a matter with you?" Pady exploded. But Ehrlich hadn't heard him; Ehrlich ran on.

"They been kidding you, Dan MacCarthy. You been taken for a ride. You crazy, silly Social Consciousness, why don't you come off the bus? Poses! The truth is a mattress cover!"

Now Holloway stood there listening. Why in Christ's name didn't Holloway stop him? Pady was appalled.

"And I git you no sympathy," said Ehrlich, with his voice hard and raucous and agonized. "I gif you no goddamn sympathy, not so much!"

Pady could see Dan's face contort as though he were going to cry, hear the pure disbelief when Dan spoke and the scorn when he said "your."

"Who in God's name needs your sympathy?"

Pady saw that Dan had won the argument. For the first time he saw Ehrlich flinch. He heard him yell something that sounded like German. Then Pady and Holloway jumped between them, and Holloway stated, "That's enough out of you, Ehrlich."

Slowly Ehrlich seemed to let his muscles loosen, and his

face got pasty once again. Then he smiled with half his face. He touched his face. "You ain't kiddin', Holloway," he said, and walked off. Flakes of snow decked his uncovered head, and Pady thought irrelevantly that Ehrlich would sure catch it if some officer caught him without his helmet.

"Ehrlich!" called Holloway.

"Yah?"

"I warned you once before. I'm going to have you busted, Ehrlich."

Ehrlich continued his walking.

The snow was right, decided Padrone. Not Dan, not Holloway, not Ehrlich, who was the worst off. They tore their hearts out and never noticed the snow.

7

THEY were both in the small barren Command Post a
good deal now in these suddenly dull and empty weeks before Cassino. Captain Fuller had stretched himself upon his
cot and read in spite of the glare of a single, flickering light
bulb. The hum and rattle of the gasoline power generator
broke loudly through the blankets hiding the windows.
David Evans, who sat upon his own cot, face cupped in his
hands, elbows dug into his knees, allowed the noise to
absorb a portion of his mind since he had nothing much to do
with it that night anyway.

Fuller's pressing that Evans stay with Baker Battery
when the Colonel wanted to keep him at the Air O.P. had
startled Evans at first. But he had grown used to the idea.
He had also grown used to Fuller's fumbling efforts to
establish a relationship between them based, as Evans remarked to himself, upon the rather inadequate fact that
Fuller no longer brought his own shoes to a high polish.
Fuller, Evans saw, had stymied himself endeavoring to fix

upon a meaning outside the normal reach of his personality. Evans, having had enough of platitudes of his own, could only hope Fuller's would continue out of range.

Evans glanced at his battery commander's athletic torso, speculated whether to address it, failed to think of anything to say to it, and forgot about Fuller before his gaze left him. It was disgraceful and it was unacceptable to Evans that the wearing on of the war never hardened his spirit against despair. He felt despair's evisceration almost daily now. At this very moment someone had scooped the substance out of this very room he sat in. He'd just tried to express the feeling. He'd written to Margaret that the world was built like an onion; that maybe he had read it somewhere, but that was the way the world went anyway. In order to get at the heart of it, you stripped away layer after layer and found in the diminishing ball only new layers to be stripped. And when, finally, you were finished you found yourself with nothing but a stink on your hands and tears in your eyes. On rereading, the passage had seemed more querulous than he'd intended and he struck it out. Nevertheless, Evans was sure that nothing lived in his experience substantial enough to love or attack, that right now he had the stink of the onion and, God help him for a fool, almost the tears.

"Say, Captain," he said, "I'm going out. Be back later."

No thinking, Evans decided, could ever enlarge into value the sum of vicious little troubles and animal fears which made up this time of his. They followed the discipline according to St. Colouris, who opposed enlargements as against the will of Things As They Are.

Evans silently buckled on his pistol belt and placed his steel helmet upon his head. He didn't know where he was going when he entered under the intense stars and felt the cold. He expected nothing and he hoped for nothing. Soon he felt better.

The joke of it was that he had secretly known he would feel better if he played out the reel to his misery far enough. Only now the joke was topped. He didn't even give a particular damn about the knowledge. Vigorously he strode down the road. He was ready for anything. Just let it come. Sadly, nothing was likely to come except perhaps a shot from an overambitious sentry. Evans wasn't desperate enough to want that. He chuckled at himself.

Well, Evans, he said to himself, make a decision like a good little officer. Decide where you're going. How about the Medics? Of course, he could drop in on the Medics. They had plenty of light at their place, a stove, a shot of liquor perhaps, or *vino*; and Doc Barnes was a friend of his, more or less. Thus, then, would he wind up his career as a desperate character, with a social call on the Medics. But he found such a windup quite appropriate. It would screw even the craziness in him. It would do the job up brown, but a real rich brown.

Evans swung down the road not minding the splash of mud upon his trousers. He accepted the mud with a kind of gaiety. There wasn't anything he wouldn't take on if it crossed his path. Only for God's sake, let something cross it!

Doc, the Battalion Surgeon, was practising his Italian on two Italian girls when Evans arrived. Doc operated on the idea that if you added an appropriate ending to an English root, the resulting sound was henceforth shifted into the foreign tongue, and any foreigner who had any sense should understand him. Evans had tried once or twice to show Doc, clever enough in other matters, the error of his principle; but Doc was a very stubborn character. Evans watched the short, slight figure with its bald head pushed earnestly forward at the girls.

"Still at it? Haven't given up since I saw you last?" Not spectacular words for a desperate character, Evans admitted to himself—but what would you?

Evans saw that he knew everyone here: Ernie the Pole, called such because the original name was beyond them all —small, sharp-nosed, wizened; Kramer, Doc's burly, eager section chief; and, of all people, MacCarthy of his own battery.

"Hello, boys," he said. They returned his greeting cheerfully enough.

Doc said, "Well, Evans! Come on in and sit down; there's room enough for everybody."

Doc liked to play the host. He motioned hospitably to indicate the large room with its circle of cots at the sides and the gleaming white medical cabinet from which he dispensed his aspirin.

Evans removed his helmet, let it drop upon the stone floor with a clatter which made the girls jump, and leaned back against the wall. He put his hands in his pockets and surveyed the group. There they were. Here he was. So what?

He said, "How you doing, Dan?" Evans noted how large and childish MacCarthy's eyes were behind the horn-rimmed glasses.

"Fine sir," said MacCarthy.

"How's the socialist?" asked Evans, because it was a

standing joke among the Medics, with whom Dan hung out lately, that Dan was a socialist.

Dan laughed deprecatingly in answer. He got along pretty well with Evans although he hadn't had much to do with him.

"Christ, Lieutenant," said Kramer, "don't get him started. He's been quiet so far this evening."

"You hear that, Dan? Your bosom buddy doesn't want me to get you started."

Evans' inspecting eyes saw thigh where the dresses of the two girls fell short. "Where," he asked, "did you fellows pick that up?"

"Oh," said Ernie, "they're two of Doc's patients or something. They give Doc lessons."

Evans nodded absently while he examined the girls further. One was an undersized, kinky-haired blonde. The other was large, black-haired and greasy. He assessed them both. The girls noticed it, he observed, and shifted in their seats while they pretended to listen to Doc's assassination of their language.

Kramer was leering at him slightly. "Have some *vino*, Lieutenant? I put some alcohol in it."

Kramer, obviously, had had some. "Sure thing," said Evans, and drank it quickly. It would help with the bitch, too. You needed to be drunk. "Any more?" he asked.

" 'Fraid that's all, Lieutenant—unless Doc can get some more from his Wop friends next door." Kramer looked suggestively at him, and Evans winked to show that he accepted the suggestion.

"Hey, Doc," Evans called. "There's no more *vino*. Is that a way to treat a guest?"

"All right, all right," said Doc placidly.

"Well, damn it, Doc, do something about it."

Doc buttoned his field jacket, pocketed his dictionary and pulled a brown, woolen cap over his shining pate. "Hold your water," he said. "Be back in a few minutes."

"Hey, *Signorini*," said Evans, wagging his head vigorously and motioning back the girls who had also risen. "Nix."

Doc held up a hand to the girls. "*Ritorno*," he said pontifically, and marched out.

The girls subsided. They traded a few giggling words while stealing traditionally coy glances at Evans, the *Officiale*, who looked at them and wondered what he was going to do next. He hoped Doc would hurry back with the *vino*. In the meanwhile . . .

"Hey, Ernie," he called, "help me clear away the chairs and boxes."

Between them, they prepared a clear space in the center of the floor directly underneath the brightly burning lamp. Evans reached over and increased the volume of the small battery radio so that it could be heard. Then, bracing his shoulders, he went up to the blonde and performed an exaggerated bow.

"*Danse?*" He tried to make the word sound Italian.

"*Si*," she said.

MacCarthy and Kramer had settled themselves to a game of cribbage. Kramer was humming off pitch to the music while MacCarthy scratched his head dully over the game. Evans and his pseudo-blonde rotated slowly under the lamp. He dragged her along, held her hard against his body, while outside the guns blew their heads off on the off-beats.

Evans discovered that her name was Francesca. "Am I

141

your Paolo?" he asked, grinning into her hair. She said,
"*Si.*"

"How you doin', Lieutenant?" asked Ernie, attempting
heartiness.

"Fine," said Evans.

Ernie laughed his cackling laugh and Dan and Kramer
looked up, smiled amiably at Evans, and continued their
game.

This slow movement with the *Signorina* under the glass
of hopelessness—this was what he needed. This killed
the tongue in his head. And now the *Signorina* panted
slightly. That pleased him in a remote, fierce manner. He
snuggled his face into her hair.

Finally Doc came back. He came in with two bottles
under his arm and announced, "It's drizzling." Doc placed
the stuff upon a small table and turned away as though he
were washing his hands of the whole matter. "There you
are," he said. "Go to it."

Doc nodded sagely and said nothing. He removed his
wool cap and squeezed it to get the wetness out, and settled
himself again.

But Evans went over to where Kramer was stiffening the
vino with long shots of alcohol, and Kramer offered the
first drink to him. He took it gladly. Picture of a desperate
man.

What the hell! Get drunk.

An hour later Evans mused how strangely sad it was
that Doc and the boys should be so friendly. He could hear
the beat of rain against the window above his head. He was
sure there was pity there. Give him a little time to get him-

self together and he would discover just where it was. But, for the time being, he just felt sad about the pity of it.

Evans' desperation had been surrendered several drinks ago and he had nothing left with which to replace it except dizziness and his poor friendly bastards. He essayed a weak, loving smile to show how he felt. He glanced sadly around him. What was he doing half sitting, half lying on a cot that way, leaning with his neck and shoulders against the wall? He didn't have the faintest notion.

He noticed his own arm around the blonde's waist. He moved it around a bit, experimentally. She turned her head. He observed the gold tooth gleam in the midst of her fetching smile and closed his eyes.

" 'Allo," said Francesca.

Who'd been teaching her English? " 'Allo," answered Evans.

He became conscious of motion on his right. It was, he noted, Ernie's girl wriggling beside him. Why the hell didn't she stay still? All sensible people stayed still. Evans noticed that Ernie had one hand inside the front of her dress, and he winked at Ernie as lasciviously as he could manage. Ernie was the reason she didn't stay still. But Ernie was also pounding the *Signorina* on the back with his disengaged hand. What was that for?

"What," queried Evans, honest curiosity in his voice, "do you expect to get that way?"

Ernie, intent, didn't answer. Instead, he interrupted his maneuvers to flash a light in the girl's eyes. He tried it three or four times. The girl blinked and tried to turn away from it but Ernie held her.

Evans began to wonder if maybe he was drunker than he'd thought. "Now what the hell you doing?" he asked.

143

Ernie turned to Evans. "Dilation test. For syphilis."

Oh. Evans felt the warmth of Francesca against his hand and pressed his fingers against the side of her stomach. Her dress was thin enough. An idea occurred to him.

"Say, Ernie," he said, "How about trying it on mine?" He was eager even if his tongue wasn't.

"Can't do it too much, sir. She'll get wise."

Evans nodded sagely, although at the moment he couldn't see why Ernie's girl wouldn't get wise and his would. But a lot of things which shouldn't be hazy, were. Evans decided not to press the matter. Instead he smiled dreamily. He feared that the haze might slip away and the world would stand out before him all chiseled and bony; therefore he smiled dreamily to fool the haze so that it wouldn't leave him.

Evans felt a pressure upon his knees. It reassured him not to know immediately what it was. "What's that?" he asked.

"What's what, Lieutenant?"

The voice seemed to come from the region of his knees. With an effort Evans raised his head and saw MacCarthy. MacCarthy was kneeling on the floor before him and resting his elbows upon Evans' knees. MacCarthy's mouth was open and his eyes blinked foolishly behind his spectacles. "Wha's what, Lieutenant?"

" 'Allo, Dan," said Evans. Things were properly confused again. Christ, but it was getting crowded in his vicinity. He couldn't move if he wanted to.

"I'll sing a song," announced Dan.

"Fine," said Evans, but it was hard to look at Dan when he had to keep his head propped up to do so. Evans let his head fall back.

144

Dan had a surprisingly rich voice hidden behind his plump face. It was a childish song he'd picked up in school, about a Doctor somebody or other. Evans couldn't make out the name. Dan sang very sadly. He leaned heavily upon Evans' knees as he sang but Evans didn't want to interrupt art. Dan was getting to be quite a weight, too—wailing dolefully the last incomprehensible words to Francesca. Did he want the bitch?

Dan turned his attention to the Lieutenant. "You don't mind my breaking in on you, sir? If you do I'll go away."

"No. Just take it easy on my legs." Jesus, he could have the bitch if he wanted her, poor Dan with his infantile sadness.

"I know my place, sir. I'm a Pfc. I know that. Just send me away."

"Hell, you can stay here all night," he said, commiserating with the bitch, with himself, with the whole goddamned world.

"Having a good time, Dave?" Doc was calling over the din from the chair into which he had first deposited himself.

Evans nodded.

"The trouble," said Doc, "is that you're not drunk enough." He poured out another glassful of the strong mixture they'd been absorbing. "Here," he said, thrusting the glass through the crowd. "Have another." Then he went back and replaced his hands about his stomach.

Doc had given him the drink as though he were handing out aspirin. Take two every four hours until the headache disappears. Evans put the drink to his lips and drank a little. It tasted like the contents of a medicine chest, come to think of it. Did he, David Evans, need a prescription?

Apparently. Doc, then, was an old bastard. Doc was mocking him and he wouldn't be mocked.

Evans handed the glass to Francesca and motioned her to put it down. Then, quietly, he began to stroke her side. It amused him that this time he made her uneasy. She knew something was up; she knew he was out to take what came his way. Soon, he predicted to himself, she would develop an acute attack of respectability, which he would thrust through according to his proper function as a man. She would expect that. Not pity. He massaged her side vigorously.

The girls said something to one another. They made apologetic gestures and rose. Evans simply refused to relinquish the hand Francesca offered him. He smiled broadly and pulled her down beside him. She made some small resistance, but not too much.

The other girl was still trying to break away. Then Kramer and Dan and Ernie rose over her in powerful drunken friendliness. The lines about her mouth were taut when they pushed her down upon a chair, affectionately.

Pitiless Evans waved his free hand at Doc. Doc motioned back and said, "You'll feel even better after you take her home."

That son of a bitch of a Doc. But this prescription felt very warm under his hand, Doc or no Doc. Evans' hand shifted to the blonde's hip. Dan babbled at his feet. Ernie pounded at his girl. Kramer stereotyped a drunk. Doc, in faint medical disapproval, shook his head charitably and watched with some interest. And the broken clock on the wall transfixed forever the same time.

But when for the second time Francesca made as if to

go, Evans did not stop her. Instead he reached for his helmet, as Ernie did for his. The two girls said, *"Buona sera,"* in chorus, and the men followed them closely as they left. The rain had stopped. The quiet mixed itself in with a damp and vaporous darkness. Paired, they stumbled the hundred yards to where the two girls lived.

Evans was a trifle surprised when the girls jabbered frantically as he and Ernie attempted to enter the doorway with them. So going in was out of the question. He shrugged and drew his girl away. She seemed reluctant. But he was not going to concern himself with maneuvers now. He placed her with her back to the wall and dispassionately commenced to maul her. When he had finished he let her go and saw her squirm into the vague outline of a door. The other girl followed.

"Coming in again, Lieutenant?" he heard Ernie's voice ask.

What the hell, Evans was in no mood for sleep. He adjusted his pistol belt and said, "Might as well."

They trudged back to the Medics.

Evans was satisfied that he had struck absolute rock bottom. His head was clear; he was hopelessly at peace. That was that.

AFTER the outside night, there was a sharp light in the room which made Evans blink. It was as though he were entering it now for the first time this evening. He removed his steel helmet and let Ernie enter first. Evans' body oriented to the warmth and dryness of the place.

The Chaplain was there now, also, a spare, nervous-eyed

officer who lived quietly in a room neighboring the Medics, and who chiefly distinguished himself to Evans by his "Er" saying.

But it was MacCarthy who was doing the talking. He was sitting opposite Doc on a box of medical supplies; the others formed a semicircle around them. MacCarthy's voice was raised and strong, his face overflushed. Each word he said was clear and distinct. Alcohol had cleared the tongue and drawn each sentence to a more or less grammatical conclusion. Evans was wryly familiar with the reaction.

"Running for Congress, Dan?" he asked.

MacCarthy didn't hear him. He was pleading with the Chaplain. "Father," he was saying, "all my life I've been a Catholic. My grandmother brought me up to be a Catholic." He dropped his voice dramatically. "It is my faith."

"Well, that's fine." The Chaplain noticed Evans. "Evening, Evans," he said heartily. But MacCarthy was not to be balked by the stratagem.

"Catholicism," he pursued, "is the faith which I learned at my grandmother's knee. Socialism I learned for myself in the world. I am," he said proudly, "a Christian Socialist."

"Whew," said Evans.

"Not many people know that about me," said Dan.

Evans seated himself. The Chaplain tried to catch his eye for support but Evans' interest was focused on the Christian Socialist.

"Yes, it is my faith, Father, and I want to ask you—you, an ordained minister of my Church—one question. The Gospel according to St. John says that we shall love one another. We are told, plainly told," said Dan with great emphasis, "that we shall not take that which we cannot give back. I cannot give back human life, Father. And I have taken that which I can never, never return."

Evans was amazed. Why, Evans was not the only one lost? Others suffered, then? He had almost forgotten.

"You're exaggerating," Doc provoked with a placid smile. "You've never done more than duck like the rest of us."

"Yes," MacCarthy said, "I know I'm a cannoneer, a Pfc. But when I carry the shells that will cause men to die, I am killing them as surely as though I shot them with a pistol through their hearts. I have killed, Father." He shook his head dolefully. "I am a hypocrite. I am a liar. I have taken that which I can never, never return. Explain it to me, Father."

His voice was sonorous. Dan felt himself pleading before the bar of the world. Dan, Evans said silently, there's never a verdict.

The Chaplain laughed nervously. "Religion," he said, "forbids murder. You haven't murdered anyone."

But Dan swept over him. "Have I not killed? Is that not murder? Have I not taken that which I can never, never return?"

"The Church—uh—gives you the right to defend yourself," said the Chaplain, intensely embarrassed to be talking religion and dogma before all these people.

"Sure," said Ernie. "You talk silly. The District Attorney gets the murderers. Fighting a war is different. You got to fight. Isn't that right?" he inquired of the others.

Everyone agreed Dan was silly. Also, drunk.

Doc said, "You're no one in particular, Dan. Keep your

149

head on your shoulders and your blood pressure down." He laughed and winked at Evans as though to say that that was good advice for Evans too.

MacCarthy's voice rose above those of his derogators. "No, no. My grandmother taught me . . ."

"Oh, screw your grandmother," said Kramer.

". . . that more important than nationalism or even than democracy is justice. And I have taken that which I can never return. I have done injustice. I have willingly done evil. I have entered the dark tent of evil." His face was redder than ever.

Evans grinned sourly. Dan certainly took matters in the serious vein. The dark tent of evil. Evans preferred even his own metaphor of the onion. It was less dramatic and, therefore, more just.

"Look at me, Father. I know I am ugly, deformed so that it is unpleasant to look at me, and I am ashamed . . ."

"Huh?" said Ernie.

". . . yet answer me this. The Sermon on the Mount tells us that we shall not kill, but love one another. The Third Baltimore Catechism tells us that. I am stupid, Father. I do not understand things easily. I am only a high-school graduate, no man of learning. Answer me in words that I can understand. Why am I here?"

This was really too much for the Chaplain. He shifted in his seat and coughed. He was obviously delighted to have Evans interrupt.

"Dan," Evans appealed. Dan was lost in the wrong forest!

"Yeah, Dan, let the Lieutenant talk," said Ernie.

"Let the Lieutenant talk? No, no. I have had enough of Lieutenants and Captains. Speak to me, Lieutenant, but not as a Lieutenant. Speak to me as David Evans."

"How can he when you don't give him a chance?" demanded Kramer.

"What have I to say to officers? I cannot talk to officers. Speak to me as David Evans, Master of Arts." The Chaplain shook his head despairingly. "Him I will listen to, to the man of knowledge, though it be a pseudo-knowledge truly, as Monsignor Sheen has said. Can I take that which I cannot give back? Or shall I accept the Hebrew eye for an eye, tooth for a tooth?"

"What difference does it make one way or the other?" Doc got in.

MacCarthy heard that, since it was said in a moment when he'd paused for breath. With intense dignity, he turned to the Doctor. "To me," he said, "it makes a difference. To me, who have an immortal soul, it makes a difference, Captain. To me . . ."

"To Lieutenant Evans also," interrupted Doc, "who has no immortal soul," and laughed.

". . . and to Lieutenant Evans also," said MacCarthy. "Doesn't it matter, Lieutenant? Speak to me not as Lieutenant Evans, but as David Evans. Can I take that which I cannot give back? Am I to descend into the jungle? Tell me!"

Kramer got up and put his hand over MacCarthy's mouth. "If you ask a question, listen to the answer." MacCarthy subsided under superior force.

"Go on, Lieutenant," said Kramer agreeably and tipsily.

But Evans was no longer sure of what he wanted to say. He knew something should be said by the same sudden warmth of feeling he had now for Dan as he had once had for Jordan by the downed plane. But how could one man talk to another, each cellophaned and vacuum-packed by dogma? And how could a man know what to say?

"Look, Dan," he said, feeling his helplessness. "You're barking up the wrong tree. Either you take the faith the Chaplain offers and stop your questions or you start out on your own hook. You can't have both independence and your faith. Dan, Dan, you take misery for tragedy and onions for evil. You tangle yourself in questions which you will refuse to have answered as long as you have any breath in you to smother the answers." Evans realized that his voice was rising and that Dan was drunk and how ridiculous it was trying to persuade Dan of what he wouldn't believe if he were sober. "Dan, you goddamned, hopeless fool!" said Evans and ignored Doc's grin and the Chaplain's curious stare. There was so screwing little one man could do for another, and here was MacCarthy again, with the drunken passion bursting in his voice . . .

"No, no, no. The Lieutenant is an agnostic, he doesn't believe. But I believe, Chaplain. I believe that Christ was God, that the bread and wine are the body and blood of Christ, that Mary, the most perfect of mortals, was enthroned in heaven."

"All Catholics believe that, of course," said the Chaplain, more uncomfortable than ever, the anger rising in his voice.

"Then why am I here, Father?" MacCarthy shouted. "How can I take that which I can never, never return? How . . ." The men shouted to him to be quiet. Kramer came over again and put his hand on MacCarthy's mouth.

But very clearly Evans perceived that Dan drew life from this farce. Who was Evans to pity Dan? Somebody else, of course, seeing how Dan could never permit himself the answers he yet had to have, might pity him. But not

Evans. Evans didn't even have a question to his name. He looked at the Chaplain. The Chaplain had the right. The Chaplain was also holding his temper admirably. But the Chaplain also had no doubts of any kind, and those who had no doubts couldn't pity in the respect in which they had no doubts. How was it, Evans wondered, to contain all the answers within your own head? How was it managed?

They were stifling the kid. Evans motioned to Kramer to get his hand away. "I don't understand," Dan protested. "Why won't people talk to me simply and explain it? Why won't they use words I can understand? Father, I want to ask a question. Why am I as I am? Why am I here? Why, Father?" MacCarthy was rolling on his seat; he cried a little.

Evans got up and put an arm around Dan's shoulders. "Easy," he said. MacCarthy of course wouldn't take it easy. And Evans, although he didn't have the right . . .

"Why don't you ever shut up, MacCarthy?" demanded Ernie, indignantly. "Why must you always be talking and no one else? Why? You interrupt the Lieutenant, you interrupt everybody."

"Lieutenant? What have I to do with Lieutenants?" Dan was off again.

Kramer approached Evans. "Don't mind him, Lieutenant," Kramer said, pushing his face close to Evans. "Don't mind him, sir. He don't know what he's saying. He always gets this way."

"My God," said Evans, collapsing into his seat.

"Gee, that's swell of you, Lieutenant, that's swell . . ." Kramer was drunkenly admiring him. "You're a good guy, sir."

Now Ernie was shouting at MacCarthy, who unendingly

pleaded away. "Keep quiet now," Ernie shouted. "Keep quiet or we'll give you first aid." He shook the boy by the shoulders.

MacCarthy's glasses fell off his nose. He reached for them ineffectually and whimpered, "My glasses." Why would no one give Dan MacCarthy his glasses? All he wanted was his glasses.

Now Kramer staggered the few feet to where Ernie was shaking MacCarthy. "You heard Ernie," he said. "Keep quiet or we'll give you first aid. Do you hear? We'll give you first aid," he menaced.

MacCarthy said, "My glasses, I'm blind without my glasses. Won't somebody please give me back my glasses?"

This was getting to be more than Evans could stand. He bent down and picked up MacCarthy's glasses. "Here Dan," he said, "here's your glasses." He handed them to MacCarthy between Kramer and Ernie. Kramer had taken up the pushing from where Ernie'd left off.

"Stop that, damn it!" yelled Evans.

Kramer's mouth dropped foolishly as he stopped.

But now that no one was threatening Dan with first aid, or pushing him, Dan managed with Evans' help to put on his glasses. Evans patted his shoulder. "Take it easy, Dan," he said, and stared angrily at the others. He was in league with Dan.

Then he began to feel foolish. Kramer was nearly as drunk as Dan and hadn't meant any harm. Evans had made a first-class fool of himself. He tried to work his way out of it. "That's no way to treat a drunk now, is it, Doc?"

Delphic, Doc said, "There are many ways of treating a drunk."

MacCarthy searched sorrowfully for Evans among the

blurred figures. He couldn't find him, but perhaps his words would. "Lieutenant, sir," he said, "I apologize. I was wrong. I know it. You go on. Talk. I won't bother you any more."

Vividly, it occurred to him that there was something he must not forget, something of immense importance, which he must ask Evans. "Lieutenant," he said, "Tell me. How can I take what I can't return? And why should I be glad to see others take that life? Why should I have been glad to see Cronin dead? Why should I have hated Cronin? Why should Cronin have hated me to hurt me so?"

The Chaplain and Evans exchanged glances. MacCarthy was too far gone. They went for their helmets.

"So long, Doc," said Evans. "Thanks for the entertainment."

Doc waved a deprecatory hand. "Come again," he said.

"Take it easy," Evans said to MacCarthy as he and the Chaplain passed by him.

"Don't go, Lieutenant. Don't be angry with me." MacCarthy tried to catch at Evans' jacket and nearly fell off his seat.

"I'm not angry with you, Dan. It's just that we'd better go."

They went. They heard the heartbroken drunk say as they left that no one, no one would talk to him. Evans hoped that Dan wouldn't think that he was deserting him —but knew that he would, and that there was no choice but to desert him.

OUTSIDE, in the cold damp, Evans said good night to the Chaplain who had accompanied him to the door, and headed back to the C.P. and Captain Fuller. It seemed to him a very long way back as he walked. He wondered vaguely why he had ever gone so far in the first place. The sloshing of his shoes through the mud sounded intimate, confiding, in the darkness. He listened to it carefully. He was with himself at last. He was with himself and tired. Tired to the very bone, for he had gone a long, long way and wasn't home. Poor Dave, poor Dave, his mind whispered. Dave's a'cold . . . The sap was out of him, out of his body, out of his mind.

Journey ended, he felt his way through the blackout curtain and entered the C.P. Fuller was lying on his back, legs sprawled over the sides of the cot, just as Evans had left him. He was still reading. The light bulb flickered as it had before. The drone of the generator still sounded through the walls. Nothing had changed. Had he expected that anything would?

Captain Fuller had heard Evans enter. He finished his paragraph and threw the book aside.

"Where you been, Dave?" he asked.

"Medics," said Evans.

"Anything doin'?" Fuller was removing his shoes.

"No."

"Never is. Put out the light before you hit the sack, will you?"

Evans nodded. He undressed and, reaching up, loosened the bulb in its socket. The light faded slowly in a reddish haze, and Evans crawled into his bed roll.

8

"TA TA TA TA," Colonel Colouris was humming in the small, dank room of his small and battered Command Post. For once he had other business to think about than stalemate short of Cassino and the minor war he fought each day now against the rise of lethargy in his battalion. "Ta ta ta." He'd just sent for Captain Berelli, his S-3.

Berelli's small, crow-footed eyes scanned the C.P. brightly, observed with amusement its undefiled order, and lighted upon the Colonel's back.

"Ta ta ta."

Berelli's eyes creased with delight. But something must be cooking. Normally, the Colonel went around worrying his and everyone else's ass off.

"You wanted to see me, sir?" asked Berelli cheerfully of the broad back. If you asked Berelli, he'd be damned before he'd let any battalion gray his hair the way this one did the Colonel's.

The Colonel swung around, but now the old, intent frown of the man had shunted off the humming. "Yes. Sit down." Berelli pulled a canvas-backed chair nearer to the Colonel, and occupied it. "You see the goddamn house you're in right now, Berelli? That's what's raising hell with us."

The Colonel might choose to deal in mysteries. But Berelli sat stolid and smiling with his hands upon his paunch, and watched the concern rise in the eyes of his Colonel behind their steel-rimmed glasses.

"The walls are too thick," said the Colonel to the 1:50,000 situation map in the far corner of the room.

Daylight. So that was what the old bastard was driving at. The Krauts had their own houses.

"The Limeys want it again," said the Colonel with a sudden happiness that made Berelli blink. "I've got orders to send up a forward observer to adjust our big stuff on some more of those damned houses."

Berelli whistled. "You don't say."

Colonel Colouris glanced at him sharply. "I'm for it, Berelli. It makes sense. They say they trust our gunners even that close to their lines, and they've got good reason."

If that was the way the wind blew . . . "We've got the best shootin' outfit on the front," affirmed Berelli.

Colouris' face worried over. "They trust us—but we've got to send down at least a captain to direct fire. We gave 'em a bad habit last time."

Uh-oh. "And," said Captain Berelli, "the question is, who?"

"Exactly. But damn it, I can't afford to lose an experienced officer. I'd hate like hell to lose one of my captains."

158

"We've got a lot of lieutenants who could do the job as well as any captain," offered Berelli helpfully.

"That's what I told Group. But it's no good." The Colonel looked curiously at Berelli. "Who do you suggest? You're gunnery officer now."

Berelli sat considering. Two to one the old man knew damn well whom he wanted to send and aimed to feel out his new S-3. But let's see. The firing battery captains were out, probably, as far as the Colonel was concerned. Old Moore of Service battery was too old for this sort of thing. The S-2 had had his turn at it already; Colouris wouldn't want to hit him with it twice. He himself would be needed at Fire Direction. All of which, of course, left Berelli's old big-assed drinking buddy. The Colonel didn't like to pick him, didn't trust him. But, after all, there wasn't much to do which the Assistant Como couldn't handle.

"I don't suppose there's any choice, Colonel," said Berelli. "Captain Crown."

The Colonel was nodding. Success. "That was my decision," Colouris was saying while Berelli's slight smile reached his eyes. "And maybe," Colouris had added angrily, "the experience will do him some good. Separate him from his bottle and teach him his goddamn responsibilities."

"I'll tell 'im," offered Berelli.

"I hope to Christ I'm not making a mistake," brooded the Colonel.

Berelli could just picture it. He'd walk into Crown's C.P. Oh, the poor Crown bastard. Could he help it, he'd say, if Crown got stuck? Besides, he'd say, he thought Crown wouldn't mind getting away from the battalion for a few days where the Colonel couldn't chew him out. Oh, he could just picture it. The poor fat bastard. Berelli chuckled inside.

"I'll go tell him now, Colonel, if that's all."

THE next day, soon after dawn, in the mid-March cold, Captain Crown, pistol-belted and helmeted, with a stuffed musette bag on his back and a blanket tied to it, heaved himself miserably into the righthand seat of his peep. Hand on gearshift, the driver waited. Crown twisted around and said to Sergeant Knudson, who occupied the rear seat, "You set?"

Knudson nodded and gripped the barrel of the submachine gun he carried. As the peep lurched forward out of a rut his six-foot emaciated body stiffened and his hollow-cheeked, almost lipless face set so that the jaw muscle quivered. Gently, he breathed in the cold air. He wanted to fight, more or less. He was the only man in the battalion the Colonel knew who really wanted to, even more or less. That was why, long and quiet, he sat behind Crown with a submachine gun and gave Crown what comfort Crown had.

For Captain Thomas A. Crown's head hurt like hell. The jolts of the peep moving up Route Six sent pain circulating through his head, while with puffed eyes he waited for the aspirin to take effect. Crown had gone through a rough night. Berelli had come in about nine in the evening and given him the score—which was two out and two strikes against Crown. But Berelli had enjoyed himself, the bastard. He'd brought along the Tommy gun for a parting gift, said he thought Crown might need it. Crown had told him to go to hell and writhed inside. One day he would kill Berelli. By God, how much had they drunk last night?

Yesterday Crown had been safe and warm, but now he didn't feel so good. Now he buttoned the top button of his combat jacket and slumped upon the end of his spine feeling a shiver go through it. The sonuvabitch Colonel, what a stinking thing to do to Captain Crown. His long lashes drooped over against the rising sun as he watched on either side the muddy land move away and more of the same rush down the roadside to replace it. He watched the war-beaten earth jerk with the halts and spin with the quick, rushing turns, and he watched it all with a great desire that it be stepped upon, earth, sun, morning, the whole crapped-up world. Smeared out.

Knudson leaned forward. "Where we goin' to first, Captain?"

Crown's head turned profile. "To the screwin' Limey regimental C.P.," he said.

Knudson sat back and grinned at the back of his Captain's head. He didn't see much good in the Limeys himself, for that matter. Bloody. Everything was bloody. Bloody, and their goddamn tea in the middle of everything. No wonder they'd lost the war until the States came in. But guts they had. Did Crown, Knudson wondered.

The driver swung cursing around a parked British lorry that appeared to the Americans like a tan box with wheels. Crown looked back at it viciously, his full red lips contorting with hatred and disdain.

"Stoppin' for tea," said Knudson to the front seat. Crown didn't answer. Screw him. Maybe he didn't like this business too much. Knudson smiled.

Finally they got there. After wrong turns, blown bridges, detours and conferences over Crown's road map they found the spot which on the map had a cross upon it. A British soldier directed the peep into a wooded place which showed the deep mud signs of military use. Then Crown and Knudson had to leg it in up to their ankles. A sentry pointed out the C.P., the eternal messed-up farmhouse over there, and Crown suddenly found himself longing bitterly for just one house with no scars but clean inside and out and with some good American whisky in it to warm a man.

They walked in. A tall man with three pips on his coarse brown battle jacket saw the short, plump man and the tall, thin sergeant with the bony face.

"Good day, Captain," he said to Crown. "You are, I presume, the officer from the 794th?"

"I presume," mocked Crown to himself. "Yes."

Knudson looked suspiciously around him and got a wink from a British noncom. He winked back.

"Won't you come this way, Captain? The Colonel's been expecting you. Your man can wait here."

Out of the corner of his eye, Crown saw Knudson giving the Englishman that flat, deadpan stare of his. "Your man." Crown smiled happily for the first time that morning.

He followed the British officer into a small room which reminded him of what Colonel Colouris used for a C.P. That was the Limey Colonel, a big, fat fellow, cheerful looking too, built like Moore of Service battery. But plenty of rank. Crown saluted.

"Very glad to see you, Captain. We can use your assistance," boomed the voice which owned the crown and two pips. "Name's Andrews." The Colonel held out his hand.

"Crown, sir." They shook hands. Not bad at all. Mama's little boy Tommy was getting up in the world.

"Scotch?" offered Colonel Andrews.

He said "Yes, sir," so strongly that the older man laughed as he poured out a shot for each of them. Crown reached for it eagerly. The Colonel gestured slightly with his glass and Crown returned the gesture. Then they tossed the stuff down and Crown closed his eyes for a second, feeling the smooth, hot caress in his throat, in his chest, in his stomach.

"Do you know," Colonel Andrews was saying, "I admire your gunners greatly, Captain. Delighted to be working with your people."

Crown wanted to say something generous but couldn't think of anything.

"We'll be obliged to you if your heavies can smash their bloody fortresses." The Colonel laughed gently. "I know you're anxious to get about the business. I won't keep you long."

Sure Crown was anxious to get about the business, by Christ. All he had needed was a pick-me-up. "We can do it for you, Colonel," Crown said. But he couldn't help fixing the bottle of Scotch with a steady, hopeful stare.

"Have another, Captain?"

He had another. He'd just swallowed it gratefully when a lieutenant entered and saluted. The lieutenant wore his World War I tin hat rakishly and he looked young. Still, Crown speculated abstractly, he was ready for business.

"This," said the Colonel, "is Leftenant Wilkes . . . Captain Crown. Bloody bad luck I can't be there to see the shoot myself, but Wilkes will show you around. He knows the houses we need blasted."

So it was Crown's business this Wilkes was ready for!

"If you will come with me, Captain," Wilkes was saying, "I have a man waiting with the wireless and maps. We'll take care of all communications for you while you direct your guns. I say, it will be a sight to see your heavies hit 'em."

Yeah, some sight. But there was nothing Crown could do but take his leave of the cheerful Colonel with the cheerful Scotch. Outside he and Wilkes picked up Knudson with a can of beer in his hand and a smug look.

FOUR men flung themselves into the mud and prayed. The shell struck in the steep ravine beside the trail they'd been walking, and the sound waves which were broadcast up at them made their legs soft. They waited for a few moments, perceiving no alternative, but nothing happened. They got to their feet. The sergeant resented the mess he was in for no good reason, and looked disgustedly at his plastered front.

"The screwin' thing wasn't even close," he said.

"If it weren't for the ravine, it would have been. Cheer up, Sergeant," said Leftenant Wilkes.

Captain Crown said nothing. He felt the wet cold next to his chest and couldn't help think it a dirty trick. He followed wearily behind the British officer when they resumed their march. The fourth member of the party also kept his peace. He was too loaded down with radio, equipment and discipline to have breath for words. He followed the Captain as they plodded forward. Last, after the radio operator, came Sergeant Knudson, Tommy gun in the crook of his arm and wary, delighting in wariness.

A machine gun sounded off somewhere ahead. Its stammerings had broken into their labored passage for the last half mile. It had kept gathering volume and insistence. It kept sending forth walls of occasional sound which got thicker and heavier and harder for Captain Crown to push through. If he let it, it would stop him in his tracks and force him back faster and faster; and he couldn't do that because—he couldn't. Knudson had noted the firing, also, and asked on whose side it was. The Leftenant had answered that it sounded like one of Jerry's. Then they had simply kept on walking.

"Well, sir," offered the Englishman finally, "we're nearly there."

"Where," said Crown between gasps for the rough going, "is there?"

It hadn't seemed important before: one place was as stinking as another; but now some places were far more stinking than others; they were those places which had something to do with that particular hard steel rattle. It came again. . . . "Stink-Stink-Stink-Stink." It chattered quick-time. Crown hated it.

"A few hundred yards forward from the base of this bloody hill, in the general direction of those machine-gun bursts," said the Leftenant.

THEY were going downhill now. The walking was simpler. The packs on their backs pushed them forward and they went faster. Crown didn't want to go faster but he did. He became aware that Wilkes was crouching a little as he walked. Crown realized that he, too, was crouching more than the weight of his burden warranted. He looked back.

Knudson, too. That made Crown feel better. But his legs bothered him. They hurt; by God, they did. He wasn't used to this kind of thing. The heavy jowls under his girl's face quivered.

Soon they reached the flat. It was marshy, low. In a wooded area they passed an infantry aid station. Crown saw two British Medics approach down the trail. His party stepped off to give them passage way, since they were carrying something in a stretcher. Crown quickly looked away and saw Knudson, who hadn't looked away, staring. That was something, thought Crown to himself, that was something to choke up that black look of his. Knudson looked up suddenly and caught Crown's eye and his lips twisted into an abrupt grin. What was so screwin' funny, demanded Crown of himself. They entered a narrow gulch twisting through the flat fields. Wilkes warned them all to keep their heads down, but the warning was unnecessary. They encountered holes dug into the front-facing side of the gulch. An infantryman poked his head out of one of them and mumbled something which struck Crown as unintelligible and vile.

Leftenant Wilkes stopped. He stopped in front of another British officer. They talked quietly among themselves. Crown suddenly realized how quietly they were talking, and where they were.

He had to get out of here.

The truth of it leaped out of the sky at him and shook him. His large black eyes quested desperately for reasons, for means. "Stink-Stink-Stink." There it was again, only louder. Christ, did Crown see tracers streaking over his head? Knudson's mouth was open. He'd seen them too.

Get out of here. Only find a reason, a small, good little reason or, Jesus, he'd have to stay here for hours, hours.

"Oh, Captain." A quiet voice was calling him.

With hunched shoulders he went to the two officers, but the long, peccable hours were rising in front of him.

"If you look over this parapet, Captain, you will see the two houses we need destroyed." The quiet voice was quietly apologetic.

Crown nodded. He dug his fingers into the mud bank and forced his reluctant head up slowly, his thick neck straining, until he could see over.

One hundred fifty yards away the heavy, squat Italian house screamed whitely with the sun. He could see every detail of the thick, gouged walls. Crown's eyes dilated. One hundred fifty yards close to him. He was to shoot at that with two-hundred-pound projectiles. His head would be taken off—if the machine guns or a sniper didn't get him first.

Suddenly his mind iced over. He was thinking clearly while someone inside of him was blessing him for thinking clearly. He drew back his head and turned to the waiting officers with his answer.

"Well," said Wilkes eagerly, "what do you think?"

"It won't do," said Crown, flat voiced, impassive.

"It was the Colonel's suggestion, sir. He considered that this was a very opportune gulch, with the infantry covering us." Wilkes looked very much disappointed.

"To hell with the Colonel," whispered Crown, seeing his answer clear. "It's a poor O.P. It's not an O.P. at all for heavy artillery. It won't do."

It was working, it was working, the Limeys didn't know

what was inside him, not even Knudson who was nearby and listening hard. They weren't laughing at him. He was pulling it off.

"You can't see enough here," he said. "A round that went out of the way too far would be lost, and we're too close to your own troops to experiment tossing around stuff like ours."

By God, what he was saying was the truth. Crown felt strong and exultant. He was carrying it off. And with the truth. The truth was his reason. The two Limeys were looking at him with respect. Knudson appeared puzzled. Crown smiled to himself as the "Stink-Stink-Stink" went off again. Let it. He went on; he bit his words off in a military manner. "We'll have to find another O.P. One higher up where I can see more." That meant the hill back there, of course. Christ, wasn't he pulling it off! What did he mean, pulling it off? Wasn't it the truth? Sure. "Your Colonel was just mistaken. I've got to use my own judgment in this." Target. Right on the nose. He was a man of independence. "We'll start back up the hill." Look at the Limeys stare at him. He could say crap was gold now and they'd believe it.

Crown had an idea.

"Say," he said to the new British officer, "do you happen to have a shot of something back at your place?"

"Why certainly, Captain," said the officer. "If you gentlemen will accompany me a short way. . . ."

"We'll get started as soon as we have a short one," Crown said to Wilkes and winked at him. Head carefully lowered, he strutted a bit on his short legs. He was no coward, by God. He was an artilleryman. And they were heading in the right direction this time.

On the forward slope of the same hill they had descended to reach the gulch, Crown had found his new position. The others had never even noticed that cavelike mound with the small opening at the rear through which you could see what had to be seen on the terrain below. The Germans themselves had improved and camouflaged it when the lines were south of the hill.

Inside, the shelter was even remotely comfortable. Crown enjoyed the close walls, the snug overhead protection, even the damp earth he lay upon. It had been a mouth-drying business, searching for an observation post within seven or eight hundred yards of the enemy's white, suggestive houses. That shot of gin of the Limey's had helped Crown a lot.

He and the Leftenant edged close to the aperture through which they would do their observing. Now they could see considerably more than the two houses which alone had been visible from the flat below. They could see a dark ravine just beyond them, a bulk of hills, even Monastery Hill with the squat, indifferent monastery astride the top of it. They focused their field glasses, and the holed earth flew at them to be measured off in mills by the fine lines in their instruments. There was no movement, neither man's nor the quick spurt of fire. Silence drew off the valley's harm except where, periodically, the invisible machine gun reinstated it to make Crown squirm and Knudson, behind him, search.

"Well," said Crown suddenly, making his lips thin, "what are we waiting for?"

Well back in the shelter the blank-faced radio operator switched on his machine. He'd located it near the entrance of their shelter so that the long antenna could reach out delicately and unobtrusively into the wind. Leftenant Wilkes instructed him to contact regiment, and informed Crown that regiment would contact Crown's own battalion.

Impatiently Crown shifted his weight. "Have 'em shoot out the first round whenever they're ready."

Everything had been settled in advance. Berelli had made his plans and calculations in advance. The gun crew which would do the firing had been warned in advance of how precise they must be. The firing would be slow but each round would be in there on the target. There was nothing to worry about, Crown told himself. In the business conference before they started drinking, they had even decided which house they would hit first. And now, with the maps he'd brought along, there could be no doubt which one it was on the ground. Everything had been taken care of. The rest was up to him.

Then why the hell was he worried?

"On the way," said the radio operator.

Crown nodded, and hoped the others saw the self-sufficiency of his nod.

Fascinated, Leftenant Wilkes watched with his field glasses the shape of the enemy pictured on the terrain, while Knudson regarded the quiet land disinterestedly and put aside his Tommy gun.

The noise the projectile made rushing over their heads made them quail so that Crown missed the sharp red heart of the explosion. But when he peered over the defensive earth in front of him he could see the house partly silhouetted against a widening column of smoke. He had expected that since they had arranged, in order to avoid risks to the infantry, that the first shell would strike beyond the target.

"One hundred over," said Crown to the radio operator.

Crown's heavy chin protruded. This wasn't so bad at all. "Nice burst, eh Leftenant?"

"Very," said the Leftenant. "You should pound 'em to bits."

Crown pursed his lips in scientific detachment at that.

It seemed to Crown that the second round struck almost on the site of its predecessor. He looked angrily at Knudson. "The bastards aren't givin' me what I ask for." But Knudson shrugged. He looked at Wilkes. Wilkes smiled affably and made a soft, deprecatory movement with his hand. Crown raised his voice. "One hundred over." With his glasses he examined again the walls of his target, but they gave him no suggestions. The machine gun yelped again.

The next burst took a great leap and flashed a grave distance below and to the left of the house. Crown said "Sonuvabitch," and noticed that Wilkes wasn't smiling. Crown laughed uncertainly. "That must have scared your boys more than the Krauts," he said to Wilkes, who became more unsmiling than ever. They were waiting for him now, he saw. He shouted, "Five-zero left, one hundred short."

Knudson said coldly, "You're jumpin' your bracket, Captain."

"I know what I'm doin', damn it. Got to protect the infantry." He hoped for justification from Wilkes but got none. All right, then. The guns were a little wild. Could he help it if the guns were a little wild? No. He was doing his job, that's all.

But Knudson's silence was distinctly skeptical. He showed it. He thought Crown should have made it five-zero short if he had any sense and that it was bad Crown should lose his head. Knudson watched sharply for the verdict of the next round. There it was now—and just as he had thought.

. Crown, too, saw the burst flare quickly to the right of the target. It shouldn't have landed there, it shouldn't 've—because now he couldn't tell whether the range of the gun was great or small or right, and now Knudson would be laughing at him and there was nothing he could do about it. "Two-five right." He halted, searching his judgment and finding it tightened and wordless.

Crown heard Knudson's hard voice. It wasn't laughing. It was worse. It was telling him what to do. "Tell them," it was saying, "to repeat range."

And Crown followed the voice because he couldn't think of anything else to do. "Repeat range," said Crown. Why did it have to be him in this mess? The unfairness of it rubbed him, sandpaper on nerve endings. He couldn't look at the British officer.

"I see," Crown said to Knudson, attempting to laugh, "I see you're learning gunnery, Knudson," while his eyes concentrated on the house which he hardly saw; and he wanted a drink more desperately than ever.

The machine gun was laughing brief, hard laughs like a metal madman. Their shells were goading it, tickling it, making it laugh. Crown wanted it to stop laughing almost as much as he wanted a drink.

The rush of air overhead, the deep caromph again. Sense it, Crown, sense it, he warned himself. This one was in closer, though. It was a little right and beyond the target. "One-zero right," he said, "Five-zero over," and when he looked directly at Knudson he could tell that Knudson was laughing at him inside that skull of his because Knudson had been right all through and he had been wrong.

172

"Do you think we'll be hitting it soon?" It was Wilkes talking. Crown turned to answer him. But Wilkes wasn't looking at Crown. Wilkes was addressing Knudson.

"Next round should be damn close," said Knudson. Crown hated them both with all his force.

While they waited, Knudson extracted a pocket knife from his pocket and punched two holes into the top of his beer can and poured the beer into a canteen cup. Then he looked out again over Crown's shoulder.

The next round blocked the house from their view. Crown could see that they were in on it close, real close. The pride in him took one last fling. He summoned all his resolution. "Repeat range." He said it strongly and turned to the other officer while he prayed in the background of his mind that all was redeemed now. "We're in on it," he said emphatically. "We didn't hit it last time because of dispersion." Dispersion. That was it. Dispersion was what had blocked him. Nothing of his doing. Of the gun's. Of the rotten, rotten gun's.

"I hope so," said Wilkes, dryly.

So Crown took refuge in the knowledge that the machine gun was silent and that that, at least, was one thing—and who the hell was Wilkes? But no. There was the rattle again.

Sergeant Knudson said nothing but picked up his canteen cup. "Some beer, Leftenant?" He grinned his lipless grin and he was speaking to Wilkes, not to Crown. "English beer."

"Yes, thank you," said Wilkes, and he was speaking to Knudson.

Wilkes took a few swallows and handed the cup back. Knudson raised it to his lips, then halted. "Beer, Captain?"

173

"No," said Crown. It had been hard for him to get the word out.

Crown saw the explosion blast at the same spot, and groaned inside. The gun was still short. There was no end to torment, after all. Dispersion, maybe it was dispersion— weakly he offered the consolation to himself, and then realized that he didn't care any longer. Just let him go back where it was warm, in his cozy C.P. with the *vino* bottles lined up under the cot. Knudson was talking. Shut up, Knudson, damn you, shut up.

"Better make it Two-five short, Captain," Knudson repeated.

Crown hid himself in an island of despair. He renounced responsibility so that his insides wouldn't writhe. "Two-five short," he echoed, dully.

The two-hundred-pound projectile smashed down upon the roof of the target. The smoke plume was red in the sun this time, charged with red dust. Black fragments dotted it. Soon the wind moved it away so that they could see the black hole in the roof with the gray wisps trailing out of it.

The sight roused Crown. It enticed him from his island. "Target," he said, "repeat range." The rest was easy. He would sit there and tell them to repeat range. He shoved his hands into his pockets. He still didn't care—but what the hell. He no longer bothered to hate Knudson. If they didn't like him, they could go screw themselves. The whole world could go screw! But God, how he wanted a drink.

Some shells struck before the house, hiding it, some beyond it, framing it. Others bored into its walls, into its ceilings, its inner chambers. Some with special fuses reached even into the cellars and burst there. When it was clear that nothing could be gained by pulverizing jagged walls,

Crown called "Cease Firing" to the radio operator and gave an accounting of the results.

Leftenant Wilkes said, "Splendid," thinking of all the power allied with him.

Knudson, with his deep-sunken eyes alive for once, agreed with Wilkes.

Captain Crown said nothing, for he was dreading the next mission. Wilkes found him tiresome. But Crown was not interested then in Wilkes or in what Wilkes might think. Crown was interested in Crown, and thought of the next mission, which was inescapable. The machine gun coughed again. Soon he could see the question on their faces. What the hell was he waiting for now? All right, all right, he'd give them their mission.

"Fire number two target when ready," he said. The radio operator passed it on.

It was at that moment that the Nazi concentration began. Four men heard a shell roll screaming down the harmonic scale and initiate the concentration. A pure white flower rose on the slope below them, scattering burning pollen in high red arcs. They heard the crash of its birth. Then the wind took the billowing petals and unfolded them over the slope. They caught the mordant scent of the petals. Other rounds coming in filled the air with screaming and the slope with the blossoming flowers.

The air coagulated whitely. Wilkes rose up against it. "Bloody rotten white phosphorus," he shouted, and subsided helplessly because all his shouting would not help him to see his target through the thickness.

One after another the smoke seeds sprouted closer to Crown. The red burnings searched for him, the smoke rose and seeped into the shelter. He could hardly see the others because the silent wisps were turning into bandages before his eyes.

Soon none of them could see. Each was alone with the screamings and the poundings all around, with burning phosphorus streaking through the whiteness and with the stink and with his own sneezings and coughings. Only Crown was the most alone because Wilkes was cursing bitterly the bloody smoke which stopped their mission and Knudson was angry and interested at once and the radio operator didn't count. Crown, who was the most alone, didn't want that whitened kind of loneliness. He was coughing with the stink lodged in his throat; his ears were bursting with the vast caromphing around him.

A bush before the aperture of their shelter caught the fire and flamed. They saw its branches outlined in red against a white, choking world, and caught in their chests the bush's further fumes. Tears filled their eyes.

Crown yelled in his terror that the screwin' woods were on fire. He would have run. But where? Into the white outside with the burnings in it? He couldn't run—but God, he wanted to. He didn't hear Wilkes croak that it was too wet for fire, because at that moment all the murderous, foul invective within him exploded in one obscene batch; it came out of him in whispers to do battle with the wrapping, seeping, indifferent enemy.

Suddenly the noise of the shelling stopped. The stream of Crown's whispered curses crawled over the silence until he, too, realized that the noise had stopped. They sat waiting for the next shell in the white silence. Was it over? The radio operator said that Fire Direction wanted to know what the delay was about. Wilkes told him to answer, "Smoke barrage. Wait."

But how much longer would it be before the smoke dissipated? They couldn't tell. They had to sit there waiting.

All at once, Crown was certain that he wouldn't wait. He was getting out of this. The others couldn't even see him. He stumbled to his feet. He'd get out of it and when the smoke cleared, they'd wonder.

A tide of noise anticipated him, stopped him open-mouthed where he stood and sent him to squeeze himself against the earth wall. The tears which came to Crown's eyes were more than tears from the smoke.

Wilkes, who kept his station by the opening, noticed no thickening of smoke and saw no red lines traced through it. Yet the heavy explosions trampled rapidly on their hill. He wondered. He felt a body lie down beside him.

"High explosive." It was Knudson's voice.

"Yes," said Wilkes, seeing reasons now. "Perhaps they'll blow us a rift in their own smoke screen," he added hopefully.

"Or maybe they'll blow us," said Knudson. "They're tryin' hard enough."

"Yes," said Wilkes.

But it was too difficult to speak, and there was too much booming in the air.

Crown, too, sensing the smoke density lessen, felt the truth come upon him. "High Explosive." The words exploded in his mind. "H.E." around him. He sensed death. And then his mind went white and blank as the sightlessness around him. It closed down. It called it a day. He simply sat in his corner—and listened.

"Look there," said Wilkes, shaken with excitement.

Abruptly displayed in its cloudy frame was the fortress

house they had sought to hit before the smoke came. But it was more than that now. It was many small figures rising and falling, rising and falling in their long green overcoats while the house covered them with fire.

Wilkes squeezed the Sergeant's arm.

"Captain Crown," Wilkes shouted, "Captain Crown."

Crown was listening for the H.E.

"Damn it, man, wake up." Wilkes couldn't see the Captain. "Wake up, damn you, it's an attack," he cried.

Knudson placed a hand upon the Leftenant's shoulder. "Screw the bastard," he said. "I'll adjust on 'em, Limey." There was no insult when he said "Limey."

Knudson had the operator relay to Fire Direction the news of the attack and called for battery fire.

Once, before the smoke curled over again and hid the field of action, the two men saw four huge blobs of flame strike among the enemy. "Target," said Knudson. "Continue fire for effect. Repeat range."

The two men stopped their futile attempt to penetrate the smoke screen. They found comfort in distinguishing the greater sound of their own shells overhead from the lighter noise of the enemy's. They couldn't see their rounds landing but knew they must be. They forgot fear. They forgot even their own discomfort. When a halt came in the enemy's fire on their hill, they were able to hear the caromphing of their shells upon the enemy and that cheered them even more.

Crown knew that the halt had come, too. He smiled happily. With the white bandage tight around his eyes, he felt his way by the radio operator. This time he knew that he would make it. After a moment, he could tell that he was outside, and that he had made it. He broke into a blind trot, stumbling and falling in the cloud.

Then he heard the whir of the incoming shell. He started a wild run back to where he thought the shelter was. At the last moment he threw himself prostrate, but as he fell he saw the sharp flame illumine the shelter's thin earthen roof and crumble it.

His jaw sagged with awe. He regarded the blood streak on his right arm. This was his payment for being alive. It didn't hurt at all.

He felt like laughing. He had pulled it off. The others were dead. No one was alive to know himself a better man than he was. It came to Crown only vaguely at first. It came to him in its intensity little by little as he crawled away on his stomach. It rose stronger upon him when the shelling finally stopped and he got to his feet; and it propelled him as he ran. No one would ever know!

Eventually he made his way beyond the smoke screen and found help. They sprinkled sulfanilamide on his wound, bandaged it, and sent him back to his unit.

Some days later, Lieutenant Colonel Colouris was seated in his C.P. with Captain, soon to be Major, Berelli. Suddenly, with a grin, Colouris picked up a sheet of paper and handed it to his S-3.

"Take a look at that," he said, "Crown's citation."

Berelli raised his eyebrows.

"Do you remember I told you the experience might be good for Crown?" Colouris chuckled briefly. "I admit I was worried, by God. But it made a soldier of him."

179

Comfortably, he lit a cigar. "Now I'm going to make it stick. I'm going to get him decorated. Psychology, Berelli, psychology." He puffed deeply on his cigar. "And he deserves it. I'm very pleased with Crown," Colouris added.

Berelli decided that the Colonel was too contented for it to be only Crown.

"I've gotten all kinds of congratulatory messages lately because of his work. The English colonel sent me down a note praising the battalion to the skies. I want you to have copies mimeographed and distributed among the officers and men. A copy will go in the 201 file of each officer. Good for morale. . . ."

Right on the nose. But Berelli never winked an eye.

"Go on, Berelli, read it."

Berelli read while his Colonel watched him with a pleased smile.

". . . Captain Thomas A. Crown, in the course of one afternoon's work as forward observer for the 794th F.A. Bn., succeeded through an unusually precise adjustment in destroying an enemy strong point which had held up Allied troops for days. He had begun the destruction of a second when the enemy laid down a heavy smoke screen and followed it by an intense barrage of high explosive. Crown would have been justified in vacating the position since the smoke made visibility impossible. But with great tenacity he maintained his post. That tenacity was rewarded when a rift in the screen made it possible for him to observe the formation of an enemy counterattack supported by the remaining strong point. Prompt and vigorous action enabled him to direct heavy artillery fire on the attack with the result that it was dispersed with large casualties inflicted on the enemy. He achieved this during a constant bombardment which resulted in the destruction of his party and the wounding of Captain Crown. Only then, when his party was destroyed, and he himself wounded, did he leave his post—and with his mission accomplished. His actions were in accordance with the finest traditions of the Field Artillery . . .”

“. . . so Crown's in for the Silver Star,” mused Berelli.

“Do you know what I like even better than all this in the citation, though I couldn't very well put it down in black and white?” the Colonel was asking. “The way he selected a position other than the bad one the Limey colonel had suggested. That showed,” said Colouris, “moral courage. Moral courage, by God.”

The Colonel heard a knock, said “Come in,” and the opening door showed Captain Crown, pink and ruddy, recovered, as far as Colouris could make out, from the strain of his experience. Colouris was delighted that in a few days a valuable officer had recovered from the strain of his experience.

The Colonel rose. “Crown,” he said. “I've interesting news for you.” He was beaming on his captain.

“Yes, sir,” said Crown.

“Yes. I'm putting you in for the Silver Star. I don't ordinarily mention this sort of thing before it's a fact but in this case I don't think there's any doubt but that the award will go through. We all heard the progress of your mission over the radio relay. The results are definite and important. We don't have to depend on hearsay or your own report of what happened.”

“That,” said Berelli cheerfully, “is the beauty of it.” But he was watching Crown carefully.

Crown ignored him. "Yes, sir," he said to the Colonel.

Berelli couldn't understand it. It didn't make sense. He thought he knew Crown, and he couldn't figure it out.

When the congratulations and the modest acceptance were over, Berelli accompanied Crown outside. Outside the C.P. it was gray and drizzling. Berelli took Crown by the arm intimately.

"Say, Crown," he asked, "what's the lowdown?" His voice was intimate and secretive. It tried to say that he was ready to laugh with Crown.

"Lowdown?" said Crown coldly.

The fat ass was too damn self-possessed. The little round butterball of iron! Why?

"You heard me. Lowdown!" Berelli leered maliciously. "You must have gotten the breaks somewhere to get through all that. What's the story? Where the hell did you get so lucky?"

"Did I get the breaks?" Crown smiled with sheer delight. "Screw you, Berelli," he said and walked away.

Berelli watched the heavy buttocks disappear around a corner of the house, and shook his head. There was no doubt about it. Never again could he needle Crown so that the fat ass really felt it, nor did he see anyone else managing the trick. Crown was no longer the same Crown. He had won free. Berelli scratched the gray stubble at the back of his neck, and gave it up.

9

◤

SPRING came upon the officers and men of the 794th. Before they could turn, the warm air slid in beneath the cold, roused them from their dugouts, made them dream the merciless, impossible dreams of home. Headquarters grew big with plans. The turbaned soldier of the Empire passed across their fields.

Preparations for assault against the German battle line began on May 11th. One hour short of midnight every howitzer in the battalion fired at its scheduled target, joined in that vehement movement by every gun and howitzer on the Allied front. The false, flickering dawn blew out some stars. The spring sky howled in the night below Cassino. Then the battalion had fired through its schedule. The men waited. They waited for targets of opportunity and to go home.

The Poles came fiercely from the North; the British died in Cassino and at the Rapido; to the West, Americans warred across the Garigliano River. The men waited. Cannoneers of the 794th stared at the pin-filled maps the officers exhibited for their benefit. For the map changed, the surface of the earth changed! The future warped the past's ancient routines; you could see it in the faces of the maps. What news? They were greedy for news of change; the herded prisoners filled them with uneasiness. What of the men on Anzio? Never mind Anzio. Any man could see that this was breakthrough, spring thaw of the eternal battle line; and Rome lay ahead and beyond Rome, in the non-Euclidean geometry of the war, home! Sudden hope, like the flash of the barrage over the poppy fields at night, illuminated their hearts and devastated them.

But they waited. No one knew where to send them. The Colonel couldn't find out.

PRIVATE SIGMUND EHRLICH at the gun he served let the slight rain fall upon his dirty blond hair. He had been waiting for a phone call half the night. He had watched his howitzer slide in slowly from the insides of the night. Minute by minute, fifteen tons of metal, rooted in the mud, bedecked with the green and brown garnishings of the suspended camouflage net, had moved in out of the darkness.

A few yards away William Padrone, Pfc., filled his steel helmet with water from a five-gallon can and splattered his thin and naked torso with icy handfuls from the helmet. Long-nosed, elfin, he saw Ehrlich and the howitzer shimmer through the film of water clinging to his long lashes. "*Guten morgen*," he jibed across the flat at Ehrlich's motionless back. "*Guten morgen*, Herr Ehrlich," and wiped the mist away.

184

Meanwhile Dan MacCarthy, pudgy, bespectacled, soft-faced, meditated upon the panorama of the four impassive howitzers of Battery B dispersed before a rotting strip of road. His fingers remembered how hard the steel was to the flesh, and his shoulders the push of the rammer staff when he and three others stuffed the shell hard into its tight chamber. The gun, he suddenly decided, was a large frog sitting in the mud and he was a servitor of the frog and the frog in the mud would go in a letter to his aunt. . . . He found his way down to the howitzer.

The phone beside Ehrlich rang once, sharply. "Number One gun, Private Ehrlich." Private, private, eternally private Ehrlich. The impotent eagle eyes stared at Dan MacCarthy.

"Yes, sir, I give you ammunition report in one minute." Ehrlich added and subtracted the neat figures with the stub of a pencil. Dan MacCarthy turned away. Ehrlich was phoning the Exec position, calling back numbers. "At howitzer, 21 H.E., 12 White Bag . . ."

Dan sat down on the trail opposite Ehrlich and dreamed fitfully about how he had long since forgiven Ehrlich and how he wanted Ehrlich to forgive him, seeing how it was spring and the gun was a large frog . . . When the phone rang again, Dan jumped.

"Number One gun, Private Ehrlich. Yes, sir, I do it now!" But Dan noticed a kind of glee underline Ehrlich's voice, and decided this must be another fire mission. Ehrlich loved to fire the guns—that was about all that Ehrlich loved. Dan saw the frost-eyed Ehrlich glance at him briefly, then, strangely, smile from ear to ear, of all things, and then . . .

Dan squirmed to have Ehrlich's shout assault his ears this morning. "CLOSE STATION MARCH ORDER." There was nothing Dan could ever do about Ehrlich, nothing—but did he have to shout so loud? Close station, march . . .

"Hey!" yelled Dan MacCarthy. His jaw dropped, his round cheeks quivered. "C S M O," Ehrlich was bellowing now. "C S M O"—the initials of change.

Pack up and leave, it meant. Close your station, order yourself, but principally the howitzer, for the march, wherever the hell the march went. It meant the end of no mere year, but the end of an era. Happy New World, Happy New World! "C S M O, C S M O." The sounds beat in Dan's ears, penetrated his muscles. In a second, before a man could blink, here it was! Dan didn't know what to do. "C S M O," he heard himself yelling. He began to dance about between the gun trails. "C S M O," he shouted.

Cannoneers came on the run to the pieces they served, stumbled through the field, cursed their heads off. At point after point their shouts speared the morning mist. Everybody yelled together.

"Well, who woulda thought it?" asked Padrone. "We're movin'!"

Already the debris they themselves had scattered, the householdings they themselves had improvised these long months past, the four howitzers of the battery, the strung wire, leaped up and dropped their long familiarity and, as they all shouted, turned into the objective features of an alien field. Their released minds sprung squarely at the future. They expected nothing in particular, they made no claims. But this they had, this much of sureness; so much was done with. They were taking a step. Their equipment, their guns, their battalion, were displacing forward.

186

"Whadaya know?" mock-marveled Padrone.

For now the Colonel had found out where to take them. How to get the goddamn gun out?

It was almost twenty yards through this soft-bottomed, poppy-interspersed field to that road, Holloway observed. There was no sense sending the Mack prime mover in here after the piece. They would never get the prime mover out, let alone the howitzer. In point of fact, the howitzer should never have in the first place been moved into the field from its convenient place at the road bank. They had tried to cross up the Germans and now, by God, they'd crossed themselves up.

Carefully, Sergeant Holloway picked his way through the yard-deep mud ruts the howitzers had torn when first dragged into the heart of the field. He had wrenched his back a while ago helping the crew of Number One howitzer prepare the piece for traveling. His back made Holloway delicate with his steps. He grimaced and struggled up the yielding embankment upon which the churned road sat.

They would have to winch the piece out. The other gun sections would probably have to do likewise. It would be one hell of a job, but there was no alternative. You were going somewhere. The large mongrel gazed plaintively at him as he stepped onto the harder surface of the road.

"Have to winch 'er out," he said to Grostock, the Exec. Grostock with his worried face—at least he knew enough to steer clear of another man's job.

"One o' the Ammunition Macks will have ta pull you out," said Grostock. "Yours is still bein' fixed." Snafu again. Holloway kept his face still.

That must be the Ammo Mack now. The enormous truck chewed the beat-up road as it moved in on them.

Holloway glanced critically at the driver ten feet in the air. Holloway would have preferred his own man and his own prime mover, but was quite prepared to take what came his way.

"You," he said to the driver. "Get out your chain and hitch it to the Mack's pintle. Fasten the other end to that hunk of tree over there." Holloway stretched out a long arm to a thick stump extending two limbs in a splintered benediction over the road. "We're goin' to winch the piece out." Without the stump's additional support, Holloway calculated, the dead weight of his howitzer, slumped to its axles in the mud as it was, would drag clear off the road even the Ammo truck with its several tons. Critically, Holloway watched the Mack maneuver. It suited him well enough to manage circumstances, but he never had much trust in them.

The men were standing around the howitzer, useful as so many third tits. Regular WPA. Ehrlich stood leaning upon a crowbar. Holloway's jaw tightened. "Ehrlich," he shouted across the twenty yards to the howitzer. "Ehrlich, goddamn it!" Ehrlich looked up from his crowbar. "Come here and lend me a hand." Ehrlich's squat and heavy figure didn't arrive until Holloway had finished helping the driver secure the Mack to the stump. Holloway said nothing but he noticed. Ever since he'd caused Ehrlich to lose his stripes, Holloway noticed every move he made; and every other move angered him.

Holloway removed the stiff canvas cover from the winch drum in front of the Mack. There was rust on the steel cable. He paused in disgust. Shrugging his high and bony shoulders, he seized the iron hook at the end of the cable.

"Let 'er go," he called to the driver. "Play out your cable. Herr Ehrlich and I will carry it over to the piece."

Bleakly, Ehrlich eyed the masking hill before him and drew an arm across his running nose.

"All right, Ehrlich, get the lead out of your ass." The dry, flat-toned insult of Holloway pried at Ehrlich. Ehrlich could do nothing now. He joined Holloway at the cable hook.

They pulled together. The further from the Mack they dragged the cable the more the weight and drag of it increased. A mongrel dog kept sniffing at their heels. It was the mutt that he'd seen following Holloway around all morning. Ehrlich kicked at it as he pulled at the cable. The mutt yelped, and Ehrlich could see Holloway's face twitch. Ehrlich grinned at Holloway. Then they were at the howitzer, and Holloway, aided by some of the crew, secured the cable to the front of the howitzer's carriage. Ehrlich shied a stick at the dog. The dog wagged its tail and looked foolish. Ehrlich thought, the poor lousy sonuvabitch of a mutt, it should be dead.

"Keep away from the goddamned cable, you guys," Holloway warned and made the voyage back to the road again. The wet wind smeared the mud upon his face. This had better work because it was the only way of getting the piece out. And they were going forward.

"Pull her in now," he said to the man up in the cab, and moved impatiently at the nag of pain in his back. "And take it easy. You're going to be pulling half the goddamned field along with the piece." He wished it were his own man. Holloway shook his head at all the trouble required to go from here to there.

Little by little, accompanied by the beat of the engine, the slack left the cable. The Lieutenant was watching, too. But he would keep his hands off Holloway's responsibility. The cable became a straight, shivering line between the Mack and the howitzer.

"Easy," shouted Holloway.

The howitzer shook. Its wheels pushed against the banked mud in front, but could not rise above it. The squealing winch dragged the whole mass forward and the mud rose higher. The big Mack skidded slightly on the road.

"Gee," said Padrone, "look at that pooch sniffin' 'round the cable."

"Take it easy," Holloway repeated, flicking his eyes briefly from side to side to see that no damn fool stood anywhere near the cable. The thick stump which moored the Mack down cracked the earth above its roots.

Then the howitzer pointed its eight-inch muzzle at him like a big eye and lunged a foot forward. The encouraged driver made the engine roar louder. "Cut it!" yelled Holloway but the goddamn fool never heard him. The mud distended in bulging piles before the wheels and undercarriage of the howitzer. The cable sang with tons of pull. And the gun stopped dead!

"Cut it, goddamn—LOOK OUT FOR THE CABLE!"

Twenty yards of wound steel cable snapped into two huge and slashing whips. They writhed; they went wild with energy. One hurled itself back at the howitzer, the other struck at the winch drum. Mack and howitzer skidded and recoiled and rang with the blows.

"Jesus Christ!"

No one could even think.

Padrone opened his eyes. The howitzer simply squatted in the mud. The faint rain continued. Instead of the whips, two pieces of cable lay quietly in the mud. One section of the cable even stretched at his feet. Padrone shuddered. But there were all the others standing there. Everything remained the same.

"Anybody hurt?" Grostock was yelling. "Fer Chris' sake, anybody hurt?"

Dan MacCarthy began to run around, he didn't know where, looking for somebody who was hurt. Nobody was hurt. Only there, there, right in the middle of the field, Dan could see it quite clearly, all quiet and dead like the cable except where the slight wind moved its fur, lay the neatly bisected parts of a dog.

"Look!" he shouted. He stumbled over the gun ruts running to the poor mutt in the field. He couldn't get there fast enough. He fell once and fouled himself in the muck and got up again. He had to see the mutt.

The fresh insides were coming out.

Others joined Dan. The mist snuggled closely upon the men who, in wonder, on this early spring day watched a dog's blood puddle at their feet.

Padrone knelt down and touched the dead animal's ear. Gee, look how dead it was. Poor little, poor little, poor little pooch. Why, it wasn't fair at all. Little dog with his long tongue hanging out of his mouth. All dead now it was, dead as a man. An enormous wave of sadness flooded over Padrone's heart.

"Another screwin' casualty," said Padrone.

Dan MacCarthy turned away and threw up.

And quietly Holloway surveyed his howitzer, and his men who served it clustered around the dead mutt, and on the ground the remnants of manifest power, two pieces of cable. But the war was still on. He still had to get the gun out. A quiet anger grew within him, grew over the pull in his back, became big with that dull ache, and bigger. "Come on back, damn it," he flared suddenly at the men in the field.

Sagely, Ehrlich nodded his head.

B BATTERY's vehicles were aligned on a tree-shaded lane which, just ahead of where Number One gun sat behind its prime mover, entered over a muddy, rutted joint upon Route Six. After Number One gun, at ten- or fifteen-yard intervals, the other three howitzers waited; and after the howitzers, the two-and-a-half-ton trucks. The lighter vehicles scrambled upon an adjacent field, prepared to move into the lane when their heavy associates had cleared it.

Lieutenant Grostock, standing beside the right front wheel of Number One's prime mover, glanced down the lane for the tenth time to reassure himself that all was in proper order, cannoneers disposed upon the loaded tops of the Macks, all drivers ready to start. He made out an officer standing at the edge of the field where the light vehicles were. Grostock knew he was watching for the first signs of movement to organize the light column and follow behind with his maintenance crew. Grostock turned away; he had only to wait for Evans to return and lead the battery forward to wherever Captain Fuller waited at the new position.

The new position would be, of course, beyond Cassino. A broad and innocent grin of delight illumined Grostock's face, but only for a moment. When he looked at his guns again, his eyebrows merged into a straight line. He wouldn't be happy until he was up there in that cab and they were moving. Where was Evans? What the hell was the delay?

Grostock mumbled something under his breath. Sergeant Holloway, standing by, heard him. "You say something, Lieutenant?"

"Nothin'," growled Grostock.

"Thought you said something," said Holloway peaceably. The pleasant spring breeze, the afternoon shadows over the guns, made him feel peaceable—not like an offensive at all.

"Nope," said Grostock sullenly. "We're waitin' fer Lieutenant Evans ta pick us up."

"Think it'll be soon?" Not that Holloway minded waiting in the quiet with the war moved far out of range. Besides, it would rest his cannoneers.

"Dunno." But what was the delay? Evans should have been there half an hour ago. But what the hell, mused Grostock, it wasn't his ass. He was in the clear. The reflection made him feel better.

"Hey, Sarge," bawled Padrone from ten feet off the ground, sprawled on the tarpaulin which covered cases of powder and looking at Grostock, "let's get goin'."

"Hold your water, Pady," said Holloway affably. "We're waiting for Lieutenant Evans."

"What the hell's keepin' him, then? He pick up a *Signorina* or somethin'?"

The men ten feet off the ground with Padrone laughed.

"Let's get goin'," wailed Padrone again.

"Yeah," said someone else up above. "All we do all screwin' war is wait. When do we win it?"

Horse laughs. The boys felt good. The spring and being

on their way made them a little crazy. Holloway smiled affectionately at the afternoon shadows. Someone else on Number Two was yelling, "Let's get the hell outa here." The boys must be in damn good spirits, all right. Only Grostock looked as though he didn't know whether to laugh or blow his top.

"I suppose Lieutenant Evans'll be here soon," Holloway said to him.

(But suddenly Holloway found himself praying vehemently that Evans would never come. He shook his head to clear it.)

"Hope so," muttered Grostock. That screw-up Evans was spoiling the whole thing for him. Everything always got spoiled. Nothing ever went like it should. Christ, he was sore.

"Gee," Grostock said suddenly. "I bet the war's over in no time!" and his soreness vanished in a happy smile.

Holloway didn't say anything because Grostock was praying, not talking. "Let's get goin'," yelled someone. Holloway lit a cigarette. His hand shook slightly. He found it strange, but this final moving hardly seemed real as yet. Perhaps the men were trying to talk themselves into thinking it was real. How about that? Holloway shrugged.

(His back hurt. For the first time in his life he didn't want to go ahead. He was deadly tired of the war. He blinked in his amazement.)

"Wisht we'd go an' get it over with," muttered Grostock.

"Hey," yelled the driver in the cab of the Mack, who'd been watching Route Six for lack of anything else to do. "Here comes a peep."

194

Everybody looked up. They could hear the noise of the peep, even those who couldn't see it. Grostock waited anxiously to hear signs of its slowing down to turn off into their lane. If it slowed down, that meant Evans. It did. Grostock grinned from ear to ear. There was the peep coming up to him now; and Evans was in it.

The small dust-covered vehicle stopped near Grostock and he went the rest of the way. He could see Evans' face lathered with dust. "Hey," he said, and laughed. "What happened t'ya?" Then he remembered the business on hand. "What the hell was the delay about?" he grumbled.

"Traffic," said Evans hoarsely because his throat felt as though it were lined with felt. "Too damn much of it. Tanks, trucks, infantry, guns—everything's on the road. Whew."

"Yeah?" said Grostock eagerly. "We're really pushin', ain't we?" Back in Hoboken in no time.

"The whole army's moving up," croaked Evans. "Look, Grostock. I'll lead you into position. There are route-marking signs posted—all the drivers know 'em—but in all the damn traffic sometimes you don't see 'em. Fuller says to make sure all the vehicles stick close together as possible or someone'll get lost." He seemed tired by his speech. He sank back into his seat while the driver maneuvered in the narrow space to get at the head of the column.

Grostock turned happily to Holloway. "Y'heard, Sergeant?" he said. "Supposin' ya pass the word t' the drivers, huh?"

Holloway went about his business. So they were moving? He examined curiously the field he'd left. They were really leaving. He shook his head. It was still hard to believe . . .

He broke into a trot down along the line of vehicles.

Grostock saw Holloway returning to him. "Ya tell 'em, Sergeant?"

Holloway nodded and swung himself up into the cab beside the driver. Grostock took one last earnest look at his column, shouted, "Let's go," heard the rising lion-growl of the motors of his prime movers and followed his sergeant up.

Evans' peep rolled up the grade to Route Six. Grostock's prime mover lurched forward. He put his head out over the door and satisfied himself that the others were following. Slowly, heavily, roaring with the effort, his vehicle pulled the fifteen tons of dead weight behind it up the slope of the junction and boiled the dust on Route Six. He could see the other prime movers and their long-stemmed guns swinging wide as possible to make the turn. One after the other. By God, this really was it. Then the two-and-a-half-tonners essayed the turn, and then he was too far down Route Six to see more. Grostock fixed his attention on the road ahead and Evans' peep leading him on.

"Well, Sergeant," he said, "we're on our way."

Suddenly he felt very proud. He wished that he could be standing on his feet as they advanced northward toward Cassino. He wouldn't mind the dust in his face even if it made him gray as Evans was. He would be a leader with his guns following him up Route Six, with his men following him. Grostock was surprised at himself. He never went in for that kind of crap!

They had moved at five miles an hour until all the battery's vehicles were mounted on the road; now they were accelerating slowly. Holloway leaned back. He might as well enjoy the ride. There'd be work ahead. Of course, thought Holloway, he wasn't as excited as he should be. But they had been too long waiting, much too long. He turned his attention to the flat lands on each side of the road.

"Screw it," said Holloway, half to himself and half to Grostock.

"Yeah," chuckled Grostock.

It was a murdered land on each side, the corpse of a land, twisted, with holes rotted into its substance, where no green sign showed, though it was spring. But Holloway regarded it all equably enough. It was no skin off his back. He was merely passing through the country, taking it in on the way.

He observed that it wasn't a very good way. Route Six was becoming vilely pitted as they moved toward Cassino. (He perceived the whiteness of Cassino at the flat's end, and his gorge rose.) But the driver was unable to make much speed. The great Mack would lurch into a pit and demand that it be nursed out with care.

"Maybe," he said to Grostock, "traffic will be lighter after Cassino."

"It better," said Grostock darkly.

Holloway smiled. Grostock was an angry child. Wait until they hit the traffic Evans had promised further down the line; then he would really boil. Probably he was already worrying about that. But Holloway wasn't worried.

(Not about that. But, my God, where were they going? An enormous rebellion passed its peristaltic action through his body and left him shivering. Oh, that blasted back of his!)

Evans' peep crossed the makeshift bridge. Carefully, the prime mover followed and the boards creaked as it pressed its formidable weight upon them. Now Holloway noted dust fog dead ahead. Out of the corner of his eye he caught Grostock grimacing. Holloway was going straight into it. He was inching in painful line behind an endless progress of wheels and exhaust and skin-roughing, eye-smarting, fine-ground particles of war.

"Sonuvabitch," protested Grostock. "Oh, sonuvabitch."

This much wasn't bothering Holloway. Grostock, perhaps, but not him. Holloway had yet to encounter a nuisance which some other nuisance would not supersede. Snafu or no snafu, he was quite accustomed to taking care of his own. Holloway set himself more comfortably with reference to the backboard which came no higher than the small of his aching spine.

(But how much could he bear to see on the other side of the dust fog? Holloway was angry, cold angry. He hated Ehrlich!)

Now Baker Battery was moving behind a column of British lorries in a jerky, dislocated fashion. On the battery's left, squeezing by the Macks and howitzers, rearward went a column of empty trucks.

Pfc. Padrone on the broad back of Number One's prime mover balanced himself beside Sigmund Ehrlich, Private, the white marks showing on Ehrlich's sleeve where the stripes had been. Padrone touched his face with his finger tips and absently contemplated the smudges. He shoved his hand in front of Ehrlich's face. "Look at that," he said, he being almost the only one of the gun section who bothered much with Ehrlich. "Whew."

"I don't haf to look for your fingers to know it's dusty," said Ehrlich.

Ehrlich was pondering bomb craters half filled with water on the field beside the road. "You look at that," he said, and pointed to a great hole in the earth which, with part of its circumference, scooped out the edge of Route Six. "Some bomb," he said. "Yah, a beauty.

"That," he added abruptly, "iss the way to do it."

"To do what?"

"To fight war," said Ehrlich with a kind of pride, "to fight war."

Padrone rubbed the dust out of the corners of his eyes. It didn't seem that Ehrlich expected an answer. He himself was not too impressed with fighting war. But he regarded the few broken piles of masonry which denoted the outskirts of Cassino with a sort of awed respect. He himself had had a hand in that! Padrone shook his head in sheer disbelief.

"Christ," he said, "I betcha I could walk faster'n this. *Blitzkrieg*. Christ."

"Never mind," said Ehrlich. "We go."

The prime mover swayed heavily and Padrone had to hang on. "Yeah," he said, "on our ass." He removed his helmet. It was getting warm.

We go, Ehrlich was thinking, we go slow but we go far. Soon, maybe, it would be the end. Soon it would be Rome and after Rome, Paris, and some day Berlin. It would be good to chase and smash the German Army. Yes, and this breakthrough went for a sign. The thought tightened Ehrlich's lips and shot light into his eyes. It obliterated his sense of isolation and the casual, indifferent curiosity of his comrades.

They passed larger piles, unidentifiable now, mute, cut off from their former existence. Ehrlich glowed when he

199

saw them. British sappers had roped them off with white tape, and posted warnings. Mines. Ehrlich shrugged. Of course there had to be a price tag for every victory. To break the bastard enemy, he would gladly meet the price. Gladly!

"Hey, Pady," yelled Grossberg from where he perched among a group of men further to the rear of the Mack, "did ja see that?" Grossberg was in high glee and intensely interested.

"See what?" Padrone yelled back.

"That thing over there." He stretched a heavy arm toward what had once been an amphitheater. The outline remained. "What ya think it was?"

"Search me," shouted Padrone.

Ehrlich looked where Grossberg had indicated. It didn't matter what it once was. That fool Grossberg didn't know that. Ehrlich smiled gently. What mattered was what it was now. Now the powdered granite belonged to Ehrlich, not to them. For they were like the guns which wrought his vengeance, as blind, as senseless. The victory was his, then, his alone. He alone knew the great, victorious pain of hatred and eternal war. They could never touch his victory.

OCCASIONALLY, David Evans in the lead peep would look back over his shoulder to make sure the column was behind him. His driver was reaching over the windshield of the peep to wipe it clean of film for the twentieth time. They were going slowly enough to make the feat simple. Evans shook his head in disgust. The dust had become as personal to him by this time as his own skin—but it was by no means as comfortable. He was weary of travel, dust and confusion.

At that moment he wasn't too sure he wouldn't rather be back in the old C.P. without an offensive to scatter dust into his eyes.

But this was the dust of victory, the dust of breakthrough long planned and persevered. Surely, that made a difference. What was he bitching about? That victory had dust? What did he want, scimitars and armor? They passed a burned-out Sherman tank. There was armor. Near it, only a few feet off the road, were three tilted crosses smeared as anonymously gray as the rest of the world. Those might be the warriors buried outside of their armor. . .

A tank retriever hauling a battered armored car passed him on the left. He looked anxiously back to see whether the many-wheeled vehicle would pass the guns successfully. He could see Grostock in his cab waving his arms at it. But it got by and Evans relaxed.

Now he was passing at the dead march before the Hotel of the Three Roses. Surely, he thought, surely no other day in May had ever been provided with such rubble. Cassino in May . . . Here we go gathering nuts in May, it went in the old rhyme . . . But it wasn't nuts they were gathering.

Evans glanced at his driver. "What do you think of it, Morgan?" he asked him casually. Since Evans had accepted that he could never win, that victory for him was a contradiction in terms, he found it easier to talk to people.

The driver's gaunt, unshaven cheeks moved with the chewing of the gum in his mouth. His helmet, tilted sharply over his right eye, hid the rest of his face from Evans.

"Cassino, y'mean?"

"Yes, Cassino," the fruit of their labor, and of his.

Morgan thought for a moment. "Helluva mess, ain't it?

Never seen nothin' like it." He paused and chewed. "A lotta guys won't be goin' home," he said, and continued to chew his gum.

A passing medium tank made a fearful racket and threw mixtures of carbon monoxide and dust into their faces. Morgan looked at the tank keenly, squinting to avoid the dust. "Know what kind of tank that is, Lieutenant?" he asked.

"Didn't notice," said Evans.

"Sherman," said Morgan. "Like the wrecked job we passed." He nodded his head in satisfaction.

"That so?"

"Yeah." Morgan chewed lazily on. "I like t'know the makes. Too bad there ain't more."

"Why?" Evans had thought there were more than enough.

"Oh," said Morgan, " 'fore I got inter the Army I useta know all the diff'runt makes a' cars. Spot a Pontiac or Chevy or Packard a mile off. Like that." He snapped his fingers. "Useta have my own."

"You'll have it again," reassured Evans, feeling himself called upon to say something. But this wasn't at all what he wanted to talk about.

"Yer damn right, Lieutenant," said his driver vigorously. "It won't be long neither, the way we're goin'. It'll be better'n this lousy peep, too." He fell to musing.

"Ya know, Lieutenant," he said suddenly, "I been thinkin' 'bout them poor bastards back there near the tank."

"The three crosses?"

"Yeah. Imagine bein' dead in a uncivilized country like this. Think it makes any diff'rence, Lieutenant?" He stared straight ahead, and nursed his vehicle forward.

"Well," hedged Evans. "It's hard to say exactly . . ."

"Yeah."

But Evans was curious. "What," he asked, "do you have against Italy that you wouldn't be caught dead in it?"

The driver cocked a surprised eye in Evans' direction. "Like I tol' ya, Lieutenant," he said. "It ain't civilized."

"Not civilized?"

"Sure. Ya know I ain't seen a single decent car in the whole goddamned country? An' the road . . ." Morgan shook his head in utter disgust. "The roads is crap. Lieutenant, it ain't civilized. I tell ya," he said positively, "there's only one place in the world. The States. Sooner we lick the hell outa the Krauts so's we c'n go back, the better. Glad we're started . . ."

And what, Evans asked himself bitterly, what after victory? More dust? More victory with a dirty lining? Oh, some May they would no longer gather death in May. In Mays to come they would gather Fords by the wayside, and the sum of victory would roll out on four wheels to send, however hard the macadam, more dust into his eyes.

Evans looked around him, at the white, powdered bone of the town, at the thin line of gray British infantrymen plodding at the side of the road, at Morgan chewing by his side, and suddenly he was heartily ashamed. In this serious hour, in the shadows of the rock piles of Cassino, to mock at a man and play the snob—who in hell was he to do that? On what ground, by what mandate, did he declare their hard-earned triumph suspect? Let him be still!

Lord, give them their toys, he prayed quietly in his mind. Give them their bathtubs, their comic books, their movies and their Sunday drives. Lord, give us all our small desires . . .

"I am, too," said Evans gravely to his driver. "Glad we've started."

On the far side of Cassino his vehicle passed the gray-faced, chin-raised Colonel standing by the road to watch his column. David Evans offered him a salute. Negligently, his eyes on the vehicles beyond Evans', Colouris returned it.

IO

∿∿

THEY came to the outskirts of a small town south of
Rome, a comparatively unscathed town, but the war had
run ahead and once more they parked their howitzers, their
Macks, guarded and useless for the night. Weary and over-
traveled, still . . .

"Holy cow, will ya look at that!"

Gee, civilization. Whole houses. Middle-class houses
with broken windows. Right smack in a regular suburb!
Civilization, but nobody here. Empty. Where had they all
gone? Snoop around, but remember: NO LOOTING!

Who wanted to loot this crap?

Shove the furniture into the corners, big clumsy stuff—
empty drawers, too. Toss the chairs on top. Not at the
goddamn mirror, ya fool! Look what ya done! Sweep up
the glass. Throw your blankets down, make yourself at
home.

Well, fer Chris' sake, toilets! Hey fellers, look, toilets!
Busted! The lousy Krauts! Hey, the sonuvabitch sergeant

got himself a bed! Stamping up and down the stairs, real wood stairs! Look out for yer screwin' carbine, you knucklehead, watcha' wan'na bust things for? Ahhh.

Nuts. When's chow?

They had chow. They came to a time when the rooms had nothing more to offer. They wrote letters. They talked. They remembered how tired they were. But some of them wanted something to do even though they were tired. Settle down, you bastards. Some of us wan'na sleep. The funny, bleedin' heart pictures looked indifferent-like over their heads.

Sometime short of midnight, most of the men stopped searching for something to do and went to sleep, body lying by body in the packed rooms.

EHRLICH was having trouble sleeping. The loud snores, the flicker of the candle someone forgot to gut made it hard. He tossed around a bit and sat up. For all he could tell, everyone else was sleeping. They seemed to be putting all their effort behind their sleep. They breathed slowly, forcefully and deliberately; they breathed in obstructed rhythms, with intensity in their breathing as though they were hunters after prey, throwing themselves upon sleep. And the gargling noises and the whistles they made were to Ehrlich dark snarls twisted in the jumping shadows of the one candle left burning. Ehrlich made as if to put his hands over his ears. He had forgotten the deep, communal sleeping of the barracks.

Finally, he threw aside his blankets and felt for his shoes. He had trouble finding them. He had to feel under the edges of his close neighbor's blankets. After he put his shoes on, he stared for a moment, fuzzy and disconcerted, at those wrapped-away forms he lived with. He rose unsteadily to his feet.

Sometimes Ehrlich wondered how he had come among these men. Especially at times like these, when they all inflated their chests and snored together and only he was awake. He was tempted to push Padrone, to have someone to talk to, but all that concerted sleep was intimidating. And who was Padrone to him? Ehrlich picked his way through the long room to the door.

The door was wide open. But the candlelight could not stretch to the stairs outside the door and Ehrlich saw only a black rectangle as he stepped over the ranked bodies. He wasn't sure, but he thought he heard a faint noise of steps coming through the doorway; then he was sure that they were steps; and suddenly, there was Tomlinson come in out of the black. Well, very well, Ehrlich recognized the slight crouch of Tomlinson. But he did not understand his enemy's weaving motion, nor the way Tomlinson turned his head slowly from one side to the other.

Ehrlich frowned. He could sense Tomlinson looking at him. He distrusted the readiness of the man, the slow, coiled movement. But Ehrlich kept on his careful way to the door. He was no longer conscious of the noises of the sleeping going on around him. He was conscious of Tomlinson. He pretended not to be. Even if Tomlinson made no move to leave his position blocking the way, Ehrlich would still keep on coming.

Tomlinson stretched out his arms and supported himself against the sides of the doorway and blocked the doorway.

Ehrlich would have to push Tomlinson out of the way. He didn't want to do this. He wanted peace instead, for now; but he was about to do it when Tomlinson spoke.

"Goin' somewhere, Corp'ral?" Tomlinson trumpeted the drawled words through the room. A few of the men started in their sleep and the regular beat of more than one snore was cut off with a sigh and a groan. Ehrlich was affronted. It was unnatural for Tomlinson's drawl to be uttered with such force anywhere, let alone in the midst of sleep. But "corporal"? Ehrlich regarded him steadily, not wanting trouble, being thoroughly tired of it, but prepared.

"That is my business," said Ehrlich. "Get out of my way." He discovered his own voice to be louder and harsher than he had expected.

But Tomlinson grinned at him and stayed just as he was. By the faint, persistent weaving of his body and his lop-sided grin, Ehrlich decided that Tomlinson was drunk.

"Sonuvabitch!" drawled Tomlinson. "Ah bulieve yuh still mad, Corp'ral."

Corporal? Again. Ehrlich controlled himself. He musn't fall for kidding. Angrily, he said, "Cut the corporal."

"Huh?" said Tomlinson. "Ain't you Corporal Ehrlich? Oh, sure. I clean ferget. Sure. Yuh one o' the guys now, ain'tcha?

"Yuh know," went on Tomlinson, mild and unconcerned, "Ah come back heah lookin' fer company. An' ah'll be screwed if'n ah don' find you jus' waitin'. Ain't that some-thin', now?"

"Yah," laughed Ehrlich. "It sure as hell is." Oh, he was on to the bastard. Ehrlich had to admit he would sort of like getting in again with the others, admit that a man couldn't always go around with an iron up through his spine. If only it were someone other than this bastard! "Get outa the way." A gust of rebellion carried the words out of Ehrlich.

"Sure, Corp'ral, sure." Tomlinson examined him with speculation in his eyes and let one of his arms fall away from the doorway. He began to laugh softly. The laughter came through his open mouth in short spurts. When Tomlinson put a hand lightly on Ehrlich's shoulder, Ehrlich stepped away from it and the hand dropped. Tomlinson's laughter expired.

"Why, Herr Ehrlich," he said gently, "what yuh 'fraid of?"

"Not of you," snapped Ehrlich, not liking the gentleness at all, and prepared, God in heaven, prepared now and always.

"Sure, y'ain't. Only ain't we gonna be friends?"

"Chesus!" said Ehrlich. Friends! With Tomlinson? Ehrlich laughed silently. (This he had never expected. This tickled the living hell out of him.) "Sure," said Ehrlich suddenly and harshly. "Why not?"

"Y'know," said Tomlinson eagerly, moving close to Ehrlich so that Ehrlich smelled his breath, "what say me an' you go out an' git us some *vino*? Ah already got me some at one place. We c'n go back, huh, Ehrlich?" His short laugh exploded jerkily in Ehrlich's face, and Ehrlich moved away.

"Sure. Wait 'till I go get my hat."

Ehrlich heard Tomlinson's laughter continue as he went for his helmet. He picked up his carbine along with his helmet because he had noticed that Tomlinson carried a carbine. He had the right to have some fun, too. Who would stop him? So what, if he had it with Tomlinson? That made it better. Better, Ehrlich insisted fiercely to himself.

"Okay," chuckled Ehrlich. "Let's go."

Tomlinson leading, the two of them tramped down the narrow staircase. Under space Tomlinson suddenly appeared unimposing to Ehrlich. On the long street, with the two-story shadow-houses lined beside the street in rigid order, Tomlinson shrank. It was strange the way Tomlinson made you forget his hollow chest and shoulders.

"Well," Ehrlich said, "Where we go to now?" His voice, which in the room had crowded the sleepers and stuck against the wall, vanished quickly under the stars.

Tomlinson led on without answering. There was no one in the street. The street was emptier than a street had a right to be. They stepped on the broken glass of smashed windows; the hard and brittle crushing of it cut the night silence. Tomlinson made a point of kicking the glass in his way. There were no other noises. The war had rushed on away from this town so rapidly that even the big howitzers were out of range and nothing was in range of these two men. They were passing by the house which Captain Fuller used for his C.P. A splinter of light came through the edge of one of the windows.

"Chesus," laughed Ehrlich. "You wan' ta go here, maybe?"

"We ain't a'goin' heah," said Tomlinson. "See the house down the road aways? That's the sonuvabitch."

Tomlinson had pointed to a building isolated from the main body of the town and about a hundred yards from the C.P. house. The building was a dark shadow created by the moon, a shadow of a house living its own secretive days away from the others. Still, Ehrlich felt, it was too close. They shouldn't be fooling around so close to the C.P.

He said so. He said, "We get the hell away from here."

Tomlinson laughed in that way of his which grated Ehrlich's nerves so badly. "Why, Corp'ral?" he asked. "We all doin' anythin' wrong?"

Ehrlich had to admit there was nothing much wrong trying to get some *vino*. He shrugged his shoulders and followed Tomlinson. He would go any place Tomlinson would go. Walking to the house along the road, Ehrlich decided this was better than trying to sleep and not being able.

"There's Wops in there." Tomlinson slanted the words out of the corner of his mouth.

Ehrlich shook his head sagely. "That's goot," he said.

Then they were at the house. Even on this closer inspection, it looked exactly as the others did. There were the same half balconies outside the second-floor windows. There was the same simple door on the level of the street staring them blankly in the face. Ehrlich didn't know how they were going to handle this bulky, noncommittal mass in front of them.

"What we do now?" he whispered. "Knock?"

"Yeah," said Tomlinson, not whispering. Lazily, he removed his carbine and then, with the butt of its stock, knocked hard three times; the hollow, massive sounds hurried through the house and through the night and were lost somewhere in the Big Dipper.

"Maybe they're sleeping," said Ehrlich, loud.

Tomlinson didn't answer. With the butt of his carbine he drove three more wedges into the quiet, splitting it open.

Why the hell didn't those goddamned Wops answer? In sudden glee, Ehrlich slapped Tomlinson on the back. "Maybe we should shoot in the screwin' door, huh Tom?" He didn't mean that but it was the way he felt. Tomlinson

211

laughed. Tomlinson had been laughing more tonight than Ehrlich had ever heard him laugh before.

"Gif 'im hell," Ehrlich chuckled.

They thought they heard movement on the other side of the door, and listened for it. A man's quavering voice came through to them. "Who is there? What do you want?" it asked. The accent was strong and Italian but it was English.

"Chesus," said Ehrlich. "He speaks English."

"Sure," said Tomlinson, "that's mah pal Pietro. He's the Wop who give me the *vino*." He lifted his carbine and struck once more against the door. "It's me," he shouted. "Yuh know me, ya sonuvabitch. Open up."

Ehrlich slapped Tomlinson on the back again as the door opened part of the way. The same voice said, *"Nix vino."* It tried to be friendly and definite at once and fell off into uncertainty. Tomlinson applied his shoulder to the door and pushed. They heard the Italian stumbling away as they walked in.

". . . Wop," said Tomlinson, and slammed the door shut behind them.

The only light in the room came from the primitive lamp which the Italian carried in his hand. The Italian was a man getting on in years, Ehrlich saw. He didn't hold the lamp very steadily, either. Its light, coming from below, illuminated the under portions of his face, and shadowed the eye pits so that they appeared deeper than they were. When he tried a smile the wrinkles of his pallid cheeks and forehead were sharpened by the way the light came. Ehrlich saw a drop of liquid quivering at the end of his bulbous nose and Ehrlich shook his head in contempt.

Tomlinson inspected the Italian also, looking him up and

down and leaning slightly toward him. "Remember me, Pietro?" asked Tomlinson. Pietro opened his mouth to speak but Tomlinson cut him short. "Sure as hell, Corp'ral, ah think the sonuvabitch don' wanna remember me. Ah jus' guess we gotta git acquainted all over agin."

Tomlinson pushed his helmet to the side of his head. "Pietro," he said, "meet Corp'ral Ehrlich. Corp'ral Ehrlich meet Pietro. Pietro, meet me."

Fine. Ehrlich would be Corporal Ehrlich again—for the Wop!

Pietro began to shake his head vigorously. They were playing with him, he could see it. *"No Fascisti,"* he protested. *"Viva Roosevelt . . ."*

"Damn," said Ehrlich laughing, "he is scared stupid." Ehrlich slapped his hand against his thigh in huge amusement. "You, *Fascisti*," he said, "go get us *multi vino*," and roared, absorbing confidence he had lost, sucking it into himself from the other man's fear of him. *"Pronto,"* said Ehrlich. "Goddamn it."

Pietro, bewildered, said, *"Nix vino,"* wailing slightly. He pointed at Tomlinson. *"Finish'e vino."* He smiled ingratiatingly. "You go?"

"Hell, no!" said Tomlinson. "We stay heah. We like it heah." He balanced himself precariously on the balls of his feet. "Listen you, ah wants the *vino* now. Git." Pietro shrank back as Tomlinson extended a hand toward him, but Tomlinson merely took the lamp from his hands. "Git," said Tomlinson mildly, and his mildness froze his pal Pietro. *"Vino. Pronto!"*

Waving his hands and muttering, Pietro left them. Tomlinson laughed. "Y'see, Ehrlich," he said, "when yuh wants somethin', this heah's the way t'git it."

Ehrlich watched Tomlinson's lean, stooped figure bear the light to a table in the center of the front room and put it down, then he examined the place. The big picture with the bleeding heart, the heavy overstuffed chairs, the iron stove to one side of the room, made him laugh. Soon, with the light of the lamp making foreign things more foreign and Tomlinson inspecting him with that funny look of his which could mean anything or nothing, Ehrlich felt the ties of everyday snapping. A sudden exultation seized him for the freedom which the snapping brought. He plumped himself down on one of the stuffed chairs. Nobody ever felt freer than he did. He flung his steel helmet upon the wooden floor.

He noticed that Tomlinson held something in his hand. "What you got there, Tom?" he demanded. He let his voice ring enjoyably through the house and listened for the reverberation of it.

Tomlinson, grinning, held up a bottle in front of him. "*Vino*," he said. "No Wop sonuvabitch ain't gonna screw me." He pulled out the cork and swallowed deeply from the bottle. Ehrlich could hear the gurgling of the swallow. "The lousy bottle was right smack on the table." His lips curled. "*Nix vino*," he imitated. He thrust the bottle out to Ehrlich and Ehrlich tilted it high and drank the remainder.

"Ain't much in it," said Tomlinson. "Pietro's bringin' more," he confided, and winked.

"Where the hell's Pietro?" Tomlinson shouted suddenly. His shout released a pressure of energy in him. He strode around the room taking long strides. He opened a drawer, felt around in it, hurled out the contents, and slammed it shut again. He went on to another drawer. He stumbled against a chair and shoved it out of his way. "Pietro," he yelled. There were glass and porcelain figures upon a shelf. He swept them to the floor with one outflung hand. "Pietro, ya sonuvabitch, come down heah."

He stopped in front of Ehrlich and grinned cunningly at him. "That'll make the bastard come," he said.

Ehrlich felt a quick trembling of uncertainty and laughed out loud. The crazy bastard Tomlinson—but he knew how to get what he wanted. Tomlinson laughed with him. Tomlinson's laughter spurted out of his mouth in jets, it was forced out of the tight insides of him in splashes of laughter. Crazy bastard, thought Ehrlich, and laughed louder himself.

Quick steps scampered toward them and Pietro was in his room fearfully assessing the damage done to it. He held his hands clasped tightly in front of him as though he were a small boy, and shook his head as though the small boy were watching some impossible wonder. At the sight of him Ehrlich's and Tomlinson's laughter renewed itself. They saw his wife behind him, not daring to come in, large-eyed and fat, leaning against the door to the room, attempting to make her large bulk small; and that was even funnier.

"Y'ain't got nothin' t'be 'fraid of, Pietro," said Tomlinson softly when he had finished laughing. "Only thing we want is the *vino*. Ain' that right, Corp'ral?"

"That is all we want," confirmed Ehrlich.

"*Vino, vino, vino!*" Pietro was shouting at them. They were amazed. "*Nix vino. Tedeschi take'a vino. Nix vino.*" He waved his hands at them.

For answer Tomlinson picked up the empty bottle by the neck and dangled it in front of the Italian's face. Then he opened his hand. The bottle shattered at Pietro's feet.

"*Nix vino?*" asked Tomlinson quietly, and smiled.

"*Nix vino*," wailed the Italian and wrung his hands. "*Finito.*" Why wouldn't the Americans believe him? He had no more *vino*. Why didn't they go away? "*Nix vino*," he pleaded, trying to be reasonable.

Tomlinson stopped smiling. His lips were very thin and pressed together so that they were bloodless. "Yuh cain't screw me, Pietro," he said. His carbine hung by its carrying strap over his shoulder. Fixing with his steady, feral glare the man who wouldn't give him what he wanted, he removed the carbine from his shoulder.

Ehrlich was a little startled but he grinned to see the Wop shaking. Tom knew how to get what he wanted. Ehrlich heard the quiet, unnerving sobbing of the Italian's wife. Maybe Tomlinson was pulling his bluff too far.

"Aw, what the hell," Ehrlich said. "Maybe Pietro don't haf more *vino.*"

Tomlinson merely raised his carbine. "Ah never bluff, Wop. Yuh better go git it." The carbine traced small circles in the air but at each point on the circle its thin tube reached toward some part of Pietro's body. Pietro's mouth dropped open.

Ehrlich heard the faint click as Tomlinson pulled back the safety. Maybe he wasn't bluffing? Tomlinson was drunk, crazy drunk! Alarm rose over Ehrlich.

Pietro's wife put her hands upon her large bosom and said, "No," once, very softly.

"Cut it out, Tomlinson," Ehrlich said harshly. "Enough iss enough."

"Yuh buttin' in, Kraut?" Tomlinson's mouth was twisted in the parody of a smile. He stepped back lightly and Ehrlich saw that the muzzle of the gun aimed at him and that Tomlinson's finger was within the trigger guard. He thought he must be dreaming because this couldn't be . . .

"Chesus," said Ehrlich. "He iss crazy." Ehrlich's brain spun. They were friends a minute ago!

"Ah ain't a'bluffin'," said Tomlinson. Tomlinson was master now. No one else. Their fear delighted him. He laughed briefly. "Looks like ah got me a Wop an' a Kraut on mah hands."

He looked intently at Pietro. "Git that *vino!*" He had flung back his head and yelled the words at the Italian with all the strength in his lungs and vehemence in his spirit.

The command paralyzed Pietro. Pale and quivering he stared at Tomlinson. "*Nix vino . . .*" The words came puzzledly and sadly out of his mouth; they were reflex. He wasn't actually thinking of them or of anything else because the unbelievable enormity of the pointed carbine soaked up thought in a sponge of fear. "*Nix vin . . .*"

There was a sharp crack that filled the room and shook it, and Pietro's wife screaming, and a steel-jacketed bullet ripping through Pietro's stomach and making him finish his word in a soft grunt. Then he crumpled to his knees with his hands upon his stomach, swayed there for a second while everyone watched him, tried to hold on with his hands pressing tightly against his stomach; and then he was sprawled forward on his face.

Tomlinson looked faintly surprised. He simply stood in his place and held his carbine as he had fired it. He looked at Ehrlich, and his eyes were at once mocking at Ehrlich, curious at Ehrlich and, also irrevocably uncertain. Then, while Pietro's wife was crying over Pietro, and aghast Ehrlich had risen to his feet, the mockery and fierceness went away and only puzzlement and a strange kind of speculation were left.

Ehrlich was moving aside carefully now because Tomlinson had his carbine pointed at him, followed him with its tube. Ehrlich was sidling toward the door. Ehrlich was neither puzzled nor uncertain. He had, instead, horror at Tomlinson whose carbine followed Ehrlich's sidlings in little broken arcs and whose eyes were so inquiring that the brain behind them might send word to kill again. Ehrlich sidled toward the door, leaving his helmet behind, desperate to leave. Although his wide-open eyes took in only Tomlinson and although he focused his life upon that hesitant figure which wasn't getting its *vino* after all, Ehrlich knew a sudden, terrible certainty that he himself was finished, *finito*, *caput*. Even if Tomlinson never pulled the trigger.

Slowly, Ehrlich reached for the door handle. He knew he must not disturb the delicate balance in Tomlinson's mind. His hand stroked the wooden door for the handle. Then he had found it; then he had flung the door open and hurled himself into the street and Tom hadn't fired after all! Since they must not find Sigmund Ehrlich here to court-martial him, since he would never be able to explain to them or to himself his unbelievable complicity in somebody else's crime, Ehrlich began to run with all the strength he owned.

LIEUTENANT EVANS took his ease outside the C.P. house. Fuller was away somewhere. Evans smoked a cigarette in the May night weather, cupped the burning tip within his hand and watched the faint traces of its smoke wreathe among the stars. He was feeling rather sentimental but refused to let it bother him. He'd been writing to Margaret. He'd written, *I think it creditable of the Lord for making a distinction between man and woman. It is a far more fruitful distinction than any I myself have been able to draw.* This new note would surely surprise her after the letters he'd been sending. But, after all, she was newly his wife, discounting Army time; she deserved his folly.

Evans smiled at the night. He found he'd been busted up enough to grow a sort of humor. Of course, it was pretty much a flop as such growths went. But, in all truth, he considered the failure entirely appropriate for a man who flopped even more hopelessly in all other businesses under the Italian sky. He knew also, and had known it ever since his involvement with Dan MacCarthy in the Medic's place, that such pity as he had was largely (but not entirely, not entirely) reflex of his own failures. Since, then, he could be neither Colonel Colouris nor Jesus Christ, nor certainly the Stoic hero, Evans thought a wry and flat-based humor suited him best; and if others found his humor hardly humorous, then that was merely to be expected and made it the more proper.

Evans found himself sleepy. He was aware that he would have to take what came his way and suffer for it—but not before it came his way, not before. Evans yawned heavily. This spring night—he would have to reject it and turn in. Evans had turned on his heel when the report of a carbine cracked down the street and paralyzed him.

He would have to do what was expected of him.

"Sergeant!" he yelled back into the C.P. house. The First Sergeant came out on the run, buckling on his pistol belt. "House up there," said Evans indicating where the shot had come from. "Come on." They ran carefully, toe dancing upon the broken glass, holsters banging against their thighs, through the peaceful night. When they were twenty yards from the house Evans suspected, they saw someone break away from it and run up the road ahead of them.

"Halt!" Evans shouted. "Halt, damn it. Halt."

The figure didn't halt. This was serious, then. Evans and the First Sergeant slowed down and tugged at the automatics in their holsters as they ran. They snapped shells into the chambers but when they looked up the running figure had disappeared down the street.

They were almost at the door when another figure leaped out of the doorway and sent them back upon their heels. What in God's name was going on? "Halt, you goddamned fool," shouted Evans. By God, he couldn't let this bastard get away too. When the shadow ran even faster, he opened fire, and the First Sergeant, too, so that the sudden reports nearly deafened them both. Evans made a face in the dark at all the racket he was making, while his hand jerked up at each shot. He had to do what he had to do; he wasn't Jesus Christ.

But Tomlinson, running in the moonlight while a fusillade of shots cut through the moonlight after him, felt a powerful thrust between his shoulders hurling him forward. Momentum made Tomlinson skid in the road and then he lay quietly in the dust which he had disturbed with his falling and which settled around him and upon him and absorbed his blood. He was beginning to forget Tomlinson while he lay there quietly. The two men who ran to him and stood over him never reached through to his consciousness, though one of them bent down and fumbled helplessly with his body. The blood was carrying all hatings and all puzzle-

ments out upon the accepting dust. Everything was softening inside. There was no more of pressure in the chest of
Tomlinson, whom he had so nearly forgotten, no more of
that pressure which had pressed for vengeance during the
day, during the night, no more mazes to be lost in, no further
constraints. The strength of Tomlinson was finally breaking through containing walls; it was spreading now under
the faint touch of the moon on the gray road. And no one
could stop him now and no one could get in his way and stop
him any more and he felt all soft and easy, and then Tomlinson had forgotten Tomlinson utterly.

Evans and the First Sergeant stood over Tomlinson. They
had immediately recognized the profile flattened against the
dust. When they perceived that he was dead, Evans looked
from the body to his .45 and from his .45 to the body.

"He should have stopped," said Evans.

"We couldn't help it," said the First Sergeant defen-
sively. "Might have been Krauts for all we knew." The
fault was elsewhere, somewhere in the world, in something
which had brought them to this, which they had never for a
moment wanted.

"The poor bastard," said Evans suddenly. The warm air
stroked his cheek. After a few seconds, in an angry, hard
voice which protested against whatever it was had happened, he said, "What was he doing?"

The guards had already found Evans and the First Sergeant, stood clustered a few feet away, and didn't answer.
No one answered. The dead man threw them off balance.
Dead men always did that. They whispered a little but
didn't dare to speak out.

"Two of you stay with Tomlinson," said Evans, doing
what he was supposed to do. "Come on, Sergeant."

221

Evans and the First Sergeant returned to the house from which they'd seen Tomlinson run. If a carbine shot had brought them, something must be wrong, very wrong where the shot had been fired. They entered, automatics drawn, and saw Pietro's wife sobbing over Pietro.

Murder.

Evans roused himself and, putting his hand upon the woman's shoulder, asked what happened. A flood of tears answered him, a quantity of vengeful Italian. He quickly took his hand away from the woman's shoulder and didn't know what in hell to do with it. But he remembered that he still was holding his automatic and, carefully, he put it back into the holster.

Murder.

He heard Captain Fuller calling for him outside.

EHRLICH's heart pumped with vicious rapidity. As he ran, the vein in his forehead pulsed so hard he could hear it. His face burned. He staggered from one side of the road to the other, he leaned his weight forward to overcome the steep incline of the hill and pushed desperately the numb muscles of his legs. Hardly conscious of running, conscious only of terror and the next step, he had heard shots behind. Clearly and distinctly he had heard the shots run up the long rising street after him.

Sigmund Ehrlich was on the run again. He fought along the way to nowhere.

There were black areas obtruding before portions of the road, tree-cast blacknesses which hollowed out the moon-light and filled him with old fear, Munich fear, Munich hatred. He ran writhing with anger.

And then suddenly he could go no further. Suddenly he

didn't give a damn if only the pain in his chest would cease and his brain stop pounding against the top of his skull and so that he could breathe one painless breath. Halting, wavering, saying to hell with everything, with room enough in him only for the roaring blood beneath the skin, he dropped his body into the deep, triangular ditch which ran parallel to the road.

The ditch was lined with grass, with cool grass and soft spring earth. He lay upon his side in it. The two sides of the ditch moved up close to him and cradled him and his exhaustion. He listened very carefully; he convinced himself that no one pursued. After a while awareness touched him of the softness of the earth, of the cool, feverless breath which hung upon the air about him, and he could wish no better home than this and no other comfort than the infinite condolence of his returning breath.

Sigmund Ehrlich was on the run again. Cold-eyed, implacable, he had enemies. Once again Tomlinson waved a carbine before Sigmund Ehrlich's face and men shouted "Halt." Alas that Sigmund Ehrlich should feel this pain and nameless trouble expand immeasurably within his chest so that he couldn't contain it, although there was no alternative but to contain it; that neither May, nor earth, nor running, nor hope, could erase it! Sigmund Ehrlich, self-sufficient, had his weakness and burned his own heart out for it. He had gone on out with Tomlinson, blundered. Why?

And Italian Pietro died. Though Ehrlich could feel no compassion for the dead Italian, he had not shot him, would never dream of shooting Pietro in the stomach for a glass of wine. How had he become a part of it? Sigmund Ehrlich was on the run again. Considering the matter carefully, he did not see how he could escape court-martial.

He would never watch from his peculiar position the

other men again, never be part of their entanglements, nor with them in the mud and rain and shellings nor when they turned their little radio on and laughed together. Sigmund Ehrlich had no place to run to, not even men's dislike. This rage of his shook him, not them.

All this was true, unless—unless no one found out!

His mind scampered rapidly over its thoughts. No one could know who was with Tomlinson in the dark, except Tomlinson and Pietro's wife. In the day or two before they left he might avoid the old woman. Tomlinson would hold his silence, if he were not killed by the blast of shots Ehrlich had heard. And eventually Ehrlich would kill Tomlinson. He would want to kill Tomlinson in any case—this much of vengeance he would give himself.

There was still hope. Hope sent an electric shock through Sigmund Ehrlich's spirit. Hope evoked a vast anxiety in his mind which lifted him to his feet. It made him shake with desire to be back in his quarters, hidden under his blankets, or awake with the others asking, "What happened, anybody know what happened . . . ?" If only he could get back in time no one need know.

Ehrlich began the walk back slowly at first because he might have to dodge men on the way—men sent looking for Tomlinson's companion. For this reason he kept within the tree shadows along the road. He would have to be most quiet. If he were careful and quiet he need be on the run just a little while longer. He could deny everything and wait for his time with Tomlinson. He could hold off Holloway. Had he not learned how to fight on the run? Sigmund Ehrlich could not help but break his walking gait and trot. He didn't mind the carbine jolting his side any more than he had in his first flight. These men who oppressed him from continent to continent were fools, fools. He felt crazily exalted.

Waving his hands helplessly, he stopped dismayed in the middle of the road. It was very obvious. Tomlinson might have been caught. Then Tomlinson would grin with that lopsided grin of his and consider it worth it to him if he could also pull down Ehrlich. That pig Tomlinson. Dismay and fury rolled over Sigmund Ehrlich. There was no way out of wondering, out of doubt. Ehrlich was impaled on doubt, left squirming.

He would have to go back and take his chances. He would take one last fling. Of course. He, Sigmund Ehrlich, had been a corporal in the German Army once. In the American Army, too. Sigmund Ehrlich chuckled on the run. Then his whole spirit erupted in revulsion, and he threw up by the side of the road.

Sigmund Ehrlich changed his pace in fits and starts as he moved in the shadows over the road. He was whistling softly. That was, he confided cunningly to himself, to make anyone who saw him think how innocent a fellow he was. Ehrlich chuckled. Then he cried a bit. Then he went on whistling his song. As he had said to himself before, that was to give him a way out in case anyone saw him.

"*It's you, Lili Marlene,*" he sang. "*It's you, Lili Marlene . . .*" The words went through his head along with the whistle. He was sorry for Pietro.

ABOUT an hour after the shooting, when Tomlinson had been disposed of and Fuller finished playing detective about Pietro's body, Evans and Fuller had nothing to do but wait at the C.P. Fuller was dragging impatiently on a cigarette. He got up in exasperation and sat down again.

225

"Where the hell are those guys?" Fuller demanded. He smarted under a personal injury. Just when he had been finding his footing again—murder! Well, he was through eating his heart out about what the people in his battery did.

"What do you suppose made 'em do it?" he asked Evans bitterly, striding around the room.

Evans shook his head. But Evans should know, Evans was a knucklehead himself. Fuller was getting tired of Evans. Fuller was getting tired of the whole goddamned mess.

"You know," said Evans, calmly regarding his Captain. "I went through an entire campaign without killing anyone, directly. It was very easy. Now, although the Sergeant fired also and I'm hardly a good shot myself, it seems that I began the shooting which makes me responsible for the death of one of our own men."

"Yeah," said Fuller. "But," Fuller added savagely, "why in hell should a guy go out in the middle of the night and kill a Wop?" He had been sure Tomlinson was a solid soldier. The bastards were beyond him.

Evans had been lying flat upon his cot. He sat up and swung his feet to the floor. "I have come all the way from Philadelphia for the war in order to shoot Tomlinson of Kentucky." Evans stared calmly and questioningly at Fuller. "And I have no sense of guilt whatever. I have no desire whatever to make a stink about it."

Fuller turned his back on Evans. Fuller had more important problems on his mind than the way Evans felt about doing what he had to. Fuller would have all kinds of investigations on his hands. He'd have to fill out ten thousand forms. He'd catch it from the Colonel, the blasted Colonel who never realized that those bastards weren't

Fuller's to handle as he liked. Fuller's mind filled with anger at the thought of the Colonel.

"What the hell's keeping those guys?" demanded Fuller.

A steel helmet rested on the thickly carved table in one corner of the room. If Ehrlich hadn't only left his goddamned helmet with his name printed in the liner he might have gotten away with it. Now Fuller had half the battery under the First Sergeant's direction looking for Ehrlich. What was keeping them? Fuller had a court-martial on his hands over a goddamned Wop because Ehrlich couldn't keep his screwing hat on his head.

"They'll be here soon, Captain," said Evans quietly. "Ehrlich has no place to go."

"So will the goddamn Colonel," said Fuller. He paced up and down the room, then said "Screw it!" and sat down.

Soon they heard a knock and Fuller said "Come in," viciously.

It was the First Sergeant with a great smile on his wide, flat face. "We got 'im," he said. "Got the bastard tryin'ta sneak inta Number One's place. He put up a fight. Holloway poked 'im in the jaw. Holloway says he's his man. Says he'll keep him guarded for the night, if you don't mind."

"Mind?" ejaculated Fuller. "Mind? He can have him permanent." The Sergeant grinned. "All right, Sergeant," said Fuller. "Stick around until the Colonel comes. He'll want to know the whole story."

"I'll wait outside. See you later, Lieutenant," the Sergeant said to Evans.

Evans nodded affably. He and Fuller were alone. The single, garish Madonna stared blandly over their heads. The gasoline generator roared from outside and sent the electricity flickering through the light bulb dangling from the center of the room. Evans watched Fuller sit himself upon the large oak table and play with Ehrlich's helmet.

"The Sergeant and I have a lot in common," said Evans. Evans straightened up. More deep-voiced than Fuller had ever heard him before, Evans said, "I'd like to go down to the Exec house with Grostock, Captain, if you could see your way to transferring me there again. I'd like once more to try it down there close to the men."

Fuller shrugged. He was getting damn fed up with Evans, who along with everything else had to go and shoot Tomlinson. But a recollection struck Fuller and broke the frown upon his face, made him look up quickly and with sudden amusement. "Hey," he said. "Hey! You're becoming a regular man of decision!

"All right," Captain Fuller added, forgetting his amusement, "suit yourself." The officer he had doing the assistant exec-ing now would do as well up here anyway.

II

COLONEL COLOURIS strode up and down the room
Fuller had converted into Baker C.P. Fuller was red-faced
and obviously angry; Evans seemed paler, tenser even than
usual. Both men were fidgeting. This kind of thing made the
Colonel scowl. "Sit down," he said. They sat down.

"Evans," said the Colonel. "Are you sure you have that
Italian woman here?" That brought a bit of color to the
man's face.

"Yes, sir. I have also sent for Ehrlich."

Naturally he had. The Colonel deliberated over the thin
figure before him, saw the pale eyes of the man somewhat
steadier than usual, the straw-blond hair of him only slightly
mussed. No, the man was in order; and for all the surface
order, looked as irrevocably unmilitary as Colouris' perpetually unkempt medical officer.

"Evans," the Colonel told him, "you conducted yourself
in a properly military manner, shooting this Tomlinson.
You have my congratulations."

"Yes, sir."

Critically, the Colonel regarded Fuller, whose gradual return to precision and the military pattern needed encouragement and direction. For Fuller had exhibited an ugly self-centeredness of late, a self-centeredness which Colouris was not sure might not exclude his battery.

"Fuller," said the Colonel, "any breakthrough will tend to produce these cases. Discipline, old habits weaken. The swine go hog wild. You know as much. You're here to keep them in line. Why weren't you here with your battery?"

Fuller was gasping. Colouris waited for him.

"I was at the battalion C.P., Colonel," said Fuller finally. "You saw me there." He had been in a poker game the Colonel had been watching. Fuller bit off the words. "And I can't follow every sonuvabitch in my battery to see he doesn't get in trouble."

Gleefully for a moment, Colouris grinned. Then he said, "Of course not. Who could?" and paused. "Nevertheless, you are responsible to me for every one of your sonsuvbitches. Your job is to keep the men under control no matter how you do it. You are given officers and noncoms for that purpose. You are backed by the entire weight of the army. If your men fail, you fail. And you should know all this by now. By God, I want no excuses." But Colouris kept his voice level.

Fuller was redder than ever. "Justice," added the Colonel, "has nothing to do with it. Justice to you personally has nothing to do with the job of a battalion. Forget justice. Organization necessarily makes you responsible to me for everything within your control and beyond it."

Colouris was inclined to think he'd hit the nail on the head watching Fuller squirm. Fuller was too concerned about himself. Now, in order to continue concerning himself about himself, he would of course include the battery in his concern. Colouris turned away from Fuller. Where were the men with the prisoner? Colouris thought he remembered the fellow, a squat, barrel-chested refugee Jew. Jew? Colouris didn't go in for race prejudice. Only for the demands of effective action, of . . .

"Sir!" Colouris turned to the voice. "Sir," Evans was saying, "I don't believe I'm accountable to my superiors, although of course I realize I have to follow orders. I know I'm not important enough to be accountable to myself. I think I'm accountable to those unlucky bastards who get the brunt of what I do."

Colouris stared. "Evans," erupted Fuller, "you are the goddamnedest knucklehead I have ever seen!"

Colouris nodded slightly. All was well. Fuller thought of Evans as *his* officer and was appropriately fearful. Slowly, Colouris walked up to Evans and when Evans rose, tapped him gently on the chest.

"The Captain is probably right," said Colonel Colouris. "But I'm going to surprise you both. The fact is you haven't contradicted me, Evans. You may think as you like as long as you behave as I tell you to and as I desire. Your mind is your own. What makes you think I care what you do with the damn fool thing? What I want are your actions, Evans."

Slowly, Colouris smiled. "And haven't you given them to me? Didn't you shoot this Tomlinson boy because you knew I expected it? Or did you shoot him for his own good?" Colouris' broad mouth stretched across his face as he chuckled, watching the unhappy smile on Evans'.

"Oh," the little fool was saying, "you're right, Colonel. Not for his own good. But you shouldn't think that makes your point, Colonel. I very often make mistakes. Perhaps, sir, in the future I might not shoot?"

Colouris made his voice sober and clear in the small room. "God help you, you had better!" Colouris looked at him reflectively. "Besides, the moment you put aside your responsibilities you become an obstacle in the general enterprise of the war which, I'm sure, Lieutenant Evans, you have set yourself up to win." Colouris chuckled.

They heard a knocking at the door, and looked toward it.

"The requirements of organization, my boy," the Colonel was saying in his amusement, "facts—what are you going to do about them?

"Evans," he said, "will you please go to the door?" Evans went.

But Colouris was frowning. He had handled this Fuller-Evans thing rather neatly, hit them from the inside. Nevertheless he wasn't at all sure he'd brought them around. More and more Colouris found himself in opposition to his officers of late, and did not like it. In fact, as he thought about it now, the opposition was making him quite angry.

Down the street, with the entire house balancing overhead on the turning spring earth, in the cellar, insulated from the spring night and the swelling push of the soft night wind, at the very bottom of the house, Holloway waited for Sigmund Ehrlich who sat beside the little wooden table open-mouthed. Now Holloway watched the slight trickle of blood at the corner of Ehrlich's mouth; Holloway had made that trickle.

"Well?" said Holloway, throwing his voice roughly at the shadows and Sigmund Ehrlich. But the little red finger

of the candle on the table flicked at the eyes of Ehrlich, and
the red blood warmed his mouth, so that he said nothing.
Holloway seized a broken-backed chair and set it down on
the other side of Ehrlich's table, sat himself down and
stared at Ehrlich over the candle flame.

"Why did ya kill the Wop?" Holloway asked confidentially. Ehrlich only smiled. "Why did ya jump on Dan that
time after the shelling? Why did ya take it out on all the
boys that night we got Lili Marlene? Who do you think
you are, Ehrlich? What do you want?"

Ehrlich played with the wax curled at the base of the
candle and the tendril which delicately grew along the
slender, waxen side, Holloway concentrated upon him
across the top of the candle until Holloway's eyes were
caught by the spearhead of flame.

A long while ago this stranger had come into Holloway's
squad and Holloway recommended him for a corporal. The
stranger had been a good corporal. He'd handled his gun
sight well, never muffed a mission or an order. They
shipped overseas together. Holloway watched him carefully, but the stranger knew his job, and Holloway was
quiet. More and more the stranger kept to himself but for
the occasional aggressions he seemed to think funny. Still
Holloway was quiet because the stranger did his job. But
slowly the stranger grew more insistent and more offensive.
He broke into their pleasures, which were slight enough;
he questioned their purposes; wouldn't be silent, laughed;
waited out their weaknesses; his sudden laughter grated.
So that eventually Holloway had to warn him. The stranger
pulled in his horns for a time. Holloway was quiet, but
watchful—as most of the section were watchful. But then,
in crisis, when nobody could deny in his heart the sickening

sad mess they were in, when Holloway had fully realized how much he needed the childishness of the bunch of bastards under him, the stranger stuck his finger in. Cruelly, cruelly he prodded, without good reason, for the sake of cruelty, Holloway's charges and Holloway himself, blurted the truth which everyone knew as well as the stranger, but hid decently. Then Holloway could no longer be quiet. He took the man's stripes away. He left him on the outside, thoroughly, with no place in the outfit beyond the fixed job he had to do. Holloway would never regret this, although he hated cruelty. And angrily, Holloway had baited the stranger. He would never regret this, either. For Holloway had always expected some final outrage of Ehrlich. Now it had come. Two men were dead. Why?

"I'll tell you a story, Ehrlich, while we're waiting," said Holloway, while the candle flame danced in his eyes. "Long while ago my brothers and me used to take two, three weeks off during the fall from my Dad's farm to go deer hunting." Holloway could see Ehrlich on the other side of the table, see New England fall. His voice came flat and hard for Ehrlich and full of memory for the fall. "There was specially good hunting one year. If you moved really quiet you could watch them nibbling at the little stalks and catch the crest of horns swing on a good-sized buck when he thought he heard something. You could see 'em spurt through the trees like a bunch of old brown leaves in a storm wind. I shot one the first day of our trip with a sawed-off Enfield. He was a big old buck. Had a spread of antlers good enough for wings."

Holloway looked deeply past the little flame into the shadow-caverned face of Ehrlich, and Holloway's voice grew in balefulness. "He was my buck, Ehrlich, the best damn buck any of the three of us ever saw. Made me feel big to realize he was mine, that I'd taken him in all this empty forest. We strung 'im up for the night a little distance away from the camp. The next morning he was gone, mess of footprints in the neighborhood of the tree. We hadn't realized anyone was in the country with us."

Holloway paused. When he resumed his voice vibrated. "We'd hunted and we'd camped out in the open. No hiding, no guarding ourselves. Who in hell's so low to swipe another hunter's deer?"

Holloway shrugged his shoulders. "That day we went hunting again. Combed the area, but no game. But we weren't going to move very far from the camp site where they'd taken my property. We set up just far enough away so it shouldn't look as though we had any purpose in staying around. And the next day, one of my brothers got a deer. We dragged him back to camp and tied him up same as we had the other one. Made a specially big camp fire that night and after we ate the three of us lay back and watched the stars get strong. When the fire died down, we hid in the brush.

"All night long we stayed quiet in the cold, holding onto our rifles, watching my brother's game turn in the wind. You see, Ehrlich, that buck they'd stolen meant more than venison. We'd come a long way to get it. Never mind if it was worth the trouble. I had shot it in the forest myself. Out there in the woods, it was private to me. My brothers thought so, too. That's why, instead of chasing off after the men and maybe getting the buck back and maybe not, they waited with me with rifles on their knees.

"All night long, Ehrlich, I wondered who the men would be when they showed up because for some reason or other I was sure they would and I would see their faces. But they never showed up. I never found out what sort of fellow enters another man's camp and takes what is personal when there's enough and plenty in the forest." Holloway's eyes gleamed in the candlelight. "But I can learn, Ehrlich, if you're willing to teach me. I'm here alone now. I sent all the boys away. Let's see what's inside you. Look, I'm dropping my pistol belt on the floor. You've got clear sailing. See if you can pick it up!"

Ehrlich had been listening to Holloway with his mind on the long, empty street up which he ran, on Tomlinson and Pietro and the insufferable long misery within him and the closed four walls of the cellar; and with an enormous, helpless desire to burst beyond them all. Holloway's words had touched only the periphery of his brain. Now, drop by drop, their meaning soaked through, and the level of mirth rose in his brain. Slowly, he turned his head to Holloway. His voice creaked and rasped; he forced the words with his thick and tired tongue; his cut lips mimicked his old sarcastic grin. "I have stolen what is personal from you, Herr Holloway, I?" He giggled. The level of mirth swamped his brain, made the laughter come in spasms from his chest. He had injured Holloway, he! He had stolen from Holloway. Surely he would write about this to his friend Alfred and to his friend Hansi. "Oh," he gasped, "this is a wonderful, wonderful kidder, this Herr Holloway." Then the laughter lifted him up from his seat, spurted over the cellar stone and dinned into Holloway's ears from every side its utter mirthlessness.

"Cut it," shouted Sergeant Holloway.

But Ehrlich never heard him, holding his sides, bending with laughter, sending the waves of his laughter from his flooded brain flowing and breaking over Holloway's head, pounding in upon his own lungs, exhausting them, reaching into the streets, into the sleeping rooms above . . .

Holloway poured his curses into the laughter but it wouldn't stop. And he had to stop it. His gray eyes widened and darkened as he leaped at Sigmund Ehrlich, as he had to leap at him, the great cable slashing once again, slashing . . . He pounded Ehrlich in the face and on the head with hard short punches. Ehrlich grunted in his laughter, covered his face with his arms, and laughed, laughed! Holloway struck at his chest and stomach and punched the laughter out of him. Ehrlich dropped his arms. Holloway smashed him upon the jaw and sent him scuttling backward into the corner of their little room.

Ehrlich stood there for a moment with his mouth wide open, blinking at the pain which cut across his face and became entangled with the sorrow in his heart and made him frantic. Then he walked slowly toward Holloway, crouching, with his hands across his bleeding face, and let Holloway strike at him. When he had got close enough, Ehrlich lowered his fists and drove them with all his strength into Holloway's stomach.

Ehrlich stared at Holloway on his knees bent double. Ehrlich's eyes sparkled because there was no question of what he had to do now, no question if he could ride this last surge of power in him. But for a moment he stared at Holloway because Holloway on his knees made Ehrlich laugh strong and hard and gave him strength.

But Ehrlich heard a running and thumping overhead and down the stairs. There was no doubt in his mind why they came or whom they came for. Quickly he snatched at Holloway's pistol belt and kicked away Holloway's hand when he, too, reached for it. Then Ehrlich stood back against the far wall. When the door burst open he had the automatic pointed at it.

It amused him to see the men stop dead in their tracks, open-mouthed and foolish, to hear their carbines clattering down upon the stone floor, to see Holloway, pale, wheezing, struggle to his feet. "Stand still, Sergeant Holloway," he ordered. And Sergeant Holloway stood still, swaying. With infinite amusement, Ehrlich regarded them all. "Nobody chases me any more," he told them gently, dispassionately, grinning with his cut and bleeding lips, pointing at them with his cold, strong automatic.

"You, Sergeant Holloway, Herr Unteroffizier Holloway," he announced from his distance. "You want to know who I think I am. Maybe you all want to know. I tell you. I am somebody in your cellar who cannot walk back and who cannot walk forwart." This struck him as a joke; he grinned at it. The others just watched. "My name is Sigmund Ehrlich. I am not a Kraut, not a Chew, not even a sonuvabitch. A Kraut, a Chew und a sonuvabitch have places. Not me." Calmly, he looked them over while his heart hurt horribly. "I am thirty-three years of age. I am like you think, Sergeant Holloway, all the lousiness in your world und all your misery about it. All of it is in me. I be glad to get rid of it. Sergeant Holloway, I was born in Mannheim und I am tired with fighting, always fighting. *Es tut mir leid, dass ich das getan habe, aber ich konnte mir wirklich nicht anders helfen; ich bin allein, so furchtbar allein. . . .*"

The automatic glistened beautifully, sat very comfortably in Sigmund Ehrlich's hand. Ehrlich raised his automatic and put it to his head and pulled the trigger but it didn't go off . . .

NO MATTER HOW HARD HE PULLED, IT WOULDN'T GO OFF!

238

THEY rushed upon Ehrlich, bore him down, tore the pistol from his hand.

"Safety was on," said Holloway, still-voiced, impassive, as they stood Ehrlich on his feet and held him.

"Damn lucky," said Grossberg, hulking over Ehrlich, twisting Ehrlich's arms behind him.

"I don't think so," said Dan MacCarthy. "He killed an innocent man. We should have let him kill himself."

Pady said, "How do you know he shot the guy, Dan?"

And Sergeant Holloway, looked away from Ehrlich's bleeding, star-eyed face, stared at Padrone, and rasped out every harsh and foul name he could think of and threw them at Padrone. Padrone looked at the ground flushing. "There were two of them," insisted Padrone.

Holloway made a motion forward and checked himself. "Ehrlich," he said. "Ehrlich, you sonuvabitch—why the hell should you hold everything back when you were just going to knock yourself off? You did the shooting, didn't you? You were behind the killing. Tell it to the little snot-nose. Tell him!"

But Sigmund Ehrlich never said a word. They waited for him but he said nothing. He had not even heard Holloway. He stood limp and still between his guards.

"I wonder what Ehrlich meant," said Padrone. "Herr Ehrlich," he said gently, "Herr Ehrlich—what did ya mean before?" But Padrone felt painfully what Ehrlich meant, though Ehrlich said nothing now and simply stared with his empty gaze fixed upon the burning spearhead of the candle on the table.

"Look," said Grossberg. "Wha' do we do with 'im? Hold 'im like this all screwin' night?"

Holloway looked blankly at Grossberg for a moment.

239

"Yes," he said. "Of course." What was he to do with Ehrlich? "Tie 'im up," he ordered. "Tie 'im to the screwin' chair." That would have to do for the moment.

They tied Ehrlich up. One of the men found some rope. Dan MacCarthy got one end of the rope and wound it around Ehrlich's waist, then clumsily around Ehrlich's wrists. Eagerly he fumbled, making knots while Grossberg held the patient. Then Dan sat down upon the floor to work upon the legs. His breath came heavily. He tied as tightly as he could.

Slowly Holloway shook his head. Ehrlich was putting up no resistance at all and even then Dan was lousing up the job. Dan would never learn. Holloway would have to do the job himself.

"Get away from there," he said to Dan MacCarthy.

Carefully, Holloway retied his murderer. When he had finished and stood up to ponder quiet Ehrlich, the First Sergeant came in and said, "Hey, what the screw you guys doin'? Untie the bastard. Colonel's over at the C.P. Wants to see 'im right now."

The First Sergeant laughed. "Wash his face first," he said, and winked at Holloway.

THE First Sergeant came in and saluted and then came Grossberg and Holloway with Ehrlich between them with his hands tied. Evans knew them all. Ehrlich's face was swollen out of shape, cut, his eyes shockingly vague. Evans looked questioningly at the First Sergeant and the First Sergeant nodded.

"Why are this man's hands tied?" demanded the Colonel.

"Can't two armed men take care of him? Particularly," added the Colonel dryly, "since he seems already to have been taken care of."

"Sir," said Sergeant Holloway flatly, "Private Ehrlich tried to commit suicide."

"Hey," said the First Sergeant. "Nobody told me!" while Evans held himself together and Fuller said "Damn" and even the Colonel stiffened and looked curiously at Ehrlich, this sudden visitor from some other planet. Unaccountably, Evans felt his chest grow full. "Nobody told me," protested the First Sergeant, incredulously.

Colouris raised his eyebrow. Holloway spoke at his eyebrow.

"Yes, sir. I put my pistol belt down and told him to see if he could get it." Holloway halted a moment. "He got the pistol. He didn't know what to do with it when he got it. Said something. Aimed the pistol at his head, pulled at the trigger but forgot the safety was on. Whole thing's nobody's fault but mine," said Holloway, "that he nearly got away."

This, then, was the bony, red-headed sergeant with the thin neck and beaked nose who long ago had sent the guns ahead, who had fronted Colouris when Colouris inspected his gun, whom Fuller considered the best noncom in his battery. In the sudden quiet Colouris had a moment to consider him, this man standing at attention, immobile-faced, waiting.

"Sonuvabitch's got more guts than sense," whispered the First Sergeant to Evans.

"Very well, Sergeant," the Colonel was saying to Holloway, while his voice throbbed slightly with a hint of pride in what a man was capable of, "let's say you were preserving the discipline of your own section in your own way and let it go at that."

But Evans was puzzled, very puzzled. Long ago he had heard from Doc Barnes the story of Holloway and Borman. Evans had felt that, given the confused boundaries of war, Holloway stood on his side—distant, self-sufficient, but on his side. That deliberate cruelty would be beyond Holloway, that at least Holloway's individualism would never turn for support to the easy judgments of necessity or the custom of the army . . . Had Evans indeed been mistaken in this?

"Private Ehrlich!" grated the Colonel at this disruption of the peace. Evans heard him, saw Grossberg unsuccessfully shake the prisoner to make him stand at attention. The Colonel's eyes narrowed. "Attention, Private Ehrlich!" ordered the Colonel. Ehrlich's eyes were wide and empty. His leg muscles jerked, his face twitched. Grossberg shook him again.

But the Colonel flushed; his lips were tight; there was a rush of blood in his head. Opposition came now in the damnedest place. But never had he been so preposterously, needlessly, resisted, in all his days in the army. "Attention!" he yelled. Once and for all this mounting resistance would be crushed! "Attention!" Colouris yelled in his passion.

Desperately, Grossberg shook his prisoner. "Fer Chris' sake, Ehrlich," he said, forgetting Ehrlich was a prisoner, "Ya loon, stand up!" It seemed to Grossberg that Ehrlich was standing squarely in the path of the incomprehensible machine of the army, and the sight terrified Grossberg.

"Ehrlich," called Holloway, "Ehrlich, for the last time,

cut the crap. We're on to you. We know who you are!"

Ehrlich's bruised mouth opened and closed. Then it relaxed half open as he giggled a little, having beaten off this sudden eruption of the world now and forever—while Colouris' eyes widened at this rip, this tear in the fabric of order, this grinning blue-eyed slot in the universe. And Colouris advanced upon it with his fist raised.

"Christ, don't! Don't, Colonel," said Evans.

Colouris half turned his head. "Evans?" he said, "Evans?" The passion, the passion in the Colonel! Evans had never suspected it. And the childishness! Evans was appalled.

"The man's not in his senses, Colonel," said Evans rapidly. "Look at him. For God's sake, look at him, Colonel."

Colouris turned and looked at the open mouth and the vacant gaze fixed upon the shining silver leaf upon his collar, and dropped his fist.

These men, then, these treaders of outward going paths, rulers, sharp men, manipulators, they didn't know the distinction between sanity and insanity! Evans wondered at it. They would never know! They would always have to be told, always controlled, their energies and passions taken in hand and guided. But by whom, by God, by whom?

"Yes," said the Colonel, adjusting his collar. "My error. See to it Captain Barnes gets a look at him, Evans." Error? But they would think twice before they crossed him.

"Very well," said the Colonel sharply, "if we can't question him, we can at least identify him beyond doubt. Lieutenant Evans, bring the woman in." Still, Colouris was startled at himself. He had really flown out of hand for a moment.

Evans returned with an Italian woman and the battery

clerk. The heavy-breasted woman walked with her head erect. Her eyes were red, her nose bulbous and swollen, but she walked with her head up and swept by the men and officers with contempt. Evans put a hand upon her arm but she brushed it off. He had the battery clerk ask her in her language to point out the man who had come with Tomlinson. She looked at Ehrlich with great distance in her eyes and gestured with her head at him.

"She wants to know," said the battery clerk, "if he will be hung."

"Take her out," said the Colonel.

"She says," said the battery clerk, "she would like to see us all hung. All the soldiers in the world."

"I said take her out," said the Colonel.

Evans took her out. He thought he understood the Colonel. But he didn't understand Holloway. The thought troubled him.

HOLLOWAY, having brought Ehrlich back, dismissed the men. For by this time he'd recovered the strength and breath Ehrlich's blows had taken from him. He would be cautious now. Objectively he watched over Ehrlich, Ehrlich the stranger, the intruder, thief Ehrlich, sitting in his old place behind the candle. Though through Evans' folly Ehrlich had escaped the Colonel, he would not escape Holloway.

Holloway was determined to wait him out through the night. He would watch for the first signs of a break in Ehrlich's front. And Holloway would not let him recover. He would drag him into the daylight. Gladly would Holloway wait a night for this man. Coldly he watched the hard, square face with its swollen flesh, with the cut over its right eye, the blue mark under it, the vague aimless blue eyes from which the mockery had quite gone, and was not taken in.

The old strength was there—strength which assaulted men outrageously, that battered Holloway to his knees, that killed without reason, that, caught, attempted even suicide. Strength like this must not go unwatched and scarless from its work. Holloway knew it could not die; and he was here to strip away all camouflage, to press into the core of illicit, adversary force. In the meanwhile, he was an old hand at waiting.

Just before the candle stump gutted, Holloway replaced it by a large, clean candle. That was when he heard a clattering down the cellar steps, and, turning half way round in his chair, found Pady coming in. Holloway frowned— he'd sent the men off upstairs. But Lieutenant Evans followed right after.

"Thanks, Pady," said Evans. "Pady showed me where you were," he said, looking past Holloway at Ehrlich and then back at Holloway. Holloway didn't get up. Evans must not interfere again.

"How's Ehrlich?" Evans asked.

Holloway shrugged his shoulders, coldly stared at the officer who could tell for himself that the bastard still was hiding. This was the man who had told the Colonel that Ehrlich was not in his senses. Holloway found his hostility hard to suppress. But Evans didn't seem taken aback, eyed Holloway curiously instead.

"I wonder," said Evans, "what you hope to gain watching him all night?"

Holloway could barely hold back from throwing the

man out. Then he saw Padrone. Padrone had obviously told Evans that Holloway had taken upon himself the guarding of Ehrlich through the night. Coldly he regarded Padrone and said, "Someone has to."

"But," said Evans, "you don't think anything's wrong with him."

How did the skinny little officer know that? Holloway stared at him. Holloway said, "Doesn't matter what I think. He has to be guarded." Then Holloway added sharply, "You don't have to worry, Lieutenant. I'm not going to play any more games with him," because that, Holloway could see now, was the natural reason for the visit. "He won't get away."

"No," said Evans, "I don't think he will." He removed his steel hat and looked around the narrow cellar, and Holloway followed his stare until it came to rest again on Ehrlich, Ehrlich the foolish, Ehrlich the thief, Ehrlich the killer; and Holloway wished devoutly that Evans would go and leave him with his own.

"Suicide, Sergeant. He tried to commit suicide and failed. Do you think there can be enough left of him to try escape?"

Holloway's jaw muscles quivered as he regarded Evans. But Evans didn't know Ehrlich.

"What do you think would make him want to kill himself?" asked Evans gently.

Balefully, Holloway regarded Ehrlich. Behind the foolish mask Ehrlich would be listening, listening and mocking and noting down every word they said. He was on to Ehrlich.

"Lieutenant," said Holloway, staring at Ehrlich, talking to Ehrlich, to Ehrlich, by God, "my guess is the bastard knew he'd hit the end of his rope. My guess is all his talk about being Sigmund Ehrlich and nobody else, with the hate of the whole goddamned war on his shoulders, was talk." Intently, Holloway peered at Ehrlich. Ehrlich, are you listening? "Ehrlich knew he was finished. He just got a little weak-kneed. He just got a little talkative in the end." Mockingly, Holloway regarded Ehrlich.

"Holloway," said Evans. "Holloway," Evans called to him. Holloway turned around to Evans. "Why did he think he was so completely finished that he would try to shoot himself?"

"Look, Lieutenant," said Holloway, "is this a goddamn cross-examination?" But Evans pursed his lips, pulling no rank, so that Holloway hadn't succeeded in fending off his interference, after all.

"No," said Evans. "No cross-examination. Nothing official. No chain of command. Only, why? It's true that Ehrlich was there. It's true he was in on the *vino*-extorting end of it, or so we gather from the woman. And all this is certainly enough to get him into a great deal of trouble, considering what happened . . ."

And the joke of it was, Holloway thought, the joke of it was Ehrlich was taking in every word while slowly, with that stupid grin on his face he recovered his energy!

". . . but, after all, at the worst he could be considered an accessory to something he had not planned. Tomlinson . . ."

"Wait a minute," rasped Holloway.

". . . did the shooting for some reason which we'll never know, I suppose . . ."

"Wait a minute!" Holloway shouted.

". . . and seems to have threatened Ehrlich, although the woman isn't too clear about this last part." Evans paused. "You wanted me to wait for something, Sergeant?"

Holloway swallowed hard. "Are you crapping me up, Lieutenant, are you?" he said slowly. "Christ!" he said, and smashed his fist upon the table.

Evans smiled in a wry, sad fashion. "No," he said, after a moment. "You have it straight now. Perhaps it's too bad you didn't have it straight before, eh? Good night, Sergeant."

Holloway listened to the steps trudging up the wooden staircase, and then forced himself to look at the foolishly grinning Ehrlich. As Holloway had said before—or had he said it?—the joke of it was Ehrlich had been listening to every word.

WHAT then was the truth? The questions rattled in Holloway's brain. Holloway's back ached, horribly, horribly once again. The truth was that from the very beginning of this final night Ehrlich had known of Holloway's presumption, laughed and scorned to tell him! That was the truth.

"The bastard should have told me," he grated fiercely. "The dirty bastard never told me." Ehrlich was blinking his eyes at him. Who was Ehrlich? What he said he was? The cellar walls yawned open about Holloway.

"How?" someone was saying coldly, in Pady's voice except that Pady never spoke that way. "You would've thought he was lying." When Holloway turned around, it was Pady, all right. Pady hadn't left. He was standing against the door with his thin, long-nosed face all white and cold, Pady, the little white mouse . . .

Holloway propelled himself abruptly to his feet. The wooden chair clattered, overturned on the stone floor. He advanced on Ehrlich. Ehrlich was Ehrlich! Now and forever! "Cut it!" he bellowed. "Cut it! You dirty, lousy screwin' Kraut, you dirty Jew, you Jew, you're not fooling me, I know you're there! Cut it! I've had enough, Ehrlich. Cut the goddamn act!"

Ehrlich was shaking his head from side to side at him in a funny little way. Holloway was getting to him! Blasting him out of his hole at last!

"Come on, Ehrlich, come on you old iron gut. Guys like you don't crack. Guys like you are too smart. You're no goddamn Borman. Get up on your feet, you bastard and show your face!"

And Ehrlich shook his head and gurgled in his throat.

"You fooled me once. You made me think you did the killing. But you can't do it again, Ehrlich. Underneath that silly grinning, there's the stinking squarehead who told MacCarthy what the world was like, and loved it. Loved it, by God. Loved the fighting and the killing. Loved every goddamn smash-up in the world!"

But Ehrlich's gurgling was turning now; Holloway could see the Adam's apple of the man rising up and down his neck. Come on, by God, Holloway implored to himself, come on, you bastard! Ehrlich was weaving back and forth in his chair. Slowly, from side to side he weaved and, fascinated, Holloway watched him. The corners of his mouth were jerking. A steady sound was rising in Ehrlich's chest. There were tears in Holloway's eyes as he waited.

But the sound in Ehrlich's chest was not becoming talk; the sound in Ehrlich's chest was keening, loud, full keening spreading through the narrow cellar, rising, assaulting Holloway, wrenching at his ears with the pure, uncomprehending agony of it. The saliva bubbled at Ehrlich's lips.

249

His fists thumped at his chest. His mouth stayed open and he was keening forth now one continuous great sweep of agony. Holloway covered his ears, but the cry penetrated, and then the edge of the scream wore off and the scream became a suffusing agony and finally a constant moan in Ehrlich's chest.

With a long sigh, dropping his hands to his side, yielding, seeing who Ehrlich was, Holloway surrendered all the wrath in his heart and all the great pain in his back. "Get out of here, Pady," he said. Then he took his automatic from its holster, carefully released the safety, and dropped it on the table in front of Ehrlich. "Here y'are, Ehrlich," he said. "You don't have to fight for it this time."

Holloway turned his back on Ehrlich and walked slowly toward the door, waited for a moment facing the door with his back to Ehrlich, then opened it and pushed by Pady holding off half a dozen of the men.

"Jesus," he heard somebody say, "I don't want ever to be waked up like that again." But he pushed by them all and walked out into the open, empty street.

After a while, Pady came out and joined him. Pady handed him back his automatic.

"I thought I'd give him what he wanted," Holloway said to Pady.

Pady said, "He can't use it any more. You're kinda late."

"I thought I'd try," said Holloway.

Pady's profile was blurred, cold in the moonlight. His voice had been remote and dry. There was also a great poignance in the warm air and the faint, shifting breeze. But Holloway had a kind of peace. At last he knew who Ehrlich had been. Ehrlich had been who he said he was.

And Holloway had destroyed him.

Pady and Holloway sat for a while together on the little stoop outside the house. Finally, Holloway said, "Take over until I get back. See nobody makes fun of him. I won't be gone long."

HOLLOWAY walked away along the glass-cluttered streets. The brittle glass cracked and screeched when he stepped on it. He walked into the Medic house without even knocking. Very likely Ehrlich would now be swaying backwards and forwards on his chair.

Behind the cold blue eyes had been a man; a poor, sad sort of a man who moaned in his sleep; who was now given over entirely to sleep and its enormous fears.

"Hey!" yelled someone, alarmed. It was entirely dark in the Medics.

Holloway asked for Doc Barnes.

Someone struck a light. "Goddamn it, what the hell's the idea bothering . . . ?"

Holloway turned around to him slowly. The candlelight reached up and reddened the deep taut lines, the grime, the pain in Sergeant Holloway's eyes and his pure anger. The man pointed to a door.

Holloway stood looking down at Doc Barnes undressing.

"I told Evans," said Doc Barnes, "there wasn't a god-damned thing I could do any more tonight. Keep him alone and quiet, that's all. Now get the hell out of here and let me get some sleep."

Holloway said, "Don't you want me to make any decisions this time, Doc?"

Wearily, Doc Barnes looked up at him. "Look, Hollo-way," he said, watching the large mouth of the man work,

"I've put two stiffs to bed for your battery tonight. Do I have to put you to bed, too?"

But Doc was squinting up at him behind the rimless glasses with pain and fellowship. "Doc," said Holloway, "I want to know—what do I do? Ehrlich's finished up. He's not Ehrlich any more."

Gaunt and tall, swaying slightly, Holloway stood over him, questioning him, waiting. "Evans told me about Ehrlich and you," said Doc softly. "Go somewhere else with your goddamned questions."

Holloway didn't seem to hear him. Holloway said, "I don't seem to have anything left. I don't seem to believe much I used to believe in. I screwed up."

Holloway paused and gravely Doc nodded his head.

"Screwed up everything," said Holloway. "Can't do a damn thing about it any more. But I got to," Holloway wondered, "I got to make it good!"

In the silence, distinctly, they could hear the snores of Doc's Medics coming through the closed door. They could hear their own breaths, too.

"Christ, Doc," said Holloway. "What do you do when you got nothing and you owe everything?"

12

THE 794th caught up with the war.

B Battery's Executive position dug eight feet into the field's flat breast. They had ceilinged it with thick wooden beams, shoveled earth over and thickened safety with sandbags. Ten yards away Number One gun hulked under its camouflage net. Over a makeshift bridge, about the same distance on the gun's right, Route Six crossed a dried-out stream.

In the Executive position Lieutenant Evans removed the spectacles he wore and smeared them with his handkerchief. "Well," he said, "now it's their turn." He flung himself upon his sleeping bag.

"Huh?" said Lieutenant Grostock.

"I said it's their turn. We just threw it over at them, right? So it's their turn to throw it back."

"Very funny." Grostock turned to his ammunition report. He checked and rechecked a column of figures.

253

"Say," he said a minute later, regarding his assistant suspiciously, "do ya really think we're gonna get it?"

Evans rubbed his head. "Sure," he said in his nasal voice, "This is an artillery duel, isn't it? That's what the radio always says. 'Artillery duel on the Italian front.' You can't have a duel unless the other side is in on it. So naturally, the Krauts will shoot back."

Grostock weighed that. "Oh, crap," he said, and went back to his figures.

"Just what it is," said Evans. He grinned at Grostock perched on his water can, brow furrowed over his figures. Good old Grostock. Grostock had no pretensions. It was a quiet good to be back with him and the men.

"How's it coming?" asked Evans amiably.

"It's comin', it's comin'," grumbled Grostock.

The recorder, third man in the hole, cocked his head to one side. "Yow. Listen to that," he cried. But Grostock and Evans were already listening; and at the end of the expanding rush of sound they too felt the enormous crash. It was quite familiar. They winced. Little streams of dirt dropped down from between the beams of the Executive position's roof.

"You called it, Lieutenant," said the recorder to Evans.

Grostock was on the phone telling Fire Direction somebody dropped a shell in Baker area, somebody should see who did it. Then Grostock joined Evans and the recorder pressing against the earthen wall furthest from the light into which the rough steps ascended. They jammed their helmets upon their heads and made themselves small. How many times had he done this before, Evans wondered. But fear was now part of the natural order. He didn't object. Dry-mouthed, he blinked his eyes.

Another jar caused small particles of earth to drop from the sides of the hole. Grostock automatically brushed off the dirt which now filmed his collar. "Smack in our area," he said, terribly earnest and amazed. Evans said, "They're probably registering on the bridge near Number One."

Explosion shook the ground again. "Yeah," said Grostock, "that helps a lot." Grostock's eyes quickened with fright, glanced desperately around the underground chamber, looked for an opening out of this.

Evans breathed quickly. He felt extreme fear and an exaltation. He realized that this periodic racking of the world was what he deeply wanted—and wished to God it would end. Evans smiled ruefully. He was down with the guns, all right. Except that he wanted no food, he felt as though he were hungry. Except that no one stood behind him, he felt as though there were someone there with a fist raised to crush his skull. Evans looked up at the thick railroad ties which gave them overhead protection, imagined them suddenly caving. "No," he said to Grostock, "I guess it doesn't help much."

"And," said the recorder, "here we go again."

The earth shook. The salt smell of powder sifted through to them.

OUTSIDE a thin lifting scream slid across a space of quiet. It penetrated the Exec hole, touched the three men there, and died; but the brains of the recorder, Grostock and Evans, palpitated with the memory of it. Evans, tensing for its return, leaned forward. The cry came again.

Evans decided he would stop writing to Margaret. He no longer had any connection with Margaret. With one hand holding his steel helmet firmly upon his head, he scrambled into the light.

He saw the powder burning hot and high. The heat of it stroked his face. He saw Number One gun. He heard the man cry again but a long wail dropped sheer down the scale and pounced upon the cry, howled away with it and then exploded. The concussion rocked David Evans where he crouched upon his hands and knees. But now Evans could see near the burning powder, in the midst of punctured five-gallon cans of gas jetting their gas, the crying man busted and struggling.

Evans was running the twenty-odd yards to where the man lay. Evans' mind was frozen tight except that he was very indignant. He ran bent over, his torso almost parallel to the ground. It was outrageous that anybody should lie out there near the flames like this, crying. Another shell exploded. Evans hurled himself flat. The thrown mud spattered all over him. His ears rang. But he was there.

The two men stared at one another in a kind of amazement. Evans licked his lips, sought his voice and found it. "Put your arms around my neck, we'll take cover between the gun trails. Can you manage it?" If not, in a very short while the man would burn to death.

"Yes," said the casualty. But the word was broken on pain.

Evans got to his feet and dragged at the man. The man screamed, but the powder flame was hot on Evans' cheek. He pulled the man up, and the man seized him around the neck. They set off together staggering. Evans was crazy dizzy. The idea was to get away from the gasoline. To hell with the shells. A short distance away there was no gasoline. There was no one in sight. There was only the gun, the powder burning, the pain in the groin and the wheeze in his lungs; and then the shell cry arching against the sky. Luckily, they were within the gun trails.

Carefully, Evans placed his burden at the apex of the trails where the mass of the gun protected it, dropped himself flat and let the damn shell explode. Then he peered over the side of the trail and saw the intense flame touch the five-gallon tins of gas and the soaked earth where his man had been. The blast shocked him; the heat flared viciously at his face. He ducked down again.

Evans regarded the still face before him curiously. "How about a cigarette?" he asked. Evans was awed and amused. It had been very, very close for the fellow.

"Thanks," said the man in a low voice which Evans thought was friendly.

Delicately, Evans placed a cigarette between the man's lips and lit it. He did the same for himself. "We'll just wait it out here," he said. "Where are you hit?" How long had he known this fellow?

"Side. It don't hurt much." The man's eyes were wide open with pain and trust.

"I won't be moving you any more," said Evans. "Medics'll probably be here in a minute."

The hurt man sucked on his cigarette while Evans stood guard for him and surveyed their situation. "Krauts seem to be letting up," Evans said. It was about time. He ignored the black fumes given off ceaselessly by powder and gasoline, and looked around.

Damn it, damn it, here in the very same space with him, ten feet away, leaning against the other trail, was Holloway and another casualty. Evans had never even seen Holloway. Evans smiled with delight. But his nerves were quivering from the pull of the crazy afternoon so that he could hardly keep himself steady. No, he would never have believed he could feel so damned fine with his pulse yammering in his head and his heart full of fear. Never believed that he would feel himself at this time of all times at the very top.

"Holloway," he called out. His voice creaked. It amused him to hear it creak that way. "Everything okay over there?"

Holloway turned around quickly and saw Evans. Evans noted his surprise and chuckled. Holloway was grinning at him like a fool.

"Hell, yes," said Holloway.

Both men turned to their wounded.

"EVERYTHIN' all right, Lieutenant Evans?" Grostock was calling to him querulously from near the Exec hole.

Evans was watching the Medics take away the wounded, was saying, so long feller, good luck to his own special casualty. He had never been busier. He turned distractedly toward whoever was calling him.

"I said if everything's okay," Grostock yelled resentfully. "Colonel wantsa know! He's worried t'hell, 'fraid we can't shoot."

"Tell 'im everything's fine," said David Evans.

Later, when he had seen the men drift apart, the old order return to the battery, he realized his occasion was finished and turned on his heel and went back to the Executive position. Evans let himself down gingerly, smearing his trousers with earth from the narrow sides of the entrance. He was very tired indeed. Gravely, he sat down upon the edge of his bed roll, removed his boots and lay back.

Grostock said to him, "You did damn good t'day, Dave. More'n I could do."

Soberly, Evans regarded Grostock. "Nuts," he said.

So much, just so much of clear value Evans had gained. He'd had the trust of one man and said hello to another. No more than this, though it was a good deal. He would not mar his gain by overblowing it, nor expect anything more from the war's future. David Evans knew himself. He would cling to his calm assessment. Risking his neck came easy to him.

13

~~~~~~

THE whole front was moving. Even Rome had been taken and passed. Once again the war had slipped from Colonel Colouris' hands, but he pursued it with his howitzers diligently. Now, for the first time in weeks, he was about to catch the war.

In an hour or so, that was to say. The battalion wouldn't begin to come by and enter its firing positions for an hour. The June sun was warm upon his steel helmet; he ordered his driver to pull into the shade. He rather liked such intercalatory hours as these. The late morning sky was clear blue. With a slight smile, sitting in his peep, he placed a pad upon his knee and quickly managed the perfunctory statement of thanks, interest, and concern.

Had a talk with Colonel Grey the other day, he went on to write. Natalie would certainly remember Colonel Grey. They had passed occasional week ends with the Greys, back at Fort Bragg. Colouris paused at the memory. *Grey's heart hasn't bothered him lately, I'm glad to say; and the old boy*

260

rode his favorite hobby horse at the old-time pace. Bureaucracy: That the government governs as a government. Confusion piled upon bureau and bureau upon confusion. The toadies on top. You know the story.

I no longer agree with it. This is not the talk of a single-minded and clear-minded man. Probably, Grey is explaining that no one has made him a Brigadier. But I see no alternative to large-scale organization, military, political or industrial, much as I dislike them. Undoubtedly, they cut into the area of freedom. But even if one has no choice but to fit into some great, bumbling organization—and to refuse to admit this is a form of senti-mentalism, the ruggedness of Grey notwithstanding—it has lately occurred to me that the situation is far from lost. The conditions of individualism are changed, not the possibility of it. With a little wit, a man can clear an area for himself, I think, and run his own business. With a little wit, and one prime condition.

This will amuse you, Natalie, coming from me. The one condition I have in mind is the very confusion of the bureaucrats of civilian and military life against which Grey rails. Their confusion is my chance. Within the limits of that confusion I can make my decisions unchecked. They will be my own deci-sions, since no one will understand sufficiently what he wants to circumvent me. So, you see, I would never want, even if I could, to bring the whole state into the kind of idiot precision which appeals to some senior officers of higher rank than Grey. This is why I consider myself a democrat: given conditions as they are, a democratic society is the only one in which independent men can flourish.

You will question whether I extend to my battalion for the sake of my officers the same condition of freedom. Of course not. Why should I? Few men are concerned to be individuals; and most of those who are lack the stamina. As for the former sort, they are benefited. One of my officers—but you know Crown, come to think of it—in consequence of my authority over him received the Silver Star, stopped his drinking (the man, oddly enough, refuses to take a drink under any conditions), learned how to treat a subordinate as a subordinate and, in general, developed a sense of self-respect. On the other hand, my organization deflates the exaggerated egos of the incompetents and offers them their proper place—which is all to the good.

But I will admit the unpalatable truth. I like needless cruelty no more than the next man—but eventually the rule of life in all fields of enterprise is a free competition which normally destroys more than it preserves. Sentimentalism for sentimentalism, the refusal to see this condition of the individual's independence is perhaps worse than Grey's.

Had I told Grey all this, he would have thought that I was degenerating; and I would have been. Colonel Grey is a good soldier but incapable of learning. An invaluable superior. I would hardly wish to destroy his value by shooting my mouth off. Now he tells me that if I agree he's prepared to work his influence and my points for a transfer to a staff job calling for a full colonelcy. What do you think of that, for a National Guard officer? But I have no intention of accepting, although in courtesy to the offer I asked Grey for more time to think it over. I'll not be some exalted nobody's man when I can have my battalion.

Let me know how you and the children are. The children hardly ever write any more. I daresay they're too thoroughly involved with their own lives, eh Natalie?

Love,
John

Carefully, Colouris sealed and addressed the envelope, and settled back in the peep, frowning as he thought of the mail he hadn't received and watching the road for the first appearance of Headquarters battery. But this bright and sunny morning in June he thought of Colonel Grey again and of his own battalion, and his sorrows ended. Colouris had to admit to himself that he'd worked things out well.

Soon, not very far from the point at which the battalion had bivouacked for the night, the Mack developed brake trouble so that it dropped out of column with its howitzer while two-and-a-half-ton trucks, weapons carriers and peeps swirled indifferently by; and British drivers who somehow had interjected their vehicles into the column made comments retributive for past insults.

Lieutenant Evans, bringing up the battery's rear with the maintenance truck and crew, found the derelict and its crew waiting on the road's right edge. The motor sergeant spat, rubbed his hands, cursed the Mack driver and went to work with the two mechanics who had piled out of the rear of the Maintenance six-by-six. Evans put his hands upon his hips and frowned impatiently. Labor such as this took time. He watched Charlie Battery, next in column behind Baker, spiraling up the long road beneath him, and realized that unless the damage here was repaired before the remainder of the battalion went by he would have to lead the Mack and maintenance truck forward to a place he'd neither seen nor heard of. He would have to depend upon road markers alone, upon the small green-and-white arrows nailed to some tree or post which he might or might not notice.

Then the great vehicles of Charlie Battery edged by. Evans ignored the by-play of the cannoneers, trying to guide Charlie's Macks and guns past his own; but the Macks got through even though their drivers didn't seem to Evans to pay much attention to him. Then the six-by-sixes came by at a faster pace, and Evans had to stay off the road and make sure nobody wandered off. Finally, the small vehicles of Charlie careened along in the effort to catch the others, making Evans sneeze with the dust. Following wrong roads, Evans knew, could be disastrous even if you traveled alone. But with a howitzer behind you, you could not even hope to turn around.

Yet one could hardly hurry the mechanics. They were doing their best. Evans asked how much longer they thought they would take. They answered about ten minutes. One of them was at work underneath the chassis, flat on his back in the dust of the road. Evans would have liked to help. But he didn't know a gasket from a carburetor, whatever a gasket was. He thought he knew what a carburetor was.

A group of Bren carriers came and were gone, driving dust in Evans' face while he waited. And now he could see the first trucks of Service Battery ascending the long winding slope. Service Battery was not going to be delayed after all, as Evans had hoped. Then the first six-by-six of Service passed him; Service was the last, the very last of the battalion. Evans glanced furtively at the mechanics. Both of them were under the truck now. He could see their feet sticking out. The motor sergeant came over to Evans, stood beside him for a moment in greasy coveralls, shook his head, wiped his nose with the back of his hand, and went back to his work. Then the last of Survey's weapons carriers went by, and then the weapons carrier which would pick up the men who were posted by the green-and-white arrows to make sure no one in the column missed them . . .

That was that. The battalion was gone. Evans would have to find his way forward alone on the basis of what signs he could discover. So he lit a cigarette and lounged, indifferent to his grayed clothing, against the side of the Mack's front wheel. There was no more reason to hurry.

During a lull in the traffic Evans could hear sharply and clearly the cannoneers of the stalled gun section talking to one another in the warm June air; and he reached up to pull a leaf from an overhanging bough in order carefully to wipe away the dust and feel the young green underneath. Interspersed along the road below him he could see concrete proofs of victory, the fire-soiled tanks, eighty-eights with muzzles splayed outwards, small cars and trucks all smashed like tin cans by an axe. It went on that way for miles, through the green-gray fields and along the lithe roads moulded to the soft, curved landscape. But the wind must have shifted. Evans turned his head away. A powerful stench rose from the bloated bodies of horses decaying by the roadside. The stench overspread the warm June air. Evans could see the stiff-legged clump causing the trouble now, just a little bit forward along the road.

Quite possibly, Evans figured, he would find their way without too much trouble. Objectively, he lit another cigarette. There was nothing special anywhere. Jordan, who had piloted him a long while back along the Rapido, had been quite right. Discovering the bit of green leaf still in his hand, Evans smiled and tossed it gently aside.

TWENTY-FIVE miles ahead and early that afternoon Colonel Colouris stood among his battery commanders watching his battalion pull in. Things were going as they should go.

Headquarter and Able Batteries commanders had already driven off at the head of their columns, heading for their specified positions. The other captains standing beside Colouris now would soon do likewise. Colouris was in high good humor. They had come halfway up Italy in perfect order. This was Colouris' organization.

"Damn it," he said to Fuller at his side. "It won't be long before we've chased 'em clear into the Alps, eh, Captain?" while the tail end of Able battery swept past him.

"Yes, sir," emphasized Fuller, looking up quickly. "Won't be long." Colouris in a good mood was sometimes vulnerable. "I hear the chippies have a lot more talent up north there, Colonel," he confided.

Colouris laughed and Fuller grinned. In the distance Colouris made out the misshapen outline of Baker's first Mack. "There are your boys now, Andy," he said to Fuller, putting a hand on Fuller's shoulder. This was Colouris' battalion and it was coming through. To stand at the nerve center of a battalion, with every man in it finely attuned to the commander's impulse (or else God help him), to stand as Colouris stood now, in entire control, this was somewhat better than to rise in the world to be some exalted ass's man. Here, where he stood now, was the only freedom our time had to offer.

Now Baker's first Mack was close at hand. Colouris watched Fuller hop into his peep and cut across in front of Grostock to lead his battery in. Colouris watched with satisfaction. Colouris was happy to think no asinine professional soldier had built a better battalion. Nevertheless, here, off the main roads, in the shade of the large oak, the war seemed hardly to have ventured, and Colouris was reminded vaguely of country lanes at home. Then the first prime mover and its howitzer was gone, the second, the third—where was the fourth, he asked himself impatiently —but only the six-by-sixes rolled along, then the light vehicles, weapons carriers with trailers, weapons carriers without trailers. Everything came in perfect march order, but where was the missing gun section? The Colonel stepped into the center of the road and waved down the last of Baker's vehicles in considerable irritation. The corporal beside the driver looked out at the Colonel with a slightly scared face. Yes, he admitted, he had seen the other gun section back aways. Probably motor trouble or something, he thought. Colouris waved him angrily on.

But at least, Colouris calculated, Evans and his maintenance section hadn't come up either. That meant Evans was with the missing section and that the section hadn't gone astray. Colouris cursed to himself, then calmed himself down. He would chew Fuller for it later. Perhaps the howitzer would yet show up in Charlie or Service Battery.

SOMEWHERE north of Rome an American maintenance six-by-six led a Mack with an eight-inch howitzer in a slow crawl through French Army traffic, jam-packed to the front, to the rear, at times precariously on both sides. Moroccan troops grinned broadly at the isolated Americans perched all over the Mack and gun and waved to them. Glumly, the Americans waved back and noted sarcastically that the Moroccans rode in brand-new weapons carriers, six-by-sixes and jeeps. Where the hell was the goddamn war taking them?

Lieutenant Evans, up in front in the cab of the maintenance truck, had only the most general idea where he was, nor did consulting his road map help, when he never could be sure he hadn't missed some outgoing path in all the traffic. Of course, knowing where he was when he didn't know where he wanted to go made very little sense; but still he held on to his map. Evans was intensely uncomfortable. It was a long time since he had seen one of the green-and-white arrow-shaped markers which the battalion used to point the way. He recognized that it was his responsibility to see them.

Of course, Evans reassured himself, he might not have seen the things because traffic moved so infernally slow he might not have covered enough distance—although he could swear he should have seen another by now. But whether he had missed a marker or not, there was nothing to do about it. Truck, prime mover and howitzer could never conceivably turn in the mass of vehicles which pressed upon them and made his driver curse profoundly. They would have to go straight on and take the consequences. It cheered Evans only to consider that as long as they stayed with the main stream of traffic, there was no question but that they were on the right side of the lines—if there were any lines. Evans grinned wryly. As usual, with respect to the small authority he held at any time, he had no alternatives. He was compelled to exercise his authority with respect to alternatives which weren't there.

Evans observed that the motor sergeant, squeezed in between himself and the driver, had removed his helmet—contrary to regulations, so what?—and, with his dirty-faced head slumped forward, was sound asleep. Evans thought it admirable that the sonuvabitch could sleep in all this, and, shifting closer to the door, projected his shoulder partially out of the cab to give the sleeper more room. Then Evans turned again to the straining vigil for a sign and a road.

He blinked as fright caught him by the throat. Just in front the road broke into two routes, and he couldn't see a marker, not a single solitary marker, anywhere. Had he been complaining of a lack of alternatives? The driver slowed down. The Mack behind slowed down. The French column behind began to honk its horns. The driver looked to him for a decision. Where in hell was the marker? He had to get going.

Very well, he would follow the main road. He started to tell the driver as much but in the haze of dust through which the afternoon light penetrated more dimly than ever, he couldn't tell which was the main road. The whole column behind was honking at him. "Screw the bastards," said the driver. Evans raised himself half out of his seat searching for some clue. He found nothing. Neither did the driver. Evans pulled back the corners of his mouth mirthlessly. When in doubt, stay with the main body. He waved his thumb for the driver's benefit toward the right-hand split which most of the traffic ahead of him had taken. When they had left the junction behind Evans hoped only that it wouldn't be too long before a marker nailed to some tree justified his choice.

Occasionally as they rode Evans put his head out of the cab and looked back to make sure the Mack and its howitzer followed. Once he saw the Mack all but run down a light French vehicle which had attempted to work between the prime mover and the truck it followed. And all the while as the light slanted more and more from the west,

Evans became more uneasy. It was bad enough in daylight, but being caught out lost at night . . . He didn't finish the thought.

As they traveled on he noticed the traffic thinning. They were going faster, also, the speedometer reading twenty miles an hour on the instrument-cluttered dashboard of the six-by-six. At this rate he would find out soon enough whether this was the right road or another. Evans was feeling better until it struck him forcibly that perhaps the thinning out came from being where he shouldn't be with a six-by-six, a Mack and an eight-inch howitzer. "Damn," he said aloud, and the motor sergeant woke up. "Nothing to do with you," said Evans. "Where the hell are we?" asked the motor sergeant. Evans glared at him, then had to smile.

But after a while the road began to make turns which, in their implications, frightened Evans, since his map said bluntly that the main road ran straight for a long, long way. And the road was now quite empty. Evans decided he had made the wrong choice somewhere along the line. That was clear—or was it? Perhaps he was supposed to choose as he actually had and there had been a marker at the junction which he hadn't seen, or perhaps the marker had been destroyed. Maybe this, maybe that.

The driver was quite stolid behind the wheel. The sergeant had gone back to sleep. But when at the next junction no marker appeared, Evans knew he could dodge the truth no longer. He had taken the wrong turn.

"Pull over," he ordered. The Mack behind followed the truck's example.

When Evans dismounted, the section chief of the first gun

section did the same. "Piss call, Lieutenant?" Holloway asked. They had been on the road for three hours.

"Yes," said Evans. "A long one. You stay here with the gun. I'm going back to find out exactly where we went off." Evans realized how bitterly he had dreaded exhibiting to Holloway the plain truth about the road and, more, far more than the road, about himself, David Evans.

But gaunt, beak-nosed Holloway looked at him without reproach. "Okay, Lieutenant," he said. "We'll break open some C rations," and quickly turned away.

"Sergeant," Evans called, "Sergeant!" Holloway turned around again.

"Holloway, did you see a marker which I didn't follow anywhere along the way?" This much Evans had to be sure of, though the question spilled the rest of his guts before Thomas Holloway.

"Hell, no!" said Holloway. "I'd of let you know before, by Christ!" Holloway trotted back to his Mack. "Okay, you guys," he heard Holloway call out. "Piss call. A long one," he heard Holloway quote him.

Quietly, Evans climbed back into the cab of his six-by-six. "Let's go," he said to the driver. "Back." Holloway had given him a minimal peace. The peace was rather new to him. After considerable maneuver the truck turned around and set off down the long path. The sun carved with its light a low swinging arc which cut the tips of the grass with shining on the eastern side of the road.

Nevertheless it was he, David Evans, who had led them astray, not Thomas Holloway; and this was an objective fact which held the background of his brain, provoking sickness and a vague regret. But in the foreground of his

271

mind Evans traced again the route he'd taken and sought the error.

WHEN Colonel Colouris had seen every one of the 794th's vehicles go by him, he stared for a long moment at the empty crown of the hill down which guns and trucks had rolled. But the missing howitzer did not come. Then Colouris rose up in his exasperation. He strode angrily to his peep, climbed in and gestured sharply to his driver. "Back the way we came," he said, and clamped his lips together.

This was almost a personal affront, this one provoking failure where nothing else had dared to fail in the face of his vigilant planning. For one day in many months Colouris had watched events pour into the mould of his foresight— and now, for no damn good reason, they poured right out again. But he would not easily be robbed of success. He, in his peep, crossing over to the main road, was out to rectify events, to dam the gap in foresight. His long, bony jaw protruded angrily and the blue, shaven skin around it was taut. He was out to get that goddamned gun and bring it up with the others where it belonged.

For by this time Colouris was convinced that the gun must have gone wrong and the maintenance truck with it. Unless the breakdown were serious there was no other explanation. But he refused to think that the breakdown of the prime mover could be a serious affair. Before the offensive began he had provided too thoroughly against mechanical failure with innumerable checks and inspections. What was wrong then? What was the root source of this interference with what should be? It must be that some one had gratuitously fumbled his part—had neglected his part. Colouris' gray eyes narrowed in wrath when he thought of that man.

Evans. It must be Evans who had failed in responsibility, who had marred the scheme, punched the hole in his commanding officer's foresight not with words but with behavior. Let it darken, by God, let the damned star appear over the graying hill and the road grow blue on which he sped—Colouris would send no one else to take Evans up on this.

Colouris smiled sourly. The howitzer was important, not Evans. Evans had probably simply bungled. But for that bungle Evans should be hurt.

EVANS had been riding up and back, searching. He'd found no signs. No one knew where the battalion was. The French had never even heard of it. Harshly, he ordered the maintenance driver back to the junction where Evans first suspected he'd made a wrong choice. In the six-by-six, the warm wind rattling the canvas roof of the cab, they careened down a desolate road and Evans felt that once more the guns had escaped him, as once before long ago they had.

Evans could hardly believe his eyes. There, just ahead, coming toward him was a peep and that man in the peep must surely be the Colonel. No one else sat stiffly as he did . . . Panicked, Evans reached over and banged at the horn in the center of the driver's steering wheel, ordered the driver stop, goddamn it, stop. Evans darted out of the cab before the truck came to rest, but the Colonel had heard and seen. The Colonel was waiting.

"Colonel," Evans said, "Colonel," a bit winded. "I'm sure glad . . ."

"What," said the Colonel grimly, husbanding his judgment until he was sure, "happened to you and the howitzer?"

"Well, sir," he said. But he was coming back from the Air O.P. all over again with Jordan hit, himself rebuffed again . . . Evans swallowed hard to regain his balance. "I found the howitzer a little way below here out of the column with bad brakes . . ."

"You should have sent it on to be fixed at the new position." Colouris made his tone flat.

Evans paused. Of course. What else had he expected? "Yes, sir," he said. "After we fixed the brakes, I tried to lead her in. The gun's up the road to the right." He pointed to the split he had taken. The junction was only a dozen yards away from them. "The gun's about ten miles up that road," he said calmly as possible, not wishing to lose this battle too hopelessly. But the Colonel merely stared at him. "I guess I went wrong," he added lamely, but kept for all of that a last note of challenge.

"I guess you did," stated Colouris. "Didn't you see the goddamn marker?"

Evans was about to say with certainty that there wasn't any, but he looked again as he opened his mouth and there was the green-and-white arrow, neatly hammered to the tree trunk on the other side of the road, visible now at the end of the day. Evans blinked at it. How had he ever missed it? "No, sir," he said. "Must've passed it in the dust and traffic."

The Colonel looked him over quietly for a moment. The Colonel obviously thought Evans was making excuses. He was.

"Go tell the maintenance truck to turn around and follow

the signs to the battery. They will find their way alone easily enough."

Deliberately, firmly, the Colonel was trying to force him into his proper place, to reduce him, not knowing that Evans had long since reduced himself. Evans saw the process and recognized it for what it was. But he obeyed the order. The Colonel had the justice of events on his side.

"Jump in here," said the Colonel, when Evans had sent the six-by-six on its way. "Now you and I will go back for the howitzer, eh, Evans?" Evans barked his shins getting into the rear seat of the peep. Through the ending twilight, the peep pursued its light and rapid way. Evans was quite willing to admit he was himself rather absurd. Why wouldn't the Colonel let it go at that? The insolence of the man, the enormous assurance with which he sat upon his kernel of truth! The Colonel let it go at that? Evans shook his head in the back seat. He'd almost forgotten: this crafty man could not distinguish sanity from madness.

"Evans!" said the Colonel suddenly, turning his head slightly to the left, making Evans lean forward to hear what he had to say. "You had the Mack and howitzer turned around, I suppose, since you knew you were heading in the wrong direction?"

There was no sarcasm in the Colonel's voice, but strict objectivity. "No, sir," said Evans. "I didn't want to turn her around until I was surer I'd gone wrong." His own words didn't convince Evans as he spoke them, but he had mustered his energy and kept his voice from fading at the end of his tale.

The Colonel didn't trouble to answer. And the Colonel was right in his contempt—Evans was sure of it. The Colonel had judged him rightly; Evans would never win a place in the Colonel's organization. Nor could he beat that organization. The Colonel was mistaken only in thinking that this was news to Evans, and in thinking that it was this which hurt Evans to his core.

Quickly, the peep was eating away the blue space between junction and Mack. Its motor sang in the quiet, its wheels swished on the long blue road. No, what hurt Evans to the core was not the Colonel. What cut Evans was the charity he must redeem, not the insolence he could ward off. What tortured Evans was peace and sanity. He saw them now, guessed what they would mean, knew that he must make a place for them—and could not. What caught at David Evans' throat was the vivid clarity of a responsibility truly his which he could never, never redeem in this war-shot Italian world which was all the world he had.

The cannoneers, disgruntled, bored, scattered all about the Mack and howitzer, wandered short distances up and down the road, lounged where they could.

Holloway sucked on a pipe. There were many new faces around here now substituting for Borman and Ehrlich and Tomlinson and Cronin in his section; for other men in other sections.

"Goddamn it, you guys," he shouted, "keep out of those goddamned fields." You would think they would know better after six months of war. Sometimes Holloway doubted that people had much sense. Not that he had any exaggerated ideas about his own.

"Wonder whether we'll be stuck here for the night," said Pady to him.

"Wouldn't mind at all if we were," answered Holloway,

scratching his head. "Peaceful." Pady was making a good corporal. He didn't pass so many bad jokes any more, also —which was just as well. "One place is good as another," Holloway added.

"I got a prejudice in favor of eating," said Pady. Pady was growing up, Holloway thought.

When the men saw the shape of the Colonel's peep, they gathered together at a distance and watched their chief of section, Holloway, salute the Colonel who, followed by Lieutenant Evans, had immediately left the peep.

COLONEL COLOURIS said nothing. Standing underneath the muzzle of the howitzer, he looked at Evans and waited, fists on his hips.

"All right, Sergeant," said Evans. "Have the driver swing the Mack around and we'll get going." It wasn't much to say. Colouris was sure that Evans would remember whose will he was echoing in saying even this much.

In the dim light Colouris could see the Sergeant assessing the road.

" 'Fraid it's too narrow," said this Sergeant Holloway. "We'd have to cut into the field."

"Yes," said Evans. "I suppose the field might be mined. We might move ahead and look for a better place. . . ."

Irresolutely, Evans stood there while the Sergeant waited silently for his command, and Colouris' mouth grew grimmer. Evans was wondering, of course, whether they might not find mines ahead, or perhaps get lost, or perhaps . . . Colouris shook his head from side to side and watched Evans simmer in his indecision.

"Well," said Evans. "I think . . ."

"You think!" gritted the Colonel. "You think! Damn it man, you made a decision!" Colouris could hardly contain himself. Evans, wavering in his position, loosened the fabric of the batallion. "Sergeant," the Colonel rasped, "you heard the Lieutenant!"

Holloway looked at him for a moment, then said, "Yes, sir."

"You men," said the Colonel to the watching cannoneers, "stay off the Mack until she's turned around." They half flinched. This was the way to handle it. You took necessary risks; you didn't chase around looking for a riskless alternative. But you took no more than the necessary risks. And then you didn't lose.

Colouris stood with his hands upon his hips. The Mack driver climbed into his high seat and turned the motor over. Holloway, the section chief, prepared to direct the action. Colouris was tightening up the structure of his battalion; soon he would have the howitzer in its proper place.

The Mack's gears ground as the Mack lurched forward. "Cut her hard," yelled Holloway. The great wheels turned slowly to the left as the vehicle moved. "Straighten her out and pull her forward." The driver pulled her forward. "Now back up," yelled Holloway over the roar of the motor. "Cut hard, hard!" And then as the Mack moved backwards, slowly the howitzer jackknifed. "Hold it," said Holloway. "Now . . ."

Colouris smiled at Holloway's impossible attempt to turn her on this narrow band of road. "That will be enough of that, Sergeant," he said. "You can't hope to turn the Mack without hitting the field. Now send her in and let's get it over with." It amused Colouris to note how even the best of them—and he was convinced Holloway was one of the best of them—would balk at the necessary, unless they were controlled.

"Now take her in," continued Holloway. "We've made as much of the turn on the road as we can," he said as though he hadn't heard the Colonel.

Colouris grinned broadly. Holloway was tough. Colouris liked toughness, by God. Under no circumstances would he want to break a man like that. Nevertheless . . .

"Can't see a goddamn thing in the field," said the driver from his perch.

"I'll guide you," said Sergeant Holloway.

Colouris nodded his head in approval. He would let Holloway alone, then. But what was Evans doing? Without a word to his Colonel, Evans was approaching the Sergeant!

"I'll take over, Sergeant," said the dim little figure in the oversized helmet. Colouris saw the Sergeant look at Evans for a moment, then salute, and saw Evans return the salute and Holloway step aside. Well, well, well! Colouris had forced Evans' hand, after all. This was actually more than Colouris had bargained for! Out of the confusion and error, he was forging success with the poorest materials—and perhaps even improving them in the process!

Evans walked slowly backward just before the left front wheel. He glanced frequently over his shoulder to make sure that in the rising darkness the Mack would strike no obstacle. He was glad that the field was dry. There'd be small danger of the Mack's miring down. He had to think of such things now.

There was starlight and moonlight, but even so Evans

279

had to take care. In the grave distances of the early evening, on the horizon in the west, the last purple light caught the corner of his eye. Also, in the midst of his guiding and concentrating on the black earth, a faint chill traveled the air to him.

But his gestures to the man in the Mack who could hardly see them were definite. Evans walked backwards. He glanced regularly over his shoulder. But his steps were firm and he called out his instructions clearly to the man in the Mack. "Cut her a bit to the right. That's it! Hold it!" Evans was a member of the working whole again, and his admission ticket cost him only a few chances.

He smiled to see the others watch. He had taken on a responsibility. Holloway had offered to take his place. But he had stepped in front of Holloway. This he'd done independently of the Colonel. Of his own free will, he made his choice. He hoped Holloway had seen, and the men with him. In the future, Evans knew, he could never do more than this.

"Watch it, damn it, watch it," he called as the Mack dipped in and out of an unseen hollow. His own voice mixed with the noise and the silence nicely. There was a breeze, too, which, when it moved the poppies of the field—Evans remembered them from the afternoon—moved them in accord with the silence, gently. And beyond doubt, the poppies stood quite gay and firm, those in the Mack's path, until the massive wheels ground them out of life and color; and even then, the others, Evans considered, would sway with no less grace. "Straighten her out!" he yelled. There was a wry sweetness to a June evening, Evans thought, which could justify a great deal.

Evans had to jump to get out of the way of the sliding front wheels. "Take it easy," he called to the driver. They would be out on the road in a moment. Then he would confront the Colonel again.

COLOURIS watched the bulk of the Mack slip a bit, then prepare to mount the slight incline to the concrete road. Slowly Colouris smiled and rubbed his chin. But a blast, redder than any poppy, bloomed horribly beside the left front wheel of the Mack where David Evans stood, hammered at Colouris' ears, exploded in his brains, pried open his eyes to see the smoke rising from the smashed front of the Mack into the evening sky, and from what must have been David Evans.

He noticed that the Mack's motor had stopped with the explosion. The Mack was dead. Someone had betrayed Colouris.

Holloway had his hands to his head but he heard someone scream. Then he saw Colouris lead the wild, stumbling charge. Holloway went with them to see who was screaming and found that it was Dan MacCarthy screaming as he ran and screaming as he looked down at a legless torso. Holloway shook him, but he still screamed. Then Holloway struck him on the jaw, and there was silence.

But quiet no longer existed. There was merely absence of sound. Above, in the cab of the Mack, Holloway could see the pale, numbed driver in his seat and, down below, the Colonel, Padrone, all the others, all staring at the mess. This was Evans, Holloway told himself. Evans was dead.

Someone had betrayed Colouris, who struggled with a

crest of thought and conquered it. Colouris summoned his strength and pushed the thought below the level of his mind. He didn't need thought.

"We didn't need to turn around here, Colonel."

The loud voice of Holloway was talking to him, penetrating the evening sky, penetrating the fumes, loud, clear. Colouris needed neither thought nor Holloway. He needed to do something. Hard as he could, he grasped at the handle of action, holding on . . . He swallowed hard and raised his head and looked Sergeant Holloway in the eye.

"Sergeant," he said coldly, forcing the mechanism of his tongue, swallowing. "Sergeant, you wait here with the men. Keep them off the field and I'll be back soon with transportation for your men and a wrecker for the Mack and gun."

"It was a damn fool mistake to turn around here, Colonel," said Holloway loud and clear.

Calmly, with stiff, braced shoulders, head erect, not looking to right nor to left nor glancing back over his shoulder, above all not looking back, Colouris completed his march to the peep. Getting the Mack and gun out would be a problem. It would be tough. He must think of that problem because it was important. He must think of what it meant in morning-report terms to secure another Mack and another officer for replacement.

But how could he know there were mines here? "Get going," he said to the peep driver. The peep driver had been waiting here all along, which was the way it should be. He had been trained that way. Colouris turned once as the peep started up to see the cannoneers turning away slowly like weary men, to see Holloway's tall figure stock still and facing toward the peep. Then Colouris had left the Mack, the howitzer, the tired cannoneers and Evans.

Then Colouris had nothing to do. He sat in the moving peep with the handle of action broken off in his hands. And he could no longer hold his thoughts down. He had failed. How could he have known there were mines? But he could have led them until they found a wide and open crossroads or a town. How clearly he remembered Holloway. Holloway was tough. The bottom was out. In public, before the cannoneers, Holloway had spoken the truth and Colouris had not been able to answer it. Colouris had demonstrated incompetence.

And the structure of his organization was irredeemably torn.

Colouris went straight to Service Battery. "Holmes," he told the battery commander in the C.P., "take my peep, your wrecker and one of the Ammo Macks. Baker's Number One Mack hit a mine a little while ago. The howitzer is in traveling position. Send the busted Mack back to Ordnance and take the howitzer back to Baker. My driver knows where to take you."

When Holmes had left, Colouris called Fuller. Luckily, the lines were in. But it wasn't luck. The battalion had been well trained. Colouris squared his shoulders. "Fuller," he said, "your Number One section—I found it. Turned it around. But the Mack struck a mine. Lieutenant David Evans was killed. Shut up, man, I'm talking. No one else was hurt. Holmes will bring your gun and crew into position." Then he hung up. Sergeant Holloway would probably tell Fuller the complete story. There was no need to go into details.

Evans had threatened once, more or less threatened, in his weak way, to counter his commander's will with more than words. Colouris' broad mouth twisted.

Colouris removed from his inner pocket the letter he had written this morning and tapped his fingers with it, then in a gust of rage tore it to small pieces. When he quieted, he sat down at the phone and told the operator to get him Group. "Colonel Grey?" he said. "Been thinking it over. Think perhaps I could use some staff experience." Grey sounded surprised. Colouris laughed harshly when he hung the phone up. Grey would never guess that his recommended officer could no longer stay commander of his battalion.

Then Colouris sighed deeply. It was over. Let someone else take the responsibility from now on out. Colouris need never carry the world on his shoulders again. But let them be careful how they talked to him! Heaven help the man who tried to ridicule Lieutenant Colonel Colouris, soon to be full Colonel Colouris!

It was quite dark now. The cannoneers stayed together on the side of the road away from the truck and the legless body of Evans. Pady stared at the stars which seemed to spiral in the clear spaces where they were not caught among the leaves. Poor Evans. Evans was alone, no officer now.

"Hey!" Grossberg suddenly whispered to Pady, "wasn't that some'pin? Whad'ya think's goin' ta happen to ol' Holloway now? Look at the ol' bastard standin' there!" Pady looked.

"Man," said Jablowsky fiercely, "man, but he sure gave it to 'im. D'ya see the Colonel, Pady, d'ya see him?"

Jablowsky did a little dance. He slapped Pady on the back. "This was worth waitin' for," he said. "Man!"

"I been two years in the Army," said Grossberg reflectively, "I been waitin' two solid screwin' years, and I ain't never seen anything like it until now."

"I could see the look on the Colonel, the Big Authority!" said Dan MacCarthy.

"Yeah," said somebody hoarsely, "yeah!"

"Justice," said Dan MacCarthy, slapping his legs. "Justice, by God!"

Nobody was whispering any more. They were talking out loud, having a great time. Pady watched Tom Holloway standing aside, his big old beak, his long neck, his long legs . . . Pady shook his head in amusement at the nerve of the guy. Everyone was dancing around now, laughing. Pady couldn't help but feel the general glee himself.

"Shut up!" yelled Holloway. "Goddamn it, you men, shut up!"

They all stopped their prancing. They stood stock-still and silent.

"D'ya think they'll do anythin' to him?" whispered Grossberg. Then he chuckled. "They can't do more'n take his stripes. Hell, he din' really say anything in so many words, did he, Pady? We c'n testify in a court-martial, eh, Pady? Christ," marveled Grossberg, "we got 'em licked!"

"Y'know," said a new man to Pady, "I'll do anythin' for that Sergeant. Anythin'," he prayed. "We licked 'em. For once!"

After a while the fellows got over their excitement. Pady watched them break into twos and threes and wander up and down the road. "Stick around," said Pady. "Don't go far," because he was Corporal.

285

"Go screw yourself," someone told him.

Pady shrugged. There was no more howitzer to bother with any more. Just themselves! Pady grinned and scratched his head, watching a bunch of people wander up and down an empty road. A bunch of civilians, it struck Pady. A bunch of lousy civilians!

Pady shoved his hands into his pockets and strolled over to Holloway, curiously looked up at the heavily shadowed face.

"Tom," said Pady after a moment, "whatever it is, you sure have done it."

Holloway didn't answer. He seemed to be looking toward the spot where Evans lay. But he couldn't see Evans in the dark, Pady noted. You could only see the jagged hulk of the prime mover and its howitzer black against the stars.

14

~~~~~~

THE woman was in a state of raw fear. She wrung her hands and dribbled at the mouth. She clutched at the wide peasant skirt she wore.

"Well, for Chris' sakes, Pady—what the hell does she want?" The soldiers gathered around her in the village street.

Pady swore. "*Parla adagio, diavolo!*" he said. He hadn't talked Italian in years. He tried to grasp the words out of the stream of her speech.

"What kind of an Italian are you anyway, Pady?"

"Screw you. My folks didn't come from this part of the country. "*Parla adagio!*" he shouted at the peasant woman. He took her by the shoulders and shook her.

"Look," said one of the new men in the section. "*Chocolati. Bono.* Slow down!" The woman pushed the chocolate away, and stared at them. Then she buried her face in her hands and began to weep.

"No one's going to hurt you," said Pady softly.

"Give 'er air! Goddamn it," bellowed the First Sergeant. "Break it up!"

- Pady nodded his head as the woman spoke in gasps. "Well?" demanded the First Sergeant. Pady, concentrating on the woman's lips, waved him down. The woman drew a finger across her throat and Pady nodded to show he understood. Pady's face was cold and noncommittal when the woman had finished her story, and he quieted her.

"Well?" demanded the First Sergeant.

Pady pressed his lips together. "The old story," he said. "One of those French Ayrabs, those Goum fellers, tried to jump her daughter an hour ago. She stepped in with a meat cleaver and yelled for the neighbors. She says she knows he's going to come back with others, because before he left he made like he was gonna cut somebody's throat and nodded his head to her. The woman says what's gonna happen to them and her daughter?"

"Nuts," said the First Sergeant. "These goddamn Wops expect me to post guard over every piece of tail they got."

As the First Sergeant walked off, the woman's fear rose up again and Padrone had to quiet her.

"She lives," said Pady to the men who stayed with him, "half a mile away with her daughter and father. Her husband is dead. Only people around are two families near by with no young men."

"What do you want to do about it, Pady?" asked Sergeant Holloway, who came in time for the translation. "The First Sergeant's got a point. We can't defend all the people in the country 'gainst a whole division of Ayrab liberators."

"Sure," said Dan MacCarthy bitterly. "The French get even on the Fascists letting loose the Goums, who get a lot of fun screwing the Italians. What in hell can you do about it? You going to change the lousy system, Pady?"

Pady looked at the ground. "These are very poor people," said Pady.

"Go take a look, Pady," said Holloway calmly. "Take a good look, and come back and tell me what you find."

Pady went into the little house and came back again with his carbine. "*Vieni e fa mi vedere, mamma,*" he said to the woman. She fell upon him; she burst into tears. Pady disengaged himself. Everybody was laughing at Pady. He ignored them, tried to soothe her. But she wailed as she led him through the single narrow street of the little village.

"Where you goin', Pady? Gonna save some ol' whore's virginity?"

In these days of rapid motion, Doc Barnes hardly ever set up. He would unload only the barest necessities and the bed rolls of his section, and let most of his medical equipment remain in the trailer. Now he was having trouble locating a stethoscope in the mass of his equipment. He was also cursing diligently. When the Colonel had announced that he wanted a check-up, Doc had recommended going back to a hospital in the rear. The Colonel then said he was too busy, he was sure Barnes could do the job. Doc grunted in disgust, spied the stethoscope, put it around his neck and walked back into the little house he had established as this day's headquarters. He thought he knew what was wrong with Colouris without giving him an examination.

But Colouris insisted on ceremony. In he came. Doc Barnes glanced at his watch. Colouris was on time to the second, with boots spotlessly clean.

Colouris smiled broadly. "Well, Doc, how are you doing this fine morning?"

Such questions made Doc uncomfortable. "Fine," he said. "Make yourself at home."

The Colonel laughed. "Came on business, Doc. Remember?" he asked in a brisk voice, but then smiled again, removed his helmet and dropped it to the floor. "I am not," he said ruefully, "as young as I once was. You were right, Doc."

Barnes nodded. He made no pretense of being much of a general practitioner. He had long ago predicted that the Colonel would have to slow down and had told him so. Doc had only not predicted the occasion for the slowing down.

"You should've gone back to a general hospital, Colonel." Why, Doc asked himself, did this man think he would assume any more of the responsibility for him than Doc could help? It was irrational to hate Colouris.

Colouris ignored his remark. "Youth," said the rueful Colonel. "We can't hold up our end without it. But the young men don't know what end to hold up. There's the excuse for old fellows like me, eh, Doc? Show the young fellows what to do with their youth!"

Doc put the stethoscope plugs to his ears. "Take off your shirt, please," he said.

Carefully, Colouris removed his spectacles and blinked his swollen eyes at Doc. "It's a wearing responsibility, Doc," he said gravely, and stripped off his shirt. The chest was deep and hairy, sprinkled with white hairs upturned. The smell of perspiration reeked from it as Doc bent forward. "Cough," he told Colouris. From deep within this middle-aged torso, he listened attentively to the intimate pounding of the Colonel's heart.

"You sweat much lately?" asked the Doc.

"Why, yes," said the Colonel. "Never quite so much before. What do you make of it?"

Doc guessed at the force which clamped down an iron lid upon the pressure within the man. "We'll take your pressure," he told him. But the sweat seeped through, Doc noted with satisfaction. Not even an iron lid could contain sweat.

"I frequently feel pain in my chest," said the Colonel. "I don't suppose it's significant. Get rather flushed."

"General feeling of debilitation?" questioned Doc.

"Yes," said the Colonel.

Doc squeezed the black rubber bulb sharply and watched the colored fluids move along the calibrations. The odor of decay was all one to him, he told himself. Colouris could stink from now to doomsday; Doc would not ease the pressure; Colouris would not get what he came for. Doc would give him no medical reason for his ego, for his reputation, to keep them from rotting. It was foolish, Doc told himself, to condemn a man for running the course of his disease, for his radical failure. But Evans was dead.

"I'd hate to have to leave the outfit," said Colouris quietly as Doc removed the tubing from his arm. Colouris was most earnest. "You know, I pretty much made the battalion . . ."

Ten minutes later, coldly, emphatically, a little pale, Doc gave his verdict. "I find nothing wrong, Colonel, that shouldn't be wrong with a man of your age and temperament. If you were well enough for your job before, you are well enough now. I see no reason why you can't stay with the battalion, if you wish."

The Colonel said nothing for a moment. Doc had blocked

him. Objectively, Doc regarded the Colonel, but Colonel Colouris was glancing up at him and Doc could swear that the glance was mocking before it vanished in the Colonel's wide-mouthed smile.

Colouris chuckled. "Now," he said, "now you know why I came to you when I felt a bit run down rather than accept your advice and go down to the General Hospital. They might not have known, as you and I know, that I'm fundamentally sound. I have no intention of being read out of the war by some pompous M.D."

Colouris was trying to retrieve his position. Doc would lend him neither aid nor comfort. "I doubt that they would read you out of the war, Colonel," said Doc Barnes. "As you say, Colonel, you are fundamentally sound."

"Exactly!" said Colouris. "Just what I'd hoped you'd say," still happy-faced, smiling, unperturbed enough to make Doc wonder at the man. "But since I've begun to feel the symptoms you so long ago predicted, and recognize that you must be right, I have no alternative." Colouris shrugged his shoulders in mock amusement. "I can no longer afford sentimentalism. The matter is decided. I'm going to accept a staff appointment. I've been put out of business, Doc—I'm joining up with the big corporation, where the job will be proportionate to what the old ticker can take, eh, Doc?" asked the Colonel, heavily, deliberately, reciting a lesson, explaining himself—clearly, very clearly.

For a long moment Doc regarded the Colonel, who had worked him so beautifully, steamed him up in the wrong direction, then used him to justify the line already decided upon as the one way out. Colouris could justify himself now. He could justify even giving up his battalion, on the medical ground of which he had now reminded Doc, and through Doc, the battalion.

But Doc smiled and stretched out his legs. "Sure, Colonel," he said, "you're entirely right," and nodded professionally to the Colonel.

"Yes," said the Colonel, "and I wish I were not right. But what can one do?" Wearily he rose and dressed. The blandness and the smile were quite gone now. Since he had accomplished his mission, they were no longer necessary, Doc noted. Nor would it be long before the man disqualified himself even for staff work in the field. Would they make him a general then? Yet, black-ringed behind the steel rimmed spectacles, how lost and troubled the man's eyes were with the smile gone! And how terribly manfully he braced his shoulders as once more behind his silver leaves he turned to Doc.

Slowly, Doc pulled himself to his feet. Slowly, with faintly lifted eyebrows, he raised his arm and gave to the Colonel and the Colonel's victory a last salute.

"Good day, Doc," said Colouris, returning the salute, reassuming the imitation of himself. Doc Barnes went to the window and watched the sunlight on the Colonel as briskly, in a proper military manner, the man snapped back the greetings of the Medics outside, climbed into his peep, and drove down the road.

David Evans, Doc felt sure, would have approved of the salute.

THE day was rich in light and heat. Shirtless, the cannoneers lay back upon their blankets and sucked in the June warmth, tanned themselves. They could see the same heat shimmer the town upon the distant hill and make the walled towers light upon their granite. Immobile, the howitzers lay under their camouflage nets behind the little village street. The war had already moved to their farthest range. Holloway had no regrets that he'd let Padrone go off upon his mission; there'd be no firing today. Someone played tentatively upon an ocarina behind Holloway on the light-shot field.

Dan, Holloway noticed, squatted over a writing pad, with his stare suspended in space. "Sick or stuck?" asked Holloway.

MacCarthy shook himself. "I was thinking," he said.

Down the scale in rapid sarcasm dropped the ocarina.

Holloway dug into a side pocket for a pack of cigarettes. Lighting one for himself, he raised his eyebrows questioningly at the two other men on his blanket. They shook their heads. Holloway lay back and asked Dan, "What are you thinking about?"

Lazily, Holloway watched the perpetual schoolboy. Schoolboy Dan. "Oh," said MacCarthy, "just about how the war will end sooner than we think, what with the invasion now."

"Thinkin'!" said the man with the ocarina. "If thinkin' about that is thinkin', me an' everybody else in this screwed-up outfit is another Einstein, we think so screwin' much."

Holloway stared at the blue overhead which had no bottom. The Germans were really going down, then? The war might have an end? Something in Holloway gleamed at the thought, for he had never believed it before. Holloway recalled Ehrlich's stumpy figure, his pale blue eyes. If the war ended before he found his way around Herr Ehrlich, how could Holloway go home? Standing very large over him in front of the blue, this must be Pady, returned.

" 'Lo, Pady," Holloway said. How serious the bright-eyed, gay little wise guy was now! Holloway was fond of him.

"The old lady wasn't lying," said Pady. "There were eight, nine people up there on the side o' the hill. They say the Ayrabs sometimes come with trucks an' take all of the women they can to a stockade."

"Goddamn! How 'bout a piece o' that?" said the man with the ocarina.

Pady was pale. "They say I'm only a corporal an' an Italian one. They would feel better if maybe they could talk to an American authority."

Holloway had to laugh himself. "How would a screwin' staff sergeant do?" he asked. "The resta you fellers stick around if there's a fire mission, but I don't see how there can be."

The way to the place where the woman stayed was a narrow trail that began at the edge of the village and went through tall grass and heavy-leafed trees. Holloway enjoyed the walking. Strolling along the hillside on a narrow trail, though his pistol in its holder rubbed against his thigh, and the howitzer was hardly out of sight, Holloway felt almost rested. He noted that Pady believed what the Italians had told him about the colonial troops; but Holloway had no clear idea of what Pady and the Italians wanted of him.

"Pady," said Holloway, moved by a sudden impulse, looking down at the slender little fellow, "think you'll ever amount to anything?"

Pady's frown smoothed over. "Hell, no," he said. "My old man useta ask me the same question in another kind of accent. Once he busted a fiddle over my head. Sure, I useta play the fiddle. Pop wanted me to be a big-time violinist, a regular virtuoso. Took me outa high school so I could practice."

The long, lush afternoon penetrated down through the shadowing trees. Pady was silent. "Did you practice?" said Holloway.

"Huh?" said Pady. "Yeah, sometimes. Pop useta get sore. 'Whatsa ma' Pete,' he useta say, 'you no likea da violin. You no wanna be somebody?' "

Gravely, Padrone led Holloway along the narrow trail.

BUT when a moment later Holloway stepped with Pady into the little clearing on the side of the hill, the clearing with the two small stone houses was bare and noncommittal. He could not imagine how in this bare, empty clearing with the ancient, weather-beaten, single-story houses, there had ever been people.

"*Vieni fuori,*" yelled Padrone. "*Tutto va bene. Son io ed il sergente americano.*" Turning to Holloway he apologetically said, "They're in the bush. The Ayrabs wear G.I.'s, too."

They came out one by one. First came the old lady Holloway had already seen. In one hand she carried a butcher knife and with the other led a girl of fifteen or sixteen, Holloway judged.

"*Mi dispiace molto d'averli spaventati,*" said Pady.

The girl was plump, dirty and sniffling. There were tear streaks on her cheek, Holloway saw. Now the woman with the knife was blabbering again, and two other women were walking toward them. The two new women might have been thirty or fifty. Holloway would have said fifty, except that their hair was jet black. Then four children stood stock-still four paces away from Holloway and watched him.

"*Dov'è il vecchio?*" asked Pady.

Holloway noticed the woman to whom Pady had been talking point at two men coming from behind the stone house nearest to him. When they came closer he could see that both were old, but the older man was hobbling. Their faces were thin, and the skin upon them shiny at the cheekbones and wrinkled and loose at the jowls. Holloway shifted uncomfortably. The women and the kids were staring at him. He decided it must be the fat girl who was causing the trouble with the Ayrabs.

The older man waved away the women and children with quick, angry gestures, and drew himself up squarely in front of Holloway.

"*Piacere!*" squeaked the old man at him, high and shrill with unexpected force. "*Viva* Roosevelt!" and raised his right hand in salute. Holloway started, but no one seemed to notice. The old man was waving his arms now and squeaking at him, squeaking like an old mouse with a white fuzz around its cheeks while the women nodded solemnly. Holloway turned to Padrone. Pady said something, but the old man ignored it, waved his arms and pushed his face under Holloway's.

Holloway wondered what in God's name he was doing here among these people. He could imagine his brother and his Dad—and Ehrlich for that matter—among these strangers!

Pady looked up at Holloway surrounded by the women, the children and the two old men, and began to translate. "He's a very oratorical old gent," said Pady. "Near as I can get it, he says first of all welcome. You got the *Viva Roosevelt*. He says he is very glad to see a real American. He had never seen one before, although he's got a son in America. He says he feels related to his liberators because of that. Calls you a liberator, Tom. Claims he is tired of having to run into the woods all the time, first from the *Fascisti*, who he says are grafters, then from the *Tedeschi*, now from the Ayrabs. He welcomes you because you bring back his dignity. Where he gets that from, I don't know. He says if he were younger he would sing a song in your honor, but he is too old now. Claims he was once the best singer in the neighborhood. You're supposed to answer," added Pady.

"My God," laughed Holloway. It was curious. Although these characters weren't like Ehrlich at all—who under no circumstances would run into the bush—they seemed to want what Ehrlich wanted!

"That was just a brief outline," said Pady. "I missed a lot."

Holloway grinned broadly. "Tell the old bastard I'm delighted to hear he was the best singer in the neighborhood. That's what I came here for, to find out. Give him my congratulations," he said to Pady, but so Pady took no offense. "Tell 'im anything." Holloway took the old man's horny hand and shook it, gravely.

"*Vino!*" ordered the old man after Pady pretended to translate what Holloway said. Then all the women began to talk at once, except for the old woman with the butcher knife who went into the house. The children advanced upon Holloway with the palms of their hands outstretched.

A woman put a big mug in Holloway's hands. He and Pady clanked their mugs together, and then clanked the old

298

man's, too, which made the crowd all laugh and cheer. They didn't seem to be frightened at all any longer. It occurred to Holloway that he was the reason. The thought of it made him a little angry.

"Ask them," he said to Pady, "what the hell they expect of me?"

"The old guy told you," said Pady, shouting over the noise, but then the noise suddenly stopped. Pady's voice trailed loud in their ears over the silence.

Three men in G.I. clothing were sauntering by on the other side of the clearing. But they were not G.I.'s. They waved to Holloway and Padrone and grinned from ear to ear. The Italians had come together in a small knot behind Holloway and Padrone, with the young girl in the center. The men in G.I. clothing came closer and jabbed their fingers at the Italians. They laughed.

"The screwin' Goums," said Pady, dry-mouthed. "They want to be friendly."

They raised their clenched fists and struck their forearms with their other hands at the Italians. They seemed to be having a lot of fun. They kept pointing to Pady and Holloway and saying, "*Amis, amis,*" and jabbing their fingers at the Italians, and Holloway guessed, swearing at them. There were whimpering sounds coming from the Italians. The sounds seemed to excite the Goums more.

Holloway and Pady stood in front of them. One of them tried to get by Holloway to the Italians, but quickly Holloway stepped in front of him, hands on his hips and his right hand next to his automatic. The Goums carried rifles. Holloway could see that they didn't get him at all. They would get the idea soon enough.

"*Ey,*" said one of them, "*Americani, bono. Italiani nix*

299

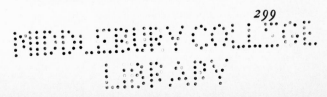

bono." Grinning happily, he pointed to the whimpering children and women behind the Americans. "*Italiano, bono figi, figi.*"

Holloway looked down at the three gesticulating men who were trying to make him understand common sense. "Look, boys," said Holloway in a loud voice. "We're all pals, allies, all that kinda crap. Now why the hell don't you clear outa here?" They looked at one another. "Scram," said Holloway, motioning with his hand but keeping a grin upon his face so they wouldn't think of their rifles.

"Sure," said Pady, "*Allez-oop. Marcia, su!* you sons of bitches."

"Aahh," they said, nodding their heads as though they understood and laughing, pointing to the women and to the Americans and nodding their heads knowingly, and making no move.

"It looks to me like they think we want all the tail," said Holloway, "and it looks to me like there's going to be trouble." The poor dumb bastards naturally expected to be let in on the fun, unless . . . Holloway's eyes lit up. "Pady," he said, "I want some respect from you and I want it fast."

"Huh?" said Pady.

"Promote me, bub. Promote me fast and make it loud, because in just a little while they're not going to think it's so funny. Lieutenant!" he bellowed at Padrone. "The caissons go rolling along. Why?"

Luckily, Pady didn't smile. Pady drew his slight frame to ramrod attention. Pady, thank God, caught the fool trick. Christ, it was the only trick Holloway could think of. "And how, *mon Capitaine*," Pady was saying, making the

300

title loud and clear. "*Mon Capitaine*, I sure as hell hope this don't make these characters shoot us, *mon Capitaine!*"

Sharply, Pady saluted. Holloway tossed back the salute. Pady pointed to the trail. "On your way, bums," he was snapping at them in a military manner. "The *Capitaine* and I wish to be alone!"

The Goum troops wavered. "*Officiers?*" said one.

It was working, then! Holloway could hardly believe it. The Ayrabs were saluting and walking down the trail. They were turning only to draw fingers across throats for the benefit of the Italians. And the women were wailing their thanks while the old man was making Holloway another speech. And, "Hooray for the goddamn army," Pady was saying to him fervently, crazily. "Hooray for a lousy private gettin' taught respect for an officer's going first! Wow!" Pady was shouting, slapping his leg, "God bless Dandy Andy, every one of him all over the screwing world! And it's me saying it!"

"Calm down," said Holloway.

But Holloway was looking at the three peasant women and the young girl and at the children. He could see that the women were crying. And suddenly he believed their tears! He believed that their plight was real, real as the plight of Ehrlich, real as his own. For almost the first time he found that he believed what he knew, and he didn't know what to make of it.

"Pady," he said slowly, "suppose we weren't here?" This was the earth under his feet, the spring earth, good and green. What might not have happened on this solid earth? Those three men who had left were ordinary Ayrabs certain they were entitled to a little figgin', sure these other people were honest spoils for themselves. Holloway could suddenly see that the world moved on different axes simultaneously, and the sight made him dizzy.

Pady said, "They're not gone. I saw a bit of G.I. clothing move in the brush. They're waiting for us to leave."

"Pady," said Holloway abruptly. "Tell these people to put their things together. We'll convoy 'em back to the village and put 'em in a house near the sections. We got to take care of 'em."

Pady nodded and began to translate.

But Holloway watched the long planes of the late afternoon incline through the clearing. The Goums would be watching, he suspected, but there was nothing to be done about that. Soon the old man brought out an ancient phonograph with a huge horn. Holloway looked at it and smiled. He knew that if he were to make his way home again nothing must happen to these people, no matter how the axes of the world turned.

Somewhere from the direction of the guns Holloway heard a voice calling him. He had nearly marshaled his charges and their possessions. "Hey, Holloway, Sergeant Holloway!" He and Pady exchanged glances. Pady looked relieved.

"Reinforcements," said Pady. Holloway raised his head and bellowed, "Down here!"

"Phew, *mon Capitaine*," said Pady. "I was kinda worried what those Ayrabs might do if they saw us pulling out."

The two fellows running down the trail were all excited.

"Jesus," said one of them, "where the hell you guys been?"

"Here," said Pady.

"We been lookin' all over for ya," said the other. "Fer

Chris' sake, we jus' got close station march order. We're goin' in a half hour!"

Holloway gaped at the messengers. Pady seemed to collapse into a very sad and gray mouse. Holloway glanced toward Pady, but Pady turned his head away. The Italians looked at one another. Holloway could almost see the apprehension in them as he just stood there. Then the women began to moan. How did they know what was up? But they sat down on their packages and began to moan, and only the old man stood upright.

"*La guerra,*" Pady managed to begin.

The old man nodded gravely. "*Si,*" he said. "*La guerra.*"

"The *guerra* be damned," said Thomas Holloway. "Look, Pady. You go back with these fellows. Tell Captain Fuller the score. Say we got to have a guard on these people. And run, damn it!"

It tickled Holloway to see Pady's eyes open wide with new hope.

"And how, *mon Capitaine!*" said Pady. "C'mon, you guys."

Holloway turned to the Italians. "Don't worry, folks," he told them. "Things are going to work out." They seemed to understand what he meant. "In the meanwhile," he added, "put your stuff back." They didn't understand that. He had to gesture. He had to pick up one or two pieces of their junk and motion toward the house and pat the man on the shoulder. He felt ridiculous. But it had to be done.

Holloway saw the last of the Italians enter the house with the last of their bundles; then, turning once to check the brush and the little trail down which the enemy had left, he went in himself in order to make sure all of his people were concentrated together. There was an old table, a madonna askew on the unplastered wall, and a couple of rough wooden chairs. Even the children were quiet. The people had dumped the junk in the center of the floor, and the women and the old men sat on the junk, broken off from one another, waiting. Holloway counted heads. He figured that if he got his guard, whatever noncom stayed in charge could use the other house for his men to sleep in during their reliefs.

But the room was vaguely wrong, vaguely out of balance. Holloway rubbed his chin, then he saw what bothered him. First he went to the old man who'd made the speech, took the old codger by the arms and pushed him gently into the chair. Then he went to the woman who still held onto her butcher knife and led her to the second chair. When she was seated too, Holloway stood back and decided things looked somewhat better. But all at once the old man began to wrinkle up his face cheerily, and the woman with the knife dropped it, and life returned to the faces of the others too. Holloway became aware that the young girl and the children were giggling; soon the old people were shouting at one another; pretty soon he smelled garlic. Now there was nothing wrong with the room at all; but my God, how it smelled. Holloway stepped outside for fresh air.

Soon, when Pady came back with the guard, as surely he would, these people would be taken care of, and Holloway could relax. In the meantime he would stand just outside the opening of the house. Considering the matter, he didn't believe the Ayrabs would take a pot shot at him, if indeed, they were out there at all. Of course, they might. But more, very much more, Holloway feared the danger of their blundering in—of their forcing the showdown that could result only in killing. But when the guard came with its show of force, everything would be okay.

In the midst of the clearing Pady stood before him at this last of the afternoon, breathless, choked up and wild. Holloway had walked quickly to meet him. "The sonuvabitch," Pady was saying, "the sonuvabitch said no soap. He was sorry but no soap. I argued with 'im, Tom. I tol' 'im about these people. He said he was sorry, he couldn't help it, he didn't know where the hell the battery was going, but things were moving fast and we couldn't keep a guard posted back in the woods for a bunch of civilians—he couldn't spare the men or the vehicles. I tol' 'im you were out here now. He said to get my ass out and get you back. He said we had to think about the screwin' battery. He said if I didn't get my ass back here in a hurry, you'd get left here. He said he'd hold up the battery twenty-five minutes for you and me t' get back."

Pady was sobbing. Pady was crying like a baby, all angry and helpless. Holloway put his large hand on his shoulder. It had finally come to the point where Holloway had no choice.

"Pady," he said, "did you say anything to Captain Fuller that might get you in really serious trouble?"

"Christ," said Pady, "how the hell should I know? Who the hell cares?"

"Did you," said Holloway patiently, "tell him off? Did you refuse to follow an order?"

"Didn't get around to it," said Pady bitterly. "But it

makes no goddamn difference at all, and you can get the hell back to Captain Fuller. I'm stayin'. Ya get that? I'm stayin'."

Holloway shook his head as though to clear it. "Don't go getting your balls in an uproar, Pady," he said. "You're rushing to conclusions. Fuller's not a bad guy. There's a lotta good sense to what he says. If you go on back now, I don't think Dandy Andy'll hold it against you long."

Pady's face went pale and icy and full of contempt. "I'm stayin'."

"No," said Holloway. "We need someone to take over the gun section. I've been thinking as you talked to me. The gun section's important, too. Dan can't handle it, neither can any of the other guys. You're next in charge of the gun section. You got to take over, while I take over here."

Pady was blinking foolishly now.

"Time for you to go," said Holloway urgently, "if you want to make it back. Don't make it tough for me. Someone's got to be with the section. Go back, Pady."

Pady said quietly, "They're my people, Tom. Not yours. Why should you get a court-martial for 'em or maybe cut up by the Ayrabs?"

Holloway straightened up, and his face became severe and drawn. "We haven't got time for a conversation, Pady," he told him. "Try to understand and if you don't understand, then trust me anyway, and clear out. I'll put it simple. It's because they're *not* my people that I got to stay. It's because they're strangers. It's a very big debt and maybe this is my only chance to pay it off. I don't know. I only know I got to stay, and I can't stay unless you go back and take care of the gun for me, because I'm accountable for the gun, too. Pady, if only you help me and stop being a stubborn little sonuvabitch, we can balance things off! Between us we can fit things together. So for God's sake leave me your carbine and get goin'." Holloway laughed. "Everything's going to be fine," he said. "I'll see these people through, and then I'll join you. I feel damn good about it. Tell Captain Fuller I'm not deserting. Tell 'im I'll be back."

Pady handed him the carbine. "Be seeing you, Tom," he said.

Holloway watched him walk off quickly into the gathering dusk and then break into a trot—then the small familiar figure had left him alone in the clearing. Holloway could hear inside the house the crying of the children and the women chattering their funny talk, and, no doubt, putting their belongings away once again. Thinking it over for a moment, Holloway was a little surprised. This, then, was the way to answer Ehrlich and go home, by leaving the section and the outfit for the strangers in there? Of course it was. What surprised Holloway was that the answer seemed perfectly acceptable

AFTER a while the children fell asleep on straw pallets the women had prepared for them. The women sat together in the far corner of the room surrounding the old lady who had long since put down her butcher knife; while the head of the house stuffed an ancient pipe with weed and puffed the foul aroma into the garlic-ridden atmosphere of the room which held them all. All of them except the children watched Sergeant Holloway standing squarely in the doorway.

He would have to work on a new angle. The last candle

burned now in its clay receptacle. When that candle burned down, it would do no good for Holloway to pass now and again before the open door, helmeted and armed, so that anyone outside would see he was still there and not blunder in. Holloway wished he could know whether anyone waited there in the bush or not. But he couldn't. He only knew that when the light went out the Goums, sometime in the night, might take a chance that he had gone.

But patiently now the women regarded him, and curiously he looked at the stout limbs of the young girl. It made Holloway angry to consider so much unquestioning dependence. The thick candle stump settled slowly in its lake of wax.

It occurred to him again and again that he might conceivably patrol outside. But if he did that, he might blunder into the Ayrabs and force things in the dark. He would certainly be separated from these people. And, whatever it was worth, the enemy would see he was no officer. Again and again he decided that he needed a better answer.

He had to work something out sanely and calmly. He had to come through this night and bring these strangers with him because otherwise his staying would be pointless. It never would even begin to meet his guilt, to fail with good intentions. Holloway was in charge to see that certain terrible things did not happen, and only for that reason. Therefore he must stay. And win.

It must have been about eleven when he thought of the old man's ancient phonograph. Holloway adjusted the fool horn under the old man's proud and worried eyes, and set the contraption up near the entrance of the room so that the horn faced outside. Then he wound the machine and checked the turntable. Luckily, the turntable worked. He got one cracked record from the old man. He would have to handle it very carefully.

For when the light went out music might convince any-one outside that the American was still there having a good time for himself. Holloway shrugged his high shoulders. You never could tell. It might even work.

What was his anthem for the night? He held his one record close to the candle but the inscription was blurred and he suddenly remembered that he couldn't read Italian even if it weren't. He put the record on the turntable, adjusted the arm and held his breath. The thing played. Holloway grimaced and took the arm away, partly to save the needle. That was that.

Then suddenly he became aware that these people, mute in the ancient room which the candle made huge, had been watching every slight motion of his hand, every turn of feeling upon his face; and that these people had no idea of what he wanted to do, that he couldn't even tell them what his problem was, that he had only their grave, uncompre-hending sympathy. He tried waving his hand in a friendly fashion. He needed these people, and this was the best he could do. They waved back. They gave him some more wine, and he sat slowly sipping it.

This, then, was what you did when you had nothing and owed everything? Holloway remembered asking the question of Doc when Ehrlich had gone finally under. He wished he could tell Doc the answer now. But what could he really say to the man? Holloway rubbed his long jaw ruefully. Not a damn thing. And at the court-martial which would surely follow, if anything followed this night's work, also not a damn thing.

Still, once again he had his seat before the candle flame

which licked so delicately at the shadow, and once again he waited during the dark night for a thief. This much was fact. This much, and the sudden flood of calm surprising his heart. Holloway rubbed his jaw now because what he felt now was very different from the calm which shrouded him in hunting or in shooting or in dragging the great howitzer from the mud. This was new to him. This went together with keeping his eyes wide-open all night long, together even with what he'd done to Ehrlich in that old, terrible calm.

Once again he had his seat before the candle and waited for the thief. But the sureness he felt now, it was not calm, it was . . . What? Holloway chuckled quietly. It didn't matter that he could no more tell himself what he felt now than he could hope to tell a court-martial. Let the court-martial judge as it would. This time, this time, by God, he had won through to a real choice, and a good gamble. He was content.

The candle sputtered briefly before the room turned pitch black. The after-image of the flame within his eyes, Holloway waited five minutes, felt for the arm of the phonograph, sent the turntable spinning and scratched the record with the needle. He heard the long, flaring horn blare in his ear the center of a note, after which he heard a thump, a blare and a thump, a blare and a thump, and on and on. He figured that the racket should make anyone outside pause and wonder. Holloway grinned. It made him pause and wonder himself. He let the record run through until the end, then removed the arm. He would play it through the night, at odd times. It would serve to keep him awake. It would serve to tell the Goums that he was still there.

But there must be no mistake. They must have no reason

to think for a moment that it was some helpless man or woman who played the record on and off throughout the night. If they were there now, they must be told who it was. Holloway seized the carbine Padrone had left him and stepped into the empty doorway.

"Hey," he called into the darkness. "Hey! I'm still here, you bastards! Don't forget it out there. I'm takin' over!"

Then he went back in again. They might not understand the words, but they would get the idea.

My God, it occurred to Holloway, the whole damn world was private to him!

DATE			
NOV 2 4 1980			
MAR 1 2 1998			

WILLIAM A. ST

CIRCUM

THE VIETNAM C

Alfred A. Knopf, New York, 1978

CHANCE AND CIRCUMSTANCE

LAW

CHA

THE DRAF

This is a Borzoi Book
Published by Alfred A. Knopf, Inc.

Copyright © 1978 by Lawrence M. Baskir and William A. Strauss. All rights
reserved under International and Pan-American Copyright Conventions. Published in
the United States by Alfred A. Knopf, Inc., New York, and simultaneously in
Canada by Random House of Canada Limited, Toronto. Distributed by Random
House, Inc., New York.

Library of Congress Cataloging in Publication Data
Baskir, Lawrence M. (Date)
Chance and circumstance: the draft, the war, and the Vietnam generation.
Bibliography: p.
Includes index.
1. Vietnamese Conflict, 1961–1975—Draft resisters—United States.   2. Vietnamese
Conflict, 1961–1975—Desertions—United States.   3. United States—History—
1945–   I. Strauss, William A., joint author.   II. title.
DS559.8.D7B37   1978   959.704'38   77-75000
ISBN   0-394-41275-3

Manufactured in the United States of America
First Edition

To Cecily and Melanie we dedicate this book
with a father's prayer of peace

CONTENTS

ILLUSTRATIONS

FOREWORD

This is the first comprehensive study of the Vietnam generation, those 53 million young Americans who came of age—draft age, that is—between 1964 and 1973, roughly the decade of the Vietnam war. Because of the lingering unpopularity of that war, it may well be the only such study written, the single contemporary historical record, since the American people tend to put unpleasant and unsuccessful events far behind them as quickly as possible. While the decade was in progress, one heard or spoke of the war many times every day. It was an omnipresent incubus. Now one rarely speaks about the war or hears about it, unless something unusual happens, like another presidential pardon or a commission to search for those still "Missing in Action."

However, the American people cannot commit to oblivion the malevolent experience of the quarter of all Americans who directly confronted that war and the many heartrending personal decisions it demanded. Granted that half of the more than fifty million coming of draft age were women. They were also sweethearts, sisters, classmates. Granted that more than 60 percent of the 27 million men escaped service by a variety of legal and illegal means. That action, too, left its moral scars when one views the composition of those who were drafted, the quarter of a million who were wounded in Vietnam, the more than fifty thousand who died, the hundreds of thousands who became legally entangled in resisting the draft, and the other hundreds of thousands who, mainly for family and not antiwar reasons, committed military offenses, many after serving a full year in Vietnam.

The great bulk of all these Americans deeply scarred by Vietnam were those already economically, socially, and educationally disadvantaged. They not only carried the burden of the fighting and dying, they now bear the lion's share of the penalties occasioned by the war and its aftermath. One often hears shocked people excoriating the President for pardoning deserters and draft resisters, but do these self-righteous critics ever advert to the fact that 15 million men of draft age completely avoided even one day of military service without penalty, and that only twenty-four soldiers were convicted of deserting under fire in Vietnam, fewer than three a year?

What occurs to me in commending this unique study to Americans is the key sentence in the authors' opening chapter: "Until Americans evaluate the conduct of these men [deserters and draft resisters] in the context of the entire generation's response to the war, there can never be any real understanding of the tragedy of Vietnam."

I should perhaps add a personal note regarding how this book came to be written and why I am writing this introduction. I lived out the war in a university and had my share of antiwar protests in ever-growing crescendo. One would think that it was a students' war but, in fact, only a minuscule percentage of college graduates ever saw service in Vietnam. I had my own change of heart and conviction during the war years, coming at last to hate the whole involvement with a passion. Once the war ended, although I had come out for unconditional amnesty, I was invited by President Ford to serve on his original nine-member Presidential Clemency Board to administer, case by case, his well-intentioned program of conditional clemency for convicted draft offenders and military deserters. After one year and several thousand case studies, I had become profoundly moved by the basic injustice and all-pervading inequity of closing one's eyes to the great majority of young Americans (mostly white and advantaged) who protested but did not serve, while lowering the boom on those who protested and took their punishment here or in exile, or who served and deserted mainly when called by a higher duty to their family in crisis. Poor families are almost always in crisis.

Granting that there are a few thousand out of millions whose felonious behavior in or out of service does not deserve forgiveness, the great, great majority of the hundreds of thousands scarred one way or another by the war they did not create deserve relief from this one more burden, since they are already carrying so many burdens. Read the book and see for yourself what I am saying—the evidence is all here.

At the conclusion of the one year's activity of the Ford Presidential Clemency Board, it appeared to me, and to my generous good friend Mr. McGeorge Bundy, president of the Ford Foundation, that we might use much of the monumental evidence assembled by the Presidential Clemency Board to strike a well-deserved blow for justice and equity. The Foundation provided the modest funds needed, and I persuaded the two most talented and dedicated members of the Clemency Board staff to make the study and to draw the public policy conclusions that were otherwise likely never to come to light. It was not, and is not today, the most popular of enterprises, but to their credit, Larry Baskir and Bill Strauss did it, with the help of a very balanced and wise committee that we assembled to counsel them along the way.

Already this study and a preliminary publication, *Reconciliation After Vietnam,* have influenced the courageous actions of President Carter to address some legal aspects of the problem. It is our present hope that *Chance and Circumstance* will contribute to the solution of the more intractable side of the problem, the need for the American people to find a true measure of compassion in their hearts.

In the end, it is justice that really counts. Americans are, in my view, a fair people. If enough of them read this book and ponder its implications, I am sure we may then legitimately put the Vietnam experience behind us, for we will have restored justice to what is now a very unjust residue of a very unpopular war.

Rev. Theodore M. Hesburgh
University of Notre Dame

PREFACE

As we complete this book, it is almost exactly two years since three decades of America's Vietnam involvement ended with the entry into Saigon of North Vietnamese and Viet Cong troops. To most Americans, Vietnam already belongs to another era. It is hard to remember how our national soul was wracked, so quickly and so eagerly have we put those years behind us. Yet nations have psyches just as do individuals. And this conscious effort at forgetting may only mask a period of internal healing. The time will come when we openly begin to reexamine Vietnam and try to digest that experience as a people. We have written this book as our contribution to that effort.

Chance and Circumstance focuses on that part of the American people who were confronted most immediately with the reality of Vietnam—the 27 million draft-age men we call the Vietnam generation. Yet this book is not about those who actually fought the war. Their firsthand accounts are eloquent, tortured, and tragic, and are perhaps the most important single chronicle of the Vietnam experience. We have written instead about the 25 million men who did not fight. Our purpose is to show who they were and how they escaped the war—and yet, in truth, did not escape it. Vietnam was, as a Washington *Post* editorial once observed, "a generation-wide catastrophe." In its wreckage lay an astonishing variety of victims.

It is altogether fitting that we be the authors of such a book. Had our luck been different, or had government policies been otherwise, we might have written a firsthand account of Vietnam. As it is, California is the closest we have ever been to Southeast Asia.

One of us (Baskir) finished law school in 1962, in those prewar days when the draft kindly permitted young men to continue in school as long as they wished and were able, until the magic age of twenty-six. Yet the law degree came at twenty-four. Wishing to avoid two more years of education or the indignity of two years as an enlisted man, he took one of the routes especially designed for the thinking man and joined the reserves. Basic training at Fort Dix, New Jersey, was no more distasteful than it had to be. The training company was composed exclusively of reservists, and all were recent college or professional school graduates. The unit was well insulated from the real army of draftees, volunteers, and lifers. The final two months of active duty were spent as a battalion clerk, sufficiently free from the rigors of military life to spend every day reading Gibbon and every night at Princeton, playing bridge. The one clinker in the reserves was the fact that for six years you were liable to call-up in an emergency. The example of the Berlin crisis hung like a pall for all that time, a danger made increasingly real by the escalation in Vietnam. But it was not like Korea this time. President Johnson found his soldiers elsewhere.

The other (Strauss) lived for years with the threat of the draft, but good luck kept him away from a personal confrontation with Vietnam. He graduated from college in 1969, six months before the first Selective Service lottery. While his friends were under pressure from their draft boards, his San Mateo, California board mysteriously left him alone. Meanwhile, he cooked high-calorie meals to help a friend eat his way over the weight limit and out of the draft. The first draft lottery designated his February 5 birthday as #214. The government later announced that #215 would be the cutoff number, and he lived for months with the lonely horror that he might be among the last to be drafted. On a hot July evening on a subway station outside Yankee Stadium, he saw a folded New York *Post* under a man's arm with the partial headline "195" in ten-point type. An instant later, he learned that his escape from the draft was as narrow as nineteen pellets in a scrambled drum. But this was not just luck; statistics experts later proved that the first lottery had a bias in favor of January and February birthdays, whose pellets had been put in the drum first and ended up at the bottom.

Neither of us can say what we would have done had we actually been faced with orders to Vietnam. Would we have had the courage to go, or the courage to refuse? We could not answer that question then, and we still cannot. But we strongly suspect that even without the luck of the lottery, or Johnson's reserve policy, we would have avoided combat via some other manifestation of chance and circumstance.

Our involvement with President Ford's clemency program gave us an opportunity to consider our personal experiences in a broader context. We were both senior officials with the Presidential Clemency Board, Baskir as general counsel and chief executive officer, and Strauss as director of planning and management and editor of the Board's final report. During our year with the program, we came to recognize how much we, like so many Americans, had misunderstood the amnesty issue. The clemency program, despite the President's good intentions, was an inadequate solution.

Among those who shared our opinion was Father Theodore M. Hesburgh, president of the University of Notre Dame and a member of the Clemency Board. At his urging, and supported by a special grant from the Ford Foundation, we undertook this "Vietnam Offender Study" as faculty fellows of the University of Notre Dame, working through the law school's Center for Civil Rights. In January 1977, the University of Notre Dame Press published our report, *Reconciliation After Vietnam,* in which we recommended a specific program of relief for draft and military offenders.

President Carter's response was less comprehensive than we proposed, especially for Vietnam veterans, and we persist in the belief that the wounds of the war have been more covered over than healed. Just as the government proved incapable of punishing draft resisters and deserters as effectively as most Americans believed, so has it been unable to devise an adequate means of relieving the punishment it did impose. Yet the most severe punishment suffered by draft resisters and deserters has been the condemnation and misunderstanding of their fellow citizens. No government program can remedy this. True forgiveness can come only from understanding.

As we began our study, we were surprised at how little careful analysis had ever been given the subject. To get the necessary background information, we visited several military bases to learn about past and current disciplinary problems; we interviewed hundreds of counselors, lawyers, government officials, draft resisters, and deserters throughout the United States; and we visited Canada and Sweden to speak with exiles. With the aid of the University, we researched draft and military law and analyzed the raw data that emerged from President Ford's program.

Finally, we conducted our own survey of 1,586 men who were of draft age during the Vietnam war to learn of their experiences with the draft and military. This "Notre Dame survey" was not a national sample. It consisted of roughly equal groups of men from South Bend, Indiana; Ann Arbor, Michigan; and Washington, D.C. Subjects were chosen through neighborhood spot-samples, with a special effort to get a representative number of interviews in low-income or minority neighborhoods. We have used the findings of the Notre Dame survey to draw conclusions about the entire draft-age generation, recognizing that there is some margin of error.

The nine flowcharts have been constructed through analysis of the best available data, much of which is not very good. But we are confident that the data is sufficiently accurate to put all issues in proper perspective. Some of our statistics conflict with those commonly cited elsewhere—for example, the number of Vietnam troops or the number of Vietnam-era bad discharges. This is generally because we have defined our terms differently from other sources. The notes should help explain any discrepancies.

To protect the privacy of individuals whose cases we describe, we have used fictitious names. The only exceptions are well-known legal cases, public figures, and persons who requested that their real names be used.

We wish to thank the many people who have given their time, energy, interest, and advice in the preparation of this book. We are especially indebted to the members of our advisory committee, Hon. Charles McC. Mathias, Jr., Professor Morris Janowitz, Professor Jefferson Fordham, William Klaus, Eddie Williams, Roger Kelley, and the chairman, Father Hesburgh; to McGeorge Bundy, Peter Bell, and Sandy Jaffe of the Ford Foundation; to Dr. Donald Kommers, director of the Civil Rights Center of the University of Notre Dame; to the university's provost, Rev. James Bertchaell; to Mike Wise, Tom Linn, Dave Curry, Jim Carr, Susan Zwick, Barbara Gaal, Bonnie Katz, Bill Miller, Bill Valentine, Rick Drucker, and the many other fine people who helped immeasurably with our research; to Rick Tropp, Bob Knisely, Rob Quartel, Neil Broder, Tom Alder, Ed Sherman, and Henry Schwarzschild for their editorial help; to Ash Green and Lee Goerner, our editors at Alfred A. Knopf; and above all to our secretaries, Paddy Shakin, Anita Listman, and Harold Peltz, and our research assistant, Larry Vogel. For the support of our wives, Marna and Janie, we can only offer a special thank you.

Lawrence M. Baskir
William A. Strauss

CHANCE AND CIRCUMSTANCE

I | THE VIETNAM GENERATION

When John F. Kennedy was inaugurated on January 20, 1961, the new President told the nation and the world that "the torch has been passed to a new generation of Americans," under whose leadership America would "pay any price, bear any burden . . . to assure the survival and the success of liberty." These were brave words, very well received.

This "new generation," described by Kennedy as "tempered by war, disciplined by a hard and bitter peace," consisted of World War II veterans then in their late thirties and forties. Their "best and brightest" would later steer the nation through a very different, much more controversial war in Vietnam. Yet this time it was not they who had to do the fighting. Fewer than five hundred members of this generation died in Southeast Asia, most from accidents, diseases, and other causes that had nothing to do with combat. The rest paid the taxes to finance this $165 billion venture. It was their children, the baby-boom generation —the product of an enormous jump in the birthrate between 1946 and 1953—who paid the real price of Vietnam.

Fifty-three million Americans came of age during the Vietnam war. Roughly half were women, immune from the draft. Only six thousand women saw military service in Vietnam, none in combat. But as sisters, girl friends, and wives, millions of draft-age women paid a heavy share of the emotional cost of the war.

For their male counterparts, the war had devastating consequences. As Figure 1 illustrates, 26,800,000 men came of draft age between August 4, 1964, when the Tonkin Gulf Resolution marked the nation's formal entry into the war, and March 28, 1973, when the last American troops left. Fifty-one thousand died—17,000 from gunshot wounds,

7,500 from multiple fragmentation wounds, 6,750 from grenades and mines, 10,500 from other enemy action, 8,000 from nonhostile causes, and 350 by suicide. Another 270,000 were wounded, 21,000 of whom were disabled. Roughly 5,000 lost one or more limbs in the war. A half million were branded as criminals, more than two million served in the war zone, and millions more had their futures shaped by the threat of going to war.

These were the sons of parents reunited after a long but victorious war, parents who, in columnist George Will's description, "were anxious to turn from the collective task of history-making to the private task of family-making. Like Studebakers and toothpaste, the next batch of children would be 'new and improved.' " Having faced depression and war, they wanted their children to know nothing but peace and prosperity. As William Manchester noted in *The Glory and the Dream,* their offspring would be "adorable as babies, cute as grade school pupils, and striking as they entered their teens. After high school they would attend the best colleges and universities in the country, where their parents would be very, very proud of them." They were the Dr. Spock generation, the Sputnik generation, the Pepsi generation, and eventually the Woodstock generation. But above all else, they became the Vietnam generation.

As children and teenagers, they had grown accustomed to the existence of the draft. Some looked forward to military service as an exciting and potentially valuable experience—a chance to demonstrate their manhood, serve their country, and get some adventure before settling down. Others saw the draft as an unpleasant but nonetheless tolerable demand on two years of their lives. Many, especially those from well-to-do families, looked upon the draft as something to avoid, an unwelcome interference with their personal plans. But most never thought much about it. Consciously or unconsciously, they put the draft out of their minds; it was something that happened to someone else, never to them.

But when the generation and the Vietnam war collided, the draft became a preeminent concern. In 1966, a survey of high-school sophomores found that only 7 percent mentioned the draft or Vietnam as one of "the problems young men your age worry about most." But when the same question was asked of the same individuals after their

FIGURE 1: VIETNAM GENERATION

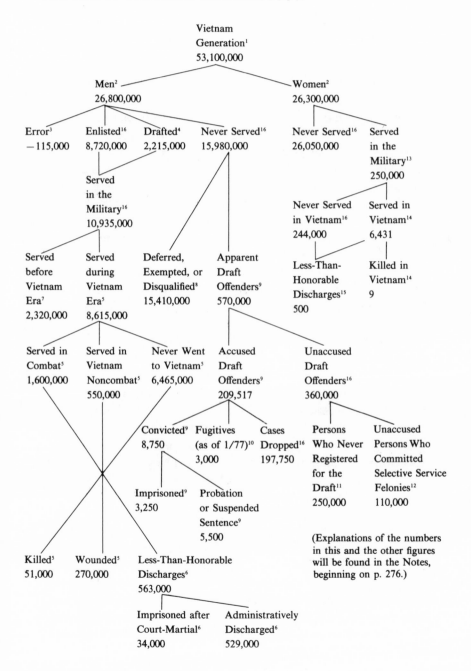

high-school graduation in 1969, that number had grown to 75 percent. Few nineteen- to twenty-six-year-olds were eager to risk their lives in Vietnam.

Although only 6 percent of all young men were needed to fight, the Vietnam draft cast the entire generation into a contest for individual survival. The draft was not, however, an arbitrary and omnipotent force, imposing itself like blind fate upon men who were powerless to resist. Instead, it worked as an instrument of Darwinian social policy. The "fittest"—those with background, wit, or money—managed to escape. Through an elaborate structure of deferments, exemptions, legal technicalities, and noncombat military alternatives, the draft rewarded those who manipulated the system to their advantage.

Among this generation, fighting for one's country was not a source of pride; it was misfortune. Going to Vietnam was the penalty for those who lacked the wherewithal to avoid it. A 1971 Harris survey found that most Americans believed that those who went to Vietnam were "suckers, having to risk their lives in the wrong war, in the wrong place, at the wrong time."

Much of this sentiment reflected the public's growing disenchantment with American involvement in Vietnam. The outspoken antiwar views of many young people helped sway public opinion and turn around the nation's policies. Their activism involved moral courage, but little concrete sacrifice. Except for occasional individuals who, on principle, abandoned deferments and exemptions to go to prison or take exile, opposing the war was in every draft-age man's self-interest. The sooner the war ended, the less likely it was that he would bear personal hardship.

This sense of self-interest was best illustrated by the attitude of antiwar collegians toward their student deferments. Harvard College graduate James Glassman recalled that in 1966, before the draft calls began to rise, "students complained that the system was highly discriminatory, favoring the well-off. They called the II-S an unfair advantage for those who could go to college." But as the war escalated, "the altruism was forgotten. What was most important now was saving your own skin." In 1967, when graduate-school deferments were abolished, the Harvard *Crimson* published an editorial entitled "The Axe Falls," accusing the government of "careless expediency" which was "clearly unfair to students."

Many students defended their deferments—and their draft avoidance —with a measure of class arrogance. A Rhodes scholar, now a corporate lawyer, observed that "there are certain people who can do more good in a lifetime in politics or academics or medicine than by getting killed in a trench." A University of Michigan student commented that "if I lost a couple of years, it would mean $16,000 to me. I know I sound selfish, but, by God, I paid $10,000 to get this education." These attitudes were shared by millions of draft-age men with other deferments and exemptions. "I got a good steady job," a Delaware defense worker said. "I'm making good money and having a ball every weekend. Why the hell should I want to go?" Why should he have wanted to go? Vietnam veterans were held in no esteem, and the fate of the nation hardly lay in the balance.

"The result," as Yale University president Kingman Brewster noted, was "a cynical avoidance of service, a corruption of the aims of education, a tarnishing of the national spirit, . . . and a cops and robbers view of national obligation." Avoiding Vietnam became a generation-wide preoccupation. According to the Notre Dame survey, approximately 15 million (60 percent) of the draft-age men who did not see combat took positive steps to help fate along. More than half of all men who escaped the draft, and almost half of all servicemen who escaped combat, believe today that the actions they took were wholly or partly responsible for keeping them away from the fighting.

Avoiding Vietnam did not necessarily mean emerging unscathed. For one in four, it meant hurried marriages, unwanted children, misdirected careers, or physical impairments. But millions emerged untouched, triumphant in what New Orleans draft counselor Collins Vallee called a "victory over the government." They never went to war, and they never faced the costly alternatives of prison, exile, or court-martial.

Avoidance was available to everyone. Ghetto youths sidestepped the draft by failing to register. High-school dropouts married and had children. But by far the greatest number of escape routes were open to youths from privileged backgrounds. Through status deferments, physical exemptions, or safe enlistments, they had little difficulty staying far from Vietnam. Even doctors, who were subject to special draft calls, were seldom involved in the war. Fewer than one of every ten medical-school graduates was drafted; many of the rest found refuge in the National Institute of Health, Public Health Service, or the reserves.

The draftees who fought and died in Vietnam were primarily society's "losers," the same men who get left behind in schools, jobs, and other forms of social competition. The discriminatory social, economic, and racial impact of Vietnam cannot be fairly measured against other wars in American history, but the American people were never before as conscious of how unevenly the obligation to serve was distributed. Few of the nation's elite had sons or close friends who did any fighting. Leslie Fiedler, commenting about his university community, wrote that he

> had never known a single family that had lost a son in Vietnam, or indeed, one with a son wounded, missing in action, or held prisoner of war. And this despite the fact that American casualties in Vietnam are already almost equal to those of World War I. Nor am I alone in my strange plight; in talking to friends about a subject they seem eager not to discuss, I discover they can, they must, all say the same. . . .

The racial inequities became a major scandal of the late 1960s. General S. L. A. Marshall commented that he had seen

> too many of our battalions come out of line after hard struggle and heavy loss. In the average rifle company, the strength was 50% composed of Negroes, Southwestern Mexicans, Puerto Ricans, Guamanians, Nisei, and so on. But a real cross-section of American youth? Almost never.

At the end of World War II, blacks comprised 12 percent of all combat troops; by the start of the Vietnam war, their share had grown to 31 percent. In 1965, blacks accounted for 24 percent of all Army combat deaths. The Defense Department undertook a concerted campaign to reduce the minorities' share of the fighting. That share was reduced to 16 percent in 1966, and 13 percent in 1968. In 1970, the figure for all services was under 9 percent.

hundreds"—and that the judicial system dealt with them swiftly and severely. None of this was true, but it helped reaffirm traditional values.

The national conscience was also salved by comparing the cowardice of draft resisters and deserters with the courage of combat soldiers. This helped blind the nation to the fact that 25 million men of military age did not serve in Vietnam, and that relatively few were touched directly by the sacrifices of those who did.

After the fighting was over, draft resisters and deserters served one last, tragic purpose. They became scapegoats, much like Eddie Slovik, the only soldier executed for desertion in World War II. Slovik was a misfit totally incapable of being a combat soldier. He performed so poorly in basic training that his commanding officer tried, without success, to get him discharged or transferred to a noncombat unit. Slovik never actually ran away, but he confessed to desertion as a way of staying out of the fighting. On the day of his execution, a few months before the end of the war, Slovik told a reporter, "They are not shooting me for deserting the U.S. Army. Thousands of guys have done that. They just need to make an example out of somebody, and I'm it."

Those who feel a deep, unarticulated resentment about what happened to America in Vietnam have made whipping boys of the draft resisters and deserters. They are the ones to blame for the tragedy of a lost war and lost illusions, symbols of the nation's lack of resolve to win. For those who condemn the antiauthoritarian values of the generation, the resisters and deserters represent the worst of a bad lot. For those who suffered personal tragedies in the war, these are the men who should have gone in place of loved ones.

As important a symbol as the draft resisters and deserters have been, Americans know little about them. They are, like the draftees who saw combat, society's "losers"—disproportionately black, poorly educated youths from low-income families. Had they been better advised or more clever, most could have found one of the escape routes used by so many others. The disadvantaged not only did more than their share of the fighting; they also paid too much of the penalty for not fighting.

Vietnam-era draft and military offenders number more than a million. An estimated 570,000 men committed draft violations that could have sent them to prison for five years. Yet fewer than half were reported to federal prosecutors, only some 25,000 were indicted, and fewer than 9,000 convicted. Just 3,250 went to prison, most of whom were paroled within a year. In the military, a quarter of a million men were punished with Undesirable, Bad Conduct, or Dishonorable Discharges, branding them as deserters or military criminals of other sorts. Yet only 13 percent of them were convicted by court-martial, and even they seldom spent more than a few months in prison. Another 300,000 servicemen were sent home with General Discharges, which are technically given "under honorable conditions," although they are nonetheless a handicap in these men's search for jobs.

A great many escaped the brunt of the law because of legal or administrative problems. More than 100,000 draft cases were dismissed because of draft boards' failure to obey court-imposed rules. The overburdened military justice system gave 130,000 servicemen undesirable discharges as plea bargains, sparing the armed forces the expense of trying and imprisoning them. But, in part, this leniency reflected the views of many prosecutors, judges, and military officers that these individuals did not deserve the stiff punishments the public thought they were getting.

It is inaccurate to assume that the "evaders," as a group, did anything fundamentally worse than their 24 million peers who also escaped Vietnam, but by legal means. The term "evader" says little about each individual's attitude toward his responsibility to serve in the military. A great many men who legally avoided combat service would have been evaders had the necessity arisen; the Notre Dame survey found that 15 percent of all draft avoiders would have seriously considered breaking the law if that had been their only recourse. As one resister commented, "Almost every kid in this country [was] either a draft evader, a potential draft evader, or a failed draft evader." According to Michael Brophy, a Milwaukee draft counselor, the epithet has been misapplied:

> To evade is to avoid something by deceitful means. The draft evaders are in the Reserves and the National Guard, seminaries, and other educational institutions. . . . A man who [breaks the law] may do so to avoid the draft, but he is not deceiving anyone.

The opprobrium of "evader" is inappropriate for large categories of Vietnam-era offenders. About one-third of all draft resisters could have avoided the draft through deferments, exemptions, and legal loopholes, but they insisted on accepting exile or punishment as the consequence of their beliefs. One-fifth of all deserters never actually evaded Vietnam service. They finished full combat tours before running afoul of military discipline back home, often because of postcombat readjustment problems.

The law has worked its will on these men. By the mid-1970s, all but a few thousand had paid the legal penalty. They were prosecuted, punished, and officially forgiven. Still, the question remains whether the American people will continue to condemn them.

Until Americans evaluate the conduct of these men in the context of the entire generation's response to the war, there can never be any real understanding of the tragedy of Vietnam. The memory of the war may be too bitter for any to be cast as heroes. But perhaps the American people can begin to understand the extent to which so many young men, veterans and law breakers alike, were victims. And, with the passage of time, critics of the generation may stop setting victim against victim, fixing blame that only exacerbates the tragedy of the war.

Vietnam wrought havoc on millions of lives in a manner that most Americans may never understand. The war was, at root, the personal calamity of the generation called upon to fight it. They are the ones who faced the terrible choices, and they are the ones who suffered. "You were damned if you did go and damned if you didn't," said Ursula Diliberto, whose son was killed in Vietnam two weeks before the end of his tour. "My son was a victim, my family was a victim, all boys of draft age were victims in one way or another."

II | AVOIDERS

Channeling

In the summer of 1968, Paul Milligan received an induction order from his Des Moines draft board. On the day he reported, no military transport was available to take him to Fort Polk for basic training, so he was given a job for the day filing case histories in the local draft office. He read about young men who had avoided the draft through one ruse or another. At first, Milligan resented what others had done, but later he began to feel the fool. That night he telephoned his mother: "The whole setup is corrupt. I don't need to *be* here! I don't need to *be* here! I don't need to *be* here! I simply didn't *need* to be drafted!"

Paul Milligan became one of the 2,150,000 draft-age men who went to Vietnam, and was one of the 51,000 of his generation who sacrificed their lives in the war. He had been chosen from among 27 million men by military manpower policies that did not care who was drafted as long as enough people were drafted.

Combat was the basic mission of the war, but even at the height of American involvement fewer than 1 percent of all draft-age men were needed to fight at any one time. For every combat soldier, many others had to perform support functions in Vietnam and in the United States. Troop commitments had to be fulfilled in Germany, Korea, and American bases in other parts of the world. The Navy, Air Force, Coast Guard, and National Guard had to maintain readiness for an emergency. Civilians also had functions to perform for the nation's long-term security. Scientists and engineers had to stay on the job in vital defense industries. Students had to complete their education to become the next generation of doctors, scientists, and engineers, and to provide the quality officer corps needed by a technologically oriented military. Because Vietnam was a limited war, civilian society had to operate with as few disruptions as possible. Family life had to go on, and as many people as possible had to stay financially self-sufficient. And, of course, no person with a severe mental or physical handicap could be asked to do anything beyond his abilities.

That was the plan. Manpower policies were designed to allocate the draft-age generation among these different functions, in addition to combat, the least desirable job in the minds of most young men. The nation might have relied on the marketplace, paying whatever was necessary to attract qualified applicants for every position. But Vietnam was already costly. Even paying combat soldiers the federal minimum wage would have made the war prohibitively expensive. The nation was not ready to experiment with a volunteer military in time of war. Alternatively, selection could have been left to chance, using a lottery to assign men to military service. Eventually, both of these policies were implemented, but too late in the war to make much difference for the draft-age generation. Through most of the war, men were directed into desirable civilian and military avenues through a comprehensive manpower policy that Selective Service Director Lewis B. Hershey called "channeling." The draft system, and to a somewhat lesser extent the armed forces personnel system, used the threat of induction to "channel" people into a variety of more attractive civilian and military pursuits that were considered to be in the national interest.

General Hershey became director of Selective Service in 1947. He had been heavily involved in the total mobilization of World War II, and had seen the nation mortgage its future by depleting its colleges of students and emptying its laboratories of scientists. The lesson of that experience was that future military manpower procurement had to be viewed in a larger context. According to Hershey, "we are [not] so rich in human resources that we can afford deliberately to ignore opportunities we have to channel people into training and the application of training."

The Selective Service, in Hershey's view, was an instrument of human resource planning, exerting "pressurized guidance" to encourage young people to enter and remain in study, in critical occupations, and in other activities in the national health, safety and interest. . . . The psychology of granting wide choice under pressure to take action is the American or indirect way of achieving what is done by direction in foreign countries where choice is not permitted. . . . From the individual's viewpoint, he is standing in a room which has been made uncomfortably warm. Several doors are open, but they all lead to various forms of recognized, patriotic service to the Nation. Some accept the alternatives gladly—some with reluctance. The consequence is approximately the same. . . . The club of induction [could thereby drive men] out of areas considered to be less important to the areas of greater importance in which deferments were given.

During General Hershey's tenure, he expanded the functions of Selective Service so that the drafting of soldiers was only an incidental part of its mission:

Delivery of manpower for induction . . . is not much of an administrative or financial challenge. It is in dealing with other millions of registrants that the [Selective Service] System is heavily occupied, developing more effective human beings in the national interest.

In his twenty-two years of leadership, Lewis B. Hershey came to personify the draft system much as J. Edgar Hoover did the FBI. He shaped it to his own image, converting what was originally a civilian agency into a paramilitary organization, 90 percent of whose top-ranking officials and state directors were officers in the armed forces. In turn, they appointed local board members with perspectives like their own. At all levels of Selective Service, turnover was low and morale high.

Hershey was a master at the skills of politics and bureaucracy, and for years he withstood attacks by his critics. Four Presidents and a long string of Congresses gave him frequent praise and near-total support. By the 1960s, however, the consequences of one-man rule, low personnel turnover, and a dated philosophy left Selective Service extremely vulnerable to criticism. Hershey might still have weathered the assault had the Vietnam war been more popular. As it was, the controversy about the war put the draft system in the public spotlight, and Hershey was discredited. Reform was exceedingly gradual, however, and the remnants of channeling persisted throughout the war.

General Hershey and other supporters of the traditional system failed to foresee the extent and the implications of the Vietnam generation's compliance with the channeling policy. For seven years, millions of draft-age men looked for doors out of Hershey's "uncomfortably warm" room. Draft critics marshaled their forces and, through a nationwide network of counselors, took advantage of every imaginable weakness in the system. The draft became a sieve for men who got the right advice at the right time, or who were clever enough to wage an independent fight against the system.

Like the tax system, the draft was seen as an instrument of public policy capable of inducing socially acceptable behavior. But unlike the tax system, little care was given to fashion incentives to ensure that lawful avoidance served useful national purposes. And unlike the Internal Revenue Service, the Selective Service System never made a serious effort to keep pace with sophisticated efforts which enabled people to distort the process to their personal advantage.

Aside from giving the armed forces the soldiers needed to fight the war, the draft did little to "channel" a generation of draft-age men in directions that served the national interest. Instead, it created distortion, dislocation, and above all, class discrimination. This cannot be blamed on General Hershey alone; he was merely the most vocal advocate of a manpower policy deeply rooted in American history.

The Civil War provided the first American experience with the draft as part of a national manpower policy. The first Confederate conscription law exempted whole classes of citizens from military service—railway employees, minor government officials, lawyers, newspapermen, schoolteachers, druggists, and others. Plantation overseers were exempted at the rate of one overseer for every twenty slaves, through the notorious "20-Nigger Law." The purpose of these exemptions was to maintain a functioning civilian economy, but the effects were scandalous. Schools were established without pupils, newspapers without readers, and drugstores without customers. Wealthy landowners were able to take advantage of the "20-Nigger Law" to keep their sons home from the front. It was not until late in the war, with the Confederacy facing a shortage of able-bodied men, that most of these exemptions were canceled.

Draft avoidance was rampant in the Union. More than 750,000 names were selected by lot, but only 50,000 were conscripted. In the Confederacy and Union alike, a man could avoid military service by hiring a substitute at a price agreed on by the two. In the North, this served the same purpose as the southern exemption of professionals and plantation overseers; the well-to-do could avoid the draft simply by using the marketplace to their advantage. The fees for substitutes ran as high as $1,500 in the Union and $600 in the Confederacy, the equivalent of several years' earnings for most. The Union policy prompted draft riots in many states, including one in New York City that caused 1,200 deaths. The Confederacy abandoned this practice entirely in 1863, but the Union made it cheaper and easier by enabling any person to avoid the draft by paying a $300 fee.

In 1866, General James Oakes, assessing the experience of the Union draft, recommended that any future system be administered by civilian boards composed of friends and neighbors of draft-eligible men to assure that decisions would be fairly made. His report lay dormant for fifty years, but it was the origin of twentieth-century America's conscription policies.

The 1917 Selective Service Act created a structure of local boards, deferments, and exemptions as an integral part of the World War I system of conscription. According to President Wilson, the draft had to be used as a comprehensive manpower policy so that Americans could

> speak, act, and serve together. . . . The nation needs all men, but it needs each man not in the field that will most pleasure him, but in the endeavor that will best serve the common good. . . . People who work in deferred occupations will be serving the country and conducting the fight for peace and freedom as effectively as the men in the trenches.

More than half of those in the first draft call of World War I made formal claims for exemption, usually for occupational or physical reasons. A hundred thousand shipbuilders were given a blanket exemption because of the need to enlarge the nation's merchant fleet. So many registrants had their teeth extracted to avoid induction that the War Department publicly warned that dentists could be prosecuted for aiding draft evasion. A "Student Army Training Corps" enabled 145,000 students to defer their service for three years; by the time deferments had expired, the war was over. Throughout the war, no one was reclassified from his original deferment or exemption, no matter how much his personal circumstances had changed.

By all contemporary accounts, the World War I draft was a great success. It registered nearly 24,000,000 men, and it drafted 2,700,000 soldiers, two-thirds of the manpower needed to fight the war. The only acknowledged problems were nonregistration and "draft desertion," the willful refusal of induction. Two years after the war was over, the War Department tallied 325,000 individuals who were still wanted for those offenses. Those who could not be found and those whose offenses were not considered "willful" were given military discharges *in absentia* ("this man . . . performed no military service whatsoever . . .") and forgotten.

World War II required a much more complete mobilization. In all, 10 million men were drafted. Only the most essential jobs in war industries qualified for exemptions, but a great many draft-age men maneuvered their way into deferred jobs or safe military duty at the homefront. As General Hershey recalled, "we deferred more damn people to build battleships." The most common way to avoid World War II was to fail the preinduction physical exam. Almost one-third of all registrants were exempted for physical, emotional, or mental defects; in some southern states, the rejection rate exceeded 50 percent.

Student deferments were a matter of considerable controversy before World War II. In France and England, college students had been among the first to fight and die in World War I. This left these countries with severe shortages of skilled professionals and potential leaders. America did not want to repeat that mistake, so the 1940 draft law deferred anyone whose activity was considered essential to the nation's welfare. Higher education was included in the definition, and more than 100,000 college students were deferred when the Japanese attacked

Pearl Harbor. As manpower needs increased, however, student deferments were restricted to men preparing for critical occupations in
engineering, science, and medicine. Some inductees were assigned to
college ROTC units, but the overall college enrollment tumbled
sharply. By 1944, the male college population was less than one-third
its prewar level.

When the war ended, there was widespread concern that the nation's
survival had been jeopardized by the depletion of the colleges. One
prominent scientist accused World War II draft policies of causing
"great difficulty and hazard to the war effort itself" by impeding the
nation's ability to assemble highly qualified people for such tasks as
the Manhattan Project's atomic bomb research. Another observed
that the war had left the United States in a poor position to compete
with the Soviet Union in the postwar era: "We were extremely fortunate that the war years were followed by a five-year period of peace
which, combined with the GI Bill, allowed us to recover at least in
part from this serious mistake [of not deferring college students]."

The postwar years witnessed a spirited debate between the advocates
of universal military training, including President Truman, and advocates of a limited system of conscription. The debate was framed entirely in terms of national priorities, with little attention given such
notions as social equity or individual liberty. The line between civilian
and military service to the country was never more blurred. President
Truman acknowledged that universal military training had only an
"incidental" military purpose, as its real goals were "to develop skills
that could be used in civilian life, . . . to develop citizenship responsibilities, and to foster the moral and spiritual welfare of our young people."
The other side argued for World War I–style policies that would meet
military and civilian needs at the same time, without expanding the size
of the armed forces.

The latter side won the debate, and one of its chief proponents—
Lewis B. Hershey—was appointed director of Selective Service. At
about the same time (1948), Congress enacted America's first peacetime
conscription law. The President was authorized to defer any category
of persons whose activity he deemed essential to the national interest.
The new law also created two special enlistment options for draft-age

men who wanted to minimize their risk of combat. Eighteen-year-olds were allowed to enlist for one year, and anyone could avoid induction by joining the reserves for six years. But the most significant new feature was the student deferment. Congress had rejected a specific proposal to defer all students until graduation, not wanting to engage in what one member called "a highly preferential action which would benefit only the sons of wealthy men." However, a special committee of educators convinced President Truman that college students should be selected for deferment on the basis of their performance, and given four months after graduation to find employment that would qualify them for further deferments. Starting in 1950, college students could avoid the draft either by ranking in the top half of their class or by scoring well on a special aptitude test. Within a year, more than three-fourths of the nation's college students were deferred or exempted from the draft.

These expanded deferments and exemptions survived the Korean War intact. Even though 1,500,000 men were drafted between 1951 and 1953, enlistments and reserve call-ups were large enough to ease the pressure on the overall manpower supply. College graduates joined the service, typically as officers, in rough proportion to their numbers. Throughout the 1950s and early 1960s, the main criticism of the channeling concept was that the underprivileged were too often barred from the benefits of military service by unrealistically high mental and physical standards.

Special interest groups sprang to the support of deferments and exemptions every time there was talk of a change. Medical, scientific, engineering, union, and farm organizations were covetous of occupational deferments. According to General Hershey, "Business was all over my back, agriculture wanted this that and the other thing, and education wanted their PhD's." The Scientific Manpower Commission suggested in 1955 that the military obligation be eliminated altogether for men trained in science and engineering. Educators joined the National Student Association in arguing vigorously on behalf of student deferments, warning that their removal could have "a devastating effect on the morale of the campuses and on the financial integrity of institutions."

Between 1954 and 1964, draft quotas were low. The operating policy was to draft all or almost all registrants classified as available for immediate induction (I-A). In this way Selective Service maintained the fiction of a universal obligation for all registrants. The draft system then controlled the size of the I-A pool by liberalizing the rules for exemptions and deferments. Preinduction physical rejection rates reached all-time highs. Deferment for postgraduate study was allowed for the first time, and the total number of all student deferments grew by 900 percent between 1951 and 1966. The most important new development was the expansion of hardship and dependency deferments to include fatherhood. General Hershey defended these deferments as necessary "to strengthen the Nation's civilian economy . . . [and to] foster the family life of the Nation."

By 1963, the draft system faced an unusual problem: the number of draft-eligible men was increasing as the postwar baby boom matured, and Selective Service was running out of defensible ways to limit its I-A pool. The notion of the draft as a universal obligation was in immediate jeopardy. A lottery was one possible solution, but Hershey strongly resisted the idea. In his eyes, the difference between the existing system and a lottery was "at bottom the difference between a human being and a machine. The people on local boards have more compassion than a machine . . . [which] cannot tell whether a man is more valuable as a father or student or scientist or doctor than as a soldier."

Hershey convinced President Kennedy to put all married men in a special low-priority I-A category, and the problem was averted. By 1966, hardship, fatherhood, and marital deferments outnumbered student deferments by almost two to one. Draft calls remained relatively low, however, and a Selective Service official acknowledged that "we have got more people than we can induct unless the inductions go up."

President Johnson's escalation of the Vietnam war solved this problem. Almost immediately, monthly draft calls rose from fewer than ten thousand to more than thirty thousand. So rapid was the escalation that Selective Service soon found itself with a shortage of I-A registrants. Even the large numbers of the baby-boom generation could not prevent retrenchment from the exemptions and deferments of the preceding fifteen years. Occupational deferments were made harder to get. Fatherhood deferments were limited to those who had never been granted student deferments. Most draft boards no longer gave new deferments to married men and graduate students, but registrants who already held them were generally allowed to keep them.

Selective Service resumed its Korean-era practice of limiting student deferments to those with good grades or high scores on a special aptitude test. A college student with a low class ranking had to take the Selective Service Qualifying Test, which General Hershey admitted was "cocked over toward the mathematical, because it's easier to grade for one thing." Three-quarters of a million students took the test in 1966 and 1967, and many who scored poorly were reclassified and drafted. The test became a rallying point for antiwar activists, who boycotted it and threatened sabotage by shouting answers aloud in the exam room. An antiwar National Vietnam Examination was published, with questions like "Who said 'I have only one hero—Hitler'? (Answer: South Vietnam President Nguyen Cao Ky)." Eventually, Selective Service abandoned the special test, and educational deferments remained available to college students who maintained respectable grades.

The Vietnam war put unaccustomed pressure on the nation's four thousand local draft boards, who had long understood the necessity of applying the rules flexibly. One draft board member described the system as "sort of like an accordion. Sometimes you stretch it out and get generous with deferments, and then other times you squeeze it up tight." Before the war escalated, most draft boards had willingly given deferments and exemptions to anyone who presented a reasonable case; when faced with borderline cases, they tended to give registrants the benefit of the doubt. Social scientist Roger Little observed a number of boards at work, learning that "many cases considered 'too hot,' 'too puzzling,' or 'too troublesome' [were] handled by granting a deferment with the statement that 'he's got several years to go to reach 26, so we'll try to nail him later.' " Once the Vietnam escalation began, the benefit of the doubt was not given so easily.

Despite the rapidly changing environment in which Selective Service now functioned, General Hershey resisted reform. Local boards consisted predominantly of older, white, middle-class men with military backgrounds from World Wars I and II. Part-time, unpaid volunteers, they were poorly trained and ill-equipped to cope with a decentralized system of subjective decision-making in the midst of unprecedented challenges. But Hershey refused to issue specific rules that would intrude upon local discretion. "Once you train them, once they learn the business, you can't meddle around in their affairs," he observed. He remained confident that board members knew enough about each registrant "to know whether he is putting something over on them."

Draft board meetings were typically held one or two evenings a month. During each meeting, board members had to determine the appropriate classification for hundreds, even thousands, of young men. They were usually able to spend only a few moments on each case and relied heavily on the recommendations of their clerks, who were lower-grade civil service employees.

Left to their own devices, the four thousand draft boards developed four thousand very different policies. Each board's monthly induction quota bore only a loose relationship to the size of its total manpower pool, and its day-to-day interpretation of the rules was often strongly affected by its own administrative requirements. Consciously or not, a board's policy usually reflected its members' traditional values, treating deferments and exemptions as rewards for young men who shared these values. According to Roger Little,

> Registrants were often lectured or quizzed on the values of thrift, hard work, obedience to the law, morality, and concern for parents. . . . They probed into many irrelevant aspects of the registrants' lives in an effort to find something on which to base a decision. Typical queries were such as these: "What do you do with your spare time?" "You don't like to submit to authority, do you?" "What kind of car do you drive?" "Were you ever in the Boy Scouts?"

As implemented by the local boards, channeling became less a means of allocating manpower to different beneficial national pursuits than a means of enforcing a set of political and social mores. Roger Little heard comments like the following:

"You ought to see this guy. . . . Well, this is the sort of guy you would take down to the latrine and scrub down with a wire brush. . . . Let's make this baby I-A. We'll fix his trolley."

This distortion of channeling reached an extreme with the practices of punitive reclassification and accelerated induction employed by Selective Service to enforce the government's Vietnam policy. In December 1965, thirty-five University of Michigan students staged a sit-in at the Ann Arbor draft board, and General Hershey recommended that they be drafted as a lesson to other would-be demonstrators: "Reclassification is quicker at stopping sit-ins than some indictment that takes effect six months later." Within a month, several of the Ann Arbor students lost their student deferments.

The policy of punitive reclassification used Hershey's "club of induction" as retaliation against dissenters who opposed an unpopular war. The armed forces strongly resisted the idea of military service as punishment, prompting Hershey to comment, "I'm as popular as a bastard at a family reunion with the military because they don't want to run a correctional institution. But they have the know-how to teach discipline." Many judges agreed with Hershey that military service was a good way to rehabilitate social misfits and petty criminals. They sometimes gave convicted offenders a choice between joining the military or going to jail. Before appeals courts rejected these practices, thousands of war resisters and convicted criminals were channeled into uniform.

Under pressure from the courts, draft boards increasingly took exactly the opposite approach with registrants they considered to be troublemakers. A good strategy for avoiding the draft was to harass local boards with antiwar leaflets, postage-due packages with bricks inside, or letters declaring an intent to refuse induction. Roger Little found that draft boards often responded by putting the registrant "into some slot . . . [where] he was no longer problematic for them." Mark Rudd, the leader of Students for a Democratic Society at the height of the war, asked his draft board for an occupational deferment as a professional revolutionary. His board refused, declaring that his occupation was not "in the national health, safety, or interest," whereupon Rudd advised them that he intended to pursue the same occupation in the Army. He was later found physically unfit under circumstances which suggested that his draft board was eager to keep him out of the military.

General Hershey's ill-fated effort to use the draft to punish his critics galvanized national opposition to his administration of Selective Service. But it was the treatment of conscientious objection that set in motion the forces that eventually undermined the system Hershey had created over the course of two decades.

Before the Vietnam war, courts had given local boards considerable leeway in making classification decisions, including requests for CO exemptions. Combined with the vague rules issued by headquarters, this led many boards to feel that they enjoyed total discretion in deciding these cases. Different standards were applied by every local board. For example, Lake Charles, Louisiana, had three draft boards: one gave CO exemptions to almost every applicant, another gave them to no one, and the third looked at the merits of each case.

The draft system quickly got into trouble with the courts for its casual procedures and inconsistent treatment of CO applicants. The resulting court-imposed rules had to be applied to all cases, not just to conscientious objectors. By the late 1960s, draft boards had to grant full due-process safeguards in every case to make their induction orders safe from legal challenge. This made them inclined to defer, exempt, or simply ignore registrants who presented legal or administrative problems, and they concentrated their attention on other, more easily draftable people.

In effect, stricter procedural requirements created a new door out of General Hershey's "uncomfortably warm" room. At the height of the war, the rules for setting deferments and exemptions had become so technical that the draft system worked more than ever to the advantage of the astute.

By 1969, the pressure on the manpower supply began to ease; draft calls peaked, and the number of draft-vulnerable men was increasing sharply. But unlike earlier times, Congress and the public were unwilling to let Selective Service keep the system in balance by liberalizing deferments and exemptions. In fact, the draft had by this time become so discredited that the public was demanding a fundamental restructuring of the system. General Hershey was replaced by Curtis Tarr, and the path was clear for the introduction of the Vietnam war's first draft lottery, the end to student and occupational deferments, and the post-war abolition of conscription.

Under Tarr's leadership, Selective Service sought to regain the trust that had been lost over the past several years. However, many problems continued unabated, and the draft still had an "open door" quality. Tarr's reforms did not stem the flood of judicial challenges and the resulting overlay of legal technicalities that the courts imposed on local boards. Knowledge about the draft's vulnerability to sophisticated legal attack continued to spread, and registrants increasingly sought help from skilled draft attorneys. As it became evident that the war was winding down, more and more draft-age men began to realize that they could outlast the war by exercising their legal rights and slowing down the processing of their cases.

With the reduction in American combat involvement and the lowering of draft calls, local boards could ignore complicated cases and be lax about reclassifying those whose deferments had expired. They still had more than enough I-A registrants to meet monthly quotas. Induction stations stiffened the physical standards, and the nationwide rejection rate jumped from 37 percent in 1967 to 58 percent in 1973.

One of the most remarkable escapes of the Vietnam-era draft was a direct result of the reforms that followed Hershey. It was, as one draft counselor called it, the "great lottery loophole." President Nixon was determined to abolish student deferments in 1971, but he did it in a way that enabled the entire freshman class to escape the draft permanently. With the 1972 election just a year away, Nixon's motive may have been political. He was able to take credit for making the draft more equitable without actually drafting college students, which might have alienated a large bloc of newly enfranchised eighteen-year-old voters.

This loophole resulted from a bizarre combination of bureaucratic technicalities. In late September of 1971, Congress passed amendments to the Selective Service law giving the President the power to terminate student deferments. By the time the deferments were actually abolished on December 10, all induction orders for the calendar year had been issued, so no student could be drafted until January. Under the rules of the lottery, individuals who lost deferments late in the calendar year could not be drafted any later than March of the following year. However, there were no induction calls for January, February, or March of 1972. As a result, no member of the freshman class of 1971 could legally have been issued an induction order, even if his lottery number was 1. More than 600,000 men with low lottery numbers benefited from this combination of events.

The December 28 announcement by Secretary of Defense Melvin Laird that there would be no draft calls in early 1972 was an unexpected Christmas gift for tens of thousands more who held other kinds of deferments. There was a nationwide scramble to drop deferments before the December 31 deadline for 1971 draft vulnerability passed. Bulletins were posted everywhere, phone lines to draft boards were jammed, and last-minute appeals were made at New Year's Eve parties urging people voluntarily to renounce their deferments. Many who took advantage of this loophole were the most hopeless cases, the ones who otherwise had no alternatives to the draft but prison or Canada.

The final quirk of the draft came, fittingly enough, during the last induction call of the war. Three hundred men were ordered to report to various induction stations on December 28, 1972. But the twenty-eighth was declared a national day of mourning for Harry Truman, who had just died. Those who reported on the twenty-eighth were sent home to await further instructions, which never came. Secretary Laird announced the end of the draft less than a month later.

Artful Dodgers

Many of the 16 million men who escaped the draft during Vietnam were just plain lucky. Some were the beneficiaries of a poorly administered system which lost or mishandled their cases. Four million were fortunate enough to get high lottery numbers. Millions more, as Figure 2 (pp. 30–31) indicates, were excused because of hardship, family dependency, physical, or mental reasons. For most, the structure of deferments and exemptions worked to their benefit without requiring them to take any significant steps to manipulate the system.

Yet the draft's channeling policy encouraged individuals to take fate in their own hands by rearranging their personal circumstances. According to the Notre Dame survey, three-quarters of those who never served admitted that they tried to avoid the draft. A majority (55 percent) believed that the action they took may have been responsible for keeping them out of the military.

Many, of course, did nothing more than exercise their legitimate rights under the law. They applied for deferments, documented cases for physical exemptions, applied for CO status, or made other claims and appeals. But others took far more drastic steps, often under the impression that they had no other alternative. To stay away from Vietnam, they "channeled" themselves in directions that were in neither the country's interests nor their own.

Many young men went to college solely to escape the draft. Nationwide enrollment statistics throughout the Vietnam years, along with the findings of the Notre Dame survey, suggest that male college enrollment averaged 6–7 percent higher than normal because of the draft. Additionally, 12 percent of the survey respondents said the draft kept them from taking one or more years off from college to work or travel, and another 5 percent changed their courses of study to keep their deferments. A student deferment was not a permanent escape, because it was almost always necessary for a student to acquire some other deferment or exemption between graduation and age twenty-six, when vulnerability ended.* Without these deferments, however, millions of college students would have faced induction before they got high lottery numbers or discovered other ways to work the system to their advantage.

The importance of II-S deferments to college students was demonstrated by a prank at Emory University. One day in 1966, the college humor magazine took over the newspaper presses, printing a special edition to announce that Selective Service had ordered local boards to deny deferments to all Emory students. In the hours before the prank

*Legally, a registrant was vulnerable to age thirty-five if he had ever received a deferment, but only in a true national emergency. During the Vietnam era, no person was drafted unless he received an induction order before his twenty-sixth birthday.

FIGURE 2: CIVILIAN AVOIDERS

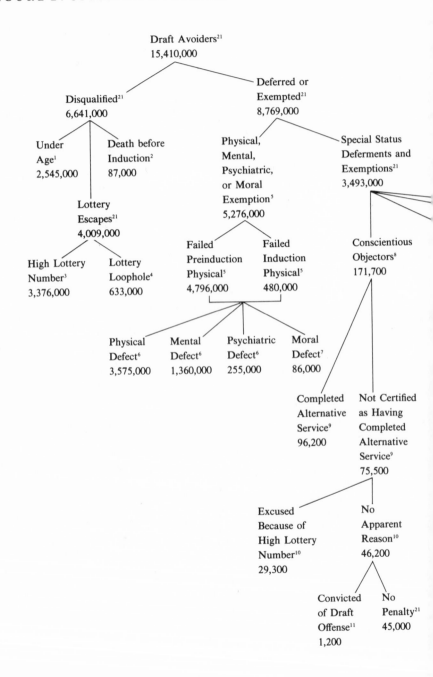

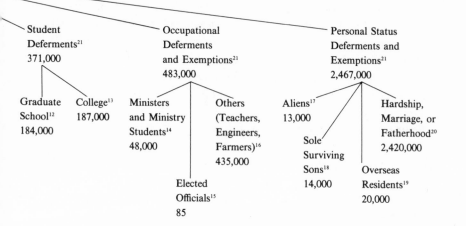

Student
Deferments[21]
371,000

Occupational
Deferments
and Exemptions[21]
483,000

Personal Status
Deferments and
Exemptions[21]
2,467,000

Graduate
School[12]
184,000

College[13]
187,000

Ministers
and Ministry
Students[14]
48,000

Others
(Teachers,
Engineers,
Farmers)[16]
435,000

Aliens[17]
13,000

Sole
Surviving
Sons[18]
14,000

Hardship,
Marriage, or
Fatherhood[20]
2,420,000

Overseas
Residents[19]
20,000

Elected
Officials[15]
85

was discovered, a number of students telephoned or mailed applications for immediate transfer to schools they thought were not affected by the order.

Before 1968, graduate schools were also havens from the draft. Three or four years in graduate school were often enough to enable a man to reach the magic age of twenty-six. In 1966 and 1967, graduate schools were besieged with draft-motivated requests for admission. The head of one well-known graduate school of business administration took a personal survey of twelve hundred male candidates for admission and found that 90 percent had applied at least partly because of the draft. Noting how the Vietnam-era draft affected higher education in the exact opposite way from the World War II draft, General Hershey said that "I feel very good about a lot of these draft-dodging PhD's, but there were some that didn't have a brain in their head. God help us."

After the end of graduate school deferments in 1967, divinity schools became increasingly popular as draft shelters—especially those that did not require strict sectarian courses of study. Some Jewish yeshivas were ideal; they offered a complete range of secular degrees, enabling students to study what they pleased while their draft boards believed they were preparing to be rabbis.

According to the channeling theory, the national interest justified inducing men to further their education. However, many university officials accused the II-S deferment of having a corrupting influence on their institutions, perhaps even contributing to the campus unrest of the period. The baby boom, along with a rapid expansion in higher education facilities, put a strain on the job market for educated people. The draft simply added to the problem.

The employment picture was especially bleak in fields like engineering or teaching, which earned almost automatic deferments from draft boards. By the late 1960s, both fields were glutted with recent college graduates. In 1968, the year New York City draft boards confirmed that all full-time teachers qualified for deferments, the city's board of education received twenty thousand more applications for teachers' licenses than the year before. By 1969, 85 percent of New York City's teacher trainees were draft-age men, and some city universities were reporting an 800 percent increase in men taking teacher education courses. Nor was this phenomenon limited to education and teaching. Ten percent of the Notre Dame survey respondents admitted that the draft influenced their choice of careers.

As an instrument of human resource allocation, the draft produced personal as well as social distortions. Bob Johnson lost his student deferment when he graduated from Yale, and his Maryland draft board promised him an occupational deferment if he taught science at a local high school. Johnson wanted to go to graduate school to study chemistry, but he decided to teach school as long as necessary to stay out of the war. By the time his draft vulnerability had passed, Johnson had married and become a father; it was too late for him to go back to school.

Altering one's family circumstances offered another way to avoid the draft. Military pay was low throughout the war, and most draft boards gave hardship deferments to people who provided the sole support for widowed mothers, younger brothers and sisters, or other dependents. A person could qualify for a deferment by inviting an unemployed or disabled dependent to live in his house. It was not necessary to be poor; George Hamilton, the actor, received a hardship deferment because his mother lived in his Hollywood mansion and relied on his $200,000 income for support.

Two common stratagems were what President Eisenhower called "babying out" and its corollary, "marrying out." Ten percent of the Notre Dame survey respondents—three of every ten fathers—said that their decision to have children was influenced by the draft. This was especially common among men who never went to college. Special draft treatment for married men existed only between 1963 and 1966; during those years, there was an immediate 10 percent rise in the marriage rates for twenty- and twenty-one-year-olds. Many marriages were hastily arranged. Colonel Harry Smith, the Georgia state director of Selective Service, recalled one week in which forty-six men who had been ordered to report for induction suddenly got married. Six percent of the Notre Dame survey respondents—one of every eight husbands—admitted that they married early as a means of avoiding the draft.

The preinduction physical, in addition to its basic function of excluding the unfit from military service, was considered a valuable means of identifying young people with serious untreated physical problems. A government manpower report, "One Third of a Nation," even hinted that the process could be used to direct people to the medical care they needed. But instead of helping identify the medically unfit, it gave the medically fit another way to avoid the draft. According to the Notre Dame survey, the preinduction screening process drove almost a million men to manipulate their health as a way of avoiding the draft. Many of their ploys were harmless, like jabbing forearms with pins to fake a heroin problem. But some tried so hard to be convincing that they risked serious harm to themselves; for example, some men injected heroin to make the addiction "act" harder to uncover.

There were dozens of ways to get an exemption by abusing one's body. Individuals who suffered from asthma, allergies, and other minor ailments often aggravated their conditions right before their physicals. Some athletes with old joint injuries deliberately reinjured themselves, hoping they would later reheal. A common tactic was to gain or lose enough weight to get outside the military standards. A University of Michigan football player ate three large pizzas every night for six months, gaining 125 pounds and the sought-for physical exemption. The grandson of a Russian immigrant pushed his body to extreme limits by staying awake for over a week before taking his preinduction physical. He could have avoided the draft in easier ways, but he felt honor-bound to use the same technique his grandfather had used to avoid conscription in the Russian army.

Some were so desperate to avoid Vietnam that they willingly suffered permanent injury. The easiest way to do this was by slicing off half a thumb, or by asking a friend to punch one's nose hard enough to cause a deviated septum. A nineteen-year-old shot himself in the foot with a .22 caliber rifle, smashing several bones and leaving himself with a permanent limp. Another youth partially blinded himself by staring at the sun.

One little-known evasion tactic, capitalizing on a loophole in the registration rules, bore an ironic similarity to the action that thousands took who fled the country illegally to avoid the draft. If a young man left the United States after his eighteenth birthday and stayed away, he faced a serious threat of prosecution for draft evasion. But if he left before turning eighteen, he acted within the law. All eighteen-year-olds living abroad were required to register with Draft Board #100 in Washington, D.C. Until mid-1971, Selective Service regulations did not allow Draft Board #100 to induct any of its registrants as long as they stayed outside the country. Teenage exiles were not the only ones who took advantage of this loophole. Sons of overseas military personnel and corporate officials were able to avoid the draft simply by going to foreign universities until they were twenty-six.

At the height of the war, Draft Board #100 had twenty-eight thousand registrants and was drafting only about two hundred per year. One board member admitted that "an awful lot of kids played games with us." By the time the law was changed in mid-1971, most of the Draft Board #100 registrants who might earlier have been drafted had turned twenty-six, had high lottery numbers, or were able to stall out the war with help from draft counselors. No one knows why this loophole ever existed, but one board member said, "It would have been unfair to make these boys travel thousands of miles just to report for induction."

In this generation-wide scramble for survival, millions of men were prepared to do whatever was necessary to avoid the war, as long as it was within (or not too far outside) the law. Many of those who manipulated their draft status were given only temporary deferments or exemptions. They were duty-bound, under penalty of law, to inform their local boards of any change in their circumstances. They seldom did.

With the war and its casualties confronting draft avoiders in every newspaper they read and every television news program they watched, many could not ignore the social and ethical implications of their conduct. Milwaukee draft counselor Michael Brophy considered each man's experience with the draft to have been his "rite of passage" into adulthood. For many men, Vietnam was their first test of personal integrity. "The long-term casualties are unbelievable," Brophy recalled. "I know someone who ate six dozen eggs and got an exemption for excessive albumin. Now, for as long as he lives, he has to maintain the lie that he is allergic to eggs." Brophy and other draft counselors still get calls from Vietnam-era clients asking for reassurance that they did the right thing.

Aid and Comfort

Beating the draft was by no means a lonely endeavor; in fact, it became more of a status symbol than did fighting for one's country. "If you are I-A, you are a nobody," observed Congressman Alvin O'Konski. "You happened to get caught because you didn't know any better. If you are not I-A, you have status." President Johnson's daughter Luci defended student efforts to keep their deferments: "Some of the students are fighting just as hard to get their education as . . . you could expect them to." A mother of a draft-deferred son spoke the minds of millions when she boasted of him as "a boy who knows how to take advantage of his opportunities." One of every four Notre Dame survey respondents had parents who openly encouraged him to avoid the draft. Outside the family, people from the most respected elements of society—teachers, employers, doctors, and lawyers—provided important help, without which millions of men might never have stayed out of the military.

Colleges were the main sanctuary from the draft, and many teachers and administrators did what they could to help their students. College grades were referred to as "A, B, C, D, and Nam," and antiwar professors sometimes adjusted their grading policies accordingly: "It's a rotten, stinking war, and I'll be damned if I'll help it along by sending over more cannon fodder. Unless he's clearly an idiot, . . . I intend to pass every able-bodied man in my class." Some professors even gave all A's in their courses, since even a B or C could affect a student's draft status.

The well-connected working man could stay away from Vietnam by getting timely help from the right people. Farmers often convinced draft boards that their sons were essential to the continued operation of the family farm. Plumbers, electricians, and other craftsmen lobbied local boards for automatic deferments for union apprentices. Employers could guarantee deferments for favored employees by designating them as supervisors of four or more full-time workers, making them "indispensable" according to the draft system's rule-of-thumb. Employers wrote letters like the following to local boards: "Braking systems for railroads and mass transit systems have been judged as essential to the welfare and safety of the nation, and our contribution as a primary supplier [is] vital for Selective Service purposes." Rural draft boards regularly granted deferments to truck drivers, laborers, and others whose employers were close friends of board members. A presidential commission reviewing the files of 199 local boards around the country in the late 1960s found that "about half" of all registrants with occupational deferments "were in neither a critical occupation nor an essential industry as defined by the Department of Labor."

Family doctors contributed to the exemption of many long-time patients. Anyone who had seen the same doctor for years had a medical history that was likely to document some kind of physical defect, and most doctors were inclined to cooperate. They gave extra tests to find heart murmurs or other minor conditions that qualified for IV-F or I-Y exemptions. As one doctor commented, "The traditional doctor-patient relationship is one of preserving life. I save lives by keeping people out of the Army." However, some doctors were staunchly against helping patients avoid the draft, even those with grounds for legitimate physical exemptions. One Bloomington, Indiana, doctor promised his patients he would write letters in their behalf, but he confidentially alerted their local boards that they were physically fit, and he urged that they be drafted as punishment.

The primary source of help came from an unprecedented network of counselors, lawyers, and other professionals with special expertise on the draft. More than one-fourth of all Notre Dame survey respondents consulted with experts, many of whom flatly guaranteed that anyone who followed their advice could avoid military service. By the late 1960s, the only real challenge left to the draft was to find the right advice in time.

Draft counseling had its roots in the pacifist movement of earlier wars. Conscientious objectors were the pariahs of the First and Second World Wars; sometimes they were jailed, sometimes they were isolated in special work camps, but always they were looked upon with suspicion by their draft boards and most of the public. Pacifist religious organizations gave them counseling and protected their rights, an unpopular task at the time.

In the early 1960s, these same groups helped establish conscientious objection as a commonly sought alternative to military service. CO exemptions were generally limited to Jehovah's Witnesses, Quakers, and members of other recognized pacifist religions, but a growing number of young people were citing personal, nonsectarian reasons for refusing to take arms. In 1965, the Supreme Court declared in the *Seeger* case that CO exemptions had to be granted to all confirmed pacifists, regardless of their religious backgrounds. To qualify, an individual's beliefs had to conform to legal standards, and he had to convince his local board of his sincerity.

Religious organizations like the Catholic Peace Fellowship and American Friends Service Committee provided the bulk of counseling in the early war years. At first, they concentrated on helping confirmed pacifists, but the growing unpopularity of the war brought an increasing number of "selective objectors" to their offices. These individuals objected only to the Vietnam war and did not qualify for exemption under the law. However, every counselor knew that CO status was only one of several ways of staying out of the military, and they rarely turned away people without giving some helpful advice.

As the war progressed, draft counseling became increasingly comprehensive, expanding well beyond conscientious objection. By the late 1960s, churches, colleges, high schools, and antiwar groups were offering a variety of counseling services. Most cities and university towns had at least one full-time counseling center. The typical center had one bona fide expert on the draft, aided by a number of paraprofessionals who relayed advice to walk-in clients. Some were volunteers, and others were paid out of church funds or donations from people they helped. A few universities hired their own full-time draft counselors, gave them clerical help, and paid for their office space. Through its legal assistance program, the Office of Economic Opportunity provided federal funds to pay salaries of lawyers engaged in draft counseling.

From the earliest days, counselors were enormously successful. Through newsletters and word of mouth, they learned each others' tactics. It was rare for a counselor to have a success rate of under 90 percent. The Catholic Peace Fellowship in New York City advised thousands of draft-age men, and all but a handful received deferments or exemptions. Even in the South and other parts of the country where public sentiment was strongly in favor of the war, counselors did extremely well.

Attorneys made especially good draft counselors. In San Francisco, Los Angeles, and other cities, lawyers' committees steered clients to participating attorneys while providing backup legal services to keep the local bar well ahead of draft boards in its knowledge of the law. Fees were fairly reasonable—usually about $200, and rarely more than $1,000. For anyone who found a competent lawyer, avoiding the draft was virtually assured. William Smith, the chairman of the Los Angeles draft attorneys' panel, told the local press that "any kid with money can absolutely stay out of the Army—with 100 percent certainty." A local prosecutor agreed with him: "If you got the dough, you don't have to go." Attorneys who charged nominal fees could represent hundreds of clients. All that was generally required was a quick interview, a standard letter, and one or two follow-up phone calls.

Expert advisers were not hard to find. They were cross-referenced with local service agencies, covered by the press, and known to most community leaders. Every state except North Dakota had at least one walk-in center, and more than half of all draft-age men had a center within a two-hour drive of their home. At the peak of the war, thousands of lawyers and paraprofessionals were doing draft counseling, serving about a million clients every year.

Most of the clients were surprisingly ill-informed about the draft and unaware of their most fundamental rights under the law. Some knew nothing about deferments or exemptions for which they were obviously qualified. Others were discouraged from filing legitimate claims by draft board clerks who misunderstood the law. Some youths were even mistaken about what their lottery numbers were. Without a visit to a draft counselor, these men might have been drafted or pressured into enlisting in the service.

Frequently, the first question a counselor heard was, "Can I qualify for a CO exemption?" Many draft-age men knew that conscientious objection was one way to avoid the war, but they had little idea about how to apply or how to qualify. The counselors' main role was to help CO applicants articulate and document their beliefs in a way that would convince draft boards of their sincerity. One organization advised people to

> sit down and think about why you are against killing people in war. Write down short sentences or ideas (for instance: love . . . brotherhood . . . peace . . . equality . . . personal responsibility . . .). Let your mind work freely, and you will probably get down on paper most of the ideas that will make a good CO case.

CO applicants were encouraged to get people they knew, especially clergymen, lawyers, or educators, to discuss their beliefs with them, and then write letters of reference attesting to the firmness of their convictions. Clients were sometimes referred to clergymen who were adept at writing letters supporting CO claims. Through schools like the Jane Addams Peace Center in Philadelphia, CO applicants were prepped on the questions that were commonly asked by local draft boards in personal interviews.

Most counselors who specialized in conscientious objection believed that no one could fabricate sincerity, but some draft board members were not so sure. Over time, CO applications became so standardized that it was hard for draft boards to tell who was sincere and who was not. As the chairman of a Denver board complained, "So many of these CO's—you could tell they were so cleverly coached. We could tell outside forces were directing these boys."

In the view of most draft counselors, almost all conscientious objectors were spurred by deep principle, not by a shallow desire to avoid going to war; some even did their alternative service by working for civilian agencies in Vietnam. A large number of CO's were Jehovah's Witnesses, Quakers, Mennonites, Muslims, and others whose churches preached total pacifism. Many others were Catholics who had to overcome their draft boards' knowledge that the Catholic church was not pacifist. One Samoan was exempted by his California draft board because of his sincere belief that if he killed anyone, his pagan god would cause a volcano to erupt. Others belonged to no established religion, but convinced their boards of their moral and ethical opposition to all wars.

However, a few saw conscientious-objector status as nothing more than a convenient way to avoid the draft. They copied examples of successful personal statements, falsified ministers' names, and wrote their own letters of reference. Draft boards rarely had time to check up on them.

Most draft counselors knew there were better ways to avoid the draft and refused to prepare a fraudulent CO claim as a matter of principle. They tried to discourage the insincere by describing CO status as a bleak alternative to military service. The Central Committee for Conscientious Objection published a handbook which *Newsweek* magazine described as "enough to convince all but the most determined malingerer that only confirmed, absolute pacifists need apply for the dirty details, civilian volunteer work, or jail terms that conscientious objection invites."

Conscientious objection did involve considerable hardship. Almost all of the 172,000 Vietnam-era conscientious objectors were asked to do alternative service in lieu of induction. CO's had to work for two years in low-paying jobs beyond commuting distance from their homes. Many worked as hospital orderlies or as conservation workers in wilderness camps. However, most draft boards were so overloaded with inductions and reclassifications that they kept only very loose contact with CO's, and alternative service was often very casually supervised. "Many of these local boards couldn't stand the sight of CO's and wanted nothing to do with them," recalled a top-level Selective Service official. "They didn't realize that they were doing these boys a favor." Almost fifty thousand CO's dropped out and were never certified as having fulfilled their obligations. Refusing to do alternative service was a federal crime, punishable by up to five years in prison, but only about a thousand individuals were convicted of this offense.

For a number of persons, a conscientious-objector claim was only the first step in a long procedural tangle with the draft system. Even a CO application that had no chance of succeeding could tie up a draft board for months or sometimes years. By pyramiding claims and appeals, a skillful counselor could enable his client to outlast his draft vulnerability. After years of exchanging paperwork with draft boards, clients turned twenty-six, received high lottery numbers, took advantage of the lottery loophole, outlasted the draft itself, or goaded their local boards into procedural errors that made induction orders unenforceable. Stalling tactics were often expensive and always the cause of great personal anxiety, making them usually the strategy of last resort. According to New Orleans counselor Collins Vallee, "The system was full of escape valves, and all we had to do was try one tactic after another until something finally worked."

By far the biggest escape valves were the preinduction and induction examinations. Every prospective draftee had to be examined twice, once before his draft board could classify him I-A and again when he reported for induction. On either occasion, he could be given a IV-F or I-Y exemption for mental, physical, psychological, or "administrative" reasons. The mental exam was hard to fake, and examiners were quick to question anyone with a peculiarly low score. But other aspects of the examination process were extremely vulnerable to manipulation and fabrication.

Young men could qualify for an administrative exemption by admitting membership in any subversive organization listed on the Armed Forces Security Questionnaire. If a person refused to fill out the questionnaire, Army regulations required that he undergo further investigation before he could be drafted. Sometimes these men were exempted without further inquiry. As one official at Selective Service headquarters admitted, "As long as there are plenty of men available, no one's going to spend any time investigating hippies." One youth was exempted simply because he claimed that his father was a member of the Communist Party.

A person could also get what one handbook called a "draft immunization" by developing a history of petty criminal behavior. Notwithstanding the movie *Alice's Restaurant,* dumping trash by a roadside was not enough—but cattle rustling, killing an eagle, or engaging in what the rules called "sexual misconduct" could qualify a person for a I-Y exemption on the grounds of "questionable moral character." In New York City, one arrest for marijuana possession was sometimes enough to keep a person home from the war. Some men were rejected for administrative reasons upon nothing more than a subjective determination that they would not make good soldiers. "The I-Y classification is sort of a dumping ground," explained one draft counselor. "It's

a place for guys the Army just doesn't want, and it's often very hard
to find out why they were put there."

The physical part of the exam was easy to fake. The military knew
this was a serious problem, yet it was never able to solve it. According
to Colonel William G. Peard, head of the Army department which set
medical standards for induction:

> Even when we suspect malingering, to prove it is very difficult. A registrant
> may play upon some defect which might be minor, and it's almost impossi-
> ble for a physician to say he's lying. . . . Only when fakery is flagrant is
> . . . any detective-type investigation of a registrant's claimed defect under-
> taken.

To help registrants fail the preinduction physical, many draft counseling centers organized special clinics, often staffed by antiwar medical
students or doctors at university health centers. A careful examination
by a knowledgeable specialist and an equally careful choice of a preinduction physical site guaranteed an exemption for nine clients out of ten.

The military's stringent standards required that each inductee meet
the physical requirements of an infantryman under stress. This pre-
cluded the induction or enlistment of anyone with a defect that might
impair training, be aggravated by military duty, or interfere with military routine. Trick knees, flat feet, skin rashes, even excessive or obscene tattoos were enough to qualify for a IV-F or I-Y exemption. As
Los Angeles attorney David Caplan explained, "There are thousands
of disqualifying physical and mental conditions, and it's a rare case that
someone does not have *one* of them." Roughly half of all draft-age
youths failed to meet physical standards, two to three times the rejection rates for other NATO countries.

Even well-conditioned athletes in apparent good health could qualify
for physical exemptions, since many of them had some history of bone
or joint injuries. As described in the House Armed Services Committee's 1967 report on the draft, many military experts believed that "the
chronically injured, deferred athlete is not physically able to meet the
full demands of service in a combat zone. . . . [Without] quick access
to whirlpool baths and other modern and elaborate therapeutic devices,

... [he] would become a quick liability to a military unit." The public's attention focused on Joe Namath and his IV-F knees, but thousands of hometown high-school athletes got similar exemptions.

Medical counselors stretched the rules as far as their imaginations allowed. "I just follow the Army's own standards," one commented sarcastically. "I'm sure the Army appreciates my help in screening out unsuitable prospects." They helped document disqualifying conditions, and sometimes advised clients of the necessary symptoms. Some conditions had symptoms that no civilian or military doctor could disprove if a person complained of them convincingly. Ménière's syndrome, for example, could be faked by attesting to persistent dizziness, nausea, ringing in the ears, and an inability to concentrate.

A determined individual with strong fortitude could fake a gastrointestinal ulcer. A few hours before his preinduction physical, he had to borrow a syringe and extract a pint of his own blood, making sure that the needle mark was in an inconspicuous place. Just before entering the examination center, he had to drink the blood. This induced vomiting a few minutes later, ideally in the presence of a military doctor. He then had to complain of severe stomach pains. When tests confirmed that his blood pressure was down and the vomited blood was his own, a IV-F exemption was guaranteed.

One draft manual, *IV-F: A Guide to Exemption*, described how a number of people could "very likely" be exempted for a defect that only one of them actually possessed:

> Since civilian doctors know their patients only by the names they give, a registrant bent on fraud with a bona fide disqualifying defect which was either intermittent (such as asthma) or unverifiable by objective tests (such as Ménière's syndrome) might receive treatment from several doctors using the names of several conspirators.

The law provided an exemption for anyone under orthodontic care, and almost every draft-age person had teeth sufficiently crooked to give braces some therapeutic value. In the Los Angeles area alone, ten dentists willingly performed orthodontic work for anyone who could pay a $1,000–$2,000 fee. Wearing braces was a common last-minute tactic for registrants who faced immediate call-up. According to one youth who wore unneeded braces, this "dental cop-out" was "very expensive and very uncomfortable. But it sure beat KP, getting up at 4 A.M., and going to Vietnam."

One could also look to a sympathetic psychiatrist or psychological therapist for another costly escape from the draft. Through a series of visits, a patient could translate his anxiety about being drafted into a psychological trauma that qualified him for an exemption. Mindful of military standards, therapists probed for a variety of mental problems: "You could theoretically be rejected for any neurotic trait from bedwetting to nail-biting." Sometimes, therapists coached patients about the necessary symptoms. "I had only one patient who was denied a psychiatric exemption," a psychiatrist recalled. "He wanted me to say he was crazy, but he wouldn't take the responsibility of acting crazy." A Washington, D.C., psychologist recalled writing a letter for one of his patients:

> I described his anxiety and periods of deep depression, but there wasn't any reason why he couldn't have served in Vietnam. The day before his interview, he accidentally cut his wrist opening a jar of pickles. He went to the examination center with my letter and a bandage on his wrist, but he never told anyone how it happened. He got an exemption.

Homosexuality was a common ground for a psychiatric exemption, and one antidraft pamphlet advised how to fake it:

> Dress very conservatively for the Army shrinker. Act like a man under tight control. Deny you're a fag, deny it again very quickly, then stop, as if you're buttoning your lip. But find an excuse to bring it back into the conversation again and again, and each time deny it and quickly change the subject. And maybe twice, no more than three times over a half hour interview, just the slightest little flick of the wrist. But above all, never admit it. Even after they're hooked, keep up the denials.

San Francisco draft counselor Paul Harris recalled that "all of my clients who faked it got their exemptions, but they drafted the one fellow who really was gay." One antiwar protester in Chicago was exempted as a homosexual, but he later married and was threatened with induction. He replied that if drafted, he would demonstrate his tendencies beyond any possible doubt at his induction physical. No one called his bluff.

The preinduction physical was a highly regimented process, with long lines of men receiving very brief attention from military doctors. Anyone who drew special attention to himself improved his chances of getting an exemption, if only because he slowed the process down. Peter Simpson suffered from a minor skin rash which he knew was, at best, borderline grounds for an exemption. While everyone else was walking around undressed, he kept wearing his business suit and carried a *Wall Street Journal* under his arm. Simpson displayed so much confidence in his claim that the examiners gave him an exemption.

One way to get special attention was to disrupt the process. Radical draft counselors often encouraged this tactic, "not only because it obstructed the smooth operation of the criminal war machine, but also because it might impress the examiners with your undesirable character traits." One San Francisco youth, tentatively stamped I-A, made a desperate visit to a draft counselor during the lunch recess from his physical. He was advised to "piss on the table" when he saw the psychiatrist. He did, and he got an exemption. In Chicago, an antiwar activist brought seventy-five demonstrators to picket outside during his examination. To keep them from storming the building, examiners summoned the military police, gave the activist a I-Y exemption, and asked him to leave.

Documenting a disqualifying condition or disrupting the process was not necessarily enough to guarantee exemption. Every preinduction examination center interpreted official standards differently, and some were alert to tricks that were popular in their areas. For these reasons, counselors often advised their clients to take advantage of a major loophole in the draft law which existed throughout the war: the right of every registrant to choose the site of his preinduction physical.

The examination process had a built-in bias which favored out-of-state examinees. Examiners had no quotas of their own, but they knew if they failed an unusually large percentage of local youths, they would draw a reaction from nearby draft boards, which did have quotas to fill. However, examiners almost never heard complaints when they disqualified out-of-state youths. Besides, many of the latter were politically oriented students whose disruptive tactics could be avoided if they got what they wanted. At the Boston examination site, for example, graduate students from Harvard and MIT were told, "If you cooperate with us, we'll cooperate with you."

The counselor network kept an up-to-date "book" on which centers were receptive to particular claims. For most of the war, Butte, Montana, was considered an easy mark for anyone with a letter from a doctor, and Little Rock, Arkansas, for anyone with a letter from a psychiatrist. Beckley, West Virginia, was well-known for giving exemptions to "anyone who looked freaked out." A number of famous rock stars avoided the draft by going to Beckley incognito with beads, bare feet, and long hair. By far the most popular place to go for a preinduction physical was Seattle, Washington. In the latter years of the war, Seattle examiners separated people into two groups: those who had letters from doctors or psychiatrists, and those who did not. Everyone with a letter received an exemption, regardless of what the letter said.

The preinduction examination process rewarded careful planning, guile, and disruptive behavior. But if a person came without a letter from his doctor, he was very likely to be declared fit for induction, regardless of any actual medical problem. All but the most obvious physical defects were easy to overlook in the confused environment and mass processing of the examination center, and disadvantaged youths who had not received adequate medical care were often classified I-A. One draftee from a low-income family spent three months in the Army before it was discovered that he was an extreme diabetic. At his preinduction physical, his urine sample had been confused with that of another person, who got the exemption. Blacks and members of other minority groups were the most common victims. In 1966, the only year for which racial data was published, a mentally qualified white youth was 50 percent more likely than his black counterpart to fail the preinduction physical.

Many doctors, dentists, and psychiatrists who specialized in draft avoidance now feel a sense of disquiet about their role during the war. The people they most wanted to help—blacks, low-income youths, and conscientious war resisters who had been denied CO status—were rarely the ones who came to see them: "The people we saw were all middle class. It wasn't that the others didn't have the money. They just never thought of going for professional help." Even at the draft-counseling medical clinic of predominantly black Fisk University, walk-ins were overwhelmingly well-educated, middle-class whites. At a large Chicago clinic, doctors refused to help any white who failed to bring at least one black with him for a medical interview.

Professionals were especially discouraged by the self-centered attitudes of many of the young men who came for help. Dr. Peter Bourne, a psychiatrist working at the time in Atlanta, commented that "some people acted as though all doctors had a moral obligation to help them dodge the draft for nothing." Dr. Bourne counseled people for free, but he sometimes had to refer them to specialists who knew more about certain disqualifying conditions. Later, he heard complaints when the specialists charged $25 to write letters to draft boards. Dr. Herbert Schwartz of Hartford, Connecticut, refused to do draft counseling after consistently encountering "opportunists who felt threatened by the war, but did not oppose the war. They were people without ideals or principles who were just looking for an easy way out."

Yet a number of the professionals were themselves opportunists. Many were far too willing to bend professional principles to help clients connive their way out of the draft. Others had a false view of what they were accomplishing. One counselor said that his goal was to encourage draft avoidance until the government could be provoked into rescinding all deferments and exemptions. "When that happens," he commented, "the sons of the rich will be drafted right along with those of the poor. And then the shoe will begin to pinch the wrong foot." But the impact of draft counseling was exactly the opposite. The burdens of war were shifted even more to the socially and economically disadvantaged.

Safety in Service

In 1966, Major General George Gelson, Jr. of the Maryland National Guard was photographed by *Life* magazine wearing a Baltimore Colts uniform, a football tucked under his arm. "We have an arrangement with the Colts," he commented. "When they have a player with a military problem, they send him to us." In Detroit, an Army reserve unit found room for the Lions' star halfback and tight end, in return for fifty-yard-line tickets and a chance to serve as the honor guard during flag ceremonies at home games. The Dallas Cowboys had ten players assigned to the same National Guard division at one time. "If we had been called up," recalled a Philadelphia reservist, "the Eagles would have been left without a backfield."

Except for one instance in 1968, reservists and guardsmen were not called up during the Vietnam war, so the Colts, Lions, Cowboys, Eagles, and dozens of other professional sports teams were able to protect their players from active military service. The Miami Dolphins almost lost a key linebacker to the draft until a club official intervened with Selective Service headquarters in Washington to get him a temporary deferment until his National Guard appointment could be arranged.

At the peak of the war, waiting lists were long, reflecting the popularity of the National Guard and reserves as sanctuaries from the draft. Many draft-vulnerable men who became guardsmen or reservists were able to leapfrog these lists by having influential persons nominate them to fill the rare vacancies. The FBI once investigated the relationship between the New York Jets and a go-between who, for a fee, could arrange for players to be put at the top of local reserve waiting lists.

Because of the difficulty in getting a position with the National Guard or reserves, not many youths from disadvantaged backgrounds were able to join. Most recruits were recent high-school graduates, but a disproportionate number were college graduates. In 1969–70, for example, 28,000 more college-trained men entered the National Guard or reserves than were enlisted or inducted into all active forces combined. Only about 1 percent of all guardsmen were black.

Guardsmen and reservists had a four-to-six-month active-duty obligation, plus yearly summer camps and monthly unit meetings over a six-year period. If they failed to show up for meetings, they were technically AWOL and subject to immediate call-up for active duty— but that did not often happen. A Wisconsin reservist (who was also a draft counselor) stopped going to meetings with three years left on his term. He never heard a word until, on schedule, he received his discharge by mail. For years, the Defense Department considered taking legal action against delinquent reservists—but, as of 1977, the matter was still under study.

Training for the National Guard or reserves was neither as rigorous nor as thorough as that given the active forces. Often, reservists had to train with outmoded equipment and then read books or watch movies to learn how to use the modern equivalents. After the National Guard was criticized for its 1967 handling of the Newark and Detroit riots, units devoted much of their training to riot control, which, according to a Defense Department report, came "at the expense of combat mission training time."

The Guard and the reserves were subject to activation and extended periods of service, including combat. Almost 700,000 guardsmen and reservists were called up during the Korean war. Most units consisted of men from the same localities, and the casualties devastated some communities. President Kennedy's call-up of the reserves during the Berlin crisis in 1961 had severe political repercussions. The lesson of that experience was that mobilizing the reserves was a drastic step with profound domestic and international implications, a step to be avoided if at all possible.

For the first three years of the war, President Johnson steadfastly refused to activate guardsmen or reservists, and the government relied on increased draft calls to fill the expanding need for troops. This was consistent with Johnson's efforts to picture Vietnam as a limited war of short duration, which could be fought with little domestic dislocation and without interfering with his administration's war on poverty. Reservists and guardsmen were better connected, better educated, more affluent, and whiter than their peers in the active forces, and the administration feared that mobilizing them would heighten public opposition to the war. Instead, they were called upon only for domestic service, during natural disasters, urban riots, and antiwar disturbances.

In 1968, a commission headed by Burke Marshall warned that the National Guard and reserves were becoming major refuges from the draft. Led by Senator Richard Russell of Georgia, chairman of the Senate Armed Services Committee, Congress made activation easier. After the 1968 *Pueblo* incident, 37,000 guardsmen and reservists were called to active duty, largely for symbolic purposes. About fifteen thousand were sent to Vietnam. But the pressure to activate them eased as the war stopped escalating, and no guardsmen or reservists were again called upon to fight.

The National Guard and reserves were attractive avenues for avoiding Vietnam. A 1966 Pentagon study found that 71 percent of all reservists were draft-motivated, and James Cantwell, president of the National Guard Association, claimed in 1970 that as many as 90 percent of all Guard enlistments were draft-motivated. At the end of 1968, with the draft still in full force, the Army National Guard had a waiting list of 100,000. After two years of shrinking draft calls, that waiting list vanished. Six months later, the Guard found itself forty-five thousand men under strength.

The nation's 1 million Vietnam-era guardsmen and reservists performed a measure of national service, as contrasted with those who avoided the military entirely. Guardsmen and reservists were willing to train, interrupt their lives, help disaster victims, and offer a show of force during inner-city riots. But they served in a way that involved much less personal hardship than did active military duty. As observed by the Gates Commission in recommending the all-volunteer force, the Guard and reserves were used by recruits to "minimiz[e] the cost of fulfilling millitary service." Draft-vulnerable men who joined the National Guard or reserves were, in one basic respect, like the millions of others who avoided the draft by letting themselves be channeled into jobs, marriages, or other situations they did not especially like; they left the fighting and dying to others.

The National Guard and reserves were not the only examples of how individuals could perform military service while minimizing the risks of Vietnam. Throughout the armed forces, there were a great many "Sergeant Bilkos," as one Pentagon manpower official described them, "men who try to look brave while making sure that someone else does the fighting." Six out of seven servicemen were never involved in actual combat. Usually, this was just a matter of chance or the military's judgment that these men had more important roles to play elsewhere. Millions of recruits did whatever they were asked to do. If ordered to Vietnam, they went to Vietnam. If ordered elsewhere, they went elsewhere. However, the findings of the Notre Dame survey suggest that a great many troops were not willing to leave things to chance. Just under half (47 percent) of all servicemen admitted trying to manipulate their military careers. They spent two, three, or four years of their lives in military duty, but they did what they could to stay far from the action.

Compared with America's other twentieth-century wars, Vietnam required the deployment of a relatively small number of front-line troops. As shown in Figure 3, about 30 percent of the 7,500,000 Vietnam-era troops went to the Southeast Asia war zone, but of these, only 1,600,000 engaged in combat. At the peak of the fighting, fewer than 250,000 troops were engaged in combat operations at any one time; that amounted to only about 6 percent of active-duty troops and 3 percent of available forces, including reserves. Overall, the risk of combat service was so low for Vietnam-era servicemen that life insurance companies did not charge extra premiums for military personnel, except for pilots and others on unusually hazardous missions.

The military's rear-echelon staff requirements grew considerably in the half-century before the outbreak of the Vietnam war. During the Spanish-American War, 13 percent of all troops were trained for noncombat roles; during World War II, 61 percent were noncombat. Yet at the 1968 height of the Vietnam war, 88 percent of all servicemen were assigned to noncombat occupational specialties. All kinds of manual, technical, and clerical skills were necessary to support combat troops. Recruits with above-average aptitude or ability were skimmed from the personnel pool and assigned special functions, often far from the combat zone. The fighting was left to those of lesser talents.

This made good management sense. The military naturally tried to use people where they would be the most productive. A college graduate with an IQ of 110 and a high-school dropout with an IQ of 85 might shoot a rifle equally well. But it made sense to give a clerical job to the college graduate, who would probably perform it better. Random assignments might have been more equitable but would have interfered with military efficiency.

The fear of combat was a powerful inducement for recruits to seek the more attractive opportunities on their own. One wartime survey

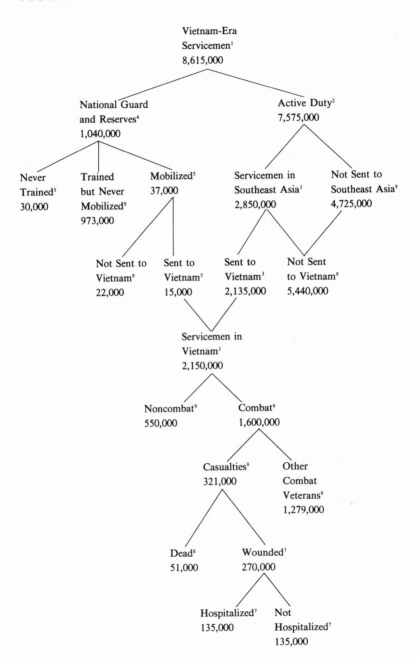

found that "less chance of death or injury" and "dislike of fighting and killing" were the two most common reasons why recruits were attracted to noncombat specialties. As a Defense Department manpower expert admitted, "We've studied this problem very carefully. People don't seem to enlist in the Army to fight. We recognize the inequity this causes in a shooting war, but we don't know what to do about it."

Sixty percent of all college-graduate enlistees were draft-motivated and not true volunteers. Competing against one another, all branches of service tried to convince the potential draftee that he had a lot to gain by enlisting. Various officer recruitment programs—especially the Reserve Officers Training Corps and the Judge Advocate General Corps —wooed university students with promises of safe assignments and deferred enlistments.

If he had sufficient education and a high enough IQ to meet their tougher enlistment standards, a draft-vulnerable man could also reduce his chances of engaging in combat by joining the Coast Guard, Navy, or Air Force. The Coast Guard lost only seven men during the entire war. Navy ships were stationed off the coast of Vietnam, but they rarely lost men to hostile fire. Almost three-quarters of the eighteen hundred Air Force casualties involved pilots, navigators, and others well beyond draft age. The Air Force's strategic bases were in places like Thailand and Guam, immune from rocket attacks or other enemy shelling. Generally, combat missions in these services involved volunteers—officers who had become pilots or patrol boat commanders with full knowledge of the risks involved, or enlisted men who willingly accepted hazardous duty. For others, the risk of combat was minimal. Altogether, the risk of dying in Vietnam was nineteen times as great for Marine and Army troops as for Navy and Air Force men.

The Coast Guard, Navy, and Air Force were well aware of these facts. Like the Air Force recruiter in Connecticut who wrote the following letter to a prospective inductee, they drove the point home that theirs were the "safe" branches of service:

> Did you know that the vast majority of the U.S. forces killed in Southeast Asia have been draftees? Wouldn't you rather take advantage of the opportunity to join the branch of service that has lost the least amount of men

in Southeast Asia as opposed to being drafted into the branch of service that has lost the most?

The Notre Dame survey found that two-thirds of all enlistees in these branches were motivated, at least in part, by the desire to avoid Vietnam, even if this meant a three- or four-year enlistment instead of the two years served by most draftees. As one sailor commented, "There ain't no Viet Cong submarines."

A Marine slogan boasted of the corps' combat mission: "Every enlisted man is a rifleman, and every officer is a platoon leader." All Marines, even members of the band, were trained as infantrymen. Yet even in the Marine Corps, a high-aptitude recruit had a good chance to be screened out of combat duty. A Marine general explained that "a computer simply and fairly assigns [them] to billets where their higher-level skills can be put to the best use for the Corps. And that's why so few of them are being killed."

The Army, home for 90 percent of all inductees, offered many opportunities for avoiding combat. In its recruiting efforts it suggested to draft-vulnerable men that they could avoid risks by enlisting. So they could: At the peak of the war, Army draftees were getting killed at almost twice the rate of volunteers. Recruitment ads hinted broadly that enlisting was the only way to avoid infantry duty in Vietnam: "Make your choice now—join, or we'll make the choice for you." As Peter Barnes noted in *Pawns,* they promoted "the image of a new 'Action Army' in which there seemingly are no foot soldiers; men work with advanced equipment, develop their bodies and leadership abilities, study, and prepare for future success."

There were opportunities in the Army, but no guarantees. Throughout the war years, enlistees were promised only that they would be enrolled in the training program of their choice, but not that they would be assigned to any specialty. Many young men complained bitterly when they passed a technical training program only to be assigned to combat units as "Eleven-Bravo" infantrymen.

"In the Army," a personnel officer acknowledged, "we plan on spaces, not faces." Beginning in 1965, the Army used computers to match soldiers with occupational specialties. In the peak years of the war, the Army had a surplus of qualified applicants for most noncombat specialties, and the computer was programmed to select the best-qualified applicants to fill quotas. Aptitude test scores, educational levels, language proficiencies, and physical skills were all important factors. An individual soldier's prospect for assignment to a noncombat function also depended greatly on when he enlisted. Most of the better-educated, high-IQ enlistees joined the service in the summer or early fall, making the competition especially fierce in those months. Recruits who enlisted in the winter or spring had a better chance.

Vietnam assignments were handled in much the same way. The standard policy of rotating soldiers out of Vietnam after one year in the war zone required a constant replenishment of troops trained in the combat arms—infantry, armor, and artillery. For them, avoiding Vietnam was usually the consequence of sheer luck. As one personnel officer explained, "A lot of guys, by the toss of the dice, went to Europe —and by the time their tours were over, there was not enough time to send them to Vietnam." Of course, some combat-trained troops volunteered for Vietnam. So many West Point graduates asked to go to Vietnam in 1966 that the Army had to select them on the basis of their class standing.

Servicemen in noncombat specialties were much less likely to be ordered to Vietnam, and not many volunteered. Periodically, recruitment shortages or heavy combat casualties required some noncombatants to be transferred to the infantry. The least productive, most expendable troops were the ones reassigned, less as punishment than as an exercise of management principles. Like regular combat troops, they tended to be low-IQ, poorly educated men from disadvantaged backgrounds.

Despite the impersonal quality of the combat selection process, there were many ways a soldier could manipulate the system to his advantage. One counseling manual advised calling the Pentagon on an Army trunk line to get special treatment:

> Don't worry about someone in the Pentagon getting angry that you're calling from Fort Sill, Oklahoma, or Fort Lewis, Washington. . . . He might just be helpful. It is possible to find the person who has your [form] on his

desk and to find out the chances of its being approved, whether it's a request to be stationed in Germany, for Warrant Officer Flight Training, for the Defense Language Institute's Swahili course, or for the Army cross-country ski team.

Not all noncombat jobs were filled by computer, and many better-educated soldiers were skimmed out of the manpower pool by officers who wanted reliable clerks, messengers, servants, or other helpers. Soldiers were given the chance to reenlist early in their terms, extending their service obligations but giving them new and better opportunities to be assigned to noncombat specialties.

Like draft registrants, soldiers could formally apply for designation as conscientious objectors, entitling them to noncombat assignments or, less often, immediate discharges. Application procedures were rigorous, requiring a lot of paperwork and interviews with chaplains, psychiatrists, and senior officers. Usually, the process took months to complete. Throughout the Vietnam era, only seventeen thousand servicemen applied for CO status.

In the early years of the war, the military approved less than 30 percent of the few hundred CO applications that were submitted. In the late 1960s, interest in CO status grew dramatically. CO applicants began to seek help from attorneys and other counselors, trying to take advantage of the same case law that courts were applying to civilian CO cases. However, the military continued to turn down most CO applicants, in the belief that it was not bound by these court-imposed rules.

Federal judges decided otherwise in 1971. In a series of circuit court opinions, they held that the military had to follow the *Seeger* rule, which entitled sincere pacifists to CO status even if they were not motivated by orthodox religious beliefs, and they further held that no serviceman could have his CO application turned down unless there were some factual basis in his military record to support that conclusion. Suddenly the armed forces found themselves defending an unmanageable number of lawsuits. In 1971 and 1972, two-thirds of all CO applicants were successful—and by 1975, 99 percent were successful.

Applying for CO status was never a good way of avoiding Vietnam.

In 1970, the Pacific Counseling Service temporarily seized upon the CO process as a Vietnam avoidance tactic. For several weeks, its counselors conducted an extensive leafleting campaign for soldiers passing through the Oakland Army Base, a primary embarkation point for Vietnam. Within a few weeks, they persuaded about twelve hundred troops to apply for CO status, postponing their orders to Vietnam. But the Pentagon quickly changed the regulations to prohibit soldiers from applying for CO status while en route to Vietnam, and the soldiers were shipped out.

In the first several years of the war, a CO applicant had very little chance of getting an outright discharge. If a CO applicant was unsuccessful—or only partly successful—his chances of going to Vietnam increased. He had to notify his commanding officer of his intent to apply for CO status, which sometimes led to expedited orders to Vietnam. Those who were granted noncombatant status were often retrained as medics and sent into the combat zone.

For the soldier who wanted to avoid Vietnam, it was better to take advantage of other opportunities for discharge provided by military regulations. A civilian counselors' handbook entitled "Getting Out" told how discharges were sometimes given "to the person who is too fat, has four or more dependents even though they don't create a hardship, is an alien, gets seasick, works for a foreign government, is becoming a minister or entering a religious order, flunks out of officer training, or has a very unusual and important civilian skill." The same booklet described how "political dissenters" could sometimes get honorable discharges for "substandard personal behavior [which] reflects discredit upon the service."

Many soldiers became increasingly restive as their Vietnam service neared. They no longer had confidence that "it can't happen to me," and they had a heightened awareness of the political controversy about the war. At antiwar coffeehouses outside their bases, and especially at embarkation points, they were urged to boycott the war. At the Oakland Army Base, a fourteen-year Army veteran sat on an upturned garbage can and exhorted troops in transit to injure themselves, engage in homosexual acts, commit crimes, or take other last-minute steps to save themselves. He was arrested and discharged from the Army, but many did what he described. Frank Paquin, a Vietnam-bound Green Beret, intentionally aggravated an old knee injury during a parachute jump. Ralph Oberstrom drove out in the countryside with a friend, shot two holes in his windshield, and had his friend shoot him in the left leg. Claiming to be the victim of sniper fire, he was sent to the Oak Knoll Naval Hospital and kept home from Vietnam. Fred Patterson tried to get discharged for enuresis (bed-wetting), but without success. He wet his bed for forty nights, and all his commander did was transfer him to a lower bunk.

A soldier with orders to Vietnam was not necessarily bound for combat. Servicemen with technical specialties were often sent directly to Saigon to serve in administrative capacities. Others underwent a series of interviews, any one of which could bring an assignment to a rear-guard support unit. According to the Notre Dame survey, almost half of all Vietnam-based troops tried to avoid combat, usually by arranging for relatively safe assignments.

The first screening took place on the airplane en route to Vietnam, where senior officers identified soldiers they considered dangerously immature and unfit for combat. After the plane arrived at Cam Ranh Bay, Tan Son Nhut, or Bien-Hoa, new troops were interviewed by personnel officers from the divisions with which they had been matched by computer. The officers had to sort incoming soldiers into four or five brigades, one of which was a noncombat supply brigade. Troops assigned to combat brigades were reinterviewed for battalion assignments upon reporting to the brigade personnel officer, and again they had about a one-in-four chance of going to a noncombat unit. Finally, they had one last chance to be assigned to a support company when they arrived at their battalions. In all, a soldier had a better-than-even chance of getting an assignment away from the search-and-destroy missions and other field operations. Anyone who made a good impression had a good chance of staying out of combat. As Pat Brannigan, now a career Army officer, recalled: "When I landed, I talked about computers to anyone who would listen. I knew that computers were always kept air-conditioned and far from combat areas. As it turned out, that's how I spent my year."

The assignment process was vulnerable to corruption. Interviewing officers occasionally arranged things to make some money or help their friends. One interviewing sergeant sold noncombat orders for $100. Others punished soldiers they disliked by sending them to the most dangerous places.

Young lieutenants and captains virtually exercised a veto over their own combat assignments. If they asked to be assigned away from combat, superior officers usually complied "out of concern for the troops they had to lead," as one battalion commander recalled. "A lot of experienced captains wanted to be company commanders until a combat opening arose. Then they suddenly became much less interested." John Markus, a West Point graduate, "went forward as an officer and gentleman" to ask to be kept out of combat duty because "I just couldn't handle the fighting." At his request, he was made a battery commander in the rear. Another West Point cadet relied on his postgraduate degree from Harvard to stay in the rear, where he helped map the day-to-day tactics of the war.

Noncombat assignments never came with guarantees. Emergencies like the 1968 Tet offensive brought massive reassignments of troops to the front lines. However, more than a half million troops in Vietnam never saw any fighting.

Throughout the war, 83 percent of all American casualties resulted from search-and-destroy missions or other combat operations. Over the course of his twelve months in Vietnam, a combat soldier faced about a 3 percent chance of death, a 10 percent chance of suffering a serious wound requiring hospitalization, and almost a 25 percent chance of getting enough of a wound to earn a Purple Heart. But those odds were not unalterable. Some soldiers committed petty AWOL offenses, staying away just long enough to miss the start of a field patrol mission. Usually, the only punishment was a small fine. Others bribed company clerks or other soldiers to find someone else to take their place, or they feigned shell shock to get sick leave.

Out on patrol, company or platoon officers were sometimes intimidated into turning their search-and-destroy patrols into "search-and-evade" missions. Faced with gross disobedience, or threatened with physical assault, they conformed their orders to the wishes of their troops, avoiding situations likely to produce casualties. One lieutenant learned of a $350 bounty placed on his head because his unit thought he was a hard-liner too eager to send them into combat. When he refused an order to attack, the bounty was lifted. Entire units sometimes wore red bandannas, signaling to the enemy that they would not fight unless attacked. The catchword was "CYA [cover your ass] and get home."

Before 1970, soldiers could get out of combat by reenlisting for a longer tour of duty. According to one account, recruiting officers were airlifted to remote firebases to greet combat patrols that had suffered exceptionally heavy losses, offering exhausted troops an immediate trip home in return for a four-year service commitment. The longer tour usually meant a return trip to Vietnam, but some soldiers were willing to do anything to get on the next plane home.

Others found easier ways to shorten their tours. Tony Palazzi wrote home to his mother, asking her to have the family doctor write an exaggerated account of her illness. Palazzi showed the letter to his commanding officer, left Vietnam eight months ahead of his rotation date, and completed his tour of duty at a missile base a few miles from his home. One combat-weary sergeant refused to take his antimalaria pills and slept with his arm outside his tent. He fell ill, had to be hospitalized, and was permanently reassigned out of the combat zone.

A few men were so desperate they deliberately tried to get a "million-dollar wound"—serious enough for evacuation, but minor enough to heal completely in a few months. Desperate to get out of combat, some soldiers asked friends to shoot them, or they took extra risks in the field. One soldier recalled that several men in his unit

. . . tried deliberately to get wounded. I saw one man casually stand up in a fire fight and get it through the head. Another stood up too, and only got it in the leg and the arm. He was sent to the hospital in Japan, and everybody thought he was the luckiest guy in the world because he was safe and free again.

III | EVADERS

The Resistance

In electronic circuitry, the ohm is a measure of resistance to the induction of electric currents. Its symbol, the Greek letter omega, became the symbol for resistance to the induction of troops for the Vietnam war. Inspired by Mario Savio's plea to "put your bodies upon the gears" to stop the machine, the organized Resistance movement hoped to end the war by provoking a breakdown of the draft—a breakdown that would dramatize the tragedy of the war and prevent conscription of the army necessary to fight it.

In 1964, three St. Louis men signed a pact of joint resistance, promising that if one went to jail for refusing induction, the others would follow. All three spent eighteen to twenty-three months in prison for refusing induction, and one of them later observed:

> I believe the most important thing about our pact was that we were translating a principle into action—not only draft resistance itself, but effective solidarity with a person who is prosecuted for acting in accord with conscience. I believe that any time anyone is arrested for any such cause, there should immediately be five or ten or a hundred or more who will say "Set him free or take us too" and proceed to enter prison to show they are not merely talking or signing their names.

Another collective act of draft resistance inspired the imagination of the antiwar movement in 1964. In May of that year, twelve students burned their draft cards at a New York rally as a general protest against American military policies. They coined the slogan "We Won't Go," and the list of places where they wouldn't go included the Dominican Republic and Cuba, along with Southeast Asia.

Out of the New York rally, a May Second Movement petition was circulated, calling upon its signers to refuse induction if called. The act of resistance would occur only as a matter of last resort, enabling deferred students to voice their opposition to American foreign policy without immediate self-sacrifice. Other "We Won't Go" petitions were circulated in the next two years, but the feeling mounted that opposition without personal risk was an empty gesture. In July 1966, angered by the rapid Vietnam buildup, a New Haven group endorsed a statement calling for unconditional, preemptive resistance on the part of its signers: "On November 16, we will return our draft cards to our local boards with a notice of our refusal to cooperate. . . ." Simply returning cards was unlikely to bring prosecution, but it risked provoking draft boards into accelerating induction notices, which would force antiwar activists to submit or face prosecution. The rising concern about the war made this provocative new tactic popular, and "We Won't Go" petitions collected thousands of signatures.

By 1967, Muhammad Ali's draft case drew national attention to the Resistance movement. Shortly before Ali's conviction, which was later reversed, *New York Times* columnist Tom Wicker saw broad implications in the case:

> A hundred thousand Muhammad Alis, of course, could be jailed. But if the Johnson Administration had to prosecute 100,000 Americans in order to maintain its authority, its real power to pursue the Vietnamese war or any other policy would be crippled if not destroyed. It would then be faced not with dissent but with civil disobedience on a scale amounting to revolt.

Staughton Lynd, a Yale historian and a central figure in the resistance, made the same point in *Liberation* magazine, and 100,000 acts of defiance became the goal of the movement—"an immense and provocative thought," in the words of one resister. This goal spurred the circulation of new petitions and led to the formation of a national resistance organization in October 1967. Scores of educators and religious leaders, among them Dr. Benjamin Spock and Rev. William Sloane Coffin, issued "A Call to Resist Illegitimate Authority." The movement wanted students to abandon their deferments, inductees to stay home rather than flee to Canada, and all resisters to go on strike against the draft. Many would end up in jail, it was thought, but this would serve an important purpose: "The existence of hundreds and perhaps thousands of young men in prison over a matter of conscience would exert a steady moral pressure on . . . every American whose patriotism demanded he think well of his country's place in the world." Immediately, Attorney General Ramsey Clark came under pressure to stem the growing resistance through prompt and vigorous prosecution. Rather than try hundreds of thousands of young people, he chose to prosecute Dr. Spock, Rev. Coffin, and other leaders of the movement. Although their convictions were later reversed, the Justice Department succeeded in conveying a public image of stern enforcement of the draft law.

The leaders of the Resistance soon learned that few were willing to join forces in this battle against the draft system. David Zimmerman, a graduate student at the University of Michigan, abandoned his deferment to express his opposition to being "channeled" by Selective Service while the war was going on, but most students played it safe. A survey taken by the New England Resistance in 1967–68 discovered that four-fifths of its members had deferments.

A number of antiwar organizations were reluctant to ask their members to adopt tactics that involved personal risk. At a national SDS conference, only about one-fifth of the mostly college-age delegates supported a plan to renounce their deferments. "I'm frankly appalled at the fear of alienating students by raising the II-S issue," a leader of the Berkeley Free Speech Movement explained.

The plan that won greater support was one that encouraged all students to keep their deferments, but to refuse induction if and when the deferments expired. The Progressive Labor Party took a similar position:

> While we must . . . oppose II-S as a divisive and class-racial-discrimina-
> tory system, we have to do this on the basis of collective struggle
> against the administration and the government, not by individual sac-
> rifice.

Later, antiwar groups explained their acceptance of deferments by reasoning, as Michael Ferber did, that "the deferred student was oppressed by the system along with the inducted soldier." According to this line of thought, the draft system's channeling policies made the middle-class white student "a legitimate revolutionary protagonist."

To counteract the widespread reluctance of white middle-class students to assume personal risks, the movement began circulating "snowballing" petitions which committed signers to acts of resistance only if similar pledges exceeded a specified number, ranging from one to fifteen thousand. But snowballing petitions never got enough signatures to make the pledges binding.

By mid-1968, the national movement counted fewer than three thousand committed draft resisters. A Boston Resistance newsletter reported that local attorneys "have expressed astonishment at our success so far in tying up the process," but movement strategists knew that they had fallen far short of the number needed to bring the draft to a halt.

Draft-card burning captured more attention from the press and the public. More than any other gesture of defiance, it reflected the widespread and growing willingness of draft-age men to break the law. The first known incident of this kind occurred in 1964; a year later, forty demonstrators protested the Dominican Republic intervention by burning their cards in front of a Berkeley draft board. Congress responded by making the act punishable by five years in prison, and Resistance activists immediately defied the new law. The first one was promptly convicted and sentenced to thirty months in prison. Draft-card burnings by other small groups in late 1965 and early 1966 similarly led to long prison terms.

Once the Resistance movement gained momentum, draft-card burnings became more popular, and the Justice Department began to be more selective about prosecutions. Technically, it could have prosecuted everyone who returned draft cards, burned or not, because the law required each registrant to have one in his possession. However, many of those who were burning their cards were deferred or exempt from the draft—one group of ten consisted of two veterans, two with physical exemptions, and six with student deferments—and the Justice Department was reluctant to prosecute cases of this kind. William Sessions, the department's chief draft prosecutor, refused to be party to what he called "a continuing, open, obvious expressed intent by many groups to absolutely swamp the system." The Justice Department prosecuted fewer than fifty draft-card burners—about forty of whom were convicted—but it never brought action against hundreds of other individuals who burned their cards during the height of the 1967–68 resistance.

The legal community expected the Supreme Court to overturn the convictions—especially in light of the strong trend developing against Selective Service prosecutions—but in the 1968 *O'Brien* case, the Court dealt the lawyers and the Resistance a harsh surprise. The law against draft-card burning was upheld, and the convicted activists who had been free on bond had to go to jail. The *O'Brien* case seemed to be an example of the liberal Warren court's reaching, possibly even over-reaching, to help the Justice Department control the antiwar movement. The decision ran counter to other freedom-of-speech cases in which the Supreme Court upheld protesters' rights to wear black arm-bands in school, Army uniforms as civilians, jackets reading "fuck the draft," flags on the seat of their pants, or flags as peace symbols. The effect of the *O'Brien* decision, and possibly its purpose, was to curtail the most spectacular means of resisting the draft.

By mid-1968, the Resistance movement was frustrated. The war was still escalating, and the draft seemed invulnerable to nonviolent resistance. More daring and violent means were tried. In a well-publicized raid on a suburban Baltimore County draft board, the "Catonsville Nine," led by the Berrigan brothers, destroyed 378 draft files "with napalm manufactured by ourselves from a recipe in the Special Forces handbook published by the U.S. government." Through 1970, hundreds of similar raids on draft boards resulted in damage to hundreds of thousands of draft files. Patterned after the Catonsville Nine, the perpetrators bore names like the Milwaukee Fourteen, the Akron Two, and the Pasadena Three. One group called itself the Beaver Fifty-five, although it numbered eight, not fifty-five, and staged a Halloween night raid in Indianapolis, not Beaver. Some of the incidents were bizarre. The Big Lake (Minnesota) One dumped two large buckets of his own and his family's excrement onto the I-A files of his draft board. The Women Against Daddy Warbucks stole the "I" and the "A" from the typewriter of a New York board to keep it from reclassifying anyone I-A. In the most devastating attack, the Chicago Fifteen destroyed the records of twelve local boards; four months, forty government workers, and $60,000 were required to undo the damage.

In these cases, government reaction was decisive and severe. The Berrigans were caught, convicted, and sentenced to prison. An activist who burned an upstate New York draft board in 1970 was sent to prison for four years. Ten members of the Chicago Fifteen were sentenced to ten-year prison terms.

Some draft resisters went to prison for less violent acts. In August 1966, twelve black demonstrators were arrested for a sit-in at the Atlanta induction center. All but one were convicted, and most were sentenced to prison for three years. John Wilson was convicted of "insurrection" and had to serve his time on a Georgia chain gang. Hundreds of others suffered misdemeanor convictions for sit-ins, unlawful demonstrations, or other forms of civil disobedience directed at draft boards and induction stations.

The activities of Staughton Lynd, Michael Ferber, Benjamin Spock, the Berrigans, and others failed to produce 100,000 signatures on Resistance petitions, and they did not bring the war machine to a halt. But they did draw public attention to draft resistance, and heavy media exposure contributed to the grass-roots, unorganized movement by more than a half million young men who broke the law and defied their draft boards. Enormous numbers of draft-age men were refusing induction, forcing local boards to refer their cases to federal prosecutors. The courts may not have been jammed, but the prosecutor's offices were. The draft did not collapse but it did lose much of its ability to enforce induction orders. For the most part, the movement's draft resistance goal was accomplished, but by members of the legal profession working within, not outside, the "system."

The leaders of this other movement were not national figures; most were local attorneys, prosecutors, and judges. Many were keenly anti-war, but the war usually was not their immediate concern. What they had in common was an abiding respect for the American system of law and a growing contempt for the Selective Service System's disregard of due process. After two decades of General Hershey's leadership, Selective Service had lost the capacity to make local boards operate fairly, consistently, and with proper regard for legal standards. When it tried to enforce the law against those who disobeyed, Selective Service had few friends and thousands of enemies throughout the legal system.

These lawyers, prosecutors, and judges did not draw public attention to the war in the manner of the draft-card burners and the Berrigans, but they did achieve the "immense and provocative" results that activists found beyond their reach. Working alone or in small groups, one case at a time, lawyers developed an astonishing record of preventing the conviction of draft violators. As the legal attacks on the draft system gathered momentum, the criminal justice system became swamped to the point where Selective Service prosecutions became almost impossible. By 1971, the enforcement of the draft law was in shambles. As shown in Figure 4, the vast majority of those accused of a draft offense escaped conviction.

The first sign of this breakdown came in late 1966, when one hundred student leaders from universities across the country sent an open letter to President Johnson, warning that many of their peers would refuse induction if his Vietnam policy did not change. In 1967, columnist James Reston visited campuses and talked with student government leaders. He estimated that as many as 25 percent of all college students might refuse their induction orders. A 1968 *Harvard Crimson* poll found that 22 percent would refuse the draft rather than serve in Vietnam, and a Harris poll taken later in 1968 discovered that 20–30 percent of all college students would "seriously contemplate" refusing induction. In 1969, the student body presidents of 253 universities informed the White House that they personally planned to refuse military service. Throughout the course of the war, more than a half million draft-age men did exactly that.

One of the first to say no was Daniel Seeger of New York, a pacifist

FIGURE 4: EVADERS

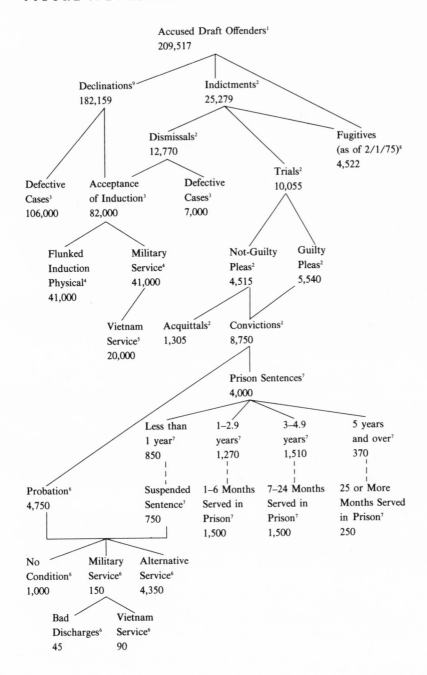

whose case began the unraveling of draft enforcement. In March 1965, when President Johnson had just begun his Vietnam escalation and war protesters were still at the political fringe, Seeger's Selective Service conviction was overturned by the Supreme Court in a ground-breaking case. Seeger had asked for an exemption as a conscientious objector, but his draft board, like most others, granted CO status only to Quakers, Mennonites, and other pacifist sects that believed in God. Seeger did not belong to any of these sects, nor did he believe in God, but the Supreme Court held that he nonetheless qualified for a CO exemption. In doing so, the Court left the clear implication that anyone with a deep-seated personal "religion" opposed to war could be a conscientious objector.

Until *Seeger,* the Supreme Court had not issued a major Selective Service decision since World War II, and the draft system was ill prepared to adjust to new legal requirements. Selective Service headquarters had no mechanism for supervising the implementation of new case law, and local boards were not eager to suffer an intrusion upon their discretion. After the *Seeger* case, many local boards still required CO's to be Jehovah's Witnesses, Quakers, or Mennonites, and many would-be conscientious objectors were wrongfully denied CO status without realizing it. The legal community discovered that draft boards were deviating not just from the *Seeger* holding, but from the procedural standards imposed upon all other federal administrative agencies. Judges were shocked by the incapacity or unwillingness of draft boards to conform to the law. "Selective Service decided not to change its procedures and decided instead to take its chances with the courts," according to one federal judge.

Increasingly, attorneys urged clients to challenge the legality of draft board decisions. However, this could only be done at great risk. No matter how egregious the draft board error, courts refused to intervene unless the individual refused induction and stood trial on criminal charges, or accepted induction and sought release from the military through a writ of habeas corpus.

Regardless of the risk, thousands of draft resisters began pressing their cases in the courts. By 1967, enough were winning acquittals and reversals to provide good case law for future challenges. Where federal judges once might have been willing to let Selective Service get by with procedural shortcuts, they now entertained arguments that probed into every last detail of draft operations.

The Selective Service System could not meet these challenges. Its headquarters kept no current account of rapidly evolving case law. It was not until 1970 that Selective Service strengthened its legal staff to help local boards avoid procedural errors, and it was not until 1972 that it prepared its own manual of draft law.

But by then, the draft system was outgunned. In 1968, a small group of Washington lawyers—Thomas Alder, Charles Halperin, Brian Paddock, and Michael Tigar—established the *Selective Service Law Reporter.* Over a six-year period, the *Reporter* published almost six thousand pages of decisions, regulations, and legal analysis—fifty times the material in Selective Service's 1972 manual. Draft law became a true industry. According to one United States Attorney who prosecuted draft cases, "We were facing a sustained, organized, and pretty well-informed bar. Young lawyers were building careers around these cases." At the height of the war, one draft attorney's handbook listed more than four hundred separate defenses that had been used successfully at least once. A Justice Department official admitted that "it would be rare, after going through [a case] with a fine-tooth comb, not to find some procedural defect."

Most defenses involved variations of the five legal arguments listed below. A few years earlier, they had been just wild ideas; by 1970, they were the law.

1. A draft board had to review an individual's draft file whenever he made an apparently valid (prima facie) claim for a new deferment or exemption. If the board did not, the subsequent induction order was invalid. Draft boards fell victim to this defense when they lost patience with well-counseled registrants who made repeated requests for deferments.

2. A draft board had to approve a request for CO status if an individual made a sincere claim that he opposed all wars, regardless of his religious background. Defense attorneys challenged any induction order that followed a denial of CO status. If a draft board claimed that a registrant was not a true conscientious objector, his attorney could

produce documents or call witnesses at trial to show that, in light of *Seeger,* the board had asked the wrong questions or drawn the wrong conclusions from the facts.

3. When a draft board turned down a request for a deferment or exemption, it had to state its reasons. Draft boards reviewed cases quickly, and many of the claims they reviewed were denied for obvious reasons. But unless they left written records, their induction orders were defective. Even if draft boards stated reasons, they could be challenged as vague, insufficient, or inappropriate.

4. A draft board could not revoke a deferment or exemption, or accelerate an order for induction, as punishment. Long before this issue reached the Supreme Court, Attorney General Ramsey Clark pressured General Hershey into rescinding his delinquency policies in late 1967. However, Hershey restated his personal view that war protestors should be inducted, and a number of local boards followed his lead. Thousands of registrants were reclassified and ordered for induction out of turn. A San Jose draft board clerk testified in court that her board had classified as "delinquents" two hundred registrants who had returned their draft cards. After the Supreme Court outlawed punitive induction orders, draft counselors advised people to pepper their local boards with antiwar leaflets and personal statements, hoping to incite punitive induction orders which were invalid.

5. The "order-of-call" defense was the most extraordinary of all. Draft boards had to issue induction orders in the right order. If a person had been ordered for induction in January when he should have been called in February, he could lawfully refuse induction. To establish this defense, the attorney had to find other registrants of the same board who were older and who should have been drafted before his client. If his client's name was at the bottom of the monthly call list, only one mistake had to be found to prove he was drafted out of order. If his client's name was next-to-last, two mistakes were needed, and so forth.

Skilled investigators scrutinized draft board records and scoured the countryside in search of someone who should have been drafted but was not. Mathematics experts were the best at substantiating this defense. A group of Los Angeles mathematicians sold cassettes explaining the order-of-call defense to draft attorneys, and a Berkeley math major formed his own corporation, Draft Research Associates, charging each defendant a fee of around $250.

Order-of-call mistakes were almost impossible for draft boards to avoid. According to one draft counselor, "You could knock five names off the bottom of any list, and some lists had only five names." The defense was often a godsend for attorneys with clients who seemed hopelessly destined for jail. Leroy Thompson was a prominent black militant and college football star who fled to Canada to avoid the draft. He was arrested on an informer's tip during a visit home, and the FBI and federal prosecutors prepared a careful case against him. However, Thompson's attorney was able to dismiss the case with an order-of-call defense one day before the trial was to start. The FBI was furious, and the U.S. Attorney who prosecuted the case later admitted that "we got blown out of the water."

Late in the war, the order-of-call defense began to be applied to cases in which draft boards had accidentally or intentionally destroyed records of registrants who had passed the age of twenty-six. A fire in the District of Columbia draft headquarters forced the dismissal of several cases. A firebombing in Santa Clara, California, destroyed so many irreplaceable records that counselors put out a call to draft fugitives from the area, urging them to stand trial and raise order-of-call as a defense.

These defense tactics were increasingly successful as the war escalated, but many judges were still reluctant to accept them. When knowledgeable defense attorneys realized that the judge assigned to their client's case was unsympathetic to technical defenses, they delayed the prosecution as long as possible, hoping for a more favorable legal or political environment. Over time, their hopes were answered.

Breakdown

At the start of the Vietnam war, there were scattered federal judges who were willing to dismiss draft cases for procedural irregularities. But in San Francisco, all eight judges dismissed cases for reasons that, in those early days, were not accepted elsewhere. One attorney tried and won a San Francisco case "with defenses that got me laughed out of court in New York." For example, four of the judges ruled that draft board members had to live within the board's geographic area. No San Francisco board met the test, and hundreds of San Francisco draft resisters went free before an appeals court reversed the rule.

One San Francisco judge privately acknowledged that the turmoil and bitter feelings about the Vietnam war affected the way he and his colleagues handled Selective Service cases. Had the war been more popular, he might have been less receptive to technical defenses. Yet like most judges, he couched his dismissals in legal terms, with no mention of the war or the social turbulence it created.

Standing behind the judges were their law clerks, who were often very sympathetic to draft resisters. "We were not that different from people who came before our judges," commented one. These young lawyers, fresh out of law school, spent much of their time looking for procedural irregularities, helping to bolster judges who were inclined to accept far-reaching defenses. Paul Harris, law clerk for a San Francisco judge, was invited to a local bar association's Law Day seminar at a nearby high school, where he found himself on the same platform with a Selective Service official: "He only told them about their obligations—so I had to tell them about their rights." Harris alerted the students that "if you refuse induction, there is a good chance you will not be found guilty because the Selective Service has violated its own regulations when it tried to draft you."

In the years before 1969, all San Francisco federal judges were reluctant to sentence convicted draft offenders to jail. Their typical sentence was two years probation, with a condition of alternative service. Alternative service was administered more leniently by probation officers than was the equivalent CO program run by Selective Service. A convicted draft offender could work nearer his home for more pay, and could select from among a greater variety of jobs.

The judges adopted a liberal sentencing policy partly because they "didn't think it would do any good" to send conscientious offenders to prison. After hearing a number of draft cases, they became convinced that heavy jail sentences did little to deter others from resisting the draft. "These people were not criminals," one commented. "I saw no point in punishing them."

When they sentenced a resister to jail, it was usually because of his defiant attitude. "Even then," one judge recalled, "I was usually reversed on appeal." The defendants were often radical activists who viewed liberal judicial attitudes as barriers to their challenge to the war and the "system." David Harris, a former Stanford student body president, refused to let his attorney argue technical defenses in his behalf. He was sent to prison, as was another defendant who challenged the "imperialist" quality of the law.

The San Francisco judges often encountered hostile reactions from defendants. One young mother spanked her child in the courtroom for giving a bouquet of daffodils to the judge instead of to the defendant, the child's father. But when the judges' lenient attitudes became apparent, the reaction changed. At the start of one draft trial, the defendant's friends contemptuously refused to stand for the judge. After the first recess, they stood.

The leniency of the San Francisco courts encouraged forum-shopping. Before 1970, a registrant could voluntarily change the site of his induction, and if he later refused induction, he would be prosecuted in the new area. One draft resister flew to the Bay Area from Washington, D.C., to refuse induction. The judge gave him probation, exactly what he wanted.

San Francisco prosecutor Cecil Poole, the nation's first black U.S. Attorney, was no more enthusiastic than the judges about Selective Service cases. Poole was convinced that he could not prosecute the cases "in the abstract." He handled them the way he did other victimless crimes, by giving due consideration to community standards. In light of the attitude of young people in the Bay Area, Poole did not believe that draft offenders should be vigorously prosecuted.

Instead of obtaining indictments that federal judges would dismiss, Poole's assistant, Paul Sloan, "began dumping cases on a wholesale basis." Although the San Francisco prosecutors pursued hundreds of cases—Sloan once personally tried thirteen in a single day—these represented a small percentage of the thousands that were referred for prosecution. In 1967 and 1968, more than 90 percent of all cases referred to the San Francisco U.S. Attorney's Office were dropped before indictment.

In 1968, Carlos Ogden, the California director of Selective Service, became concerned that too few draft violators were being prosecuted in the Bay area. Feeling that there was "a breakdown" in the enforcement of the draft law, Ogden complained to Selective Service headquarters, which complained to the Justice Department.

If a prosecutor refused to indict, Selective Service had the right to demand an explanation and special review by the Justice Department. Ogden filed a number of protests, rarely with any success. Although Justice Department officials had views on draft enforcement that Cecil Poole described as "very different" from his own, they rarely failed to support him. According to Sloan, one top official who came out to San Francisco to review his caseload "glanced at the poor quality of the cases, threw up his hands, and said 'no more.' "

Nevertheless, Selective Service officials considered federal prosecutors, not draft board procedures, to be the problem. Sloan complained that "you couldn't talk sense to them. They thought that all that we had to do was to slog away with vigorous prosecution, and our problems would go away." Selective Service officials tried to pressure Sloan to prosecute law clerk Paul Harris for giving his Law Day speech, they tried to pressure Poole to fire Sloan, and—through Republican Senator George Murphy of California—they succeeded in blocking Cecil Poole's appointment as a federal judge for eight years.

In 1969, President Nixon replaced Poole with James Browning, who promised more vigorous enforcement. Sloan resigned soon thereafter to enter private practice, frequently appearing as defense attorney in Selective Service cases. He was replaced by a specially assembled group of former military attorneys. A full-time legal aide was appointed for Carlos Ogden, the state Selective Service director, and President Nixon appointed two new judges who were not as critical of Selective Service.

During Browning's first forty-five days, more than three hundred cases were reviewed. In a marked departure from the past, over half were presented to the grand jury for indictment, and Nixon's new judges began sentencing draft offenders to prison. Gradually, however, Browning found the nation's draft law a "procedural morass," with many cases defective "because of the mistakes the local draft boards have made while processing files." Once again, Ogden complained that "many cases were not reviewed in the depth I would have liked." Despite the new regime, nothing changed very much.

The reluctance of San Francisco prosecutors and judges to convict and imprison draft offenders had a nationwide effect on the enforcement of the draft laws. Judges and law clerks stayed abreast of developments in other jurisdictions. By 1969, Selective Service cases had become the fourth largest category on the criminal docket, and they were a common topic of discussion at judicial conferences and sentencing institutes. In light of the huge numbers of Selective Service cases San Francisco judges had reviewed, their observations and attitudes could not be easily discounted. Judges and prosecutors in other parts of the country realized that many draft offenders were shifting their induction orders to the Bay Area. The ones who did not forum-shop were less affluent, more conscientious, or more poorly counseled. Some officials began to question the fairness of the arrangement.

Case backlogs were beginning to confront dozens of U.S. Attorneys, who found themselves in the same situation Cecil Poole had faced earlier. While judges elsewhere in the country were usually not as liberal as those in San Francisco, almost every judicial circuit began to expand registrant rights and draft board responsibilities. According to a federal prosecutor in Virginia, "judicially fashioned loopholes" made the draft law harder to enforce everywhere.

During the latter years of the Johnson administration, top officials at the Justice Department were concerned about the mounting confrontation between Selective Service and the courts. William Sessions of the Justice Department's Criminal Division blamed Selective Service for "referring draft violations to the U.S. attorneys without weeding out, in a majority of instances, those with fatal procedural defects." He insisted that the best way to enhance the enforcement of the draft law would be to have local boards obey the law and their own regulations. Attorney General Ramsey Clark kept a discreet distance from the dispute; General Hershey recalled that "whenever I tried to call Ramsey for help, he just wasn't around."

In 1969, Clark was replaced by the "law-and-order"-minded John Mitchell; the next year, General Hershey was replaced as Selective Service director by Dr. Curtis Tarr. Shortly after taking office, Tarr testified to Congress that the draft system was enjoying "splendid support" from the criminal justice system. Yet he soon learned of the strength of the legal challenges against the draft. Tarr was barely able to keep the draft system from completely disintegrating under heavy pressure from the courts, an expanding network of draft counselors, and a growing number of cases for prosecution. After a year, he acknowledged that enforcement was "one of the most difficult problems at the time of my appointment."

Tarr drastically expanded his legal staff to cut the backlog of unresolved cases, which by then numbered about 27,000. In 1971, at the behest of Selective Service, Congress directed the Justice Department and the courts to give draft cases precedence over other federal cases in docketing, trial, and appeal. Tarr also tried to improve the operations of local boards by training members better and supervising them more closely. In late 1971, changes in the draft law mandated a major turnover in local board personnel. Thereafter, draft counselors and defense attorneys noticed a marked improvement in local board procedures.

Tarr's efforts received a serious setback from events that were set in motion long before he replaced General Hershey. In 1970, the Supreme Court issued three landmark decisions—*Gutknecht, Welsh,* and *Mulloy.* The cases had been moving up through the lower courts since mid-1966; when they were decided, they marked the watershed in the enforcement of the draft law. Coming at a time when the war and the draft were beginning to wind down, the decisions destroyed much of whatever enthusiasm remained for enforcing the law.

David Gutknecht was a radical pacifist from Minnesota who, like thousands of others, was punitively reclassified and ordered for induction. The Supreme Court declared his local board's action "blatantly lawless," and reversed his conviction for refusing induction. Ironically, Gutknecht himself was not one of the thousands who benefited from the decision; his local board started afresh, inducted him according to proper procedures, and saw him go to Sandstone prison for his subsequent refusal to report for induction.

Elliot Welsh applied to his Santa Barbara, California, draft board for a CO exemption, and he seemed to qualify as a nonreligious objector under *Seeger.* However, his claim was denied. In reversing his conviction for refusing induction, the Supreme Court held that one need not possess specific religious beliefs to qualify as a conscientious objector.

This and the 1971 Clay (Muhammad Ali) case confirmed what many had argued—that Selective Service had misread or ignored *Seeger*, and that many accused draft offenders had been wrongfully denied CO exemptions in the late 1960s. Welsh himself reapplied to his local board and was granted CO status.

On the same day as its *Welsh* decision, the Supreme Court found that Joe Mulloy's Kentucky draft board had unlawfully failed to reopen his case after he had presented a prima facie claim for a CO classification. After the Court's decision, Mulloy's draft board issued him a physical exemption and gave up trying to draft him.

Most judges applied the new case law retroactively, dismissing old cases that did not meet the latest standards. As a result, local board actions that were ostensibly legal in 1968 were often grounds for dismissal in 1970. In effect, this placed the burden on Selective Service to set procedures in Year 1 that would meet the as-yet-unknown judicial standards of Year 2. In a sense, the retroactive application of new case law was the price Selective Service had to pay for not implementing the *Seeger* decision correctly in 1965.

The *Gutknecht, Welsh*, and *Mulloy* cases alerted federal prosecutors across the country that their pending cases needed a second look. Many cases had sat on the shelf for years because of defense counsels' delaying tactics, fugitive defendants (many of whom were in Canada), and the pressing demands of other criminal trials. Most old cases, and a lot of new ones, now could not withstand scrutiny.

The impact of the three cases went far beyond their specific holdings. Defense attorneys, prosecutors, and judges understood that the Supreme Court stood behind the Cecil Pooles and against the Carlos Ogdens. As one federal judge recalled, "we could sense the spirit of those decisions." Emboldened by this mandate from the Supreme Court, they dismissed cases for even the most technical of reasons.

After the *Gutknecht, Welsh*, and *Mulloy* decisions, federal judges also began to alter their sentencing practices. In 1968–69, the average prison sentence for draft offenders had been more than three years— more severe than the penalties for draft resistance during World War II or the Korean War. That quickly changed. Judges who once routinely gave five years were now giving two or three, judges who had imposed shorter terms now imposed probation, and probation no longer necessarily meant alternative service. During 1970, the three Milwaukee federal judges sentenced forty-six of fifty-four convicted draft offenders to prison. Thereafter, they sent only one out of twenty-nine to jail. Judges in Utah and northern Iowa stopped sending people to jail altogether, and judges elsewhere in the country began imposing sentences like a $5 fine or one hour's probation. In Madison, Wisconsin, Judge Samuel Rosenstein flatly refused to convict any draft offenders. Instead, he asked them to do some form of unsupervised alternative service for nine to twelve months, after which he ordered the charges dismissed.

Judge Rosenstein, along with a number of other judges, allowed individuals to do almost anything they wanted, even draft counseling, as their alternative service. A musician from Buffalo, New York, was sentenced to give six rock concerts in Canadian prisons. Chuck Noell, in his book *We Are All POW's,* described his own favorable encounter with a judge:

> His law clerk told me a week later that Judge Broderick had originally planned to sentence me to work in a mental hospital for two years. At the trial, he thought for a couple of minutes about what I said and then essentially sentenced me in his own words to continue the work I was already doing. . . . Both of us came out of the trial with a strong mutual respect. I've paid several social calls on him in the years since the trial, and still do whenever I have the chance.

Faced with stacks of old cases and reluctant judges, prosecutors became less and less interested in enforcing the draft law. The assistant U.S. Attorneys were peers of the accused offenders; their own problems with draft boards cooled their enthusiasm as prosecutors. One U.S. Attorney recalled that "I sometimes had to remind [my assistant] that he was not a defense counsel." In some cities, there developed what one participant called a "cliquelike thing" among draft attorneys, assistant U.S. Attorneys, and law clerks: "Everyone sat around grinning as we worked together to resolve outstanding cases, invariably to the advantage of defendants."

Aside from their personal views about the war or the draft, these were not good cases for young prosecutors to pursue. Especially towards the end of the war, they typically went to the most junior attorney in the office. His superiors screened proposed indictments much more carefully than his dismissal recommendations—perhaps because once indictments were issued, they could be dismissed only with permission of Justice Department headquarters. When cases went to trial, young prosecutors had more to lose than to gain, because their conviction rates often affected prospects for promotions or future job recommendations. They had every incentive to drop cases, and few to prosecute them.

Beginning in the late sixties and accelerating in the early seventies, the number of cases dropped reached epidemic proportions. In Milwaukee, for example, prosecutors trimmed their five-hundred-case backlog to just one hundred immediately following the 1970 Supreme Court decisions. They refused to prosecute any of the roughly fifty accused offenders referred by one local board in Waukesha County.

Other U.S. Attorneys' offices had similar experiences. In the District of Columbia, 99 percent of all 1967–70 cases were never prosecuted. "In the really gross case, if he spat in everyone's face, we would go ahead with prosecution," one D.C. prosecutor commented. A Virginia prosecutor reported that because of the volume of cases, some just "got lost in the shuffle." Prosecutors in New York City, San Diego, El Paso, New Orleans, and Miami dropped more than 95 percent of their cases. The national average was 89 percent.

Only four districts pursued more than 50 percent of their cases. In New Hampshire, which prosecuted 95 percent of its cases, the U.S. Attorney admitted that he had "quite a few acquittals." One tough-minded district's high rate of prosecutions may have resulted from a close kinship with Selective Service; the U.S. Attorney and state Selective Service director drove to work together, discussing cases en route.

In retrospect, San Francisco was not at all unique. It was just early. In 1967–70, the only years for which accurate data is available, Cecil Poole and James Browning prosecuted 11 percent of their cases— exactly the national average, and, in fact, a sterner record than two of the other three California districts.

Until late in the war, juries were the toughest enforcers of the law. Through 1971, juries convicted a higher percentage of cases than trial judges. Defendants who chose jury trials typically tried to maneuver around the prosecution's objections to appeal to the antiwar feelings of the men and women in the jury box, a tactic that usually backfired. The best hope was for a hung jury, as in one Virginia case, where a lone holdout for acquittal later admitted that he would not have voted for conviction under any circumstances. The case was later retried before a judge, who acquitted the defendant on the same facts.

By the 1970s, however, the growing public consensus against the war had reached the jury box. Jurors were instructed by judges not to let their feelings about the war interfere with their role as finders of fact —but that was too much to ask. One juror acknowledged after voting for acquittal that "although we couldn't consider the war itself, we can't ignore it." A Seattle juror admitted after an acquittal that "this war is a nasty situation. If it weren't so nasty, we probably would not have made the decision we did."

Throughout the entire war, draft cases were unusually easy to win. William Smith lost only one case out of hundreds, and that involved a client who had burned his draft card on television. Curry First, who won all thirty of his cases, commented on his shock when he turned to other kinds of law after the war's end: "Losing cases was a new experience to me. I had forgotten that any lawyer, even a very good lawyer, has to lose lots of cases."

Ultimately, of the 210,000 accused offenders, over 200,000 escaped conviction. Only 1,300 were acquitted after trial; almost all the others had their cases dropped before trial—more than half because of defective local board procedures, unenforceable induction orders, or successful technical defenses.

In this respect, Tom Wicker and the Resistance activists proved correct when they set 100,000 as the number of cases necessary to bring turmoil to the legal system and make the draft law unenforceable. There was turmoil in the courts, and for clients of skillful attorneys, the draft law was indeed unenforceable.

The Ones Who Got Away

In 1966, just after draft calls began to rise, John Morton asked his Utah local board to give him a CO exemption. A year later, they turned him down and ordered him to report for induction. Morton refused and, when prosecuted, claimed that his CO application had been mishandled. His trial was postponed while the appellate court considered an interlocutory matter. In 1971, the Tenth Circuit Court recommended dismissal of the case. Over the next year, a federal judge twice denied the government's motion to reopen the prosecution. Morton's case was not finally dismissed until June 1972. By then, it was too late for the local board to reprocess his file before the December 1972 end of the draft.

In retrospect, refusing induction and hiring a good lawyer seems to have been a good strategy for avoiding the draft. Many did engage in elaborate, expensive legal strategies to beat the system. After winning cases because of procedural errors by their draft boards, they reached their twenty-sixth birthdays, got high lottery numbers, or—like Morton—outlasted the war. Even if they were still vulnerable to the draft, the local boards frequently gave them exemptions and forgot about them. It was truly an extraordinary instance when a draft board responded to a successful legal defense by methodically reprocessing the case, taking care not to make any mistakes, and issuing an induction order that was enforceable in court. Especially after 1970, a defendant with a good lawyer had a very remote chance of ever having to enter the Army or go to prison.

But at the height of the war, the results did not seem so assured. The overwhelming majority of draft resisters thought that refusing induction would likely bring long prison terms. Lengthy legal battles involved considerable anxiety, expense, and disruption of personal plans —very real penalties for refusing induction. Tom Blackwell began law school while he was engaged in his legal battle against Selective Service. His prosecutor dropped the case three years later, just a few months before Blackwell graduated. Had he been convicted, he would have been barred from practicing law.

The 210,000 individuals accused of criminal draft offenses were subjected to FBI investigations which left permanent scars on their reputations. Their arrest records are still on file, and they often are viewed by friends and neighbors as having "gotten away" with a crime. Some men accept this as preferable to years in prison or exile, but others are bitter. They endured years of personal upheaval as a consequence of what they believed, and the courts later confirmed, were unfair and illegal actions by their draft boards.

The luckier ones were the roughly 360,000 whose draft offenses were either ignored or never discovered. The findings of the Notre Dame survey suggest that draft boards knew about roughly a third of these crimes, but never reported them to U.S. attorneys. A federal prosecutor in Los Angeles reported in 1970 that "draft boards are just so busy and have such a heavy work load that if it becomes clear they're going to have a lot of trouble with a kid, they just say 'forget it.' "

Isolated cases of unreported draft offenders occurred throughout the war. The mayor's son in a large southern city returned his draft card to his local board. The board mailed it back to him, but he rejected it a second time with a letter promising to refuse induction. He never heard from his draft board again. A young man from Detroit was ordered to take his preinduction physical. When he arrived, he lay down and slept through it. The induction station officials told him he would have to wait several hours for the next group and gave him his Selective Service file. He went home, taking the file with him. He too never heard from his draft board.

Perhaps the most bizarre story of an unreported draft offender involved Albert Jones, a Detroit youth who never really objected to going into the Army. His mother, Sister Lily, was the leader of a small black religious sect, and she wanted him to refuse induction. On the day Jones was to report for induction, his mother held an early morning service, during which he slipped away and reported. When Sister Lily discovered he was gone, she packed her congregation into taxicabs and drove to the induction station. She and her followers stormed in and rescued her son, all the while singing

"When the Saints Go Marching In." She took him home, and he never heard from his draft board again.

The largest category of unreported offenders comprised those who never registered for the draft, and whose existence was unknown to local boards. Of the untold hundreds of thousands who illegally failed to register in the Vietnam era, only a few thousand were ever identified, and just 250 were convicted.

Nonregistration was actively encouraged by some antiwar groups as a means of draft resistance. In 1967, *Peacemaker* magazine circulated a petition to enlist nonregistrants and collected 84 signatures. By the early 1970s, the antiwar movement spread to the high schools, and seventeen-year-olds were advised to resist the draft by not registering. "Check Out the Odds," a manual coauthored by David Gutknecht of Supreme Court fame, tried to persuade eighteen-year-olds that failing to register was the safest means of avoiding the draft:

> For most young men, not registering is the single most effective method of dealing with the draft. At the present time, the Selective Service has no effective method of tracking down 18-year-olds who don't sign up. If you don't register, chances are the draft board won't find out. Most of the tens of thousands of non-registrants are never discovered. And discovery . . . does not always mean that you will be prosecuted. . . . You can always register late.

The characteristics of nonregistrants have always been a matter of speculation. Peter Straub, former Selective Service general counsel, believed them to be jail convicts, patients in mental hospitals, and homosexuals. A 1974 Ford Foundation report conjectured that "they typically lead disjointed lives, moving frequently and hesitant to take permanent jobs lest their delinquent status be discovered and reported." William Walker was an Illinois nonregistrant who fit this image:

> During the first few months after I turned 18, I did confide in some friends and close acquaintances, but the resulting attitude of these peo-

ple was . . . "you'll be sorry." . . . So for the next three and a half years
I kept silent. . . . The psychological burden on a non-registrant is great.
He knows he has broken a law and that he must shape the rest of his
life with this fact always in mind.

Nonregistration was very risky for white, middle-class men. The
Minnesota State Selective Service headquarters culled through four
Twin Cities high school yearbooks, checking every name from the class
of 1969 against its records. Of the 1,082 graduates that year, only 17
had not registered. Letters were sent to them. Nine were found to have
joined the service before registering (a lawful act), and the other eight
had moved out of town. President Ford's son Jack and many other
middle-class whites inadvertently registered late, but few, very few,
failed to register at all.

Nonregistration was much more the draft evasion technique of the
poor. According to the Notre Dame survey, almost half the nonregistrants were black, and most had low incomes and little education.
Homer Singleton, a Louisiana draft counselor, believed that nonregistration was epidemic among migrant workers and bayou dwellers.
Nonregistration also may have been common in inner-city neighborhoods, where young people often lead untraceable lives. For many,
nonregistration simply reflected their alienation from the American
mainstream. Some were so ill informed that they never realized that
they had to register. Even if they were aware of their obligations, these
underprivileged youths had so few of the benefits of citizenship that
they felt no need to assume any of its duties. The war itself may have
had a significant impact on nonregistration offenses in the inner city.
The Notre Dame survey found that almost all black nonregistration
offenses occurred during the latter half of the war. Apparently, rising
black consciousness and the plight of black veterans made many inner-
city youths reluctant to join the military.

Estimates of the number of nonregistrants vary widely. Comparing
registration and census data, some have concluded that as many as two
million never registered. But most of these were seventeen-year-old
enlistees or aliens with temporary residence permits, who were not
legally required to register for the draft. In any event, many of those

who never registered are the same people who are never counted by the census. One spokesman for a community organization compared non-registration for the draft with nonreporting in the census: "It's the same thing. . . . The man with five kids says he has two. We're tired of fools coming to our door talking irrelevant statistics." The Census Bureau believes its 1970 count to have undercounted draft-age men by about 900,000, casting substantial doubt on any effort to measure nonregistrants by comparing census data with Selective Service data.

The findings of the Notre Dame survey indicate that roughly 250,000 young men broke the law by never registering for the draft. Broken down by race, 0.6 percent of all whites, 3.9 percent of all blacks, and 1.7 percent of all other minority (mostly Spanish-speaking) persons were found never to have registered. Most had very low incomes and little education.

Throughout the war, Selective Service maintained a flexible policy toward nonregistration. A young man was required to register within five days of his eighteenth birthday, but he was not subject to the draft until he turned nineteen, and draft boards seldom cared if he waited until then. Before 1973, nonregistrants were reported to prosecutors at the rate of about one thousand per year. Like Greg Hooton of Benton Harbor, Michigan, almost all avoided prosecution by agreeing to register and take their chances with the draft:

> The day after Thanksgiving I got arrested at home and was taken to Grand Rapids to be fingerprinted. There I talked to the U.S. Attorney again, and he gave me what he called "one last chance" to change my mind. When I got home, I spent the weekend talking to people about it, and the total reaction of everyone was that I should register. I don't know what my reasons were, but I did register the following Monday, and the charges were dropped.

This practice ended in 1973, after the draft expired. During that year, almost 3,500 nonregistrants appeared at their local boards, thinking all was safe, but found themselves referred to federal prosecutors. A non-registration charge was easy to prove and almost impossible to defend, and a number of individuals were convicted. But judges generally dropped charges if the defendant agreed to register, an act which by then carried no risk.

By 1976, nonregistrants were impossible to find. Draft boards no longer existed, police never asked to see draft cards, and neighbors no longer cared. The handful who were inadvertently discovered faced little risk of punishment. In a series of unusual decisions, federal courts interpreted the statute of limitations to mean that a nonregistrant could be prosecuted only if he turned eighteen between September and December of 1971. President Carter later issued blanket pardons to nonregistrants, but none would have been prosecuted anyway.

By the time of Carter's inauguration, just 2 percent of the 570,000 draft offenders stood convicted or still faced criminal charges—a manifestation of what William Sessions of the Justice Department admitted was "selective prosecution." From the prosecutors' standpoint, what happened to draft cases was roughly comparable to what happens to most criminal cases. A great many crimes go unreported, and many criminals remain undiscovered. Even when charges are filed, prosecutors routinely dismiss a majority of the cases. Sometimes the evidence is weak or inadmissible, and other times no public interest is served by strict enforcement of the law. In recent years, only about 33 percent of all accused criminals have been convicted. Yet of the 210,000 accused of draft offenses, just 4 percent were convicted, and only 1.5 percent were sentenced to prison. Had they been prosecuted as vigorously as bank robbers, the federal prison system would have had to double its capacity at the height of the war.

Federal prosecutors realized that extraordinary numbers of draft cases were being dropped, and Selective Service officials knew that the courts were invalidating thousands of induction orders. Yet at the time, no one publicly acknowledged the dimensions of the problem. While the draft was still in force, such an admission might have totally undermined the war effort.

Instead, top officials at the Justice Department and Selective Service denied that more than a small number of cases were defective. Assistant Attorney General Robert Mardian and Selective Service Director Curtis Tarr both suggested that 75–80 percent of the 210,000 accused draft offenders eventually capitulated and reported for induction. This "almost made it seem as if cooperation were the byword of the nation's young," as Stuart Loory commented. Walter Morse, Selective Service's general counsel, further alleged that the 210,000 figure referred only to "initial violations," giving the impression that most of these men were the victims of oversleeping, undelivered letters, or momentary bad judgment. But in 1971, a Selective Service survey was reported by *The New York Times* to show that these 210,000 offenders had ordinarily refused three or four induction orders before their cases were referred to prosecutors, indicating that they were indeed willful violators.

Some men did capitulate, either because their original offenses had not been willful or carefully considered, or because of the strains of being a criminal defendant. Maintaining one's resolve in the face of an FBI investigation, formal charges, and fingerprinting was not always easy. Defense attorney Conrad Lynn described the case of one of his clients who succumbed to these pressures:

> Steve was a bitter black youth who would come to my office with his indictment in his pocket and sit and brood for hours. Several months passed, and finally Steve began to open up. He had little sympathy for the Vietnamese people but a raging hatred of the U.S. Government. . . . After a year had passed the government lawyer placed the case on the calendar for trial. Steve sat in the courtroom during the trial of [another draft refuser]. Suddenly, one day he told me he wished to drop his contest of his case and submit to induction.

Often, however, accused offenders capitulated by agreeing to submit to induction under circumstances that they believed would enable them to fail the physical exam. Accused offenders in San Francisco and Los Angeles sometimes went to Seattle or other induction stations where their chances of failing were very good. Others quickly developed conditions that disqualified them.

Throughout the Vietnam era, neither the Justice Department nor Selective Service kept any statistics on the reasons for case closings. One Justice Department official was publicly quoted as acknowledging that the agency's job was "to prosecute draft dodgers, not keep figures." The only figures they released were those in a twelve-month 1971–72 sample by the Justice Department showing the reasons for case closings after indictment. These data showed that 67 percent were dismissed because of "a bona fide attempt to submit to induction." But the sample did not encompass case closings before indictment, which were usually the weaker cases—and which accounted for 95 percent of the dropped cases; nor did it include cases screened during the nationwide housecleaning of cases following the *Gutknecht, Welsh,* and *Mulloy* decisions.

U.S. Attorney's offices were generally unaware of the official contention that almost all dropped cases resulted from capitulating offenders. Informed about it afterwards, Cecil Poole said, "I can't believe it." Judson Bowles, who supervised the Justice Department's draft prosecutions during the critical 1968–71 period, disputed the official contention, saying, "I don't know where they got their statistics. A great majority of the cases involved procedural errors by the draft board." A high-ranking Justice Department official who had once publicly endorsed the 75–80 percent figure privately admitted that "the problem in prosecution resulted from sloppy preparation by Selective Service," with "a hell of a lot" of cases dismissed for that reason.

To get a reasonable picture of what happened to the 210,000 unconvicted cases, fifteen federal prosecutors were asked to estimate what proportion of their cases were dropped for procedural defects. Eight agreed to give estimates, and their collective judgment was that 58 percent were dropped because of local board errors and that, of the 42 percent who submitted to induction, half failed their physical. The official figure of 75–80 percent inducted was four times too high.

All together, the evidence suggests that roughly 115,000 accused draft offenders had their cases dropped because of procedural errors by their local boards—ten times the number later pardoned by Presidents Ford and Carter.

The Wheels of Justice

With so few draft offenders convicted, one must ask why they, and not the others, paid the penalty demanded by law. In the public mind, the convicted offenders are commonly perceived as either activist radicals who flagrantly resisted the draft, or manipulative "draft dodgers" who tried to lie or finagle their way out of the draft. If the 8,800 convicted offenders were truly "worse" than the hundreds of thousands who were not punished, then selective prosecution was justified.

Neither of these two public perceptions is correct, however. A San Francisco judge complained that "the ones we wanted to convict, we couldn't; the best people who came before us were the ones we had to convict. It was all a terrible game of Russian roulette." Flagrant or manipulative draft evaders regularly availed themselves of technical defenses that set them free. Most successful prosecutions were against those whose religious or political principles, poor counseling, or general misfortune kept them from raising defenses necessary to avoid conviction.

Manipulative "draft dodgers" were rarely caught. Stewart Horn was the exception. He stayed in college for eight years, eventually losing his student deferment because of his slow progress in school. After three unsuccessful appeals to extend his student deferment, he applied for a CO exemption. After that was denied, and after he lost two more appeals, Horn was ordered to report for induction. One day after he was required to appear at the induction station, he applied for a hardship postponement because of his wife's pregnancy. His local board granted him a nine-month extension. After the baby arrived, Horn fled to Canada. He was unhappy with life in exile, so he came home and was convicted. Still, had Horn been properly counseled at trial, his CO application and many appeals almost surely would have given rise to a sound technical defense.

The public's impression of the convicted draft offenders was reinforced by a series of well-publicized cases of fraud or deception, in which the perpetrators were caught and punished. The head of the Young Republican Leadership Conference in Washington, D.C., was sentenced to two years in prison for obtaining fraudulent deferments from his draft board. After an FBI investigation, draft evasion organizations were uncovered in New York City and Cleveland; thirty-eight fathers and sons were arrested for paying up to $5,000 for false papers that would have entitled the sons to draft exemptions. A New York City draft board official was convicted for selling deferments and exemptions for as much as $30,000. In southern California, an orthodontist gave several patients cut-rate braces that had no therapeutic value. One of his patients was convicted for conspiring to avoid the draft, and the orthodontist himself fled to Mexico to escape prosecution.

The publicity generated by these cases, along with the press attention given the more radical exiles in Canada, shifted attention away from the much larger number of persons who quietly accepted conviction as a matter of principle. Willard Gaylin, a Columbia University psychologist, conducted lengthy interviews with dozens of imprisoned draft offenders in 1968, and he was "shocked" at his "naïve assumptions" about the kind of people they were. Expecting political radicals and antiwar activists, he discovered gentle, compassionate people with deep moral and religious principles.

When President Ford's Clemency Board reviewed more than eighteen hundred cases of convicted draft offenders in 1975, the members were startled by the sincerity and decency of the people involved. As a consequence, it virtually abandoned Ford's alternative service requirement and recommended outright pardons for four out of five applicants. These individuals were rarely college-educated, upper-middle-class white radicals. An unexpectedly large percentage came from economically disadvantaged backgrounds. Many were blacks and Spanish-speaking persons. Four of every five were deeply opposed to the war, having committed their offenses as a matter of principle. Of this group, less than 1 percent had ever been convicted of other felony crimes, less than 1 percent had serious drug problems, and few had been fugitives. About a third were Jehovah's Witnesses, Muslims, or Quakers. As Gaylin noted, the persons convicted of draft violations

> . . . were service-oriented individuals who believed that a man must be judged by his actions, not his statements, and that ideals and behavior were not separable phenomena. And assuredly they were not the population at which the Selective Service Act was directed, for under the intention of the act most of these boys were indeed CO's.

These individuals were convicted because they were unwilling or unable to avail themselves of the many easier paths to escape from the draft. Gaylin found that one-third of those he interviewed could have easily qualified for deferments or exemptions, had they wished. One was almost blind, and another had a badly injured leg. Rather than accept easy ways out, they refused to cooperate with the draft system as a matter of principle.

Matt Morris wrote letters to his draft board explaining his antiwar beliefs. "The draft board said that since I was a declared Quaker they were willing to exempt me. . . . I felt that even though I qualified, there were people whose feelings were as sincere as mine who could not. If I were to cop out and take the exemption, I would be leaving them in the lurch. This would have been unethical." Morris went to prison for refusing induction.

Philip Walker's draft board went to great lengths to prevent him from committing a draft offense:

> Shortly after I had applied for I-O [CO] classification, my draft board had written that I would be so classified when my student deferment was up. . . . Three months before I was to graduate, Johnson announced that the military had been bombing North Vietnam for several months. I wrote him a letter of disaffiliation and enclosed my draft cards. An undersecretary sent them to the Iowa state draft board, and some officer returned them to me with a note saying he understood and he would direct my local board to classify me I-O. I re-returned the cards, saying he didn't understand that I no longer cared to be a member of his little organization, and that I definitely wouldn't carry the membership cards. A few months later, my local board sent a I-A classification card, which I duly returned. . . .

Walker then received an induction order, which he refused to obey. His board reopened the case, inviting him to a hearing which he refused to attend. They sent him another draft card, which he returned. Finally, after disobeying a second induction order, Walker was convicted and sentenced to three years in prison.

Clifford Jones was past twenty-five, just six months away from permanent disqualification from the draft. He was working as an aeronautical engineer for the federal government, which qualified him for an occupational deferment. Believing that the draft system was illegal and immoral, Jones refused to apply for a routine extension of his deferment. He then refused induction. When Jones's case reached the Supreme Court, it was denied a hearing. Ultimately, Jones came to regard his efforts as futile and self-destructive:

> The whole fight accomplished nothing. It took me four and a half years and $20,000 in legal fees. I went through eight different jobs and had a total of nine months' unemployment and an intense amount of personal anguish.

Just as some refused deferments and exemptions, so others resisted the temptation to raise technical defenses, preferring instead to challenge the fundamental legality of the war. Richard Lavelle fired his counsel, a nationally renowned draft attorney, who wanted to soften the antiwar character of Lavelle's defense and thereby keep him out of prison. Lavelle insisted on "maintaining my fundamental indictment against U.S. policy as criminal before morality and law," and he refused to raise any technical defenses in his own behalf. Lavelle was convicted and sentenced to five years in prison.

Frank Burton insisted on defending himself. His judge gave him a copy of the procedural rules and coached him about the defenses he could raise in his behalf. Burton ignored the judge's help, telling the jury that the rightness of the war was the issue they should debate. The judge had to overrule him, causing an uproar that left three persons charged with contempt and a cleared courtroom. It took the jury less than an hour to find Burton guilty.

Federal judges, liberal and conservative alike, refused to accept direct legal challenges against the war, and defendants like Lavelle and Burton almost always were convicted. The only exception was when Massachusetts Judge Charles Wyzanski dismissed the case against John Jeffron Sisson, Jr. Sisson was a graduate of the Phillips Exeter Academy and Harvard College whose defense, very simply, was that he refused to participate in an immoral war. Working in 1968 as a reporter for a civil rights newspaper in Alabama, Sisson refused to apply for CO status because he knew he did not qualify as a religious objector. After he failed to report for induction, Judge Wyzanski dismissed his case, declaring that Sisson could not "constitutionally be subjected to military orders . . . which may require him to kill in the

Vietnam conflict." The Supreme Court refused to overrule the dismissal, although it later declared in the *Gillette* case that "selective" objectors like Sisson did not qualify for CO status.

Many others were convicted because they failed to raise good defenses not as a matter of principle, but as a consequence of poor legal representation. Although the network of skilled draft counselors reached almost everywhere, it was most accessible to college students and others with connections to the antiwar movement. Many draft offenders never knew about this network and had to rely on less experienced local attorneys whom they discovered through haphazard means. One federal judge recalled that general practitioners had trouble with draft cases unless he personally advised them about the defenses available to their clients. A prosecutor admitted that most of his convictions "were against lawyers who were not very good." One common ploy of the inexperienced attorney was the insanity defense. An attorney would bring in psychiatrists who claimed his client was temporarily or partially insane, arguing that his affliction prevented him from submitting to induction but did not affect his other behavior. This tactic never worked. Herbert Black was the victim of poor representation. Black's attorney misplaced his CO application while redecorating his office, and forgot to mail it on time. Although Black would have qualified for a CO exemption, he was convicted for refusing to report for induction.

Many people were convicted despite the apparent illegality of their induction orders. One out of ten applicants to President Ford's Clemency Board was convicted after being improperly denied CO claims that were valid under the doctrine of *Seeger* and *Welsh*. Typically, local boards erred by insisting that CO status was reserved to members of specific religious sects. Either the lawyers representing these men failed to raise proper arguments at trial, or judges were ill informed as to the current state of the law.

A great many convicted draft offenders failed to realize that they qualified as CO's under existing law. Raul Ramirez asked his board for a CO application form in 1969, but the religious orientation of the form discouraged him from filling it out. Ramirez heard about the *Welsh* case, and he asked the board to give him another form. When they sent him the identical one, he again failed to complete it. He believed that it was impossible for him to express his beliefs properly on a form designed for members of organized religions. A draft counselor would have told Ramirez to attach his own statement to the form, but without such advice he never got CO status, later refused induction, and was convicted.

Even members of pacifist religious sects did not always receive the CO exemptions to which they were entitled. Peter Wagler was raised in an Amish family. When he came of age, he stopped attending church, although he still subscribed to the group's principles. Although Wagler qualified as a CO even under the old, pre-*Seeger* standards, his local board denied his claim, citing his poor church attendance as its reason.

As in earlier wars, Jehovah's Witnesses went to prison rather than cooperate with the requirements of the Vietnam-era draft. Despite their obvious qualification as conscientious objectors, almost two thousand Jehovah's Witnesses were convicted of draft offenses. The Witnesses were typically working-class people, polite, deeply committed, and not highly educated. They often brought their church leaders, families, and friends with them to court. Their trials were religious experiences, a confirmation of the depth of their beliefs. The teachings of the Watchtower Bible and Tract Society preclude participating in any war except Armageddon. "Actually, you can't call us 'resisters,'" commented Witness Paul Jenkins. "We believe Satan uses the worldwide political system, which the Book of Revelations calls 'a wild beast,' to cause wars, so we don't take political stands or participate in wars." Many Witnesses refused CO status and insisted that they qualified for ministerial exemptions instead. They all had ministerial duties, but rarely as full-time jobs; Selective Service regulations required that they be denied ministerial exemptions for that reason.

Most local boards did give them CO status, with or without their consent. However, many Witnesses then refused to perform alternative service, and that is what led to their convictions. Jenkins called Witnesses who obeyed draft board alternative-service orders "immature" in their beliefs, because their religion required them to refuse the command of any institution whose sole purpose was war. However, as

Jenkins noted, "if a Witness is ordered by a judge to alternative service, he can accept it then." Witnesses who were convicted and sentenced to two years of alternative service had no religious problem in completing it. After 1970, Witnesses were seldom sent to prison. Yet Abner Johnson came to court for refusing to obey his draft board, explained Witness doctrine to the judge, and promised to perform any alternative service ordered by the court. The judge, notwithstanding, sentenced Johnson to prison.

Black Muslims also felt the full force of the law. Members of the Nation of Islam refuse on religious grounds to fight in any war not declared by Allah. According to the Justice Department and many draft boards, they were not conscientious objectors because they objected only "to certain types of war in certain circumstances." The Muhammad Ali case attracted public attention to pacifist Muslims in 1966 when he asked his Kentucky draft board for a CO exemption. The board found his beliefs insincere, to which Ali replied:

> It would be no trouble for me to accept [induction] on the basis that I'll go into the armed services boxing exhibitions in Vietnam, or traveling the country at the expense of the government. . . . If it wasn't against my conscience to do it, I would easily do it. I wouldn't raise all this court stuff and I wouldn't go through all of this and lose and give up the millions that I gave up and my image with the American public, that I would say is completely dead and ruined and so I wouldn't turn down so many millions and jeopardize my life walking the streets of the South and all of America with no bodyguard if I wasn't sincere.

Ali was convicted in June 1967 for refusing induction, sentenced to five years in prison, and stripped of his heavyweight championship. Four years later (throughout which he was free on bond), the Supreme Court reversed his conviction on technical grounds. Ali went free, but about one hundred other Muslims did not.

While four-fifths of those convicted for draft offenses were confirmed war resisters, the rest were prosecuted much as if the draft law were a kind of federal vagrancy statute. Most of these two thousand individuals were hard-luck youngsters who lived at society's fringe. They often came from broken homes, disproportionately from the South. They had below-average IQs and usually were high-school dropouts. Many had serious drug or alcohol problems. Some, as Willard Gaylin found, fit "the stereotype of the self-destructive, unrealized goof-up." Robert Jackson was sent three separate induction orders, and each time he failed to report. The first time, he had gotten into a fight and been hospitalized for stab wounds. The next time, he was in jail for a minor offense. The third time, he was addicted to drugs. Jackson's draft board pressed charges, and he was convicted.

People like Jackson often moved from place to place, never bothering to tell their families or their local boards how to locate them. They used their draft cards for identification, never really understanding what the draft involved. When their turn came for induction, they could not be found. These men probably would have submitted to induction instead of going to prison, yet many were obviously disqualified for the draft. John Blass had an IQ of 49 and a sixth-grade education. Paul Allen's wife was in the midst of a serious kidney operation, which doctors didn't expect her to survive. He was her sole means of support and was qualified for a hardship deferment under any reasonable standard. Luther Wilson's father was dead, and his mother was seriously ill with sickle cell anemia. His draft board denied his request for a hardship deferment. Ernest Eckhart had a disabling physical injury which embarrassed him when he had to undress in front of other persons. He refused to report for his preinduction physical. Even though Eckhart's disability qualified him for a medical exemption, his draft board classified him I-A. But being disqualified for military service was not a valid defense to a draft violation, and each of these men was convicted.

Others committed trivial, even accidental violations of Selective Service regulations—usually for failure to keep draft boards informed of their whereabouts. When Paul Taliaferro moved to a new address, he reported his change of address to the local post office, enabling mail to reach him, but he never reported the change to his draft board. Steven Greene had his mother telephone his new address to the local board. Unfortunately, his mail often failed to reach him because he neglected to put his name on his mailbox. Robert Craig continued to receive mail at home while he was away at college. However, his father had recently died, and his mother was reluctant to see her only son go to Vietnam. Without telling him, she returned all letters from his draft board. Taliaferro, Greene, and Craig were all convicted by overzealous prosecutors.

There were obvious dangers of abuse in a statute that could be applied arbitrarily to individuals whom local officials wanted to punish. In Mississippi and Louisiana, the draft was used as a weapon to intimidate and imprison black civil rights workers. Bennie Tucker, later the mayor of a small Mississippi town, had his CO application denied because, according to his draft board, he "caused nothing but trouble." After his election to the city council, he was issued four induction orders. Hubert Davis filed to run for mayor of another Mississippi town and immediately received his induction order. Robert James was granted CO status by a Mississippi draft board that was unaware of his local civil rights activities. After working for sixteen months in two local hospitals and having his work become better known, his draft board ordered him to report to a new alternative service job in a distant town. He refused the order and was sentenced to five years imprisonment. Mississippi civil rights worker Willie Jordan reported for induction a few minutes late, and induction station officials refused to process him. For that offense, Jordan was sentenced to five years in prison.

An extreme case of harassment involved Mrs. Jeanette Crawford, a New Orleans civil rights leader who refused to testify before the Louisiana House Committee on Un-American Activities. Within a week, all three of her sons were ordered for induction or for preinduction physicals. James, her oldest son, was accused of not having registered for the draft. The fact that he had been in the Army for thirteen years did not deter prosecutors from pursuing him or the FBI from staking out the Crawford house to arrest him. At the time, James was in Germany. When his commanding officer learned of the warrant, James was put in the stockade. While James' problems were resolved in a few days, his brother Warren paid a heavier penalty. Warren refused induction, was convicted, and was given the most severe sentence of any nonviolent draft offender of the Vietnam era—six concurrent five-year sentences.

Civil rights workers and Black Muslims usually paid the heaviest penalties for draft law violations. Throughout the country, the prison sentences imposed on blacks averaged about one year longer than those given to whites. Stiff sentences were also assessed against radical activists who used the courtroom as a forum for directly challenging American involvement in the war.

However, these sentencing inequities were minor compared with the overwhelming differences in punishment from one judicial district to the next. In 1968, while San Francisco judges were offering probation to most offenders, south Texas judges sentenced fourteen of sixteen to five-year prison terms. An individual's sentence rarely depended on the seriousness of his offense; it usually hinged on the judge sitting before him.

Congress had written the law to include prison sentences, but judges still had discretion to decide whether imprisonment served a valid purpose. Refusing the draft did not indicate behavior that was likely to be dangerous to society in the future, but most violations were deliberate and would have been repeated had the occasion arisen. One federal judge observed that draft offenders "don't threaten society in the same sense as do—for example—professional bank robbers. They probably threaten it more, in the long run, by making law violation fashionable, and suggesting that every man is free to obey or disobey the law, as it pleases him." Another judge insisted that he "didn't become a judge to preside over the decline and fall of the American republic."

Some judges believed that, regardless of the moral rightness or wrongness of an individual's action, the government had a responsibility to uphold its duly constituted laws. As one noted, "I am opposed to conscription. I also believe that the war in Vietnam is both immoral and impractical. My sentence policies are based upon the fact that as long as a law exists, it should be imposed to effectuate its intent and purpose." Another judge commented that regardless of his admiration for conscientious draft resisters, "it is their duty legally to comply with the law or accept the penalty as part of their sacrifice to their principles."

A few judges imposed four- or five-year sentences as a means of assuring that individuals would serve about two years before being paroled. As General Hershey once observed,

The young man who assumes a responsibility to answer the call of his country serves a minimum of twenty-four months away from society, work, and family. I see no reason why a Selective Service rejector should be removed from society, work, and family for a lesser period.

Although these arguments made sense in theory, many lawyers and judges who saw these cases were troubled by the fact that the few draft offenders who went to jail did nothing different from the many who did not. One judge spoke with relief about how he sentenced almost everyone to probation: "If I had sentenced these people to jail, I would feel very troubled about it right now."

The moment of sentencing was often a moment of triumph and moral vindication for the draft resister. He had stood his ground in defiance of the institutions of war. One convicted offender even staged a "victory dinner," and his friends sang choruses of "For He's a Jolly Good Felon." Most could easily have left for Canada before starting their prison terms. Border authorities often checked names against an FBI list of criminal defendants, but thousands managed to cross the border without difficulty. Most judges set no bail for draft violators, even after conviction. Others set modest bail of at most a few thousand dollars, which defendants sometimes paid through funds collected by antiwar groups. A few, however, went directly to prison:

> They said that I could be released without bail if I signed a paper saying that I'd appear when my trial came up. I said that I could not honestly say —that I hadn't made up my mind yet. Since I refused to sign, they put $5,000 bail on me. This was beyond anything I could raise. I had to go to jail.

If a convicted offender really wanted to run out his string, he could remain free until all his appeals were lost, after which he would still have ten days to leave the country. However, those who took flight typically did so right after conviction. Andrew Daley of New York City, angry about living in "a nation whose laws and customs did not afford [him] the same opportunities and protection afforded to white citizens," left the country without waiting to see whether his judge would sentence him to probation.

Less than 10 percent of those convicted left the country, and of these most later returned and served their sentences. Some of the other 90 percent might have escaped if they had had more money, but most rejected the idea. Going to Canada meant cutting old ties and making a possibly irreversible change in their lives. Some viewed it as "running away from the fight," a "copout," or worse:

> Up to the very last week [I] considered going to Canada. I checked airlines, thought about the timing of when I'd have to leave, but I just couldn't do it. . . . It's my country and I'm not going to run away from it. Then, in the next few years, after this is all over, if I meet someone who has lost his son in Vietnam, I don't want to have to say that I had run away. There is this thing in me. These guys are getting killed every day, and that's the constant factor of the whole issue. They're Americans, and America is as much a part of me as it is of them. They're being shot at—I don't feel I should run away.

Frequently, the convicted draft refuser faced his prison sentence with optimism. Draft resistance manuals spoke encouragingly of what prison experience could be like for the antiwar martyr: "It can be a source of growth and satisfaction if it comes about as a result of doing what to you is the right thing. . . ." "The noncooperator can find numerous opportunities for creative service with fellow prisoners—in recreational work, education, letter-writing, and fellowship." Willard Gaylin found one new arrival at Allenwood to be full of confidence: "The experience of prison life by itself is a rare one and is a character-building thing. . . . I definitely think it will be."

But a Brooklyn judge, in sentencing Robert Modell to prison, knew better what prison life had in store:

> I take it you look with pride on the possibility of being punished. I think that's foolish. . . . I think you underestimate prison. It is not an experience that should be welcomed. Even in the best of the federal penitentiaries, it is a horrible way to spend a life. It is very damaging and, in some instances, dangerous.

A few draft offenders could not tolerate prison life. A member of the Hare Krishna sect escaped from prison because of physical threats and harassment by inmates and guards. Another developed a heroin addiction while in prison and returned a few years later after an armed robbery he committed to support his habit.

A draft offender's prison experience depended largely on where he was sent. One inmate who served his time in Allenwood, the white-collar prison of the federal system, complained about the antiwar movement's "ridiculous" claims that draft resisters were being mistreated: "I've seen in certain publications where we were dragged nude, a thousand yards, down freezing corridors and things like that. They may mean well, but the exaggerations turn me off."

Instead, abuse came in subtle ways. Prison officials sometimes offered to set up draft offenders as "model prisoners," giving them extra privileges in return for not politicizing other inmates. When they refused to comply, they were sometimes the victims of retaliation by the guards. As a fellow inmate recalled, "These kids [took] a lot of abuse that isn't in the record . . . much more than a typical prisoner." They were often denied participation in work-release or rehabilitation programs, the common explanation being that they did not need rehabilitation.

Even those who adjusted well found the day-to-day routine annoying and degrading. One spoke the mind of many when he complained about things "that sound petty on description: . . . when they distribute the mail they make cracks about your mail . . . the hassles in the clothing room . . . the trying to get the right size . . . the indifference . . . the standing up, always in line, standing for count . . . the patronizing." Above all, they were bored. One wrote, "I'm tired of being in jail. There is no fellowship here—and I am lonely." Another went over in his mind "at least a thousand times" his experiences in high school and college, thinking "who'd ever thought just four years ago. . . ." For most, prison was an unending nightmare. As nonviolent individuals, they had little in common with other inmates. As pacifists, they had little in common with prison guards. It was hard for them just to "do time" and let the months slip away. Their friends and families suffered, too. Marriages and engagements were broken off, and the wives and girl friends who remained faithful sometimes had a very difficult time:

[Our baby] arrived prematurely, early in May. Having been promised a call to Bob after the baby's birth, I eagerly called the prison. The officials refused to let me speak to Bob, even after I explained that the baby was having difficulty breathing and was in danger of death. "If she dies, call back," the guard told me, and hung up.

Few kept track of their legal situations while behind bars, and lawyers rarely watched for new law that might have overturned convictions. The Justice Department refused to review the files of the four thousand persons whose convictions had been brought into question by the 1970 *Welsh, Gutknecht,* and *Mulloy* decisions. Two years later, having done nothing about the problem, Justice Department official Kevin Maroney wrote Senator Edward Kennedy that a comprehensive review of convicted draft violators' cases would serve no meaningful purpose:

> Since twenty-two months have elapsed following the Supreme Court's decision in *Welsh,* and twenty-six months since the decision in *Gutknecht,* I believe it may safely be assumed that any individuals who were convicted prior to these decisions, and whose conviction would have been affected by them, are no longer imprisoned.

Marvin Karpatkin and the Central Committee for Conscientious Objectors prepared habeas corpus petitions for a few inmates, but nothing was done on a nationwide scale. Many months after the Welsh decision, Paul Davis was transferred from Ashland to Springfield prison, where he first learned that his case could be overturned. He then wrote a letter to a draft attorney and got out of jail. Roger Buford had been punitively reclassified by his local board, making his conviction illegal under *Gutknecht.* By the time he found out about the decision, wrote his own brief, and got out of prison, there were just three days left to his sentence. Buford's draft board then reclassified him I-A. No one knows what happened to him after that.

As a general rule, federal parole boards treated draft resisters well. Most spent six to twelve months in prison, less than half their original terms. There were exceptions: Richard Duvall of New Orleans was imprisoned for four years, most of it in maximum security at Terre Haute.

Like most other inmates, draft offenders wondered what would happen to them when they finally went home. They had spent months or years living among men who spent their lives in and out of prison. Having been warned since childhood about prisons and "ex-cons," they could not be sure how the outside world would react to them or what their own feelings would be:

What concerns me . . . is whether I will remain bent out of shape after I get out. Having been in an almost constant state of suppressed rage for two years, will I be able to relax, to regain some of the gentleness and tenderness which I was trying to nurture?

A few were just plain angry: "The one thing that has changed is that I'm no longer dedicated to nonviolence." John Peters, the founder of PISS (Prison Information and Support Service), refused to change out of his prison uniform to fill out the necessary forms of release. Guards carried Peters away from Lewisburg prison in the middle of the night and delivered him to Boston, where they left him on the steps of his parents' house. Inmate Vincent McGee admired the draft offenders' personal qualities when they came to prison, and he was saddened by the transformation that so many experienced:

The assets that they have in education, human concern, and dedication are mostly lost in the prison experience. The horror of that experience for these strong men of gentle conscience and demeanor sets too many of them against the system and cost the nation, on their release, years of dedication to community service and skill.

Back home, one of the ex-convict's first discoveries was that his draft challenge had cost him irretrievable years. Typically, five years had passed between his first induction refusal and his release from prison. The years had involved so much uncertainty and anxiety that they had seldom been used to prepare for the future.

Readjustment was not made easier by hometown receptions that were often antagonistic. One former inmate passed an examination for a post office job, only to learn that his draft conviction made him ineligible. Another entered law school and discovered two years later that his state bar would not let him practice law. In Mississippi, an ex-inmate's parents suffered so much that they had to move away from their hometown.

Others fared better, but only after years of readjustment. Don Kelleher experimented with drugs and joined the Weathermen in New York City; he later enrolled in nursing school, where he performed so well that he earned admission to one of the nation's finest medical schools. Chris Endicott was a onetime Harvard classics major who worked as a roofer in Vermont after getting out of prison; Endicott is now finishing Rutgers Law School and has been assured by local bar officials that his draft conviction will not keep him from practicing law. Paul Jenkins found that putting "Selective Service violator" on his resumé did not keep him from getting several jobs as an accountant: "The phrase was enough to prompt conversations which usually turned out pretty nicely." The legal consequences of a felony conviction—loss of voting rights, licenses, and public employment opportunities—seldom affected their lives significantly.

Some convicted draft offenders do not regret having made sacrifices for the sake of principle. Peter Halsted, who spent thirty-three months in prison, commented that "morals cease to be morals, and beliefs to be beliefs, when they are set to stew in a pot of random concerns about one's personal comfort or the fate of one's skin." Many insist that their personal stands were vindicated when America turned away from the war:

> Friends ask us if we would do the same thing again, and our answer is "yes." ... The iron bars of prison were temporary, and now we have free minds. When our children ask us what we did to stop the killing, we can answer them.

For most, however, there remains a sense of failure and frustration. The war ended, but only after many years. The time they spent in prison did not seem to affect the public's attitude about the war:

As one is ground between the massive mill wheels of the U.S. Department of Justice, one of the first things to be crushed is the belief that his action had made any difference in the imperial policy. . . . the only problems you have caused, you have caused yourself and those you love.

Some had carried the original high hopes of the resistance movement with them into prison. They expected to be joined by thousands, possibly tens of thousands of others. The prisons were to be turned into concentration camps of antiwar patriots, and the conscience of the world would be shocked. But once they got to prison, they discovered that they were just another casualty in a resistance movement that suddenly had other tactics, other purposes. Lonely and forgotten, they were unable to find any good reason why they, along with so few others, were in prison. Years of struggle against the legal system had been turned into pointless self-sacrifice:

I think this was a political act—hoping that if enough of us took this course it would create chaos in the draft. It obviously isn't working. If everyone who said he would go to jail rather than serve had gone, the joint would be jammed. It should be at its peak. I'm afraid as a political act it's a disappointment.

Were they to have a chance to relive their lives, many would have accepted deferments, exemptions, and technical defenses as valid means of resisting the war. Others would have gone to Canada. After getting out of prison, one disappointed ex-convict encouraged others to resist the draft, but warned that "one should fight the battle but duck the bullets."

All the while, the public's attention was transfixed either on the POW's in North Vietnam or the exiles in Canada. In prison and out, the draft offenders felt "the same way Antigone did—behind walls and forgotten." In one sense, however, imprisoned draft offenders were very much on the minds of millions of American youngsters. In living rooms across the country, the choice was made clear for nineteen- and twenty-year-olds who might have had second thoughts about obeying their draft boards: Report for induction, or you'll go to prison. Two million complied with induction orders, and two million others were pressured into enlisting by the threat of induction. If nobody had been convicted, if nobody had been sent to prison, then many of these people might have had second thoughts, and the draft system—and the war effort—might well have collapsed.

IV | DESERTERS

Over the Hill

In the lexicon of military crimes, few are more serious than desertion in combat. The Senate Armed Services Committee called it a "crime against one's country," a "crime against citizenship," and a "crime against fellow servicemen." In times of declared war, desertion is punishable by death. In World War II, forty-nine men were sentenced to death for desertion, although only one, Eddie Slovik, was executed. Only wartime espionage, where the death penalty is mandatory, is punished more severely. The Vietnam war was never formally declared by Congress, so no American deserters faced the death penalty. But it was a full-scale war, and battlefield desertion was no less serious a matter.

The unpopularity of the war gave desertion an added dimension. By the late 1960s, the offense began to have political overtones, and desertion came to be seen as the military counterpart of draft resistance. Yet throughout the war, politically motivated deserters were far outnumbered by those whose absences were not direct responses to their feelings about the war. Nor was desertion, despite the attention it has received, the prevailing form of indiscipline within the armed forces. The 100,000 Vietnam-era troops discharged for absence offenses were dwarfed by the 463,000 who received less-than-Honorable discharges for other reasons.

Throughout the war, tens of thousands of soldiers were separated from service each year for a variety of offenses against military authority—AWOL, drugs, insubordination, racially motivated assaults, fragging, and so forth. Much of this was not a direct consequence of the war in Southeast Asia, but the imprint of Vietnam was unmistakable on this generation of soldiers. Most of those who got into trouble were draftees or draft-induced enlistees, and they served in a military undergoing a massive crisis in morale and discipline. In 1971, for example, a random group of 100 Army soldiers would have produced the following disciplinary incidents:

7	Acts of desertion
17	AWOL incidents
20	Frequent marijuana smokers
10	Regular narcotics users
2	Disciplinary discharges
18	Lesser punishments
12	Complaints to congressmen

The crisis was a product of many factors: manpower policies that relied heavily on men whose backgrounds made them only marginally suitable for service and who were, consequently, much more likely to become disciplinary problems; social turmoil in civilian society, manifested by drug abuse, racial strife, and antiauthoritarian attitudes; the strains caused by the war itself; and the failure of military leaders to strike a proper balance between permissiveness and uncompromising discipline. These problems resulted in more than half a million servicemen's receiving General, Undesirable, Bad Conduct, or Dishonorable Discharges.*

---

*Official military terminology regarding the types of discharges is extremely complex and confusing to the uninitiated and, indeed, to many in the armed forces. Here is a short glossary: Honorable—the best and most common discharge, conferring full entitlement to veteran's benefits. General—considered "under honorable conditions" but less meritorious than the fully Honorable, likewise conferring full entitlement to benefits. Undesirable—issued "under other-than-honorable conditions" imposed administratively for substandard behavior of a culpable nature, generally resulting in denial of benefits. (In 1976, the designation "Undesirable" was abolished and replaced by "other than honorable conditions.") Bad Conduct—a "punitive" discharge imposed after conviction by a court-martial for a criminal violation of military law. Dishonorable—a "punitive" discharge adjudged after conviction by a general court-martial for an especially serious offense.

The public's perception of these half million men is dominated by its general attitude toward deserters, and its belief that all such men are simply quitters unwilling to fight. John Saunder abandoned his patrol in Vietnam, and wandered for days in the jungle before encountering some Viet Cong soldiers. They turned down his offer to help them fight, but they had him tape anti-American broadcasts and write propaganda leaflets. Eventually, the twenty-one-year-old Marine sergeant made his way from Vietnam to Stockholm. After about a week in Sweden, he surrendered to the American embassy. Convicted by court-martial for desertion and aiding the enemy, Saunder was sentenced to a long term in military prison.

John Mason was ordered to participate in a parachute drop on a hill, but he asked to be left behind. Turned down, he walked away from camp. When Mason was caught several weeks later, he was on a truck, without his rifle, heading for Saigon. His clothes torn and his face badly bruised, he claimed that he had been kidnapped by the Viet Cong. He, too, was court-martialed and sent to prison.

Every war has its Saunders and Masons, but Vietnam produced another kind of battlefield deserter—the conscientious war resister. Mark Gilman deserted from a search-and-destroy mission after his platoon was ambushed. "I saw my buddy shot beside me," he recalled. "That's what made me desert. I could think of no good reason why he should die, why I should die, why any GIs should die in Vietnam." Gilman made his way to Sweden and settled into a life in exile.

Originally discharged from the Marines as unfit, Terry Samuels worked hard to get his draft status changed so he could join the Army. "I was red, white, and blue all the way," he recalled. Trained as an infantryman, Samuels resisted his father's urgings to desert rather than go to Vietnam. But once there, his experiences scarred him deeply. "I went to mental hygiene at Cu Chi about six months after I got there and told them my head was getting pretty messed up. . . . I only kept track of the innocent people I killed, the civilians, prisoners, a lot of NVA and VC who we'd captured and who I'd been told to 'take care

---

Both punitive discharges preclude benefits. In the eyes of the veteran, anything worse than a General is considered a "bad" discharge.

of.' It came to thirty-seven." Refusing to participate in the war any longer, Samuels left his unit and found passage to Canada.

Ernest Gruening, one of only two senators to vote against the Tonkin Gulf Resolution, believed that soldiers who deserted under fire were committing principled, even heroic acts:

> It is clear that when they got into Southeast Asia and saw the innocent noncombatants, the burning of women and children with napalm, the saturation bombing which destroyed homes, hospitals, and whole families, making homeless refugees of those that were not killed, turned loose in a defoliated and craterized wasteland—these nonresisting draftees could no longer participate in this massive butchery, and deserted.

Hawks and doves alike used the image of battlefield desertion to make political and moral arguments that advanced their own points of view. This led to an "either-or" stereotype of deserters, with the public assuming that most deserters left because they refused to participate in combat. The only thing in doubt was the rightness or wrongness of what they did.

Yet, by historical standards, combat-related desertion was rare in Vietnam. More than 100,000 self-absented soldiers were still at large when the Civil War ended in 1865, almost all of them front-line troops. As recently as World War II, more than 20,000 soldiers were convicted for desertion in combat. But throughout the Vietnam war, only a few thousand men were court-martialed for unauthorized absence in Vietnam or for disobeying orders to go to the combat zone, and just twenty-four were in fact convicted of deserting with intent to avoid hazardous duty. In the Army, for example, fourteen soldiers were tried for this offense between 1968 and 1972, the peak years of the war. In only six cases did the court find the defendant guilty as charged. All but one of those convicted were sentenced to one-to-five-year prison terms.

Although there were several incidents in which entire units refused to go into combat, there was little battlefield desertion in Vietnam. Commander after commander can recite instances of short-term absences, but few can recall cases like Saunder's or Mason's. A military judge who served in Vietnam for two years at the height of the war could recall only one case of bona fide desertion, and that involved a soldier who escaped from the stockade while facing charges for a violent crime.

The simple fact was that in Vietnam there was no place to go. Almost all lengthy AWOLs involved noncombat troops stationed in Saigon, Da Nang, or other rear areas. Except for brief visits to the local hooch— and even that was risky—troops in the field were in no position to desert. "What are you going to do?" asked one. "Walk through Cambodia?" The Viet Cong were not interested in giving shelter to American deserters. As one of their spokesmen warned, "If GIs desert and go over and live with our forces, they will have a difficult life to lead." With no access to funds and no orders home, only the most enterprising of soldiers could falsify orders or stow away on commercial flights out of the country. Some did make their way to Saigon's "AWOL alley," where they sometimes hid from authorities for months. About one hundred were apparently left behind after the last American combat soldiers left the country, all of whom were eventually picked up by local police before the collapse of South Vietnam.

The easiest way to desert from Vietnam was to take advantage of a mid-tour leave. After five or six months in Southeast Asia, servicemen were allowed to take a week-long "R and R" (rest and recreation) break in places like Hong Kong, Japan, or Hawaii. Once out of Vietnam, they could travel to the United States or, with help from the local antiwar underground, head for Canada or Sweden. Throughout the war, only five thousand servicemen were discharged for deserting in the midst of a Vietnam tour. About half failed to return from R and R, and many of the rest went AWOL from noncombat situations.

Another seven thousand deserted in the United States after receiving orders to report to Vietnam. Some of these men were late-blooming conscientious objectors who did not realize how much they opposed the Vietnam war until confronted with orders to go. But most sincere war resisters chose other times and other ways to take their stands. More than any other single category of deserter, those who refused to report to Vietnam were motivated by fear, not conscience or any other mitigating circumstance. "I hate to admit it, but most of these guys went over the hill to save their necks, not because they opposed the war," said Frank Paquin, who was strongly antiwar while in the service. "The war became an issue only when they were scheduled for Vietnam, and then it was a matter of avoiding being killed." Bill Hansen, an exile in Canada, said that his reason for not going to Vietnam "was initially a fear for my life. That was my first flash. Like, man, I might be killed." Another exile recalled that "I wasn't exactly conscious of the fact that I was a deserter, I was only conscious of the fact that I wasn't going to Vietnam—it's called survival."

Sometimes, the threat of Vietnam was used as punishment, making it easier for men to choose desertion over duty. Jim McAllen described how "the sergeant in charge of my platoon told me that since I had a young wife and child, I should do extra favors for him to be kept off the West Pac quota list. I refused to bow down to his subpar intelligence, and within two weeks I had orders to go to Vietnam. I went home on leave, and I refused to return."

One exile told how his experience at a California missile base made him less reluctant to desert to avoid Vietnam:

> We had a red alert, which meant war to us—there was an attack coming. After we found out the control center made a mistake, and that it was only a practice alert, we discovered that some warrant officers and noncommissioned officers and a couple of other people in prominent positions on the base had gotten into their cars and just flat left—which as far as I was concerned was desertion in the face of the enemy, since we believed we were going to be attacked. When it was realized that "x" number of personnel had fled, we were told not to say anything to anyone, or else they would "get our asses."

In all, twelve thousand individuals either deserted during a Vietnam tour or deserted when they received orders to report to the war zone. They account for a small proportion of the hundred thousand servicemen punished for absence offenses and a tiny fraction of the nearly half million who were stigmatized with less-than-Honorable discharges* for violations of military discipline (see Figure 5). Yet the image of the

---

* The confusion over discharge terminology is compounded by the fact that a "less-than-Honorable" discharge means a General, Undesirable, or worse, while a discharge "under other-than-honorable conditions" means an Undesirable Discharge or worse.

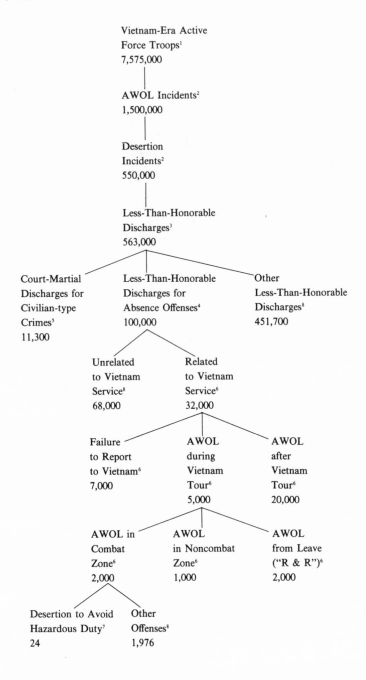

Vietnam-Era Active
Force Troops[1]
7,575,000

AWOL Incidents[2]
1,500,000

Desertion
Incidents[2]
550,000

Less-Than-Honorable
Discharges[3]
563,000

Court-Martial
Discharges for
Civilian-type
Crimes[5]
11,300

Less-Than-Honorable
Discharges for
Absence Offenses[4]
100,000

Other
Less-Than-Honorable
Discharges[8]
451,700

Unrelated
to Vietnam
Service[8]
68,000

Related
to Vietnam
Service[6]
32,000

Failure
to Report
to Vietnam[6]
7,000

AWOL
during
Vietnam
Tour[6]
5,000

AWOL
after
Vietnam
Tour[6]
20,000

AWOL in
Combat
Zone[6]
2,000

AWOL
in Noncombat
Zone[6]
1,000

AWOL
from Leave
("R & R")[6]
2,000

Desertion to Avoid
Hazardous Duty[7]
24

Other
Offenses[8]
1,976

deserter as a man who fled rather than fight persists in the public mind.

The Defense Department has acknowledged that this image is grossly inaccurate. As it commented in an official AWOL study:

> Since the beginning of military forces, the urge to go "over the hill" has been more than some could resist. The reasons are as old as man—financial or family troubles, romantic involvements, earlier misconduct that led to disciplinary action, inability to adjust to military life, or family pressure before going overseas.

Every official analysis of Vietnam-era deserters has found the same thing—that the overwhelming majority were neither conscientious nor cowardly. They were men who decided simply to put their own interests over the day-to-day needs of the military.

Personal and family problems accounted for almost half of all absence offenses. For most enlisted men, military life was their first experience away from home. When their grandmothers died, their mothers fell ill, or their girl friends dropped them, they often wanted to go home as quickly as they could. Frequently, the problem was financial. The military pay scales were so low—starting at $115 per month—that married soldiers sometimes had to go home just to keep their families off welfare. At the height of the war, a Defense Department survey found that roughly seventy thousand military families were living below the poverty level. In 1971, Republican Congressman William A. Steiger of Wisconsin complained of a "definite poverty cycle" for soldiers at some military bases. At Fort Gordon, Georgia, a community services officer told Steiger of the "bleak subsistence existence" of new recruits:

> If you take the typical married first-termer, add his base pay allowance, and subtract his taxes and savings bond payments, he has about $240 a month. You can rent a lousy place for $100 including utilities and roaches, but then you've got to add transportation and carfare because he's living off base— about $50 a month in payments for his car and another $30 for gas and repairs. If you are very frugal, and do all your shopping at the commissary, you can get by on $50 a month. So $230 is taken up, which leaves you $10

for recreation—providing everything else is perfect. Of course, if the kids need dental care or glasses, forget it.

Money problems often exacerbated a soldier's family problems. Gilly Meaks' father committed suicide after suffering from cancer for three years. His mother was partially disabled, unable to work, and his family had no money. Meaks tried to get a hardship discharge, but after a long wait he learned that his papers had gotten lost. Tired of waiting, he went AWOL to support his mother, and was later given a bad discharge.

Peter Clarke had been married for seven months and was the father of a newborn baby girl. A high school dropout, he was working in a local A&P as a stock boy. His father told him the Army would give him an education, pay him well, and help him take care of his family, so he enlisted. After finishing basic training, Clarke was shipped to Fort Ord, California, but his pay was so low that he could not bring his family with him. Upset about their three-thousand-mile separation, his wife stopped answering his letters. Clarke tried, without success, to get leave to go home. Finally, he went AWOL and caught a plane back to New Jersey. Within a week, he was picked up and brought back to Fort Ord. He was reduced in rank, lost pay, and had to pay the plane fare of the two military policemen who arrested him in New Jersey. With his financial situation worse than ever, Clarke's marriage collapsed. His wife met someone close to home who had a good steady job. When she asked him for a divorce, Clarke went AWOL again, and was eventually given a bad discharge.

The military offered a variety of measures to help solve these personal problems—Red Cross counseling, home leave, compassionate reassignments, even hardship discharges—but the mechanisms were seldom administered effectively. Complaints to Congress reached totals as high as 250,000 per year, prompting congressmen to criticize the military's inability to solve the serviceman's problems.

Many soldiers were too impatient or uninformed to ask for help, and others had commanding officers who were insufficiently responsive to their problems. John Morehead went home on leave to get married. The day after his wedding ceremony, a hurricane flooded his mother-in-law's house where he and his bride were living. They lost everything. He got an extension of leave to try to repair the house, but it could not be restored to livable condition. His wife had a nervous breakdown. Morehead asked for a hardship discharge or a six-month emergency leave, but he got neither. He stayed home anyway, in AWOL status, and was later given a bad discharge.

Many deserters complained that military officials added to their problems more than they helped: "The GI has to go to his platoon sarge, and then his first sarge, and then his CO, and the sarge has been around twenty years and knows all the answers. . . . You can't leave without permission, and if you leave anyway, or you leave to complain, you can be AWOL." A Defense Department review board, part of President Ford's 1974–75 clemency program, found many a deserter who insisted that

> the noncommissioned officers over him not only did not help but in some cases intentionally or unintentionally blocked his way from going to higher authority to obtain help. In other cases, alleged indifference on the part of unit officers to listen to or be aware of his problems frustrated the individual. Often, a promise to look into the matter or to help resolve a problem apparently was not followed through. . . .

Similarly, the Presidential Clemency Board found that 14 percent of all absence offenses were attributable to "procedural unfairness" on the part of the military.

Hugh Nolan was waiting at Fort Dix for pending orders to report to Europe. His records were inadvertently shipped ahead, and he was not paid for forty-five days. His family was evicted and forced to live in an automobile. They had no money to buy food. Nolan asked for emergency leave and a short-term loan from the Red Cross, but he got neither. He even traveled to the Pentagon to ask for help, but to no avail. Finally, he found a civilian job, and his family's financial situation began to improve. When his orders for Europe finally came through, Nolan decided to stay home. He was later arrested as a deserter and given a bad discharge.

Sometimes, however, stories of family problems or complaints about military mistreatment were mere alibis for deserters who simply did not like the service. They went home to solve minor personal problems, but stayed away permanently. One Camp Pendleton Marine told his court-martial judge that he had gone AWOL to help his invalid grandmother, but admitted on cross-examination that she lived in Boston and that he never left California while he was AWOL.

These were men whom the military called "bad apples"—immature, undisciplined, and unable to adjust to the constraints of military life. Usually, they came from broken homes and had records of juvenile misconduct. One deserter said he enlisted "because I was getting into trouble all the time, and I felt that service life might settle me down." They coped with the military no better than they coped with anything else. Robert Sherrill described two such individuals who, predictably, got into immediate trouble in the Army:

> Private Johnny Dee Smith's . . . record began with a burglary in the first grade; as he said later, "I've been pulling burglaries ever since." He dropped out of school when the school psychologist said there was no point in his trying to go beyond the ninth grade. He served eight months in jail for burglarizing a safe. The year before he joined the Army, he got into a knife fight with his father and attacked a friend with a pair of scissors. At fifteen he was arrested for carrying a pistol and a machete. He had taken potshots at cows and children. At sixteen he had been arrested for shooting up a house with a twelve-gauge shotgun. At eighteen he was picked up in Las Vegas for possessing drugs and carrying a loaded revolver. He often used narcotics—LSD, amphetamines, codeine, cocaine, morphine, opium, every-thing. At least once he posed nude for a homosexual photographer. Before joining the Army, he attempted suicide by slashing his wrists. But the Army took Smith in without a question. . . . He had just been released from the Modesto, California, State Hospital; he went into the Army as an alternative to becoming a permanent resident in the insane asylum. . . . After one day of basic training, he later recounted, "my nerves were about to blow." And since nothing was done for him at sick call, he went AWOL. . . .

> Peter Watson . . . said he never knew his real father and that his stepfather was "drunk all the time" and beat Watson's mother as well as Watson and his two brothers. Sometimes the stepfather threatened the family with a gun. The longest period Watson lived in one place was one and a half years, with

an aunt and uncle to whom the court had awarded him because his mother and stepfather had by that time abandoned him. Later he lived with older brothers. He quit school in the ninth grade. The years he recalled most fondly were those between the ages of fifteen and eighteen, when he left home and roamed the country, working here as a bus boy, somewhere else as a farm hand, on down the road in a factory—"I was free, and no one was telling me what to do or yowling at me all the time." Then he joined the Army, and everybody began yowling at him again. He couldn't take it, couldn't take the senseless punishment, the senseless restrictions. Four times he fled the Army, four times he was captured and brought back. . . .

If there is such a thing as a "prototype" Army deserter of the Vietnam era, he lived in a small town and grew up in the South. He came from a low-income family, often with only one parent in the home. He had an IQ of 90, and dropped out of high school in the tenth grade. He enlisted to get away from problems back home, to learn a skill, or just to find something to do. He finished advanced training and had almost two years "good time," which often included a full tour in Vietnam. However, he rarely progressed beyond the lowest ranks. He was arrested at least once by civilian police, and he frequently committed other minor infractions against military discipline. After going AWOL once or twice, he went home to stay, usually because of family problems. Two years later, he was arrested and given an undesirable discharge in lieu of court-martial. He entered the service at age eighteen, committed his first serious offense at nineteen, and was discharged at twenty-one. About 75 percent of all deserters were white, but a nonwhite serviceman was twice as likely as a white serviceman to become a deserter. Only about one hundred were women.

Marine deserters were younger and more poorly educated than their Army counterparts. They were more likely to desert because they could not tolerate military life and were punished more severely for their AWOL offenses. Navy deserters were overwhelmingly white, with long histories of petty misconduct and minor punishments. Air Force deserters tended to be black, better educated, and discouraged about the menial tasks to which they had been assigned. They were also more likely to go AWOL at least partly out of opposition to the Vietnam war.

Vietnam-era deserters were typically teenagers who, had they been in civilian employment, probably would have quit or been fired. Had they been in school, they probably would have dropped out or flunked out. In either case, their failure would have set them back a few years, making it harder for them to get training or find a good job. But eventually they would overcome their early mistakes, and no one would care what they had done at age eighteen or nineteen.

In the military, however, quitting is desertion, and may be punished by a long prison term and a bad discharge, a stigma that attaches for life. Questions about the discharge keep appearing on employment forms and keep coming up in conversation. The veteran continually has to pay a price for his youthful mistake.

When the Vietnam-era recruits came to basic training, they saw wall posters describing the consequences of going AWOL. One had the caption "FAMILY DISGRACE" under a picture of a forlorn mother sobbing, her face hidden in her hands. Recruits also saw a thirty-minute color film, *The Smart Way Out,* telling the story of Good Joe and AWOL Johnny. Joe followed the rules, got an Honorable Discharge, and had "years of happiness" as a result. But Johnny "couldn't take his mind off a little girl back home," got an Undesirable Discharge for going AWOL, and led a life of "bitterness, loneliness, and poverty." He ended up as an unemployed drunk, arrested by the police for vagrancy.

Pentagon officials claim that this combination of punishment and warnings was in fact successful, that the rate of Vietnam-era AWOLs was no higher than that of World War II or the Korean War. They claim that there was nothing unique or extraordinary about these offenses; only about 10 percent were motivated by opposition to the war, and the rest were no different from the AWOLs that the military has always experienced.

The statistics are correct, but they vastly understate the impact of Vietnam. Only the rate of short-term AWOL (less than thirty days) was comparable to that of earlier wars, and short-term AWOL almost always involved petty misbehavior that bore little relationship to the war. The statistics for long-term absence offenses tell a much different story. Absences of more than thirty days, administratively called "desertion,"* increased to an unprecedented level. In 1966, the Army and Marines reported about fifteen desertion cases per thousand troops. The rates climbed to more than fifty per thousand in 1969, and about seventy per thousand in 1972. By contrast, long-term absence rates during the Korean War were only about twenty-five per thousand troops.

During the entire period of the Vietnam war, there were approximately 1,500,000 AWOL incidents and 500,000 desertion incidents. At the peak of the war, an American soldier was going AWOL every two minutes, and deserting every six minutes. This had an enormous impact on the ability of the armed forces to function. Absence offenses caused a total loss of roughly one million man-years of military service, almost half the total number of man-years American troops spent in Vietnam. The Senate Armed Services Committee estimated that in 1968 alone, well before AWOL and desertion reached their peak, absenteeism was costing the military the equivalent of ten combat divisions of fifteen thousand men each. While few of these young men were consciously voting against the war with their feet, their behavior was unmistakably connected with the unusual stress which they and the armed forces experienced during the Vietnam era.

The Bottom Third

Gus Peters came from a broken home, dropped out of school after the eighth grade, and was unemployed for most of his teenage years. His IQ was only 62, and he scored around the tenth percentile in his preenlistment aptitude test. His physical condition was no better. Peters was poor military material, and before Vietnam he would have been rejected. But throughout the war, Peters and hundreds of thousands of other men like him were brought into the military via "Project 100,000" or similar manpower programs. Pet-

*Administrative desertion is easily confused with the crime of desertion, which requires the military to prove beyond a reasonable doubt, in a general court-martial, that the soldier intended to remain away permanently, regardless of the length of his absence.

ers was, as a career sergeant called him, "one of McNamara's boys."

These men represented the Defense Department's contribution to the Johnson Great Society. The ostensible purpose of the manpower programs of the 1960s was to apply military training and discipline to the rehabilitation of America's disadvantaged youth. Yet instead of reducing the effect of social and economic inequities, they had the opposite effect. The burden of the war shifted even more to society's less privileged. While these men were volunteering and filling draft quotas, their more favored peers were staying in college, joining the reserves, or figuring out other ways to stay away from Vietnam.

Project 100,000 also had important political advantages for President Johnson, whose foreign policy increasingly began to intrude on domestic concerns. By expanding the pool of potential manpower at the lower end of the scale, his administration could fight the war in Vietnam without resorting to the dramatic and politically undesirable alternatives of mobilizing the reserves or ending college and other popular deferments. The war, despite its increasing call on the nation's manpower resources, did not have to disrupt the daily lives of more affluent and politically vocal citizens.

The enlistment of men like Peters represented a dramatic shift from earlier manpower policies. Following World War II, the armed forces began studying the connection between the background characteristics of recruits and the quality of their military service. *The Ineffective Soldier,* a major postwar study by Eli Ginzburg, examined the causes of poor performance among World War II servicemen. Ginzburg stressed the need to examine carefully the intelligence and education of prospective recruits. He found, for example, that high-school dropouts were five times as likely to perform poorly as those with some college, and three times as likely as those with a high-school education.

Building on Ginzburg's analysis, the armed forces developed a series of tests designed to measure the qualifications of young men for military service. The Armed Forces Qualification Tests were designed to screen out men who could not acquire military skills and to classify those who could in accordance with their mental ability. They divided potential soldiers into five categories, with the lowest, Category V, disqualified from service and the upper three clearly acceptable. It was within Category IV, the marginal group, scoring between the tenth and thirtieth percentiles on the AFQT, that the standards could be altered in response to changing needs.

In the late 1950s and early 1960s, the military took steps to raise the quality of men accepted into service. In 1958, additional tests were developed to limit the number of persons accepted from Category IV. All persons at this level had to score 90 percent or better in at least two aptitude areas to qualify for service. The Pentagon hoped that about half of the Category IV people—who in 1957 were almost 40 percent of the total then being drafted—would be excluded. This would have reduced the total number of Category IV servicemen to about 19 percent of total strength, roughly matching the proportion of volunteers.

High standards proved to be a luxury of peacetime. As the requirements of the Vietnam war began to be felt, enlistment standards were progressively lowered. First, high-school graduates scoring in the top half of Category IV were declared acceptable. Later, Category IV high-school dropouts were allowed to join if they passed an extra battery of tests. These and other changes had an immediate impact on the preinduction rejection rate, which fell from 50 percent in 1965 to 34 percent in 1966.

This easing of enlistment standards was originally meant to be accompanied by an experimental program, the Special Training and Enlistment Program (STEP), offering special remedial programs designed to bring the men up to par with ordinary recruits. However, Congress refused even to test the STEP idea and, in 1965, rejected a $10-million Pentagon request for training, education, and social service programs. Nonetheless, the armed forces continued to accept ever-mounting numbers of recruits with marginal aptitudes and minimal education.

Once the Johnson administration drafted the armed forces to help fight the War on Poverty, military manpower policies focused on the underprivileged in earnest. The Task Force on Manpower Conservation, chaired by Daniel P. Moynihan, discovered in its 1964 report that each year the military rejected 600,000 disadvantaged young men as unfit. Eighty percent of them were high-school dropouts, and about 25 percent had not completed grade school. Almost half came from families with annual incomes under $4,000. The Task Force report, entitled "One-Third of a Nation," proposed a sweeping program of rehabilitation, a program that formed much of the basis for the Johnson administration's War on Poverty that was to come.

President Johnson immediately enlisted the Selective Service System in what Labor Secretary Willard Wirtz called "the most important human salvage program in the history of our country." Selective Service's job was to steer preinduction rejects into federally sponsored assistance programs. Local draft boards sent out 134,000 letters urging people to contact local employment offices for job training and placement. About 20 percent responded, but less than 4 percent were ever referred to jobs. Eventually, only 2,200 got jobs of any kind, and just 189 were enrolled in job training programs.

Selective Service was clearly not equipped to run employment or rehabilitation programs, so attention then turned to the armed forces. Ever since the debate on universal military training in the early 1950s, the idea of using the armed forces to educate, train, and invigorate the youth of America had attracted substantial support. Disadvantaged black youths became special objects of concern. The Pentagon noted that if black representation in the military were increased to its proportion of the population, the unemployment rate among black male teenagers would have been reduced to as little as 7 percent.

The armed forces had traditionally offered blacks more upward mobility than almost any other public or private institution. Nearly 40 percent of young blacks questioned in a 1965 survey gave self-advancement as the reason for enlisting—close to twice the proportion of whites, who were mostly motivated by the draft. Moynihan saw particular benefits for blacks in expanding the military's role. "Very possibly our best hope is seriously to use the armed forces as a socializing experience for the poor—particularly the Southern poor—until somehow their environment begins turning out equal citizens." Moynihan, who was also the author of a controversial report on black family structure, saw the military as

> an utterly masculine world. Given the strains of disorganized and matrifocal family life in which so many Negro youth come of age, the armed forces

are a dramatic and desperately needed change; a world away from women, a world run by strong men and unquestioned authority, where discipline, if harsh, is nonetheless orderly and predictable, and where rewards, if limited, are granted on the basis of performance.

With 40 percent of all blacks scoring in Category IV of the AFQT, the only way to accomplish these goals was to relax standards for enlistment. The result was Project 100,000. Unlike the earlier Project STEP, it was made applicable to draftees as well as volunteers.

Billing it as a Great Society program when he announced it on August 23, 1966, Defense Secretary Robert McNamara promised that Project 100,000 would rehabilitate the nation's "subterranean poor." These youths, said McNamara, "have not had the opportunity to earn their fair share of this nation's abundance, but they can be given an opportunity to return to civilian life with skills and aptitudes which for them and their families will reverse the downward spiral of decay." After serving in the military, they would return to civilian life with an earning capacity "two or three times what it would have been had there been no such program." The Department of Defense, he added, was "the world's largest educator of skilled men." McNamara's words were echoed by General Herman Nickerson, Jr., Deputy Chief of Manpower for the Marines: "Those of our youth who lack education, those who live in ghet-tos, combine the ills of idleness, ignorance, and apathy. Our task is to help cure these ills with education, training, and incentives."

Yet many career officers were skeptical about relaxing standards, especially for draftees who were often not as motivated as volunteers. As the *Army Times* editorialized:

> Are the services likely to get any reasonable mileage from such people? Past performance indicates not. . . . Is this any time to require the services to take on a large scale "poverty-war" training mission? We would think not. The services more than have their hands full with the fighting war.

Despite congressional resistance to STEP just one year earlier, the Pentagon revived plans for special in-service programs to help low-IQ troops pass muster. Secretary McNamara suggested the use of personalized training tapes utilizing closed-circuit television, permitting each man to progress at his own pace. But the war was already a heavy drain on the nation's resources, and once again Congress rejected the funding requests. Rehabilitation programs became but a shadow of what McNamara originally had in mind. About 17,000 recruits took courses designed to improve their reading skills to fifth- and sixth-grade levels, and a little more than 6 percent took advantage of a transition program that offered education and vocational training.

Lacking remedial programs, the military included Project 100,000 recruits in the regular training cycle. Secretary McNamara rationalized this fundamental omission by insisting that "these men should never be singled out or stigmatized as a special group." Classifying them as potential problems, he argued, might make that prediction self-fulfilling. Recruits who failed remedial reading courses were sent on to basic training anyway, and those who did poorly were "recycled" or sent to motivational platoons for extra discipline.

Because low-quality recruits were rarely offered special help, they often performed as poorly as manpower experts predicted. Gus Peters failed basic training, largely because of his reading and writing difficulties. When he tried to learn to be a tank driver, he continued to have problems. Ridiculed by other soldiers and unable to cope with military life, Peters went AWOL and was later given an Undesirable Discharge. After six months in the service, Peters was worse off than before. He still had no skills and no useful job experience, and he now was officially branded a misfit.

Commanding officers generally had little difficulty identifying Project 100,000 men, if only by their poor performance. At least one Army post had a policy of not promoting them beyond the rank of buck sergeant, no matter how good they were. Called the "moron corps" by fellow soldiers, they were commonly abused and disparaged: "They were pretty damn bad. Somebody had to help them get dressed in the morning," explained one officer at Fort Polk. "You had to take more time to explain everything to them. Since they couldn't understand what was going on, they were greater disciplinary problems." Said another, "Lots of these guys just weren't fit to do a job. I had to help one buy a toothbrush and pack his bags so he could report to another duty station."

John Grant had an IQ of 66. He married his wife when she was fifteen and pregnant. Grant could not do even the simplest arithmetic; according to a military psychiatrist, "one couldn't tell whether he was attempting to subtract, add, or was merely stating numbers at random." In one year, Grant went AWOL fifteen times, usually by bribing guards with drugs.

Another Project 100,000 soldier, Kenny Matts, was mentally retarded as the result of a childhood brain injury. He flunked a medic training course and went AWOL. "It was hard to learn in the Army," he said. "I had to take notes, and I couldn't spell."

Grant and Matts were drawn into military service by recruiting campaigns consciously directed at disadvantaged teenagers. Centers were set up in ghettos, and black recruiters were used to "rap with the brothers" on street corners. In *Pawns,* Peter Barnes quoted white Marine recruiters in Oakland, California: "We use their language . . . we say 'man' . . . we even call the cops 'pigs.' " At that office, 120 of the 125 men recruited in one year were from lower-class neighborhoods; of the 120, 90 percent were Category IV or lower, generally with police records, and most were black or Chicano. "President Johnson wanted these guys off the streets," said the colonel heading the Army's San Francisco recruiting office. "The Defense Department gave us an objective. We never had any problem. We got more than one hundred percent every time."

Rarely did Army and Marine advertisements suggest that their main business was fighting. Instead, they stressed the glamour, training, and excitement of military service. The Army advertised the modern technological "Action Army" of helicopters, electronics, and missiles. Murray Polner wrote of an eighteen-year-old he met in basic training who volunteered as a helicopter gunner, one of the most dangerous of combat jobs, "because his recruiter said it was like riding shotgun on a stagecoach in the old west." An ad in *Hot Rod* magazine read: "Vietnam, Hot, Wet and Muddy—Here's the place to make a man."

From 1966 to 1968, Project 100,000 brought in 240,000 recruits, usually to the Army and Marines. Many more Category IV troops were signed up through relaxed standards not officially part of Project 100,000. These were indeed the people whom Moynihan and others had targeted for military service. Forty-one percent were black, and almost 50 percent came from the South. This contrasted with a military-wide black representation of 12 percent, and a southern share of 28 percent. Almost 60 percent of the Category IV recruits came from broken homes, three-quarters were from low-income backgrounds, over 80 percent were high-school dropouts, and half had IQs of less than 85. More than 40 percent had a reading ability at less than a sixth-grade level, and almost 15 percent read below fourth-grade.

Not many qualified for advanced military specialties, and they rarely were offered military jobs helpful to them in civilian life. Over 40 percent of the Project 100,000 men were given combat-related assignments in armor, infantry, or artillery, and half the Army and Marine contingent went to Vietnam. This should have come as no surprise. A study conducted in 1964, before the institution of the special programs, showed that enlisted men with poor educational backgrounds had a very high likelihood of serving in combat specialties. But this was not seen as a problem, perhaps because low-IQ troops were considered good fighting men. One officer commented that he would "prefer a company of riflemen with fifth-grade educations over a company of college men anytime."

However, marginally qualified troops also posed serious disciplinary problems. A Category IV soldier was three times as likely to go AWOL during basic training as the average soldier. He was twice as likely to be given an early discharge, and two and a half times as likely to be court-martialed. Of all those discharged for absence-related or other disciplinary offenses during the Vietnam era, about one-third had AFQT scores in Category IV. Approximately eighty thousand Category IV recruits were sent home with Undesirable, Bad Conduct, or Dishonorable Discharges, and another 100,000 with General Discharges. They may have been mustered in through special standards, but that was not the way they were mustered out.

Ultimately, the War on Poverty proved to be a casualty of the war in Vietnam. By 1970, troop ceilings began to fall, and the notion of using the armed forces as a part of the Great Society passed with the coming of the Nixon administration. Project 100,000 quotas fell to 75,000 that year, and 50,000 the following year. The proportion of Category IV troops recruited outside Project 100,000 fell at the same rate. The military became more exacting about the performance of marginal recruits. In 1968, for example, the Marine Corps dropped less than 7 percent of Category IV soldiers during basic training; by 1971, they were discharging almost half. In 1972, Project 100,000 was officially terminated, and replaced by "New Standards," an equivalent program geared to the upcoming All-Volunteer Force.

The Defense Department still considered Category IV troops to be useful soldiers, as long as they were assigned to the 20 percent of all military jobs for which they had sufficient aptitude. In an era of voluntary enlistment, the Pentagon thought lower-aptitude soldiers would fill lower-skill jobs with more enthusiasm than higher-aptitude men who usually wanted something better. As Roger Kelley, then assistant secretary of defense for manpower, commented:

> There are two kinds of quality mismatches in military jobs. One occurs when people are assigned work that is over their heads. The other occurs when people are underchallenged in their work assignments. Recruiting bright young high school graduates for the bottom fifth of jobs in the Army and Marine Corps is a classic example of the latter kind of mismatch.

With this in mind, Defense Secretary Melvin Laird directed the armed forces to accept additional Category IV troops. But senior military leaders, disillusioned by their experience with Project 100,000, persuaded Congress to block Laird's initiative. By 1975, the proportion of Category IV recruits had fallen to 6 percent, and by 1977, to just 4 percent.

The armed forces have now returned to their pre-Vietnam belief that the military is not the institution for rehabilitating disadvantaged teenagers. "There is an inordinate amount of administrative and training effort involved in handling marginal personnel," said Colonel Samuel Hays, director of West Point's Office of Military Psychology and Leadership:

They have more disciplinary offenses, more vehicle accidents, go AWOL more often, have more personal problems and more mental breakdowns. They take longer to train for the same degree of skill. They are less flexible in their utilization. Their effect on the social solidarity and *esprit* of units to which assigned tends to be negative and destructive. In significant numbers, their ways of thought and habits of life make their barracks a less desirable place to live, thereby tending to drive out the better qualified.

In the opinion of many military leaders, social planners, and liberal critics, Project 100,000 proved a failure. While it expanded the wartime manpower pool, it also required additional resources which the services could ill afford. But above all, it was a failure for the recruits themselves. They never got the training that military service seemed to promise. They were the last to be promoted and the first to be sent to Vietnam. They saw more than their share of combat and got more than their share of bad discharges. Many ended up with greater difficulties in civilian society than when they started. For them, it was an ironic and tragic conclusion to a program that promised special treatment and a brighter future, and denied both.

Kooks, Heads, Brothers

"The young soldier just does things to irritate us," said one veteran sergeant. "I obey because it's the Army. They don't, often because of no reason other than they're supposed to."

"There's a guy sitting on top of a half-truck with twenty-five people around, he's smoking a big joint, and nobody says anything about it," commented another. "They question you, they ask why. We say because we're soldiers. But that's not reason enough for them."

The attitudes and characteristics of the Vietnam generation of soldiers were unique in American military history. Even had there not been a difficult war, these young men would have severely tried the patience and resources of the armed forces, just as they did the other institutions in America they confronted. "Kooks," one general called them, "men who are coming in undisciplined, the product of a society that trains them to resist authority."

They were, in spirit, like the legendary "Kool-Aid Kid" of Fort Polk, Louisiana. The Kid balked when his commander tried to get him to buy U.S. savings bonds, and he tried to persuade his comrades to join him in refusing. In retaliation, the commander had him court-martialed for failing to salute a chaplain and for not keeping an orderly bunk. Angry at getting a six-month sentence, the Kid reached for the only thing handy—a pitcher of cherry fruit drink—and threw it at the court-martial officers. He was then charged with "assault with Kool Aid" and given a Bad Conduct Discharge.

The young men of this generation spoke a different language, affected different life-styles, and had a different view of themselves, their country, and the Army. In line with the so-called permissiveness of the times, they did not take willingly to the authoritarian nature of military society, a mode of behavior directly contrary to the casual attitudes and questioning rebelliousness they brought from civilian life.

New recruits were "like foreigners," said one colonel. Appeals to their patriotism, selflessness, and sense of duty made no impression. There was indeed a generation gap in the armed forces, a gap of more than age alone. As David Cortright, author of *Soldiers in Revolt,* explained:

> Many young people today simply do not find the military relevant to their basic needs. There is something in the nature of contemporary society that weakens the warrior ethic, some characteristic of our affluent, technological civilization that seems incompatible with the military.

These soldiers were the product of a turbulent, disorienting, conflict-ridden period. Whether or not they themselves were socially or politically conscious, they were deeply affected by the unrest in the society from which they came. It was a society in trauma—racial conflicts, riots, drugs, crime, political assassinations, a "new morality," and above all, a growing public disenchantment with the war. "I think you'd be naïve if you didn't say yes, the Army does have these problems," said Army Secretary Robert Froehlke. "It has serious problems because society has these problems. And there is no way for the Army to avoid the problems of society."

Unable to comprehend the radically different attitudes of young troops, senior officers tried, often vainly, to cajole, persuade, or order men to respond to discipline. "The Brass realize something's wrong, and they ask what it is," complained one young officer. "But they won't listen when you tell them to change the whole thing." Ward Just, a persistent critic of the Vietnam-era military, observed that "all the Army has to counter [antiauthoritarian behavior] is its traditions and its discipline, command and obedience." It could have responded to grievances by loosening its more rigid requirements, like haircuts and drill instruction. It could have improved communications between officers and men. But the military was not a flexible institution; it was slow to change, slow to respond to the changes in civilian society.

When the military did try to change, it often found that its problems ran too deep to be solved. Recruits remained unappreciative and unappeased, and senior officers grew frustrated by what they perceived as the failure of the younger generation to meet them halfway. Whatever officers did often seemed to be too little or too late.

Even under the best of circumstances, morale would have been a serious problem because of the disappointing progress of the war, scandals in the upper ranks, and atrocities at My Lai and elsewhere. But the clash between the generations made morale not a problem, but a crisis. This was, in the words of the Washington *Post,* an "Army in anguish."

Two barometers of this crisis were drugs and racial conflict, problems that the military shared with civilian society, and which grew to epidemic proportions during the war. A study of soldiers entering Vietnam in 1967 showed that 20 percent were already using marijuana. By 1970, this figure had risen to 50 percent. An employee in a drug rehabilitation center in Vietnam estimated that of the seven hundred heroin addicts there in mid-1971, 60 percent had been users before they entered the Army.

Yet Vietnam seriously aggravated the drug problem. A Harris survey of veterans found that such factors as "the pressures of war, fear of being killed, the courage to kill, coping with Vietnam, and homesickness" accounted for more than half of all drug cases. The watch-and-wait boredom of combat service accounted for another 22 percent. As one drug counselor put it, "Many GIs find the war so confusing they feel they are in a dream. Life is unreal. Values are crazy. Heroin use and fragging officers are acceptable. Everybody does it. Vietnam is a bad place, and most people want to get through as quickly and painlessly as possible. Marijuana slows time down; heroin speeds it up. The days go bip, bip, bip." The combat soldier's problem, it seemed to him, was to get through an unpleasant experience as painlessly as possible, and drugs were one solution.

In the early years of the war, drug use generally involved marijuana, not heroin. Marijuana could be obtained from bars, shops, hotels, and pedi-cab drivers in Saigon. Joints sold for 20 cents each. Yet marijuana use in Vietnam was then estimated at about twenty-five soldiers per thousand, lower than the overall Army rate of thirty per thousand. Between 1966 and 1967, however, the number of soldiers under criminal investigation for marijuana use climbed from fewer than one hundred to more than thirteen hundred. By contrast, only twenty-nine people were under investigation for possession, use, or sale of opium or morphine. Heroin was not yet in evidence.

The Army reacted to the marijuana problem, as one officer recalled, "by handling drug cases just like we handled sticking up a gas station." By 1969–70, military police in Vietnam were making more than eleven thousand drug arrests per year, 90 percent involving marijuana. Under Operation Intercept, Vietnamese troops and aircraft spotting teams located and destroyed marijuana crops. Yet despite this crackdown, the proportion of pot-smoking soldiers in Vietnam rose from 29 percent in 1967 to almost 60 percent in 1971. More than half were heavy smokers.

Heroin first attracted official attention in 1970. As late as 1969, only 2 percent of all troops returning from Vietnam were known to use heroin or morphine. But by 1971, the total exceeded 22 percent. Nearly 10 percent used heroin or other hard drugs on a daily basis, and thousands of combat troops began to be arrested for heroin abuse.

The heroin epidemic was considered especially frightening because of the type of person involved. The military expected most addicts to be blacks or Chicanos from disadvantaged backgrounds, groups that comprised roughly 70 percent of civilian addicts, according to one study. Yet, by contrast, more than 70 percent of all military addicts were white. They typically came from small midwestern or southern towns, had no history of hard drug use, and lacked any obvious character disorders. As one drug counselor in Vietnam said:

> The thing that is really eye-opening about it is that those kids, and they were kids, nineteen and twenty years old as a median age, looked like an exact cross-section of the young men coming into the Army. This business about ghetto kids and high-school dropouts—that's myth. . . . These kids are a cross-section of what the Selective Service was picking up throughout America. And this is what really shatters you.

The use of drugs was peculiarly a generational problem, and it was treated differently from alcohol abuse. In 1971, the Government Accounting Office estimated that there were 150,000 alcoholics in the armed forces. But alcohol was primarily the drug of career sergeants and officers, and it was cheap and plentiful at all military bases. Alcoholism was either ignored or seen as a medical problem. By contrast, drug abuse often brought stiff punishment. Until 1971, soldiers with drug habits often got Undesirable Discharges for unfitness. If their drug problems caused them to go AWOL, that was considered an aggravating factor which resulted in harsher penalties.

As the true dimensions of the drug problem became known, however, the military began trying less punitive approaches. In late 1970, the military initiated a limited "amnesty" program—later renamed "exemption," perhaps because of the political connotations of the original term. Drug rehabilitation centers were established throughout the Army, eleven of them in Vietnam; Navy and Air Force programs were started the following year. The Veterans Administration opened more than two dozen specialized treatment centers in the United States. Yet these efforts had little success. Many soldiers were reluctant to identify themselves as drug users, suspicious of the treatment they would get if they did.

By late 1971, with estimates of Vietnam drug use higher than ever, the military stopped relying on voluntary programs. Urinalysis was made mandatory for all soldiers leaving Vietnam, and later was extended worldwide. Those who failed the test were detoxified in quarantine centers until their habit was broken, which usually involved a long, unpleasant delay before going home. But even this did not keep the heroin epidemic out of America. Drug users learned how to bypass the test, and detoxification did not mean cure.

In line with the new, nonpunitive approach toward drug abuse, Defense Secretary Melvin Laird announced that addicts were to be treated as medical problems, given General Discharges, and made eligible for veterans' benefits and postservice medical assistance through the Veterans Administration. Individuals previously given discharges under other-than-honorable conditions exclusively for drug use were made eligible for automatic upgrades.

The new policy was generous in theory, but worked poorly in practice. The Pentagon could not accurately identify which discharges were in fact attributable to drug use. Many heavy users had been given "unfitness" discharges, yet their records gave no indication of drugs. Others went AWOL to support a habit and were punished for unauthorized absence. Under considerable pressure from Congress and the American Civil Liberties Union, the Defense Department tried to contact recently discharged veterans whose records showed drugs as a reason for separation. But the files were so incomplete that it managed to locate just a tiny percentage. As a result, the drug upgrade program reached very few of the people eligible for it.

The military was more successful with its efforts to stop the drug problem in Vietnam in the early 1970s, if only because troop levels were falling and combat engagements were becoming rare. In 1972, the Defense Department announced that it had "reversed a heroin epidemic in Vietnam" and that only 4.5 percent of the men tested were diagnosed as drug users. Yet, by the admission of the Army's legal command in Vietnam, drugs remained a problem until a few months before the last troops were withdrawn. The military solved the problem only by leaving Vietnam.

For thousands of men, leaving Vietnam did not solve anything. Their habits came home with them, causing incalculable tragedies. In Vietnam, a heroin habit could be sustained for perhaps $2 to $6 a day. In the United States, an equivalent daily supply of lower-grade heroin might cost as much as $200. General Walter Kerwin, deputy chief of staff for Army personnel, suspected that "some of the people who were volunteering to go back to Vietnam for maybe the second or third time did that for the specific purpose of drugs." When users came home, they helped spread the drug culture and drug supply at military bases, on the streets, and on the campuses of America. The inevitable results were crime and imprisonment for thousands of Vietnam veterans. Heroin became a symbol of the Vietnam war, both to veterans and to the American people.

Racial tension, like drugs, was a problem the armed forces inherited from civilian society. The authoritarian nature of military society, which placed a white and heavily southern command structure over a young and substantially black enlisted population, aggravated racial hostilities and hindered official efforts to overcome discrimination.

Before Vietnam, the military had been regarded as one of the best opportunities in American society for blacks to achieve upward mobility. Partly because of relaxed enlistment standards, large numbers of black youths joined the service during the early Vietnam escalation. Unlike their fathers, who may have been content to hide their hostility toward a white-dominated military, the black soldiers of the 1960s were openly resentful, aggressive, and conscious of their alienation. The Kerner Commission saw American society dividing along racial lines, and this was especially true in the armed forces.

Blacks found community not in the service, but among themselves. The intense racial consciousness of young blacks was hard for white officers to understand. "What defeats me," said a battalion commander, "is the attitude among the blacks that 'black is right' no matter who is right or wrong." At an official "rap" session in Germany, a general was told that all whites were pigs and he, being white, was also a pig. "I burned buildings in Chicago and shot whitey, and it doesn't bother me one bit," added the black soldier. "I'd just as soon shoot at whitey as the VC."

Black consciousness fed white racism. One soldier recalled hearing blacks called "reindeer," "Mau Mau," "jig," "spook," "brownie," "warrior," "coon," "spade," and "nigger." There was an atmosphere of mutual fear and distrust. As a white Green Beret recalled, "Blacks pretty much stuck to themselves and hated everyone else. I turned into a bigot in the military when I was on a bus with mostly black GIs, and they harassed and accosted me. You were told not to walk around the barracks at night, especially alone." A black GI responded that "whites think every time colored guys get together, well, he's a Panther, he's a militant."

Racial conflict was especially troublesome in Vietnam. By 1970, black unrest had begun to hinder the fighting effort. There was fear among white officers that black soldiers would turn their guns around and, as the soldier had said, "shoot at whitey" instead of the Viet Cong. Some, in fact, did. In one incident, two white majors were shot trying to get some black soldiers to turn down a noisy tape recorder.

Racial problems did not often translate into specific grievances that could be redressed through normal channels. A 1971 Defense Department survey of Air Force units in Southeast Asia found minority group frustration so high that many men found it difficult or impossible to articulate their complaints. When grievances were aired, they commonly pertained to offensive language, prejudice in assignments, harassment by military police, inability to buy black-oriented products in military PXs, and, especially in Germany, housing discrimination and a hostile social climate.

The resentment black soldiers had toward their white commanders often provoked harsh and shortsighted responses which aggravated the conflict. Many commanders tried to enforce discipline by banning such symbolic acts of racial identity as "dapping"—the complex handshake between "brothers"—and the clenched fist salute. Prison terms were sometimes imposed on blacks who tried to persuade others that they were being used to fight a "white man's war."

The military justice system was a major source of tension. Many blacks saw it as the embodiment of white racist justice: "If some brothers jump on a white guy, he's going to go to the authorities because all his life he's been used to going there. But if a brother goes to the police, he knows he isn't going to do anything for you, no way. So what's the use? The brothers don't even bother with the police."

Blacks filled more than their share of stockade cells. A 1971 study by the congressional Black Caucus discovered that half of all soldiers in confinement were black, a finding matched by an NAACP study in

Europe during the same year. The NAACP also learned that a white first offender was twice as likely to be released without punishment as a black first offender. At Camp Casey, an Army base in Korea, blacks accounted for 17 percent of all troops, yet they comprised 62 percent of all prisoners.

A 1972 Defense Department Task Force on Military Justice reported that blacks of comparable education and aptitude who committed offenses of comparable seriousness were receiving much harsher punishments than whites. At Camp Casey, blacks accounted for 26 percent of all nonjudicial punishment, 57 percent of all special courts-martial, and 83 percent of all general courts-martial. The NAACP study found that 45 percent of all less-than-Honorable discharges went to blacks. An Urban League study showed that blacks in the Air Force received Dishonorable Discharges at more than three and one-half times the rate of all airmen.

In part, the disproportionate impact of military justice was a direct consequence of Great Society initiatives to make military service available to the large segment of the marginally qualified who were black. In 1971, 60 percent of all blacks who were administratively discharged were in Category IV, as compared to 17 percent of the whites. The NAACP study found that many young blacks were ignorant of their rights and accepted administrative discharges even when charges against them were very weak. It noted that legal counseling was of little help because of the deep distrust blacks had for white military lawyers.

Whatever the reasons, blacks received a disproportionate share of the less-than-Honorable discharges awarded during the Vietnam-era. In 1973, this fact led the Equal Employment Opportunity Commission to hold that requiring job applicants to have an Honorable Discharge in and of itself constituted racial discrimination in employment.

Vietnam and Back

Beyond everything else, the war itself "tore the fabric of the Army," as a top-ranking general conceded. Not many soldiers deserted on their way to Southeast Asia or in the midst of combat, but every Vietnam-era deserter was, in a sense, making a judgment on the war. He chose self and family over the cause for which he was asked to fight. Had the war made more sense to him, his decision might have been different.

Enlisted men's views about the war split about evenly between hawks and doves. In 1971, a survey of men on their way to Vietnam found that 47 percent thought the war was a mistake, and another 40 percent thought America was not fighting hard enough to win. Both groups questioned the wisdom of what they were doing. Murray Polner interviewed hundreds of servicemen for his book *When Can I Come Home,* finding that "not one of them—hawk, dove, or haunted—was entirely free of doubt about the nature of the war and the American role in it."

A relatively small number of soldiers bore deliberate witness to their political or moral views by deserting, refusing to obey orders, or engaging in antiwar politics in defiance of the military. In the early days of the war, resisters often stood their ground, hoping that their commanders or courts-martial would show compassion, if not understanding, toward their beliefs. Michael Pacek, a Czech refugee, had lived through the Nazi occupation and Soviet takeover of his country, and his family later escaped to America. Pacek enlisted in the Marines in 1958, reenlisted in 1961, and was sent to Vietnam as a "military adviser" in 1963. After two combat missions, he had flashbacks of Czechoslovakia and refused to participate in any more fighting. Pacek was court-martialed, sentenced to five years in military prison, and given a Dishonorable Discharge.

In 1966, three Army privates (the "Fort Hood Three") refused to board a troopship for Vietnam, claiming that the war was "immoral, illegal, and unjust." All were given three-year sentences. In 1967, two officers refused to train Vietnam-bound troops in cases that received nationwide publicity. They, too, were court-martialed, sentenced to military prison, and dismissed from service.

Antiwar soldiers were often willing to try for a CO discharge, which was especially difficult to obtain (see Part II). Many CO applications were rejected because the law was not properly applied. Gilbert Owen almost applied for a CO draft exemption, but decided against it. After two weeks in basic training, he discovered he had made a mistake.

Owen applied for a CO discharge, but the chaplain who interviewed him found his beliefs based on contacts with "pacifistic organizations and individuals rather than on religious convictions." In the earlier *Seeger* case, the Supreme Court had declared this distinction invalid, but Owen's CO claim was rejected anyway. He then refused to accept combat equipment or to wear his uniform. A general court-martial sentenced him to eighteen months in prison and a Bad Conduct Discharge.

The hostile attitude of commanding officers and other military officials sometimes discouraged sincere war resisters from applying for CO discharges, leaving them little apparent recourse but to go AWOL. "The chaplains played a disgraceful role in the whole business," in the opinion of Maury Maverick, a Texas attorney who counseled dozens of soldiers through the CO process:

> More than anyone else, they should have understood how a man's conscience could forbid him from fighting. But instead, in the tradition of old war movies, they gave man-to-man talks about how soldiers have to do what they're told. For those who went ahead and applied for CO anyway, these chaplains invariably wrote negative reports—and that was hard for soldiers to overcome. I saw it happen again and again.

After three years in the Navy, Curt Chadwick was in no danger of going to Southeast Asia, but decided to take a principled stand against the war. He tried to apply for a CO discharge, but admitted to a Navy psychiatrist that he had experimented with drugs. The psychiatrist threw Chadwick's records in his face, telling him to get out of the office and forget about being a CO. Chadwick then went AWOL.

Alfonso Martinez decided in the fall of 1965 that he was a conscientious objector, and he refused to obey orders to train for combat. He was court-martialed and sentenced to six months imprisonment. After getting out of jail, he applied for a CO discharge. While it was pending, he again was court-martialed for refusing to obey orders, and was sent to prison for another six months. Martinez disobeyed orders a third time and finally was discharged—but not before serving yet another term in prison.

A high-school dropout with an IQ of 80, Ron Hodgkins never realized his pacifist feelings until after he was drafted. For eighteen months, he repeatedly inquired about becoming a CO. Hodgkins was not very articulate, and no one who talked with him thought he was sincere. "All I could tell them was that even if someone was trying to kill me, I couldn't kill in return. They just didn't believe me." After Hodgkins was ordered to Vietnam, he went AWOL.

Any act of defiance was regarded as a direct and dangerous threat to military authority. Commanding officers had difficulty finding the proper accommodation between the needs of military discipline and the increasingly visible efforts of servicemen to assert civilian notions of free speech and other constitutional rights while in uniform. "Resistance in the Army," labeled "RITA" by the Pentagon, led to widespread military surveillance of servicemen and civilians. In 1970, a major national scandal erupted when the public discovered the existence of hundreds of thousands of military dossiers on Americans who publicly opposed the war.

Military action against in-service dissent focused on GI coffee houses, underground newspapers, and leafletting. In Japan, six Marine members of the Vietnam Veterans against the War were arrested for leafletting. When their handouts were confiscated, military policy gave them receipts for "pamphlets contain[ing] propaganda. . . . Title: July 4th. Subtitle: Declaration of Independence." The six Marines were charged with "conduct of a nature to bring discredit upon the armed forces." Prosecutions were brought against other servicemen for failing to stand for the national anthem, picketing against the war during off-duty hours, making "disloyal statements" in servicemen's newspapers, presenting a petition to a United States embassy, and distributing Congressional Record excerpts of speeches by antiwar senators. Many were given less-than-Honorable discharges, and some were sent to prison. One soldier even got a less-than-Honorable discharge for sending home a Christmas card sharply critical of the war.

Opposition to the war accounted for perhaps 10–15 percent of all absence offenses, but the influence of antiwar servicemen far exceeded their numbers. They tended to be brighter and better educated than other troops, and they were able to draw public attention to their activities. They made indiscipline a political act and made resistance to military authority more respectable.

Yet despite strong feelings about the war, this generation of soldiers, like others before it, almost always obeyed orders to go overseas. Once in Vietnam, fighting was a matter of survival, regardless of a soldier's opinions. It was hard for him to sympathize with the Viet Cong when they were trying to kill him and his buddies. Combat troops broke rules all the time, especially with drugs and short-term AWOLs, but their superiors had a tolerant attitude. "If I caught a guy with marijuana and docked him half a month's pay, it wouldn't matter to him," commented a master sergeant who spent several tours in Vietnam. "They all had money to burn, so there was nothing you could do to stop petty drug or AWOL problems. If I had booted them out, I wouldn't have had any company left."

The most serious symptom of the crisis in discipline in Vietnam was "fragging," real or threatened assaults on officers and high-ranking sergeants. The practice got its name from the fragmentation grenade, which could be rolled under the quarters of sleeping officers. Any premeditated assault against a superior was, in effect, a "fragging." From 1969 to 1971, the Army reported more than 600 such incidents, resulting in 82 deaths and 651 injuries. One soldier recalled a planned parade for a general whom the troops disliked: "We broke into the demolition room and stole some grenades and blew up the reviewing stand." In one incident outside Hué, two dozen soldiers threw stones and gas pellets at an officers' club. The plan was to kill the escaping officers with grenades, a step the attackers did not carry out. Stories like this had a telling effect on junior officers. As one commented, "All it takes is a 'How are you, Joe,' and bang, someone will shoot you."

Toward the end of the war, the threat of fragging was accompanied by another challenge—the increasing refusal of enlisted men to go into combat. In March 1971, a reconnaissance company was ambushed by a North Vietnamese unit of much greater strength. After an intense firefight, the survivors made their way to safety only to discover that some classified documents had been left behind. The brigade commander ordered the company to retrieve the documents, but fifty-three men refused to go. Orders issued from progressively higher levels of command were also refused. The brigade commander considered pressing court-martial charges against all fifty-three, but he was overruled by the commanding general. The men were found to have had "extenuating circumstances" for refusing to obey a lawful order. During his year of legal defense work in Vietnam, David Addlestone encountered dozens of combat refusals and hundreds of minor acts of insubordination, almost always ending in little or no punishment.

The simple fact was that courts-martial were not practical in the field. The paperwork, time, and trouble they required could not be afforded. Sending a man to the rear to stand trial operated much like a reward, freeing him from the dangers of combat. As a consequence, courts-martial were generally reserved for those who committed violent crimes or desertion under the most aggravated circumstances.

Despite the attention it received, deliberate antiwar activity was not prevalent in Vietnam. Resistance usually did not occur until after the soldier returned home and had time to reflect on what he had seen and done. As Paul Starr commented, "Even for those who detested the war, refusing orders and deserting were simply not very feasible options halfway across the globe from home." Doing research for *War Resisters in Canada,* Kenneth Emerick discovered five combat veterans in Canada, each of whom had deserted only after coming back from Vietnam. He described them as having "rationalized and postponed their deeper perception of events until after they returned home."

Ron Cannille served a full tour in Vietnam as a machine-gunner. Back home, just eighty-four days before the end of his three-year enlistment, he went AWOL for eight hours to take part in a peace demonstration. He was thrown in the stockade, where he became one of the "Presidio 27" soldiers court-martialed for mutiny after a sit-down strike.

Jerry Rathbone accidentally killed his best buddy during a combat assault, an incident that turned him strongly against the war and ultimately caused him to desert when he returned:

> Most GIs get back from Vietnam and they forget; they don't say anything; they say well, it's over, I can forget about it. And that's one of the reasons I deserted, right there, I didn't want to be part of that. I had to make my

commitment. I had to make people stop and think, "Well, why the hell did he desert with only 137 days left?" This isn't one of those cases where people could say, "Oh, he deserted 'cause he couldn't get along with the army, or he deserted 'cause he's a coward."

But far overshadowing the after-the-fact antiwar sentiment among returning veterans was the problem of psychological readjustment from combat, commonly called the "post-Vietnam syndrome." Bob Dantlee earned a Bronze Star and a Purple Heart, but he deserted after coming home from Vietnam:

I didn't notice much mental strain, but it was an entirely different story when I returned. I got depressed very easily, was very moody, and felt that no one really cared that I served their country for them. And this was very hard to cope with, mainly because while I was in Vietnam I gave it 100%. I saw enough action for this life and possibly two or three more. I hope somebody understands what I was going through when I returned.

Often, drugs were part of the post-Vietnam syndrome. Sergeant John Cutter arrived in Vietnam without combat experience. His leadership qualities were so strong that his company commander promoted him to platoon leader, a job normally held by a commissioned officer. Cutter led a number of combat missions, during which he took Methedrine to stay awake. The Methedrine made him jumpy, and one of his troops persuaded him to take opium to help him relax. Over time, he developed an opium habit which he kept secret from his superiors. After his Vietnam tour, Cutter was assigned to Germany, and then reassigned to a base near his home. Rather than let his family see him as a drug addict, he stayed in Germany in AWOL status and tried to enroll in a local drug clinic. After a few weeks, Cutter was arrested. The Army sent him home with his drug habit and an Undesirable Discharge for AWOL.

The military was poorly equipped to help men like Dantlee and Cutter with their physical and psychological problems. Combat veterans could qualify for disability ratings which increased their entitlement to veterans' benefits, and military doctors were sometimes suspicious that men were faking conditions to improve their ratings. As a result, many who thought they had serious injuries complained that they were poorly attended. If they wanted to see their own doctors, they had to go AWOL.

John Rainwater, an American Indian, received a Bronze Star for heroism when he moved through a minefield under heavy fire to save wounded comrades. Later, he became squad leader of nine men, seven of whom (including himself) were wounded in action. When Rainwater came back to the United States, he was refused permission to see a military psychiatrist. Frustrated, he went AWOL several times to visit his hometown doctor. An Army psychiatrist later confirmed his combat-induced psychological trauma, but Rainwater was nonetheless given an Undesirable Discharge for his AWOLs.

Many returning veterans found it hard to take pride in their sacrifices, regardless of their views about Vietnam. Bill McKuen was "shocked by what everyone was saying about the war, and I got the feeling that I'd been wasting my time over there. That's partly why I went AWOL." Grant Johnson returned from Vietnam to an Army base near Birmingham, Alabama. As a child and teenager, he had never paid much attention to white racism; as a Vietnam veteran, he refused to tolerate it. "My first thought was how great it was to be back home, and then I began to notice the hate stares. After all I had been through, I had returned to racist America, and I was keenly aware of it." Johnson left his base, left Alabama, and eventually went to Canada.

Most of the returning veteran's day-to-day contacts were with other soldiers, the bulk of whom had never been to Vietnam, and they were no more sympathetic than the general public. Sam Jollio served in six combat campaigns, received numerous decorations, and rose to the rank of staff sergeant. He was wounded in combat, and he saw his fellow soldiers killed. After two Vietnam tours and one serious injury, Jollio came back to the United States. To the soldiers and sergeants back home, he was only a "rice paddy NCO" who owed his rank to the war. Tired of being harassed and ridiculed for his war record, Jollio went AWOL.

Garrison officers sometimes had little patience with combat veterans.

Jimmy Lee objected to the training of new men for Vietnam: "They were playing games. Half the kids were only seventeen, and if they went over to Nam with what they were teaching, they wouldn't have lasted two days." Lee told the officers what he thought about the training: "I had three courts-martial and three Article 15's in my first two months back and got busted to private. So I just walked away." When he walked back a year later, Lee was handed a bad discharge.

Men who had been through Vietnam knew what did and did not matter in the war zone. When they came home, they continued the "distinctly nonmilitary style" that Haynes Johnson and George Wilson described in *Army in Anguish:* "a floppy 'Boonie' hat, a slouching and slow-moving walk, hair parted crookedly in the middle, and perhaps a sparse mustache." But their stateside commanding officers, many of whom were young and had never been in Vietnam, told them to "act like soldiers," and they had to go through the same daily regimen of inspections, formations, and petty harassment they had experienced as recruits.

The military had no readjustment programs for men who returned from Vietnam with only a few months left on their enlistments. Short-timers were of little use. There was no point in retraining them or giving them positions of responsibility. The Pentagon knew about the problem, but never addressed it satisfactorily. In 1971, an early release plan was initiated for returning soldiers with less than five months remaining, which often meant a soldier had to extend his tour in Vietnam beyond the normal twelve months if he wanted an early discharge.

Typically, combat veterans just sat around bases in the United States with little to do, waiting for their enlistments to end. They were often assigned to casual duty—KP, picking up cigarette butts, and the like. One Vietnam veteran was given the job of "assistant runner." He ran errands only when the Colonel's chief messenger was busy, but he had to stay at the ready just in case. He went AWOL in disgust.

After processing more than five thousand Vietnam-era deserters, military officials in charge of President Ford's clemency program reported that combat veterans "were not always gainfully employed, but seemed to be assigned make-work tasks to occupy their last few months of obligated service. Some were of the opinion, upon being assigned to training units, that they were being recycled through basic training, and this was the reason they offered for leaving." As Peter Barnes wrote in *Pawns,* "The final months in a soldier's career can be almost as miserable as the days in Vietnam. He fought and bled for Uncle Sam. He now expects to be treated like a hero, or at least a man. Instead, however, the Army demands that he revert to his precombat role of nigger."

Many of these men also suffered the consequences of long separations from their families, wives, and girl friends. As with the Kentucky teenager who left an Army hospital bed the day he got a "Dear John" letter, AWOL was sometimes the only answer.

When returning veterans went AWOL, they were often given bad discharges. "If we'd let people go home just because they wanted to, no one would have been left," explained a battalion commander at Fort Meade. "Without a stigma, everyone would have vanished." "Deserter" was the stigma. To the public, these veterans were indistinguishable from those who fled to avoid Vietnam.

About twenty thousand servicemen completed full tours in the war zone and received Undesirable, Bad Conduct, or Dishonorable Discharges for absence offenses that occurred after they returned to the United States. Although no official statistics are available, the evidence suggests that another thirty thousand received bad discharges for other kinds of post-Vietnam misconduct. Eighty percent of these men had served in combat. As a consequence, they lost all rights to veterans' benefits. Jim Stokes served in Vietnam for a year, earning a Purple Heart when he let an enemy grenade explode in his hands to protect his platoon. He was later discharged for AWOL. Jim Barajian suffered a detached retina during his Vietnam tour and is now nearly blind in one eye. After his court-martial conviction for desertion, he developed a disabling back injury from sleeping without a mattress in his prison cell. Like five thousand other Vietnam veterans with combat wounds or other service-incurred injuries, Stokes and Barajian were deprived of government-sponsored medical benefits.

One senior Pentagon official described the military's treatment of the returning Vietnam veteran as "our most shameful episode of the war."

Canceling Them Out

When General David Shoup became commander of a Marine Corps division at Camp Pendleton in 1957, he opened the brig and released everyone but the felons. "Go back to work," he told them. "That's what you're here for, not to sit around going stir-crazy. If you cut out again, we'll find you and put you back to work. And we'll keep doing it until you finish your time. So settle down and serve it now." Shoup straightened out the division and cut down on AWOLs. He did so without courts-martial, prison sentences, and bad discharges. Shoup's hidden ingredient was leadership. As a 1971 Army report stated, "positive leadership is the key to low AWOL rates."

But during Vietnam, the armed forces had difficulty in applying "positive leadership." The corps of lieutenants, captains, and low-ranking sergeants—the men who had day-to-day responsibility for enlisted troops—was badly strained by the wartime escalation. General William Westmoreland, then Army chief of staff, commented that

> six years of war—and this has been the longest war in our history other than our War of Independence—has truly stretched the Army almost to its elastic limit. It has been a very traumatic experience for us. We had to lower our standards to provide the officers and noncommissioned officers to man this Army because the reserves were not called up. . . . We had to lower our standards to meet the requirements in numbers.

As a result, the responsibility for dealing with the intense morale and disciplinary crisis in the ranks fell upon young and inexperienced leaders. Captains and lieutenants were trained and given commands just eighteen to twenty-four months after joining the service. Many were not college graduates, and few, if any, had ever been in leadership positions. Yet, at age twenty or twenty-one, they were put in charge of 40-man platoons or 150-man companies. The sergeants who assisted them were often just as inexperienced. Enlisted men who showed promise of leadership ability were sent quickly through noncommissioned officers' school, made buck sergeants, and promptly put in charge of eight- to ten-man squads. Barely out of high school, these "shake and bake" sergeants lacked the military savvy and experience so vital to their roles.

The inexperience of the junior command was aggravated by rotation policies. Commissioned officers, sergeants, and enlisted men did not stay together long enough to establish the relationship of trust so necessary for effective leadership. "Whenever I am asked, 'What is the basic problem of the Army?' " General Walter Kerwin said in 1971,

> I do not respond that it is drugs or race or discipline; it is the fact that we have so much turbulence, mainly driven by Vietnam, that leadership and discipline have gone down because everybody has developed what I call the "look the other way" syndrome. The man is not there sufficiently long to get a handle on his unit. For instance, not too long ago at Fort Carson, we found a unit that had five first sergeants in one year. I think it goes without saying, no matter what the business is, if you change the leadership five times, you are going to have a certain instability in the unit . . . because there is not that feeling of belonging and pride.

The problem was especially acute in Vietnam. The rotation policy may have been humane, but it had a devastating effect on group esprit. As psychologist Dr. Peter Bourne observed,

> With each soldier concerned primarily with his own personal survival until his rotation date, at which point his own involvement with the war would be over, the conflict [took] on a uniquely individualized character. The man feels no continuity with those who precede him or follow him; he even feels apart from those who are with him but rotating on a different schedule.

In the early part of the war, officers and sergeants were shifted from unit to unit every few months. Career officers saw service in Vietnam as a way of "getting their ticket punched," earning the credentials necessary for future advancement. The military later stabilized command assignments, but senior Pentagon officials acknowledged that twelve months was still too short a time for an inexperienced officer to mold an effective unit. Some volunteered to stay in the combat zone, but many were no less eager to go home than the men they led.

Rapid turnover aggravated morale problems. Officers who inherited bad units often saw their mission as just trying to keep problems from getting worse. An inexperienced company commander, coming to a unit with men who had already seen combat, had understandable difficulty asserting his authority. By the time he had overcome that handicap, his rotation date was near. His interest then lay in suppressing the outward manifestations of resistance and resentment—just getting by until the problems could be left to his replacement.

Part of the same generation as the men they were commanding, young officers were often unwilling or unable to deal with the antimilitary attitudes of their men. "I'd say at least seventy-five percent of the people I know, young soldiers, lieutenants, and captains, have told me privately they agree with what I've said," recalled one officer publicly active in opposing the war. "Either they don't have guts to say it publicly, or they don't feel it was their place to speak up." These officers tolerated the eccentricities of their troops—the sloppy dress, the love beads, the pot smoking—which were symptoms of an undisciplined force. More significantly, they failed to deal with incipient personnel problems until they became serious.

Sometimes, young officers overreacted. Although there are detailed regulations governing discipline and punishment, military justice relies heavily on the judgment of individual commanders, each of whom has wide discretion to punish offenders as he sees fit. Company-grade punishments—loss of rank, small fines, confinement to quarters, assignment to unpleasant duties—are the responsibility of captains, lieutenants, and sergeants. Their recommendations also carry considerable weight with the field-grade officers who decide whether to press court-martial charges or begin administrative discharge proceedings.

During the Vietnam period, the result was often fickle, unpredictable justice. David Segal, a University of Maryland sociologist who coordinated a Pentagon AWOL study, found "no systematic difference" between AWOL offenders who were punished and those who were not. When enlisted men felt victimized by arbitrary treatment, there was little they could do. Each military base had an inspector general to hear grievances, but he was usually a high-ranking officer with other duties and close ties to commanders. Enlisted men could file complaints, but they took months to be processed.

Whether an inexperienced officer was too lenient or too harsh, his incapacity for leadership produced the same outcome—disciplinary problems that eventually became untenable. As one career sergeant recalled, "We spent 95 percent of our time handling the 5 percent who were troublemakers." Ultimately, when all else failed, the only recourse was to discharge poor performers. In the words of Army General William Berg, former deputy assistant secretary of defense for manpower:

> You bring somebody into the service and hope he is fully productive. Some of them, for reasons of immaturity or inexperience, cannot measure up. . . . But after you have exhausted every possible remedy that you have to make this man productive, and he has already cost you a lot of lost time and everything else, you finally reach a point at which the only thing to do is cancel this guy out.

When men were "canceled out," they were given discharges that indicated the quality of their military service.

Discharge characterizations have been part of the military system since the Revolutionary War. By the 1840s, the standard discharge certificate described a man's service as "honest and faithful." If it had not been, these words were lined out in ink. After the Civil War, each soldier's service was described in longhand at the bottom of his discharge. In 1893, a plain, uncharacterized certificate was instituted by the Army as an alternative to what by then was called the "Honorable Discharge." This new discharge was not exactly neutral, however, because it included a character description on the back. These less-than-honorable certificates were later printed on blue paper, and court-martial discharges on yellow, so veterans of the two world wars came to think of bad discharges as "blue" and "yellow" discharges.

In 1947, a joint Armed Services Committee recommended shifting to the five-tiered system still in use today. The change was thought necessary to help in the adjudication of veterans' benefits claims, because the blue and yellow discharges "did not clearly provide a characterization for those whose service was neither honorable nor less than honorable within the time-honored meanings of these terms." Five types of discharge were created: Honorable, General, Undesirable, Bad Conduct, and Dishonorable.

The purpose of the discharge system was to reward faithful service and to punish, and thereby deter, unsatisfactory performance. "Anything else," in the words of a Defense Department spokesman, "would diminish the value of the discharge to the man who has given honorable service. You need a way to characterize the service for what it truly is." Yet this theory did not work well in practice. Many officers had little understanding of the military justice system. "Many people got Honorable Discharges because company commanders didn't know their jobs," recalled one career Army attorney. "They didn't know how to do all the paperwork for bad discharges."

Nor did the threat of a bad discharge have much deterrent effect. In examining the reasons why men might be discouraged from going AWOL, an Army study found that the desire for an Honorable Discharge "might" have a significant effect, but was not a particularly important factor in deterring AWOL. Most poor performers were only interested in getting out of the service as fast as possible, without going to prison. The concept of a lifelong stigma was too abstract to have any real meaning for them. "They were told what the implications were, as plain as day, but they didn't give a damn," recalled a battalion commander at Fort Meade:

> Those with a modicum of intelligence, who thought ahead about the consequences of bad discharges, were probably deterred—but the guy who had troubles usually had less intelligence and didn't think ahead. Most of these kids weren't bad. They were just dumb.

Only after the serviceman left the armed forces and had to cope with civilian life did he begin to appreciate the far-reaching impact of his bad discharge. By then, he was a civilian, and it was too late for his punishment to have a deterrent effect on him or anyone else. As a Defense Department report on military justice commented, bad discharges "became, in reality, a punitive sanction for the individual involved, but with little positive benefit accruing to the services."

Although the Honorable Discharge is officially viewed as a reward for achievement, 93 percent of all Vietnam-era servicemen received one (see Figure 6). It did not distinguish truly honorable from merely satisfactory service. According to an Army staff sergeant at Fort

Meade, "the only thing an Honorable Discharge proves is that a guy hasn't committed murder, rape, arson, or something like that. It was given to so many people who didn't deserve it that it really doesn't mean much. I wish they had given a break to the guy who really served well."

The Honorable Discharge sometimes contained a hidden qualification which undercut its value in civilian life, especially in the job market. Before 1952, the military stated the underlying reason for each separation plainly on the discharge certificate. However, the military then began using three-digit Separation Program Numbers ("spins"). These numbers corresponded to 446 capsule reasons for discharge. According to General Leo Benade, former deputy assistant secretary of defense for military personnel policy, this system of coded numbers was intended to "mitigate any adverse effect to people who were being discharged for less than honorable service." However, the numbers were inserted in every serviceman's record, including the 93 percent who got Honorable Discharges.

The clerks who made the entries sometimes followed the instruction of discharging authorities and other times merely acted on their own. There was no precise system for determining the appropriate spin number, and the choices were not subject to review. Servicemen were not told which number they were getting: because the spin was camouflaged as the first three digits of a much longer separation number, they were often unaware that the code existed at all.

Very few of the spin codes reflected well on a man's military record, such as by describing meritorious service, honors and awards, or special skills acquired during service. About half of the 446 spin codes were neutral—"expiration of term of service," "early release for Christmas," and so forth. The remainder—more than two hundred separate codes —contained descriptions that ranged from derogatory to damning, including one—"withdrawal of ecclesiastical endorsement of chaplain (5IN)"—that may have been the military equivalent of "go to Hell." Some spin codes were phrased in generalities:

28C Unsatisfactory handling of personal affairs
46A Unsuitability, apathy, defective attitudes, and inability to expend effort constructively

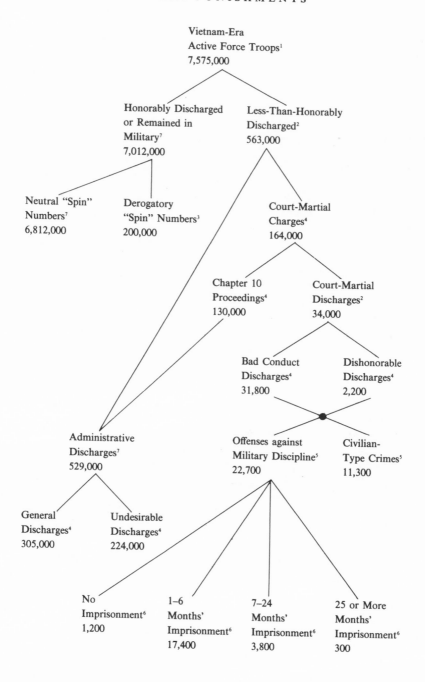

FIGURE 6: MILITARY PUNISHMENTS

Vietnam-Era Active Force Troops[1] 7,575,000

Honorably Discharged or Remained in Military[7] 7,012,000

Less-Than-Honorably Discharged[2] 563,000

Neutral "Spin" Numbers[7] 6,812,000

Derogatory "Spin" Numbers[3] 200,000

Court-Martial Charges[4] 164,000

Chapter 10 Proceedings[4] 130,000

Court-Martial Discharges[2] 34,000

Bad Conduct Discharges[4] 31,800

Dishonorable Discharges[4] 2,200

Administrative Discharges[7] 529,000

Offenses against Military Discipline[5] 22,700

Civilian-Type Crimes[5] 11,300

General Discharges[4] 305,000

Undesirable Discharges[4] 224,000

No Imprisonment[6] 1,200

1–6 Months' Imprisonment[6] 17,400

7–24 Months' Imprisonment[6] 3,800

25 or More Months' Imprisonment[6] 300

288 Habits and traits of character manifested by antisocial or amoral trend

382 Demonstrates behavior, participates in activities, or belongs to associations which tend to show that the individual is not reliable or trustworthy

461 Inadequate personality

Others used clinical terms, but were no less imprecise:

36C Maladjustment, situational, acute
36D Passive-aggressive reaction
36F Primary childhood behavior reaction
369 Cyclothymic personality*

A few described specific objectionable characteristics:

36A Immaturity with symptomatic habit reaction (somnambulism)†
36B Immaturity with symptomatic habit reaction (stammering)
41E Obesity
262 Unsuitability—Enuresis‡

Some referred to sexual behavior:

362 Unsuitability—homosexual tendencies, desires, or interest, but without overt homosexual acts in service
512 Homosexuality (Class I)
513 Homosexuality (Class II)
514 Homosexuality (Class III)

Originally, spin codes were intended only for internal use in evaluating applications for reenlistment and were kept confidential. However, copies of the codebook were given to the Veterans Administration, which used them in deciding veterans' benefits claims. Sal Horley volunteered for two tours in Vietnam before being wounded seriously enough to get an early Honorable Discharge. But he had also picked up a heroin habit during his second tour and was given spin number

*Alternate periods of elation and depression.
†Sleepwalking.
‡Bed-wetting.

384—"unfitness—drug addiction or the unauthorized use or possession of habit-forming narcotic drugs or marijuana." Horley kept trying to get medical attention for his leg wounds from his local Veterans Administration hospital. Each time, he was turned down and accused of faking his injury. Eventually, a VA official told Horley that his discharge form indicated that he had been discharged not for combat wounds, but for drug addiction.

Copies of the codebook soon made their way to large employers, who discreetly used them to evaluate job applicants. One Marine veteran applied for jobs with the California state government and a number of other places. He proudly showed them his Honorable Discharge, only to encounter strange reactions and unexplained rejections. Finally, someone asked him why he was a homosexual—and he learned about his spin number for the first time.

By the early 1970s, word about spin numbers began to spread among veterans' counselors. At first, the Pentagon reacted by "classifying" the codebooks. But faced with growing criticism, it acknowledged the unfairness of the practice. On May 1, 1974, the Pentagon prohibited future use of spin numbers and invited veterans discharged between 1952 and 1974 to exchange their discharge papers for clean, "spin-free" certificates. The National Student Association obtained and published a copy of the codebook, prompting a nationwide campaign to find veterans with bad numbers. The Defense Department refused to notify all veterans directly, however, and only a few thousand asked for new certificates. Some of those who did learned to their dismay that they will never be free of their spins. A Louisiana veterans' counselor observed that "if you ever gave your discharge form to a personnel office, chances are it's still on file. If you go back with a clean discharge to apply for a job, they'll still look at your old spin number. After all, it tells them something they want to know. I'm afraid that some vets will never shake their numbers." No official tally has ever been made of bad spin numbers, but one Defense Department sampling suggests that about 200,000 Vietnam-era veterans may have black marks on what they think are fully Honorable Discharges.

The spin code, despite its adverse effects on so many ex-servicemen, was not an integral part of the discharge system and was not a substitute for the four other discharges that characterized the service of veterans who did not receive honorable certificates. Of these, the General, next in rank to the Honorable, is perhaps the most anomalous. Roughly 300,000 Vietnam-era servicemen received a General Discharge, which the military considers "under honorable conditions," yet "less-than-Honorable." Although it ordinarily qualifies an individual for veterans' benefits, it characterizes his service as "not sufficiently meritorious" to warrant the fully Honorable Discharge.

The General Discharge was not intended to be a form of punishment. Yet its categorization of recipients as among the bottom 7 percent has an inescapable impact upon employers and others in civilian society. Macy's department store, for example, had a policy (at least during the Vietnam era) "not to hire anybody who received anything other than an Honorable Discharge." A spokesman for Macy's added that "this practice was followed by every major corporation I knew of in the City of New York that hired people in the retail field—including positions for sweepers, scrubbers, and cleaners." Recent surveys have found that while very few employers flatly reject veterans with General Discharges, roughly one-third do discriminate against them. As one veteran recalled:

> I was busted for having two joints and given a General Discharge after three years and nine months of my four-year enlistment. Adjusting back into society wasn't easy. I couldn't find a job because I had "bad paper." This caused financial problems for my family and later resulted in my getting divorced. I have two children to support.

In practice, there was no precise distinction between soldiers who received General Discharges and those who received better or worse discharges. In the Army, for example, General Discharges were given in 90 percent of all separations for personality or behavior disorders, whereas the Navy gave three-fourths of these cases Honorable Discharges. In the Army and Marines, separations in lieu of court-martial were almost invariably Undesirable, whereas in the Navy and Air Force, many of these separations resulted in General or Honorable Discharges.

Many soldiers who received General Discharges either had a history of minor infractions or else committed major offenses but were given light punishment because of extenuating circumstances. But General Discharges were also given for reasons wholly unrelated to discipline; they were used to "fire" servicemen who were incapable of performing satisfactorily because of physical, mental, or psychological disabilities and who were thus deemed unsuitable.

General Discharges for unsuitability were awarded for a great variety of reasons: inaptitude, character or behavior disorders, apathy, defective attitudes, "inability to expend effort constructively," alcohol or other drug abuse, homosexual or "other aberrant tendencies," financial irresponsibility, excessive bed-wetting, or other factors.

General Discharges could also result from unfitness proceedings, through which servicemen could also receive the more severe Undesirable Discharge. Unlike the General, the Undesirable is considered "under other-than-honorable conditions" and does not bestow veterans' benefits. An individual could be discharged as unfit for any of the following reasons: sexual misconduct, drug abuse, "shirking," failure to pay debts, failure to support his family, "unsanitary habits," conviction for a criminal offense by civil authorities, and absence for one year or more. But by far the most common ground was "discreditable involvement" with military or civilian authorities—in other words, a determination that the individual was a general troublemaker.

A comparison between the reasons for unsuitability and unfitness shows how subtle and arbitrary the distinctions were. "Apathy" to one commander might have been "shirking" to another; "financial irresponsibility" to one might have been "failure to pay debts" to another. Marijuana possession to one might have been abuse of drugs to another. These distinctions were ultimately a matter of judgment, bias, or even whim. In military shorthand, General Discharges for unsuitability were given for aptitude problems—"soldiers who would if they could, but they can't." Undesirable Discharges for unfitness were for attitude problems—"soldiers who could if they would, but they won't." To make this distinction properly, a discharging officer had to make a determination difficult even for a skilled psychologist.

Often, events beyond the control of the soldier determined which discharge he got. Bobby Banks qualified for a medical discharge after an Army psychiatrist interpreted his problem as a character disorder due to "impulsive, escape-type behavior, and unresolved emotional needs marked by an evasion of responsibility." He was processed for a General Discharge, but just before his papers came through, a race riot occurred in the unit. Although Banks was not personally involved, his commander cracked down on discipline, and he got an Undesirable Discharge.

Although the Pentagon officially defines the Undesirable Discharge as "nonpunitive," it has a serious adverse effect in civilian life. About one-third of all employers refuse to consider job applications from veterans with Undesirable Discharges, and two-thirds discriminate against them. State and local laws often bar them from employment rights, occupational licenses, and welfare benefits. As a consequence, the Undesirable Discharge has led many a veteran into a hopeless downward spiral. Paul Dodson could not afford to go to school because of his ineligibility for GI Bill benefits, so he tried to get a job as a trucker. Large firms refused to hire him because of his discharge, so he had to work intermittently for small companies. At most, he made $70 per week, but he often was laid off. In between jobs, his bad discharge barred him from unemployment benefits. James Duke, a sailor stationed in Guam, experimented with LSD one night. Afraid that his "trip" would give him continuing nightmares, he told his commander what he had done. The next day, the sailor was on his way home with an Undesirable Discharge. For the next five years, Duke drifted from place to place, unable to find a job and too poor to go to college without GI Bill benefits.

As the war approached its end, administrative discharge determinations became more and more lenient. Many of the same soldiers who once would have gotten Undesirable Discharges received General Discharges instead. The Army increased its General Discharge rate from 1.7 percent in 1969 to 8.2 percent in 1975, curtailing sharply its practice of giving Undesirable Discharges for unfitness.

The Undesirable Discharge, because it is given "under other-than-honorable conditions," was also used as a sanction in place of discharges imposed by court-martial. In the early years of the war, AWOL and comparable offenses very often meant a court-martial and a Bad Conduct or Dishonorable Discharge after a prison term. But in 1968, new legislation increased the legal protections available to servicemen facing a special court-martial and a possible Bad Conduct Discharge. Each defendant was normally guaranteed the right to a legally qualified defense attorney, a certified military judge, and a verbatim trial record. This made special courts-martial an added drain on scarce resources.

The technicalities of a criminal trial, with a heavy burden of proof and complex rules of evidence, made the court-martial a cumbersome instrument for all but the most serious of cases. One old-time sergeant griped that

> the NCO's word isn't taken at face value anymore. The other day it took four witnesses just for me to get disciplinary proceedings under way. The JAGs won't go to court if you're the only witness. The Army's got to find a better way to get rid of people faster who don't want to be here.

What made recourse to court-martial even more unattractive was the uncertainty of the result. A commander could be fairly certain that an uncomplicated AWOL case would result in conviction. But whether the sentence would include a discharge was another question. A pretrial agreement, appeal, or clemency action might result in the imposition of a lesser penalty.

"It became increasingly clear," said the chief Army legal officer in Vietnam, "that trial by court-martial was an awkward, ineffective, and expensive means of attempting to cope with a large-scale problem. . . . Soldiers whose behavior indicated that they lacked the desire or ability to rehabilitate themselves [had to be] eliminated through administrative channels."

At about the same time, Congress and the Nixon administration began cutting back on manpower levels. A congressional ceiling set in 1971 required the armed forces to separate 65,000 soldiers almost immediately. All branches of service, but especially the Army and Marines, began relying on a relatively uncomplicated, reliable means of ridding themselves of troublemakers. Criminal charges were filed and court-martial actions initiated, but defendants were then given the chance to request Undesirable Discharges "for the good of the service," popularly called "Chapter 10 discharges." This was, in effect, a plea bargain. The accused soldier waived his right to trial in return for a guarantee that he would not be convicted or sent to prison. However, he usually got an Undesirable Discharge, and the charges, which were never legally proved, remained on his record.

Commanders began resorting to this technique with gusto in the latter half of the war. In 1969, the Army issued only 532 Chapter 10 discharges, but it gave out 7,000, 12,000, and 26,000 in the next three years. The Marine Corps showed a comparable increase, from just one case in 1967 to almost 5,000 in 1971. The vast majority of these discharges—over 90 percent—were Undesirable, and this method of separating soldiers quickly came to dominate the military justice system. In fact, Chapter 10's became so prevalent that in mid-1972, the Department of the Army had to caution its commanders against using it to circumvent efforts at rehabilitation of marginal soldiers. Altogether, about 130,000 Vietnam-era servicemen received Chapter 10 discharges, more than half of the 224,000 Undesirable certificates imposed during the period.

Accepting an Undesirable Discharge in lieu of court-martial was voluntary, but there was little incentive for the average soldier to resist. Most succumbed after a little persuasion: "They started putting pressure on us to take a fast discharge," one veteran recalled. "We could be out of the stockade in ten minutes, and out of the Army in a day and a half. One Army lawyer said that the only way to avoid five to nine years in prison was to sign. It was real strong pressure, and one of my buddies took it because he had personal problems and had to get home." Some units had regular "UD days," especially when stockades got overcrowded. An Army lawyer recalled making weekly trips to the stockade, offering an Undesirable Discharge to anyone willing to sign the forms: "They were so eager to get out of jail and out of the Army, we could clean the place out in a day." But many soldiers did not realize that the evidence against them was weak, and they wrongly assumed they would be convicted.

Some soldiers never realized what they were signing. Tommy Sanders wanted to be court-martialed because he thought he was innocent, but he did not know his rights. He just signed some papers and found himself out with an Undesirable Discharge. But most soldiers who accepted Chapter 10 Undesirable Discharges did not know or care what it would mean to them later on. As one veteran described it:

> The UD is like the tattoo a young sailor gets on leave in some exotic port. It remains on him forever, and there's little chance that he can ever get it removed. It helped to believe that the UD was only temporary. There is a rumor, probably as old as the Army itself, that after six months, it automatically is changed to an Honorable or General Discharge. It doesn't.

Nonetheless, the Chapter 10 discharge was sometimes called the "golden loophole" by soldiers who were tired of the military and wanted to go home. Anyone AWOL for more than thirty days became the responsibility of the base closest to his place of arrest, so servicemen could engineer more lenient treatment by choosing where to return to military control. Counselors often recommended good places to surrender, and some bases were overwhelmed with returning deserters.

The rule of thumb was that an AWOL under three months would keep you in the service, an AWOL over nine months would risk court-martial, but three to nine months brought a quick ticket out of the service. Sam Barnes "looked around for ways to get out, and finally decided to go AWOL." He spent a few months living in a commune, surrendered at the appropriate time and place, got an Undesirable Discharge, and went home for good. So did Phil Cook, although he had a little more trouble. He went AWOL three times and then asked for his Undesirable Discharge. He was unsuccessful at first, so he left three more times. "I just decided to go AWOL as often as I had to until I got my discharge." A Fort Meade sergeant recalled how civilian employers of AWOL soldiers intervened on their behalf, asking the military to "get Jimmy Jones his Undesirable Discharge expeditiously, because we need him on the job."

However, the golden loophole was no absolute guarantee that a deserter would stay out of prison. Late in 1972, two deserters surrendered to Army authorities after having spent four years in Sweden, both expecting to get quick Undesirable Discharges. One spent a couple of months in the stockade before getting his. The other deserter, with an almost identical case, spent six months awaiting trial. His court-martial gave him two more years and a Bad Conduct Discharge.

The decision whether to court-martial was made by field-grade commanders, usually upon the advice of military lawyers. Offenses considered less serious were tried by special courts-martial, the military equivalent of misdemeanor courts, which could impose Bad Conduct Discharges and up to six months in prison. General courts-martial could impose Dishonorable Discharges and up to life in prison, but severe sentences were usually reserved for those convicted of murder, rape, or robbery. Of all soldiers punished and given other-than-honorable discharges for AWOL or other violations of discipline, just 8 percent were sent to prison, and only 2 percent served more than six months in confinement.

Military defendants who stood trial were almost always convicted, fined, and reduced in rank. Rarely, however, did they receive punitive discharges. The 450,000 special and general courts-martial of the Vietnam era produced only 31,800 Bad Conduct and 2,200 Dishonorable Discharges. About a third of the punitive discharges were for crimes against person or property that would have been punished severely by civilian courts. The other two-thirds were for violations of military discipline, usually AWOL, which were essentially indistinguishable from the type of misconduct that resulted in the 130,000 Chapter 10 Undesirable Discharges. Oddly enough, offenses committed in Vietnam or on the way to Vietnam were not punished more harshly than those that had no direct relationship with the war. Nor did the length of the AWOL have much effect on the degree of punishment. The only significant differences between deserters with Undesirable Discharges and those with punitive discharges were that the latter were more likely to be Marines, onetime exiles, or servicemen discharged early in the war.

Most Americans care little and know less about the different discharges. Personnel officers of large companies may understand the system, but the rest of the public is confused about the differences between "Honorable" and "honorable conditions," "less-than-Honorable" and "other-than-honorable conditions," "unsuitability" and "unfitness," "Undesirable" and "Dishonorable," and so forth. A Louisiana judge once concluded that General Discharges were given by general courts-martial; to him they were the worst of all possible discharges. To most people, any veteran with less than an unblemished, fully Honorable Discharge is suspect. For more than half a million men of the Vietnam generation, this means lifelong stigmas on their records.

During President Ford's clemency program, veterans of other eras wrote by the dozens, asking that their bad discharges be changed. "It's ruined my whole life," complained a World War I veteran who had gone AWOL more than fifty years ago. Father Theodore Hesburgh, a member of President Ford's Clemency Board, received the following letter from a World War II veteran with a Dishonorable Discharge:

Dear Father Hesburgh,

I am writing you simply because I understand your feelings on amnesty for the men that just wouldn't serve in an undeclared war.

I was in the Second World War. I went in the infantry in the beginning of 1942. I returned home in 1947. Why so long, you may ask. I'll tell you.

After training, we were shipped to Africa. We went in through Kasserine Pass with the First Armored Division. We were almost wiped out. . . . We were sent back for seconds, and we made it this time against the desert fox. I also went on the invasion of Sicily and the invasion of Italy and the invasion of Anzio Beach. When the Army got ready for D-Day, quite a few of the four-invasion assault troops were sent to England to join that invasion. . . . We jumped out of the landing craft on Omaha Beach (Red Beach One). . . . There were a lot of dead men there. We got off the beach, though, and something else—the men at Omaha and the 101st Airborne were the only troops to use bayonets in that war. The 29th was called the "Purple Heart" Division. No trooper got off clean. I ended my soldiering at Aachen in a mine field. Someone fell off the tape line, and the whole place blew. I went with it, but I'm alive. A lot of guys aren't.

Well, in 1945, the Germans quit. I asked for some leave, which I hadn't had for a real long time. I was refused, so I went AWOL. I went about thirty days and came back to the outfit. I was told they needed an example to scare the new occupation troops coming in, so I ended up in an Army court charged with everything they still had hanging around that had to be cleaned up. There are no lawyers in Army court, just officers who read books. I was given a general court-martial when they got finished charging me. I was sent up for ten years in a federal penitentiary. . . . They then sent me home with other prisoners, chained in the hold of a liberty ship. . . .

I tried for a long time to get justice, but who cared? Only my family. When I got out with a great combat record and a dishonorable discharge, the employers only saw my jail sentence. I finally got past that after a few years, but I never got any veterans' benefits or my insurance, back pay, or anything. As the court-martial says, "to forfeit all pay and allotments, due and to become due." Anyway, that's what I got, and I got a gang of medals, too. A five invasion man. One out of some four hundred soldiers with that ribbon for the European Theater of Operations.

I know what a jail term can do for you in the job market, education, etc. I wouldn't want these guys to get it my way. I think they need a break. Keep fighting for them, reverend. I wish to God someone would have fought a little for me so long ago.

Sincerely,
An Old Soldier

V | EXILES

On the Run

A few minutes after his ship left harbor, Keith Considine left his quarters, donned a life jacket, and jumped into the ocean. On cue, a group of Vietnam Veterans Against the War rescued him in rented canoes, taking him away to the sanctuary of the antiwar underground. Considine was one of at least fifty thousand Americans who became political fugitives during the Vietnam era, most of whom fled to another country. Not since eighty thousand Tories fled to Canada during the Revolution had America witnessed such an exodus of people fleeing its borders. Perhaps more than any other single aspect of the Vietnam war, the exiled draft resisters and deserters symbolized the conflict over the morality of the war and the values of those who refused to fight it.

While other groups of offenders were largely overlooked, the exiles captured the attention of the public and the press. Over time, they became the stuff of political mythology. Their supporters believed them to be bright, principled antiwarriors; to their detractors, they were overeducated cowards. Most people thought the law was at their heels, that arrest or surrender meant long prison terms, and that what exiles hoped for most was vindication through an amnesty that would bring them home in triumph.

Little of this was true. Exiles and other fugitives were neither the best nor the worst of their generation. They were a cross-section of young men who, for a variety of reasons, refused to submit to the draft or the dictates of the armed forces. They were rich and poor, black and white, college graduates and high school dropouts. Some were related to influential people; both Morris Udall and Spiro Agnew had nephews living in exile. Some adjusted very well to life as immigrants, but most did not. While the American public hotly debated the amnesty issue, most exiles quietly came home and seldom went to prison.

Just one-sixth of all draft resisters and deserters ever hid from the law (see Figure 7). Most of the 210,000 accused draft resisters remained home to face charges. Those who took flight generally did so long before formal charges were brought against them. Although a number were later indicted and declared fugitives from justice, most never were the subject of legal proceedings. But they all lived with the constant fear that discovery meant certain arrest, trial, and imprisonment.

By definition, all deserters were fugitives from military control, but few concealed their identities, hid in the underground, or took exile in a foreign country. For most, desertion was like walking off a job—no phony ID, no stolen jeeps, no jumping over fences, and no rescues in rented canoes. Cunning or careful planning was necessary only for deserters in the combat zone.

Four of every five deserters went home, resumed their civilian lives, and followed normal routines. They worked steadily, often at their old jobs. They were, as some described themselves, "self-retired veterans." They believed that punishment was inevitable and that it would be worse the longer they failed to report. But surrender was best left to another day. As the time began to stretch into years, many married and raised families. Some filled highly reputable jobs, acquired their own businesses, or worked for federal, state, or local agencies. A few held positions of public trust: sheriff, police chief, juvenile probation officer, narcotics agent. At times, they worked and prospered even though many people in their communities knew they were deserters.

They expected to be caught eventually. Anyone absent for more than thirty days was supposed to have a "Deserter Wanted by the Armed Forces" notice sent to the FBI and his hometown police department. After 1971, the Army offered a bounty of $25 to any police officer who arrested an AWOL soldier. But many local police never received the notices, or else just ignored them. In Berkeley, California, the city council passed a resolution barring the local police from tracking or arresting deserters.

FIGURE 7: EXILES

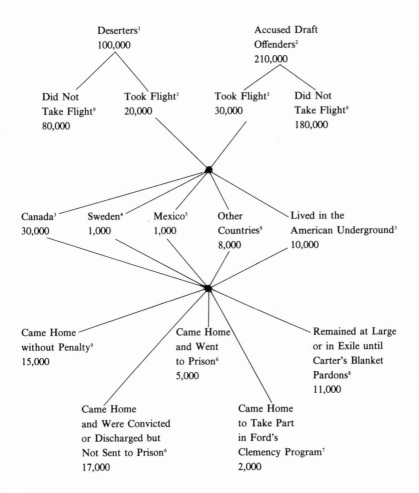

Deserters[1]
100,000

Accused Draft Offenders[2]
210,000

Did Not Take Flight[9]
80,000

Took Flight[3]
20,000

Took Flight[3]
30,000

Did Not Take Flight[9]
180,000

Canada[3]
30,000

Sweden[4]
1,000

Mexico[5]
1,000

Other Countries[9]
8,000

Lived in the American Underground[3]
10,000

Came Home without Penalty[9]
15,000

Came Home and Went to Prison[6]
5,000

Remained at Large or in Exile until Carter's Blanket Pardons[8]
11,000

Came Home and Were Convicted or Discharged but Not Sent to Prison[6]
17,000

Came Home to Take Part in Ford's Clemency Program[7]
2,000

A Seattle steelworker quit the Army, went home, and nothing happened: "I worked under my real name all the time, filed my income taxes under my real name, and got my refund checks. If the FBI had wanted me in all those years, it would have taken them about ten seconds to find me." A wildcatter from the Texas oil fields admitted he was a fugitive when stopped for speeding by his hometown deputy sheriff, but he just got a traffic ticket. A Santa Barbara deserter was visited by the FBI and admitted he was a fugitive. He asked the FBI man, "What do you want me to do?" The agent said that since the man was living at home he was not really "at large." The agent closed the case file and went away. A military attorney observed that "from month to month, you could see how much time and energy the FBI was putting in its enforcement effort. Every so often, we would get shipments from a particular place, and we always knew where the local FBI was trying to improve its statistics."

No sweep would have caught Joe Browning, even though he lived at home under his real name. His house was at the end of a cul-de-sac, and every time an unfamiliar car came down his street, he jumped out a window and ran off to the local pool hall. But fifty thousand other draft and military fugitives were not prepared to live with the fear Browning endured for years. Not willing to wait for the official-looking stranger at the door, they left their hometowns, often refusing to tell friends and family where they were going, so that no one would have to lie to the FBI. They assumed false identities, sometimes aided by documents stolen by activists from draft boards. Another tactic was to watch the obituaries until a man the proper age died. The fugitive then wrote for a copy of the decedent's birth certificate, which could be used to get a driver's license, social security card, and other identification. Sometimes fugitives were given complete sets of identification by friends, who then reported them lost or stolen. Passports were more of a problem, expert forgeries costing as much as $1,500.

Roughly ten thousand fugitives stayed in the United States, living as political outcasts—"the way our grandfathers did in Europe"—avoiding personal entanglements and suspicious of every chance meeting. It was hard to build employment records that could help them find good jobs. A young man who always thought of himself as a "termite" admitted spending virtually "every moment living in fear. . . . I worry that the longer I stay [with a job], the worse my chances are. I make up a social security number, but by the time it hasn't checked out, I've left. I can't make any lasting friends. I have to keep it all inside unless someone else volunteers he's a deserter, too. I'm lonely, but I can't get too involved with girls. They always want to know about your past, and you have to lie."

Driven by fear and suspicion, many fugitives rearranged their entire lives to avoid arrest, often eluding the FBI for years. One person changed his name, moved to a new community, raised a family, and became prosperous and locally prominent. Another moved to the mountains, where he built a tree house and lived for six years as a hunter and trapper. Other fugitives changed their routine very little. They had already been part of the youth subculture in cities and college communities, good sanctuaries for someone with draft or military problems.

Fugitives were afraid that being stopped for hitchhiking or jaywalking could mean the end of freedom. A young man from Washington, D.C., had been a draft fugitive for five years before he was arrested for shoplifting in Virginia. A Minnesota resister was arrested in Eureka, California, dressed as a department store Santa Claus. Some fugitives were caught by the FBI at antiwar rallies and conferences.

For help and comfort, many turned to the organized "underground" —a network of priests, radicals, and ordinary citizens who helped them move from place to place or settle down in a new community. Trusted counselors offered entry to the network by putting a fugitive in touch with one person, who passed him on to another. One man traveled from Chicago to New York, being handed from person to person, and he was astonished to learn who was involved: "I traveled from small town to small town, chauffeured by well-to-do young housewives who often kept small children in the car to avoid suspicion. I spent nights at wealthy farms and large houses that must have belonged to professional people. Sometimes I was taken to religious retreats and orphanages. They never showed me maps or told me where I was, and it took several days and many different trips to go from one city to the next. Frequently, I encountered other underground people going in different directions." The network was especially active in rural New England, dubbed "little Canada" because of the many farms, communes, and college campuses that hid fugitives from the FBI. These New Englanders were merely emulating their ancestors, who a hundred years earlier had run the underground railroad for fugitive slaves.

The farmers, professionals, and housewives in the underground committed felonies by harboring draft fugitives and aiding their interstate flight. "Enticing and procuring a soldier to desert" was also a federal offense. The network was never penetrated, however, and official pressure was directed only at the counselors who served as points of entry. Two prosecutions were brought against counselors in Boston and Bloomington, Illinois. One was acquitted, and the other had his conviction overturned on appeal. Both individuals had been accused of encouraging fugitives to go to Canada, rather than "enticing" the act of desertion itself.

Dozens of counseling organizations did much the same thing. The San Francisco "GI Help" program offered military fugitives "places to crash" and "information about the alternatives of exile to Canada or Sweden, open resistance to the military, going underground, or seeking various kinds of discharges." Local police once raided its headquarters and discovered a dozen AWOL soldiers sleeping on the floor, but no charges were brought against the program. The Defense Department furnished Congress with the names of twenty-three organizations, representing hundreds of antiwar counselors, "that have definitely been linked with deserter inducement programs." Although these counselors were subjected to political surveillance, they never became the targets of a major Justice Department criminal investigation.

In low-income and minority neighborhoods, there was an unorganized, spontaneous underground protecting people known to be wanted for draft or military offenses. Ed Sowders, a Vietnam veteran deserter who lived in the "poor people's underground" for three years, recalled how

> this community-based network of relatives, neighbors, and friends helped me remain in my own home, safe in the knowledge that they would inform me or my family of anything out of the ordinary. My mother received

several phone calls from neighbors and friends, informing her that they had just received visits by agents. Of course, no one provided information about me. One man said, "For christsake, if you see Eddie, tell him to get out of town, they're looking hard this time."

The network twice saved Sowders from certain arrest. Trapped in his house by FBI agents, he escaped amidst a specially choreographed pack of teenagers with baseball bats and gloves, ostensibly heading for the neighborhood park. Later, he was arrested for a minor traffic offense; with no valid identification, he was held awaiting a fingerprint check which was certain to mark him as a deserter. A number of neighbors came to the station, accused the police of breaking up a local party, and convinced them to release Sowders before the fingerprint check came through. He eventually surrendered to the FBI, but on his own terms —in a public antiwar ceremony in Washington, D.C.

Sowders was an unusually resourceful fugitive. Not many others were able to use the underground as more than a temporary shelter as they moved from place to place, making plans to take exile in a foreign country.

Taking Exile

Tens of thousands of draft and military fugitives went into exile during the war. A few nations, notably West Germany and Japan, actively pursued American deserters and returned them to military custody. But most countries left them alone if they caused no trouble. Drifters moved from border to border without difficulty, and small colonies survived for years without work permits or social benefits in Holland, France, and England. But there were few real choices for fugitives who wanted to establish roots. An antiwar guidebook rated all the countries in the world for exile, giving poor recommendations to most:

> Living in the Amazon might sound romantic, but the prospect of life in a Brazilian jail brings one back to reality and away from Brazil.
> The applicant must give proof of a minimum deposit of $10,000 in a

bank established in Haiti. Political exiles aren't rich. To hell with Haiti.

The letter which we received from [Venezuela] was rather hostile, and we would suggest forgetting it. The embassy also sent us one entire pamphlet of speeches made by Nixon praising Venezuela.

Early in the war, Mexico was a common choice of deserters from military bases in the Southwest. The border was easy to cross and living costs were low, but finding a job was difficult for a "gringo" without a work permit. Except for a few entrepreneurs who risked severe criminal penalties for drug dealing, almost all of the roughly one thousand exiles in Mexico eventually returned to the United States or left for a more hospitable country.

There were only two real choices for exiles who wanted to settle down—Canada and Sweden. Canada was an attractive refuge. It had no draft and did not consider AWOL a criminal offense, so exiles did not fear extradition to the United States. Canada offered not only sanctuary, but work permits, welfare benefits, full legal status as immigrants, and eventual citizenship. In the face of economic and cultural domination by the colossus of the south, official Canadian sympathy toward the exiles enhanced the country's international prestige and self-esteem. Many Canadians were quietly elated that America was getting its comeuppance in Vietnam. They had long worried about the exodus of talented young artists and professionals to the United States, and the flow of war resisters was helping to reverse the trend. In 1970, the northward exodus exceeded southward migration for the first time in memory. Furthermore, according to External Affairs Minister Mitchell Sharp, Canada "looked back to see what the United States had done during the period 1939–1941 when we were at war and they were not. We found that Americans had accepted deserters from the Canadian army without question. So we said, 'Well, that's fine. The Americans are in a war that we're not in, so we will apply the same policy in Canada that they applied to us.'"

Many exiles were drawn to Canada by its beauty, robust life-style, and freedom from American social pressures. The independence and the romance of the last frontier were just what some fugitives were looking for:

It isn't just in terms of geography and economy that Canada is a frontier country; it's the men and their experience. Hitchhiking in Canada, one is picked up by men who have worked in, and who talk of, the mines, the railroad, the sawmills, the oil fields, and the forest. As for me, it is a time to try new ways of living, to try new faces, to think, to remember.

Young Americans could follow the example of Jim Grady, a pacifist who fled the World War I draft, spent the rest of his life in Canada, and was an eighty-year-old prospector in British Columbia at the start of the Vietnam war. It was easy for exiles to develop an attachment for Canada: "If this is jail, it sure is a big, beautiful one."

Yet the most important attractions of Canada were its familiarity to Americans and its openness to immigrants. Throughout its history, Canada has greeted foreigners warmly, and Montreal, Toronto, and Vancouver have large, tightly knit communities of first-generation immigrants from all over the world. Americans could easily blend into Canadian life, or they could stay within their own indigenous communities.

Getting there was easy. America and Canada have the longest friendly border in the world. At more than a hundred separate border stations, guards usually wave travelers through after a few perfunctory questions. American border officials looked with suspicion on the draft-age traveler with a lot of luggage and checked the National Crime Information Center (NCIC) list before letting him pass. But most draft fugitives chose exile long before they faced formal charges, and even those who were indicted had a week to cross the border before appearing on the NCIC list. Deserters had at least a month before their names were listed.

For some, crossing the border had an element of suspense. Ron Danielson, an Army deserter, was detained for questioning at the American border station at Blaine, Washington. He raced away on foot, but was captured by American immigration officials fifty feet inside Canadian territory. The event was recorded on film by a Vancouver *Sun* reporter who happened to be standing nearby. This violation of Canadian territorial integrity prompted official demands for the return of Danielson. After spending a week in an American jail, he was delivered to the border, where Canadian officials set him free.

George Csikor, a Hungarian refugee and Canadian citizen, was awaiting trial for refusing induction into the American army. Csikor was living in the San Francisco Bay area at the time, and the president of the University of Victoria Student Union smuggled him out of the country on a flight to Vancouver, using tactics that prompted *Amex-Canada* magazine to call the episode "a veritable spy thriller escape story." Scott Peters was less successful. Peters was one of sixty-six inductees aboard a Boeing 737 en route to basic training at Fort Lewis, Washington, when he hijacked the plane and forced it to land in Vancouver, British Columbia. Within a week, Peters was deported from Canada and delivered to a Seattle jail. (The one other exile hijacking during the war involved a deserter who demanded to be flown back to the United States. He kept a knife at a Swedish girl's throat, but three fellow exiles came aboard the SAS plane and talked him out of it.)

A little pocket money was all that was necessary to enter Canada as a temporary visitor. Those who were better prepared tried to establish permanent status as "landed immigrants" right at the border. They had to score fifty out of a possible ninety points on a rating system that gave credit for education, skills, fluency in English, and other assets. An American high-school graduate with a Canadian job offer had thirty-seven automatic points, and an immigration officer could give him as many as fifteen more based upon a subjective evaluation of his character. The neatly dressed, polite fugitive had a good chance to earn the fifty points on the spot. Others entered Canada as visitors, slipping back across the border when they thought they could qualify as immigrants. Only a handful were said to have had difficulty, usually "because they were not calm and did not use common sense." For the draft fugitive with a college degree, "it was like checking into a hotel."

Canada refused to accept the less-educated, lower-skilled military fugitives until 1969. Deserters could enter Canada as visitors without work permits, but they were subject to arrest and immediate return to American military police. Even after 1969, military fugitives were sometimes turned back under Canadian immigration law, which excluded "criminals," "mentally defective persons," and "persons who are likely to become public charges." If an immigration officer suspected that an individual used marijuana, he could refuse entry. Military fugitives found it more difficult to get the fifty points necessary to become legal immigrants. Marriage to a Canadian citizen was one way to sidestep the requirement, and some deserters advertised in Canadian newspapers and paid as much as $2,000 to make the necessary arrangements.

Those who could not qualify as landed immigrants often lived for years as illegal aliens, facing the constant threat of deportation. In 1972, the Canadian government declared a ninety-day amnesty for illegal immigrants, and twelve hundred Americans signed up for landed status. Soon afterwards, a severe recession resulted in a more selective immigration policy, but by then the Vietnam war was almost over.

Sweden was almost as attractive a place to take exile. Like Canada, it offered a wide-open outdoors; it also provided perhaps the world's most generous social services and welfare benefits. Furthermore, Sweden considered the exiles more than mere immigrants; they were political refugees with international status as opponents of American war policies. Yet Sweden had a much more foreign culture than Canada, and it was an ocean away from friends and families. Exiles could satisfy their day-to-day needs by speaking English, but a command of the Swedish language was required for all but the most menial jobs. The local life-style lacked the comforting reminders of home that exiles could find in Canada with its American-dominated culture. Even Sweden's bigger cities were not melting pots, and young Americans generally suffered the same second-class treatment given Yugoslavs, Greeks, and other foreigners. The Swedish government, for all its generosity, often exhibited much the same heavy-handedness that had soured the exiles on the United States.

The exodus to Sweden began in early 1967, when the government quietly granted asylum to a black deserter from Germany. A handful of others slipped into the country illegally over the next few months, but the exile movement really began later that year with the widely publicized voyage of four sailors from the aircraft carrier *Intrepid.* In October 1967, they met in a Tokyo coffeehouse and agreed not to return to ship because of their opposition to the Vietnam war. With the help of "Beherein," the Japanese underground, they were smuggled away on fishing boats and delivered to the Russian coastal patrol. For two months, the Soviet Union treated them as celebrities. They were given the Lenin Peace Prize, 1,000 gold rubles, vacation trips, press conferences, and other amenities—all to the benefit of host and guest alike. But the four sailors, whom another deserter described as "whacked-out freaks," then began to embarrass the Russians with criticism of the opulent life-style of Communist Party members and comments like "Lenin, oh yeah, you mean John." The Russian Vietnam Committee negotiated with other countries to find a place to send them, and eventually the Swedish Vietnam Committee convinced its government to grant asylum.

The "Intrepid Four" were instant celebrities and drew considerable attention from the international press, which pleased the Swedes. But they also drew the attention of other deserters, which the Swedish government had not anticipated. As a later-arriving exile recalled, "the publicity those cats received helped guys who were fed up and refused to do any more killing for Sam. Now they knew there was at least one country in the world which would let them live like human beings." All of a sudden, Sweden became the deserters' mecca.

About a dozen soldiers and sailors from Southeast Asia followed the path cut through Japan and the Soviet Union by the Intrepid Four. They were shuffled in and out of taxis and buses by Beherein ("the slickest operators since Al Capone and his boys") and treated like heroes by the Soviet Union ("we were probably better excuses for partying than for making propaganda"). Others came from Southeast Asia via India and Afghanistan. As exiles in Sweden began to get attention in the American press, home-based deserters starting heading for Scandinavia. A few stowed away on ships, and one jumped off a Norwegian freighter and swam to safety. Some simply flew to Stockholm; one deserter showed up at an SAS reservation counter in his military uniform, bought a one-way ticket to Sweden, and took off that same day.

By far the largest migration came through West Germany and Denmark. With clothes and documents from the German underground, deserters could reach the Danish border without difficulty. Denmark did not let them stay, but guaranteed safe passage to Sweden. Sometimes, deserters found help in unusual places. Butch Dodson planned to flee to Sweden with his British fiancée, but she was killed in an automobile accident. Distraught, Dodson told his commanding officer of their plans to elope. The colonel gave him $100 and drove him on the first leg of his journey.

Sweden accepted the flurry of deserters with ambivalence. Olaf Palme's government extended a warm welcome to the Intrepid Four, but others were treated coolly. Deserters were usually put in jail upon arrival, sometimes in the drunk tank, while Swedish police made sure they were not wanted for more serious crimes. Until 1969, Sweden accepted deserters only from Vietnam or with orders for the war zone, and it rejected draft resisters altogether. Some observers attributed this restrictive policy to Sweden's own policy of universal conscription for able-bodied men. In 1901, the year compulsory service was introduced in Sweden, one of every seven draft-eligible men fled to other countries, many to the United States—leaving the Swedish government with a dim view of American draft resisters. But more important, Sweden was a neutral nation with close economic ties to the West. American stevedores refused to unload Volvos because of Sweden's acceptance of deserters, and other economic consequences began to be felt. At first, Palme's government chose to move carefully. Its ambassador to the United States commented that "nobody likes deserters," while the interior minister said that offering asylum to deserters was "necessary for humanitarian reasons," but "not an unfriendly gesture toward the United States."

Deserters who came to Sweden in 1968 paid the price of this ambivalence. They were given little help in finding jobs, housing, or language training, and were excluded from some social services available to other immigrant groups. Welfare benefits amounted to only $15 per week, and many turned to begging or stealing. The exiles became so discouraged that a delegation of twelve visited Copenhagen to inquire about moving the entire community to Denmark. But public demonstrations and political pressure from Sweden's left wing induced Palme's government to adopt a more positive attitude. After February 1969, all draft resisters and deserters were accepted at the border upon a simple declaration of opposition to the Vietnam war, and Sweden instituted generous social services to help them adjust. Welfare benefits were doubled to about $30 per week, prompting accusations from the United States Congress that Sweden was "subsidizing" desertion. At about the same time, Palme firmly declared his government's opposition to American involvement in Vietnam, regardless of any threats of economic retaliation. Until the United States withdrew from Vietnam, official Swedish policy remained on the side of the exiles.

No one can say how many draft resisters and deserters chose exile during the war years. Popular estimates of the number of Vietnam-era exiles reflected the political hyperbole of those years. Richard Nixon referred to exiles as "those few hundreds," and antiwar spokesmen often used a figure of 100,000. Each side tried to tailor the exile phenomenon to suit its own political purposes. Both the Defense Department and the Swedish government had unreliable counts, and Canada's more precise immigration tally made no distinction between fugitives from justice and other draft-age male immigrants from the United States. It is difficult even to estimate how many illegal immigrants and international drifters never settled permanently in any country. The available evidence suggests that the grand total was about forty thousand—twenty thousand landed immigrants and ten thousand illegal aliens in Canada, one thousand each in Mexico and Sweden, and the rest scattered around the world. A few thousand were not American citizens, but resident aliens who typically fled to their countries of origin rather than serve in the American armed forces.

In one sense, the 100,000 figure of the antiwar movement was close to the truth. Draft resisters and deserters were the core of a much larger American exile community that included tens of thousands of other young people who had grown disenchanted with life back home. Many went to Canada or Sweden as an act of solidarity with the fugitives. Gregg Williams had planned to refuse induction, but his Kansas City draft board gave him an unexpected physical exemption. He went to Canada anyway, living as a subsistence farmer in Ontario. Friends, brothers, wives, and girl friends often accompanied fugitives across the border and never came back. Broken engagements and divorces were epidemic in the exile community, but American women often stayed in Canada or Sweden and married other exiles.

Nor were these young Americans the only draft-age refugees. Greece, West Germany, and Portugal produced thousands of their own draft resisters, some of whom settled in the United States until they discovered they were subject to the American draft. One man refused induction in Poland, West Germany, and the United States before volunteering for the Israeli army. European countries had experienced this phenomenon for centuries, and they cared little about it. Holland even paid its draft exiles $200 to help them settle elsewhere, promising to welcome them back at age twenty-six if they changed their minds. Australia and South Vietnam produced hundreds of their own anti-Vietnam-war exiles, many of whom emigrated to Canada. To the extent that this international exile population could be called a "community," the American fugitives were its leaders, partly because of their greater number, but also because they attracted by far the most attention.

Taken as a whole, these exiled Americans were much more of a cross-section of their nation's youth than any other category of Vietnam-era offenders. Draft counselor Arlo Tatum noted that their politics varied "from very conservative to revolutionary leftist to hippie, with heaviest representation between these extremes." They were "ambitious and lazy, unkempt and neat, strange and ordinary, married and single, nervous and self-confident."

Yet some aspects of their background set them apart from their peers back home—and from each other. Draft and military exiles had very little in common, a fact that they and their host countries soon discovered. Draft resisters usually emigrated between 1965 and 1970. They were predominantly white, middle-class, and fairly well educated. Their political views were diverse, typically left-of-center but well within the American mainstream. The radical *Amex-Canada* magazine labeled them "Bobby Kennedy or McCarthy types." By contrast, deserters took exile at the height of the war, between 1968 and 1972; they were younger, had far less education, and came from more disadvantaged backgrounds. Instead of being "clean for Gene," they tended to be either apolitical or intensely radical. A Canadian social psychologist classified deserters into four groups: "nonactivists," who deserted primarily for personal rather than political reasons (over 50 percent); "refugees," who were young, unskilled, frightened, and living underground as illegal aliens (30 percent); "organizers," who were college-educated radicals (less than 15 percent); and a "salvage group" of emotionally disturbed young men who often committed serious crimes in addition to desertion (less than 5 percent). Deserters were usually more hostile than draft resisters toward the United States, but much less capable of coping with life in a foreign country. Over time, their organizations became significantly more vocal and radical.

Some draft resisters went to Canada as the last recourse after an unsuccessful campaign to avoid induction. One North Carolina youth tried three times to get a physical exemption—by falling off a bridge on his motorcycle, grazing himself with a shotgun blast, and rupturing his Achilles' tendon with a pistol. Nonetheless, he passed his preinduction physical and went to Canada. Some, like the exile who trained Saudi Arabians to use Nike-Hercules missiles, were anything but conscientiously opposed to war.

Others were violent radicals, like the Puerto Rican accused of murdering a San Juan police officer in an antiwar riot, and the two brothers charged with the bombing of a University of Wisconsin building which killed a research assistant. To quote another, "I had already been convicted and sentenced to three years for assaulting two FBI agents. I was indicted for inciting to riot, for riot, and for burglary. With new charges against me arising out of an anti-imperialist strike at the University of Buffalo, I decided that to spend the next thirty years in jail would be a waste of time." These, however, were the unusual cases, hunted as much by the Canadian Mounties as by the FBI.

For every exile who was an unprincipled draft evader or an international outlaw, there were several who refused to submit to the draft or to participate in the war on moral grounds. About one-third of all exiled draft resisters refused to accept deferments and exemptions for which they apparently qualified. Joe Britt was an A student at a top-ranking university, but his student deferment gave him ethical problems. He quit school, sent his draft card back to his local board with a "letter of resignation," and took a last tour of America on a Greyhound pass before heading for Canada. John McDermott completely ignored his draft board, refusing to play the "game" of finding an acceptable way out of the draft: "I refuse to grovel! I could try numerous dodges, but I will not lower myself to that. Groveling puts the registrant's life in the hands that have no moral right to control it and presumes that the draft board's power is legitimate."

These exiles were similar to the draft violators who stood trial for refusing induction on moral principle. What distinguished them, however, was their rejection of the Gandhian principle that one must be prepared to accept the legal consequences of one's actions. Larry Allison, now a professor of philosophy at a major Canadian university, said that he

> never intended to weasel out of the draft. Going to Canada was the only moral option available to me. I was not willing to go to jail, because the country was wrong; I wasn't. I thought civil disobedience would be futile and harmful to my life. I saw bumper stickers saying "America, love it or leave it," and well, I just chose the second option.

Many deserters were equally motivated by principle. The organizers of numerous antiwar coffeehouses and newspapers *(Head-On, The Last Harass, Gig Line, Shakedown,* and *Fatigue Press)* ended up in Canada, as did the young Marine who feared for his safety after *Life* magazine printed his name and picture in an exposé about brig conditions in Camp Pendleton. A number of deserters took exile after completing full tours of Vietnam, usually because of their growing doubts about the war. John Sheehan deserted for Canada with just four months left in his tour because he refused to "wear the label" of an "honorably discharged veteran of the Vietnam war" for the rest of his life. Gene Brooks considered finishing the remainder of his tour, but he "just felt that maybe there was a more desirable place to live without going back to a situation where there's all this social unrest, and everything from pollution to discrimination to riots to political situations. The American way of life just lost appeal to me."

Most draft exiles could have escaped conviction and avoided the draft without leaving the country, but they were ignorant of their legal alternatives. Colonel Nathan Corman, Virginia state director for Selective Service, "felt sorry" for sons of the Old Dominion who took exile: "If they had looked into all their possibilities, things might have been different." But looking into all possibilities required counseling, and many mistakenly thought that meant high-priced, untrustworthy lawyers. Stu Beecham of Miami went to Canada without looking for help, because "when you're not used to dealing with lawyers, how do you know how to find the right one?" Draft counselor Michael Brophy insisted that "upwards of ninety percent of all the men who are in Canada are there because they were unable to obtain accurate information and competent, responsible counseling." Many draft-age men who might otherwise have gone to Canada had last-minute meetings with draft counselors that kept them out of the draft. Two Los Angeles youths packed their car, closed out their bank accounts, and visited draft counselor Steve Houston to ask what to do when they got to Canada. Houston convinced them that they had other options, so they went home and eventually avoided the draft without having to leave the country.

Lack of counseling also affected exiled deserters. Half of all deserters never made any effort to solve their problems through military channels, and many of the rest never had the patience to follow through. Paul Davidov applied for in-service conscientious objector status, but he fled to Canada without waiting to see what happened to his application. He later learned that he had been granted CO status, but by then he was a deserter.

The tendency to flee before seeking help stemmed from a distrust of draft boards and commanding officers. Orin Lathrop left Minneapolis for Winnipeg because he felt "attacked all the time" by his draft board. "I was too paranoid to try to find out about anything." Don Masters was so "disillusioned and bitter about the whole process" that he never bothered to inquire about exemptions and deferments. Today, he regrets his haste, "but I felt very strongly and didn't want to spend the energy to get things resolved." Carl Scheuer tried to deal fairly with his draft board. He thought he qualified for a physical exemption, but he fled in despair when "they didn't play fair in return."

Lathrop, Masters, and Scheuer were career-oriented college graduates from middle-class families, no different from the millions who safely avoided the draft through legal devices. But their bad relationships with draft boards, coupled with their staunch opposition to the war, left them in a state of confusion and fear. They fled in haste, and they now live with the knowledge that their many years of exile were probably unnecessary. As Lathrop noted, "a lot of doors were open to me at the time, but I didn't know about them—so I guess they really didn't exist."

American-Canadians and American-Swedes

When exiles crossed the border, most were determined never to go back: "I'm a twentieth-century runaway slave, not a draft dodger. There ain't no way I'd ever go back to the United States, except to destroy it." They had to forget the past and create new identities for themselves in Canada: "Once I moved to Canada, I no longer regarded myself as evading the draft. I was immigrating. I had broken my ties with the United States." It was impossible for these men to equip themselves psychologically for the possibility of coming home, lest that interfere with their adjustment to Canadian or Swedish life. A 1970 survey of exiles in Toronto discovered that 78 percent intended to remain in Canada permanently, regardless of the outcome of the war or any subsequent amnesty. They did not consider themselves exiles; they were expatriates, American-Canadians or American-Swedes, no more interested in returning to their homeland than are foreigners who immigrate to the United States. The Toronto bus station was their Statue of Liberty, the exile organization their Ellis Island.

Today, no more than one-fourth of the original forty thousand exiles remain in their adopted countries, and they tend to be the ones who have made the most successful adjustments. They are doctors, lawyers, university professors, reporters, musicians, movie stars, skilled mechanics, teachers, farmers, craftsmen, storekeepers, accountants— every imaginable trade. One patented an invention and is now a self-made millionaire. Many have Canadian or Swedish wives and children, and one married into the Swedish nobility. They have homes, mortgages, insurance policies, and other attributes of the middle-class life they would have led in the United States.

These successful exiles responded to the challenge of immigration with an élan and self-reliance that reflects well on the adaptability of

American youth. Americans are used to moving from one place to another, shaping a new environment and making new friends. Going to Toronto or Stockholm as a refugee was more difficult than moving to another American city, but the challenge sometimes added to the determination to succeed. "It's remarkable how unremarkable it was," commented Larry Allison, now a professor at a Canadian university. "The only difficult part was the decision itself. Being an immigrant wasn't hard at all."

Even many who still scratch for a living have found personal fulfillment with life as immigrants. Pat Simpson, barely supporting himself with a part-time job loading crates onto boxcars, insists that "Canada is a good place to be a working man. I suppose I'm doing what I would have done if I'd stayed in the States, but I get more respect here." Hundreds of exiles are frontiersmen or bush farmers, working in the summertime and living for the rest of the year off Canada's generous unemployment insurance. Some exiles to Sweden have settled in the Arctic tundra, helping the Lapps with their reindeer herds. Bush land still sells for just a few dollars an acre in remote sections of Canada and Sweden, and a number of exiles have become landowners. A counter-culture shoemaker joined a hundred-acre Ontario commune and built his own house for around $6,000: "I can fulfill the American dream better in Canada than in the States. I can buy some land, build a house, and settle down. How many Americans my age can do that?"

Success rarely came easily, however. Exiles had to be resourceful to survive. Carl and Anna Scheuer were college graduates from suburban Minneapolis whose combined income exceeded $15,000 per year in 1969. In 1970, after Carl's draft board denied him a physical exemption, the Scheuers left for Toronto. "Right at the start, they told me that coming to Canada meant a five-year setback in my career plans. That's exactly what happened." Neither of them could find a job in Toronto, so they moved to Calgary. Despite their willingness to work at almost anything, it took Carl three months to find a job, and Anna a full year. Their savings vanished, and they lived in an underheated lower-class housing complex. Two years after arriving in Canada, their combined income was half what it had been in Minneapolis, and they had a newborn baby to care for. Over the next three years, Carl graduated from accounting school, changed jobs twice, and finally established himself in a promising career. The Scheuer family income is now close to $20,000 per year, and recently they bought a comfortable house in a Calgary suburb. Carl and Anna Scheuer spent six years accomplishing what they could have done in one year back in Minnesota.

The trip across the border was a pivotal point in the life of almost every exile. For Larry Allison, the decision "made me more prone to stay in control of my own life. As a philosopher, I might call myself more 'morally autonomous.' I think I'll be better off in the long run as a result." Orin Lathrop insisted that coming to Canada was the "shock therapy" he needed to get away from thinking in conventional, programmed terms. "It brought out my strengths and weaknesses, teaching me how to organize my own life." Immigration may be an acquired skill, and many exiles speak of moving from Canada or Sweden to another country if they ever hit the doldrums. They share a strong sense of individuality and self-confidence born of crisis, perseverance, and eventual success against heavy odds.

However, for every one who made the adjustment, three others did not. They came back to the United States, some to prison. Many went home after a few days or weeks. They were unable to muster the skill, hard work, or good fortune necessary to establish a home in a foreign country. Part of the problem was economic. In Canada, jobs were scarce and low-paying, especially during the recession of the early 1970s. American-owned businesses often refused to hire exiles, and some Canadian employers were not inclined to hire Americans when able-bodied Canadian workers could be found. Work could be found more easily in Sweden, but most of the available jobs were those the Swedes themselves did not want.

Deserters had the most difficult time. Young and unskilled, they had to compete with West Indians, Yugoslavs, and other immigrant groups for menial jobs—washing dishes, sweeping floors, or driving taxis if they were lucky. The job market was hopeless for the thousands who were illegal immigrants; they had to resort to exploitation labor or petty crime to survive. Illegal immigrants risked deportation if they were caught, so they had no recourse if they were paid less than the minimum wage—or not paid at all, as sometimes happened.

In Toronto, Stockholm, and elsewhere, young Americans begged in the streets, slept in the parks, and gathered empty bottles to collect the deposits. Some began to "rip off" everything and everyone they could. Leaders of the Swedish exile community granted a contrived interview to a right-wing Texas broadcaster in exchange for $2,000. Hospitable Canadians and Swedes began to notice the disappearance of valuable possessions. A few exiles resorted to bootlegging liquor or peddling drugs, creating a public nuisance that affected the reputation of the entire exile community.

Almost every exile was mentally prepared to suffer misfortune for a while, but many began to wonder whether resistance was worth indefinite sacrifice. Friends at home were leading normal lives, starting families, and prospering in careers, while exiles were still hanging in limbo. Even those who were gradually building new lives were bitter about the years they were sacrificing in the process. A former Army doctor found that his deserter status prevented him from holding all but the lowest-paying medical jobs: "Look at me. I live in a crummy house. Here I am the doctor of the family, and all my brothers have better houses than I can afford."

Separation from families back home was another source of hardship. During an exile's first few months in Canada or Sweden, the event of the day was the arrival of mail from home. Many parents supported their sons' decisions, but that often increased the agony of separation. Some parents paid a price for that support. Terry Morton's father lost his American Legion membership, and his business orders fell so dramatically that he almost went bankrupt. Paul and Roger Hodgkins were taken to Canada by their father. He took ill and died shortly after the FBI threatened to prosecute him for helping his sons flee the country. (The Justice Department later dropped all charges against his sons.)

The strain of having a son in exile was aggravated by constant reminders that events had conspired to set otherwise law-abiding families on the wrong side of the law. FBI agents often interviewed neighbors and friends, and they had a habit of visiting at Christmastime to see if the son had come home. Many exiles had to remain in Canada or Sweden when family members died, because family funerals were a favorite hunting ground for the FBI.

Yet support from one's family often meant the difference between success and failure as an immigrant. Toronto psychiatrist Saul Levine discovered that almost every exile who came to him in deep depression had parents who disagreed with the decision and had given no moral or financial support. Parents sometimes actively helped the FBI find their sons, or else sent vitriolic letters disowning them: "You have disgraced your family and your country. . . . We never want to hear from you again except to have the money back we lent you to fly back to your base. . . . We burned your birth certificate and your insurance policy. You are no longer a son of ours."

Some exiles wondered whether they were indeed as bad as their parents and others said they were. "We were taught as children that deserting the Army was the most cowardly thing anyone could ever do. We usually thought that what we did was right, but sometimes you can't help believing a little bit of what people say about you." According to Levine, guilt was pervasive in the exile community—guilt over abandoning parents and friends, guilt over leaving the country they had been brought up to love, or guilt over not having taken a firmer stand by going to prison or fighting the war effort through the underground.

What kept their spirits up amidst the economic, family, and psychological pressures was the firm belief that resisting the war was the right thing to do. However, even that conviction eventually brought disappointment. Many exiles had hoped that their sacrifices could somehow help to end the Vietnam war. As the war raged on and on, most exiles sensed that their personal sacrifices had made little difference. They remained confident that history would record their stance as morally correct, but that was little solace: "The war ripped hell out of my life for ten years, and Nixon still got his 'peace with honor.' "

The grimmest time came between 1970 and 1973. Jobs were harder than ever to find, especially for deserters, and the American pullout from Vietnam was frustratingly slow. Canadians and Swedes began to sour upon the young Americans they once glorified as moral and political heroes. The local press featured stories about deserters convicted of robbery and drug dealing, and there was a growing fear that exiles were carriers of American disease: crime, drugs, and hippie culture. Just a few dozen were imprisoned or deported, but the entire community felt the sting.

Canadians began to change their attitude as they came to perceive the young Americans more as exiles than as immigrants. Anti-American feelings were muted so long as exiles did not act like Americans. But when they began to voice counterculture philosophies, they were looked upon as cultural imperialists. Much of the criticism came from left-wing Canadian nationalists, who accused Americans "of taking Canadian jobs, money, and places in schools, of denying a Canadian identity, of spreading the American way of life, and of not learning about Canada."

Exile organizations and publications often exacerbated anti-American sentiments. *Amex-Canada* magazine, for example, commented that "we are a brand new kind of immigrant, and Canadians will have to get used to us. Maybe with a little bit of luck, they'll listen seriously to a bit of what we're trying to tell them." *Amex* was replying to a Toronto *Daily Star* editorial which warned that "unless the young Americans for whom *Amex* speaks revise their priorities, . . . they risk arousing a growing hostility and suspicion among ordinary Canadians." The radical image of *Amex* and other groups was hard for politically moderate exiles to shake. "They give an unfair and unrealistic view of expatriates," Carl Scheuer complained. "They make all our legitimate arguments sound bad."

Much of the exile community's image problem came from the Canadian media. A CBC-TV episode of *McQueen,* entitled "Home Is Where the Draft Ain't," showed an immigration official turning back a would-be exile with the comment, "He's a weirdo, a draft dodger. . . . We don't need his kind." The Canadian film *Explosion* told a story with homosexual overtones of two American youths, one a draft-deferred psychotic and the other an exile, who went on a car-stealing, cop-killing spree. Conservative Canadians began to blame the exiles for the defiant behavior of their own children: "Canadian policemen are not pigs. You will say, 'But it is Canadians who use the word.' I will ask, 'Where did they learn it?' " The heaviest criticism was directed at deserters, whom Toronto *Telegraph* editorials portrayed as full-fledged criminals who deserved no shelter in Canadian society.

The Swedes, for their part, did not want the exiles to be unobtrusive; they considered the young Americans to be heroes and international celebrities. Almost all Swedes were opposed to America's Vietnam policies, and the exiles offered a showcase for that attitude. Leaders of the exile community were the toasts of parties. But through it all, the exiles felt that they were being used, and that the Swedes showed little regard for them as individuals: "We had to be chameleons. If we were talking to a revolutionary, we had to be a revolutionary. We couldn't be ourselves." Exiles complained that the Swedes "seemed to be playing games" with their fate: "Sweden wanted all the political credit for accepting the American war resisters, but little of the responsibility for job training, housing, and schooling."

Ironically, the Swedes' favorable attitudes began to change as their government became more generous. Largely by coincidence, the counterculture came to Sweden at about the same time as the Americans: 1968 was the year of the "Stockholm summer," when hippies from Europe and the United States descended on the country. A Swedish newspaper ran a front-page article about Americans and drugs, with a color picture of an arm hemorrhaged from mainlining. Fourteen Americans were deported for drug violations, and dozens were arrested for other serious crimes. The Swedish image of American deserters shifted from antiwar hero to heroin-shooting hippie.

During the next few years, there were enough page-one stories about Americans convicted of robbery or drug peddling, or engaging in radical political activity, to feed Swedish suspicions of the exiles. Headlines like "Deserters Selling Drugs to Swedish Youth" and "Americans Lead Narcotics Subculture" regularly appeared in newspapers. A magazine asked, "If we accepted them so they would not have to kill in Vietnam, why are we allowing them to kill our children?" In Norrkoping, exiles demonstrated against the building of a Dow chemical factory by burning Swedish and American flags sewn together. Swedes began to ask why American deserters were welcome when their own sons had to perform obligatory military service.

The Americans, for their part, resented being made scapegoats for Sweden's drug culture, and became increasingly hostile toward their hosts. They complained about the "standardized and repressed" Swedish society, the Garboesque reserve of the Swedish people, and the values of a society that let speeding drivers go free while fining someone

$60 if his dog ran loose: "I've just learned to sit back, stay cool, and laugh at whatever the hell these Swedes do when they're drunk. Because when they're sober, there's not much to laugh about."

The growing alienation from Canadian and Swedish society contributed to a distinct split within the exile community. In Canada, the division was largely between deserters and draft resisters. Deserters who were having little success as immigrants became more radical and political. Organizations like the Canadian-based American Deserters' Committee and *Amex-Canada* began to abandon efforts to help exiles with their adjustment problems, turning more toward ideological attacks against their hosts and their homeland. By contrast, draft resister organizations adopted a more pragmatic "priority counseling" strategy to help exiles succeed as immigrants; they discouraged other Americans from coming to Canada and adding to the exile community's problems. The two parts of the exile community became increasingly estranged and class-oriented. Each side accused the other of vandalizing its files or carrying on "vicious whispered lobbying" behind its back. *Amex-Canada* magazine condemned "draft dodger chauvinism," commenting that "many dodgers . . . have carved their little niche in the Canadian middle class. They wish to stay invisible and resent the visibility of field jacket and combat boot clad deserters trying to survive on the street and at the same time giving the exile a bad name." The Swedish exile community had a comparable split between those who were adjusting well and those who were having problems, but the distinction between draft resisters and deserters was not as sharp.

As the years passed, the less successful exiles either clung together in ghetto neighborhoods or drifted away to live in a personal no-man's land. One deserter bicycled through Canada for years, begging for handouts as he moved from town to town. Hundreds roamed the world with their duffel bags, out of touch with family and friends, living from day to day. If they looked at all to the future, it was to the end of the interminable war. Five committed suicide. But by far the most common solution for despair was to come home to the United States.

Coming Home

As refugees, the exiles' rejection of their homeland had always been a central part of their lives. Many of them were intensely anti-American when they left: "We said no to everything American when we crossed the border of no return. The illusion of the American Dream had been crushed." They were critical of the America First attitude that many believed had gotten the nation into the Vietnam war: "Americans are floundering in ignorance that their country is the best in everything. It's a good country, but not the best in all ways. By living in another country, you can see this more clearly." "Coming to Canada taught me to look at the world as just people, not the United States versus everyone else."

Yet despite their frustration over America's persistent involvement in Vietnam, and despite their belief that the country had not faced up to the lessons of the war, most exiles remained strikingly positive in their feelings about America. Withdrawal from Vietnam and the disgrace of Richard Nixon vindicated their decisions to leave, but it also made it harder to stay antagonistic toward their homeland. Larry Allison saw these events as evidence of the strength of the American political system: "It was easy to chuckle about the problems of Vietnam and Watergate, but that's all over now. Canada doesn't have problems on the same scale, but it's often bogged down in petty squabbling. There's a joke that Watergate could never happen in Canada, because they'd never be caught. Unfortunately, that's true."

Many exiles, including some of the most radical, had a love-hate attitude toward the United States. They continued to criticize the nation's social and political problems in the apparent hope that they could make some difference, yet their separation gave them a new respect for America's social and cultural qualities: "You have to separate people from policy. Taking exile was not an anti-American move; it was an antigovernment move." They criticized Canada for its "lack of creative spirit" and Sweden for its "gray mediocrity." Others acknowledged that their own characteristically American qualities of independence and resourcefulness had helped them as immigrants. Their circles of friends often included many Americans, a fact that gave Carl Scheuer an uneasy feeling: "I find that I am both attracted and repelled by other Americans. Basically, I like them—they're doers, and they remind me about my nostalgia for the States. But at the same time, they remind me of part of my life—and myself—that I'd rather forget."

These exiles accepted the fact that their homeland would always be part of them. When McDonald's opened a branch in Stockholm, it quickly became a popular hangout for exiles. Red, White, and Blues, an all-deserter rock group, played American music to rave reviews throughout Sweden. Jack Leeds, practicing law in Toronto, described himself as "partly American, but I don't know what part."

Their vision of the United States remained much as it was when they crossed the border. Images of revolutionary politics, racial riots, and college unrest formed permanent snapshots in their minds. They kept track of major events like the Watergate scandal, but avoided the American media: "I couldn't bear to watch the Bicentennial celebration on television. I was afraid of what my feelings might be, and I didn't want to let myself get too homesick."

Some exiles maintained a deep, festering hatred for their homeland, whose war policies they considered symptomatic of fundamental social flaws. Occasionally, this attitude was given violent expression. A clandestine exile group wrote a manual for antiwar activists, explaining how to attack draft boards with time bombs and Molotov cocktails. Exiles periodically vandalized American embassies and consulates, and Richard Nixon reportedly canceled a visit to Toronto and Montreal because of advance word that American war resisters posed serious security risks. The most dramatic act occurred on June 30, 1970, when the "Northern Lunatic Fringe" led one thousand exiles across the border to lay siege to Blaine, Washington. This was the first invasion of the continental United States since 1916, when New Mexico defended itself against Pancho Villa with a National Guard troop that included the young Lewis B. Hershey. But General Hershey was not there to defend Blaine, and the incursion caused an estimated $1,000,000 in property damage before the "NLF" was chased back to British Columbia. No one was arrested.

Blaine was near the site of the "Ho Chi Minh Trail," a 250-yard swamp that was a favorite route for border jumpers until electric devices were installed. There were easy crossings elsewhere, especially in the prairie provinces, but few were willing to risk freedom for a trip home. Dave Bosman slipped across to see his family in Tennessee, and he "really freaked them out. Everybody was awfully nervous, and they talked me into going back right away." Family get-togethers usually occurred in Canada or Sweden, or not at all. The long trips were financial hardships for families with modest incomes, and impossible for the poor.

Most exiles at first expected to remain permanently in their adopted countries. Coming home was seen as an inherent admission of failure. Yet over time, some came to the conclusion that what they had done was wrong: "I've learned a lot of things about myself during the months I've been up here. I thought it was because I disapproved of the war in Vietnam that I decided to come, but looking back on it, I can see it was more just a rebellion against authority than anything else." Others grew homesick, like Roy Brasile, who quit his $15,000 job as editor of a Montreal magazine to go back to Massachusetts: "I want to go home. Even if it costs me some time in jail, it's worth the price." But most returning exiles simply concluded they could not survive as refugees. They saw a better future at home, regardless of the legal consequences.

The American government took an active interest in the exiles. After the Intrepid Four incident, American diplomatic, military, and law enforcement officials made concerted efforts to monitor the exile community. Many law-abiding exiles were visited or followed by the Canadian Mounted Police, who sometimes advised the FBI of their whereabouts. The Swedish police did not cooperate with the United States government, but leaders of the exile community insisted that American officials engaged in covert activities to undermine their reputation. Periodically, exiles in Sweden were visited by self-proclaimed "Trotskyite revolutionaries" or "Weathermen on the run," who claimed to be from the European underground. With money and contacts, they gained the exiles' trust by helping those in need. But they later were accused of taking advantage of that trust to sabotage the community.

The individual most commonly suspected of having been an American agent was a central figure in the Stockholm-based American Deserters' Committee. He radicalized the exile community and helped alienate it from the Swedish left wing, whose leaders he accused of having pro-Nazi backgrounds. Just before leaving Stockholm, he was accused of undercutting efforts to coordinate an International Exile Day by telegraphing the wrong date to Canadian organizations. Other alleged American agents were accused of giving free drugs to Swedish exiles to set them up for arrest. One exile was given 750 liquid grams of mescaline for safekeeping, but he feared a trap and flushed it down a toilet. The next day, his apartment was ransacked. Leaders of the exile community blamed infiltrators for a major part of their drug problem and the ensuing loss of reputation among the Swedish people. They accused the American government of a deliberate effort to undermine the political impact and overall well-being of the exile community.

American intelligence agencies never confirmed or denied charges of American undercover work made by the Danish and Swedish press. One observer of the Swedish exile community commented that "if these people were government agents, they were not very good ones." But covert activities of this kind were consistent with the CIA's Operation CHAOS. CIA foreign stations were asked to accumulate information on "illegal and subversive" connections between domestic antiwar activists and "foreign elements." In 1968, CHAOS was made a "high-priority program" and specifically expanded to include surveillance of draft resisters and deserters. By the end of Operation CHAOS in 1972, agents had accumulated more than 7,200 files on overseas Americans, including information that the 1976 Select Senate Committee Intelligence Report called "wholly irrelevant to the legitimate interests of the CIA or any other government agency."

The most visible American government activity was the effort to induce exiles to come home. The American embassy in Stockholm acknowledged reporting "names and other information" about exiles to military intelligence officials, who sometimes made surprise visits to Sweden. Capitalizing on momentary despair, the officials tried to persuade exiles to return right away. They occasionally succeeded. "It was funny," one exile recalled. "There were people, and then there weren't people. All they took with them were the clothes on their backs." A deserter who was heading to Sweden through the Soviet Union met an American girl in Moscow, went out for a date with her that same night, and disappeared. No one knows what happened to him.

Deserters generally expected that they would spend years in prison if they returned. In 1966, a deserter who fled to China for ten days had been sentenced on his return to five years in military prison. But in 1968, the Roy Brown case signaled an apparent change in policy. Brown had been the first deserter to go to Sweden, and his charge of racial discrimination in the American Army was extensively covered by the Swedish press. In early 1968, the European editor of the *Army Times* made several trips to convince him to surrender. Brown was guaranteed no more than a six-month sentence and told that he would never be able to come home if he refused. After repeated threats and intimidation, Brown accepted the offer. His court-martial gave him a four-month sentence, encouraging other exiles to consider making their own deals.

Prompted by the Brown case and offers of leniency from military agents, twenty deserters abandoned exile by the spring of 1968. Only one was sent to prison for more than six months, and six avoided prison altogether. One was given a $15 fine and returned to his unit. This, however, led Senator Daniel Inouye of Hawaii, who lost an arm fighting in World War II, to conduct hearings before the Armed Services Committee to inquire about the "very light sentences" imposed on deserters. Alfred Fitt, the Defense Department's assistant secretary for manpower, acknowledged that "this is awfully lenient for these people who have gone off and made a disloyal spectacle of themselves, . . . but there is another side to it." Fitt indicated that the armed forces wanted these men back, and it did not wish to "reward" any deserter "by giving him punishment which in effect will remove him from the hazards of combat." Yet of the twenty returning deserters, only two were sent to Vietnam.

Inouye's committee report sharply criticized the military's bargain with Brown, commenting that "the attitude of some Defense officials in handling this case does justice to no one. . . . It should not be in the character of those entrusted with the administration of military justice to negotiate with deserters." For a short time thereafter, surrendering exiles were dealt a harsh surprise. James "Daddy" Lovett, a thirty-five-year-old Army cook, was greeted with a four-year prison sentence when he returned from Sweden. His case rekindled the exile community's fear of stiff punishment.

After a few months, however, the military returned to its original lenient policies toward exiled deserters who surrendered quietly. But those who came home amidst press conferences and antiwar statements still risked tough sentences. In 1972, the Defense Department reported that 640 deserters had surrendered from exile, and fewer than 150 had been sent to prison. The rest were returned to their units or, more and more often, given administrative undesirable discharges "for the good of the service." The Army also gave discharges *in absentia* to deserters who were aliens and had returned to their countries of origin.

Even the appearance of severity often included a private measure of leniency. In an open display of strict punishment, Tim Poirrot, the Marine deserter who surrendered on the floor of the 1972 Republican National Convention, was tried by general court-martial and sentenced to a year in prison. However, Poirrot had negotiated a maximum five-month sentence through a pretrial agreement. Out of the spotlight, the Marines reduced his sentence accordingly.

In the years after 1972, few deserters who returned from exile went to jail. Most received Undesirable Discharges, and some were even given General or Honorable Discharges. A few came home to learn that the military did not classify them as deserters. One exile's wife received a military dependent's allowance the whole time her husband was in Canada. Civilian counselors tried to convince exiles to end their fugitive status by accepting Undesirable Discharges, but many remained fearful that they would be victimized by a sudden change of policy. Others never came home because "it just wasn't worth the hassle."

Similarly, exiled draft resisters benefited from the lack of interest of most U.S. Attorneys in prosecuting Selective Service cases. But the government kept the truth about its prosecution practices so well hidden behind a mask of enforcement that many exiles never realized they were no longer fugitives from the law. Arlo Tatum's well-respected *Guide to the Draft* warned draft fugitives that "you are almost certain to be reported for prosecution to the U.S. Attorney. A warrant for your arrest will be in time issued, and it will be waiting for you if you ever return to American territory. There is no time limit; it will be outstanding indefinitely." Tatum's warning was correct in theory, but not in practice. After the courts made induction orders virtually unenforceable in 1970, federal prosecutors dropped tens of thousands of their pending cases, including many exile cases.

Unfortunately for the draft resisters, there was no requirement that they be informed when their cases were dropped. Prosecutors thought draft boards had to tell them, and draft boards thought prosecutors had to tell them. On one occasion, a state Selective Service director canceled an induction order and asked the local board to advise the exile of its action. The board never did so, and it took the individual three years to discover that he could come home. A U.S. Attorney who dropped thousands of draft cases acknowledged that his staff never considered contacting the exiles: "If you're going to take off and go to Canada, you should keep your intelligence network to find out what is happening in your case." Few exiles had lawyers, and they rarely had reason to doubt Arlo Tatum's warning that they would be prosecuted no matter how long they stayed away. After all, Ramsey Clark, who had been U.S. Attorney General when many exiles refused induction, stated in 1974 that "more than fifty thousand young men stand charged or convicted of violating the law."

Many had had enough exposure to the criminal justice system to think it unimaginable that no charges were outstanding against them. A draft resister from Marion, Indiana, signed papers at an induction station stating that he refused to enter the military. He was interviewed by a U.S. commissioner, sent to a federal medical center for two months for psychiatric observation, and put in jail to await trial. After obtaining bond, he fled to Canada. A few years later, suddenly and quietly, his case was dropped, but no one ever told him.

Occasionally, a draft exile discovered that he was a free man. One found out from a family friend who happened to be an FBI agent. Another called up the U.S. Attorney in his district "on a hunch" and learned that his case had been dropped a year earlier. Still another learned that his Michigan draft board had been bombed; when he contacted his prosecutor, he learned that his records had indeed been destroyed and his case dropped ("Whoever did it, hey, thanks a lot!"). His draft board may actually have been responsible, because Selective Service accidentally disposed of many records that prosecutors needed to obtain convictions. Wally Krentz discovered in 1973 that his name "wasn't in the book of bad people" at the border. After two years of repeated inquiries, he was told that his file had been mistakenly destroyed and the charges dropped.

Thousands of men spent unnecessary years on the run in the mistaken belief that they were fugitives from justice. Victor Cole of Wyoming lived in Canada for nine years before learning that no charges had ever been filed against him. Andy McCoy challenged his induction, complaining to his Michigan draft board that they had unlawfully denied his CO application. But the board wrote that it refused to reopen his case because it was "in the hands of the U.S. Attorney." McCoy then panicked, spending the next several years living in the underground in six different states, fearful of visiting his family because of several trips the FBI had made to his house. Events were later to prove that McCoy had been right: it was the draft board, not McCoy, that had broken the law.

By 1972, word began to spread about the weakness of the cases against most draft fugitives. Draft attorneys Daniel Kallen and Curry First wrote *Amex-Canada,* alerting the exile community that "anywhere from a sizable minority to a slight majority [of draft fugitives] can safely return to this country." William Smith, a Los Angeles lawyer, traveled across Canada at his own expense to encourage exiles to inquire into their cases. Those who came in contact with Kallen, First, or Smith almost always received good news. Inquiring on behalf of eighteen clients in Canada, First discovered that fifteen no longer faced charges.

However, not many exiles asked for help. A good many were scattered across Canada, did not subscribe to *Amex,* and were not part of a formal or informal grapevine. Ignorance and suspicion were widespread, and rumors persisted that secret indictments had been issued to trap the unwary. Not many exiles knew how to get legal advice at a reasonable price. Dave Bosman called an attorney "friend" in Texas, who told him it would cost from $500 to $2,000 to look into his case. It was not until 1975, in the midst of President Ford's clemency program, that the exiles finally got reliable information about their cases. Of approximately 17,500 draft fugitives who still thought they were in legal trouble, 13,000 learned that they were no longer fugitives.

The reaction to this news was a mixture of disbelief and deep emotion. Some broke into tears of joy, realizing that they could finally come home after six or eight years of exile. But according to counselor Steve Pither, others broke into "tears of rage that they had wasted the last two, or four, or seven or more years underground or in exile because of Selective Service processing errors and . . . failure to let them know of their innocence once it was concluded that they committed no crime." To one embittered exile, the deceptive enforcement policy was "another indication of the moral corruption of the United States." Others were just angry with themselves for never having bothered to keep informed.

Some exiles had trouble adjusting to their changed legal status. Believing that he could be arrested by the FBI even though he was in Canada, Bob Grevey had covered his tracks for years by developing a completely new identity. He had a credit rating and an employment history, and was well established in his community. After he learned that charges against him had been dropped, he found it impossible to return to his old identity.

Most decided to stay in Canada or Sweden. Chris Parker had married a Canadian woman and started a family in Toronto: "When I left, I had to set my mind to the fact that this was a permanent change in my life. I can't turn back the clock now." Terry Morton went home in 1976 to campaign in the Wisconsin Democratic primary, but was so discouraged by his experience that he returned to Manitoba to live in a frontier town. Roy Brown returned to Sweden after serving his sentence and finding America not to his liking. Many exiles saw no reason to pick up roots and start over for the second time in their lives, especially since they feared the reception they would get when they returned: "If, after many trials, you have won a foothold, why would you want to go back? Why would you want to be an exile in your own country?"

Because the Justice Department was derelict in not informing them that their cases had been dropped, many draft exiles accepted foreign citizenship under the mistaken impression that they were subject to prosecution. They later felt that they had been tricked into paying a penalty for an alleged "crime" of which they were legally innocent. Before Carter pardoned them in 1977, the five thousand expatriates who had adopted Canadian or Swedish citizenship were unable to return to the United States, even if no charges were pending against them. They were subject to exclusion or deportation as "aliens" who avoided military service during a period of declared national emergency. This law was originally aimed at foreign nationals who tried to avoid the World War II draft, but the Justice Department enforced it against native-born Americans whom it could not prosecute for draft evasion.

Stu Beecham, a Ph.D. candidate, lived in Toronto with his American-born wife, Joanne, and their two children. Charges against him were dropped shortly after he came to Canada because his draft board had unlawfully denied his CO application. But no one told them this, and the Beechams became Canadian citizens. For years, Joanne took their children to visit grandparents in Florida, but Stu was barred from joining them. Joanne wondered, "Why couldn't they let us love both countries at the same time?" Their entire exile was unnecessary.

Whether they stayed away or came home, most fugitives paid a heavy price for their draft or desertion offenses: "Man, it'll weight you down." Five or ten years on the run or in exile did more than leave them in new places; it wholly recast their lives. They made irreversible decisions and endured irremediable sacrifices. The Vietnam war left its mark on all of them.

VI | AMNESTY

Morality and Mythology

In 1964, the year Congress passed the Tonkin Gulf Resolution, Australia enacted a conscription law to raise troops for Vietnam. Its draft was simple and precise; about 100,000 youths turned twenty each year, one-tenth of whom were chosen by lot to serve in the army. At the height of the war, eight thousand Australians were in Vietnam. As a proportion of national population, this was the equivalent of 130,000 American troops.

The draft and the war were heated issues in Australia. There were peace vigils, public demonstrations, draft card burnings (which were not against the law), and open defiance of the draft. Roughly fifteen thousand youths never registered, and seventy-five publicly refused induction. Yet only six people were ever convicted for violating the National Service Act, all of whom were sentenced to eighteen-month prison terms.

By 1972, more than 250 draft violations were pending in the courts. When Gough Whitlam of the Australian Labour Party campaigned for prime minister, he promised to end the draft, withdraw from Vietnam, and declare an amnesty for all draft resisters and deserters. Aided by newly enfranchised young voters, Whitlam was elected, and within ten days he fulfilled his promises. He also allowed draftees to resign from military service, and three-quarters of them did so. The Vietnam war and the amnesty debate quickly faded from the public's mind.

The United States found its problems with the draft, the war, and amnesty more difficult to solve. President Nixon ended the draft and withdrew American troops in early 1973, but the amnesty issue lingered for years. By 1977, when President Carter extended the largest and perhaps last measure of relief, it was too late for hundreds of thousands of people. Their lives had been permanently altered, and the American public had fixed ideas about who they were and what they represented. To some, they were conscientious antiwarriors; to others, the worst of traitors. Those in between regarded them with the same wary compassion commonly offered parolees from prison. Draft resisters and deserters had become permanent victims, not just of the Vietnam war, but of myths that personified the unresolved public debate about the war.

The stereotypes originated in the mid-1960s, when the draft-card burners of the early Resistance movement were much in the news. White, educated, well-to-do, and intensely antiwar, they were like tens of thousands of other activists who were challenging the war on the campuses and streets of the nation. By 1967, a number of draft resisters began to leave for Canada. They were a diverse group, but the ones who generated publicity were radical activists, much like the earlier draft card burners. Most exiles wanted privacy and a chance to blend into Canadian life, but the activists considered themselves symbols of the moral issues raised by the war. They were more accessible to the media, and made better press. When David Susskind's representative came to Toronto to select the right person for his show, one exile he interviewed was disgusted when "out of all the people in the room, he had to pick the most spooked-out radical, the weirdest character in the group."

When Eugene McCarthy first raised amnesty as a campaign issue in 1968, the image of the draft resister as a white, well-educated radical was firmly fixed. McCarthy described them as the best of their generation, promising to declare a "kind of amnesty" if elected President. The other presidential candidates avoided the issue. Amnesty in the midst of war had some precedent in American history. Abraham Lincoln issued two general amnesties for deserters during the Civil War, on the condition that they return to the front lines. But in 1968, the war itself overshadowed the fate of a handful of middle-class radicals in exile.

As President Nixon began his gradual deescalation of the war, interest in amnesty began to spread. Church groups passed amnesty resolutions, and "universal, unconditional amnesty" joined the list of demands of striking students. Tom Wicker, Julian Bond, and Richard Cardinal Cushing were among the first to call for the President to act. But the exiles themselves wanted no part of an amnesty. At a Montreal conference of exiles in early 1970, a visiting Tom Hayden drew sharp criticism when he brought up the subject. "Amnesty," wrote *Amex-Canada* magazine, was

> a dirty word inasmuch as it can be interpreted to mean that exiles . . .
> would be magnanimously forgiven for a crime we never committed. . . .
> Who wants amnesty? Liberals. . . . Like other liberal issues, it asks for
> sympathy and trustworthiness from the world's most viciously heavy-
> handed and conniving regime. Worse yet, it gives the impression to the
> enemy that the movement is running on nothing more threatening than
> simpering warmheartedness, by people who are not capable of shaping
> their lives themselves.

Many exiles agreed with *Amex*'s position. In 1969 and 1970, the Canadian economy was healthy, and American refugees were still the toast of Sweden. Many wanted to go home, but a mid-war amnesty would have put them on the spot. At the time, amnesty seemed an empty gesture which would have made them look like selfish draft dodgers, vindicating their detractors and depriving their resistance of all meaning. As a deserter in Sweden explained, the exiles saw amnesty as "just the start of our problems and not, as some believe, the end."

Thereafter, the antiwar orthodoxy saw amnesty as a "salve for the conscience of liberals who were silent as the war was being expanded and exiles were making their decisions not to go." Attitudes began to change in 1972, however, as the end of the war came in sight and life in exile began to sour. Noting that "the situation has changed fundamentally," *Amex-Canada* reversed its earlier position:

> For some time now, many exiles in Canada have known that many have
> been unable to adjust to exile life. More important, many have been un-
> able to get landed immigrant status and have lived underground; this
> certainly has not been healthy, physically or psychologically. Now the

question of amnesty has been raised by others, and we have recognized that there is a very serious need for it.

That endorsement made amnesty more acceptable for the antiwar community back home. New lobbying groups were soon founded by clergymen, draft counselors, antiwar veterans, and the exiles themselves.

Originally, as *Amex* indicated, amnesty was a pragmatic cause, a way of relieving suffering and reuniting families. As the war wound down, however, most of those who could not cope with life in exile quietly drifted back to the United States, paying less of a penalty than they expected. But the antiwar community found itself increasingly frustrated by Nixon's elusive "peace with honor." The government was pulling out of Vietnam slowly and reluctantly, without acknowledging that the war was wrong. The antiwar community wanted the American people to make a clear judgment about the immorality of the war.

Amnesty offered one last chance to force the issue. Where exiles once had interpreted amnesty as an admission of their own wrongdoing, they now saw it making "the moral point that our government was wrong and these young men were right." It was, as one advocate observed, "a powerful tool to make the American people aware of the character of the war that was waged in their name." The pragmatism and compassion that had launched the amnesty movement became unacceptable; the proper basis for amnesty now was as a moral condemnation of the war. "In order to lead a principled fight," *Amex-Canada* remarked, "it is necessary to make judgments about the types of arguments we put forward. . . . We have a historic duty to perform—not only winning total amnesty but also explaining the unjust nature of the Indochina War. It is that duty, not shortsighted pragmatism, which must guide our work."

The integration of amnesty into the moral and political debate over the war had four important consequences. First, it left the movement vulnerable to excess. The more radical groups embraced amnesty with zeal, tying it to the rest of their platform and giving a politically extreme cast to the whole discussion. As one activist commented:

Most of us think that not only the war and the draft, but the whole American military empire which spawns these evils is an affront and a danger to humankind. This empire must and eventually will be dismantled. I believe —though at times I will not say this too loud—that an amnesty would be a small step in this dismantling.

Second, it kept the public's attention riveted on the most politically active exiles. Few people knew or cared much about the day-to-day problems of the great bulk of the half million or more who might have benefited from an amnesty—especially nonregistrants and veterans with bad discharges, many of whom were black, low-income, and poorly educated. By making amnesty an ideological issue, the movement eliminated the possibility of obtaining substantial active support from civil rights groups, liberal unions, and other potential allies. Even those who were sympathetic to the amnesty cause were unwilling to accept the antiwar orthodoxy that the movement demanded. As one movement participant observed, amnesty forces

> failed to develop a centrist core, though it is an issue that could sustain support by a broad coalition. Ideological orthodoxy is exacted at the expense of communicating with the people who will have to vote to return to office those Congressmen who dare to vote for amnesty.

Third, tying amnesty to the debate about the war encouraged strong emotional responses from the other side. As Washington *Star* columnist Mary McGrory noted, this meant "asking . . . middle-aged men with glorious memories of military service in a popular war to admit they were wrong about Vietnam." The Nixon administration capitalized on that point to turn public opinion against amnesty. "Now that the antiwar movement has collapsed, all those idle protestors have to have something to shout about," Spiro Agnew told a VFW convention. Amnesty was out of the question for "draft dodgers who bear a deep-seated and unabating grudge against their country, who revile its principles and its traditions, and who see nothing wrong in ducking out on their obligations." As for deserters, said Agnew, "it almost makes one ill to hear about how . . . they fled from an immoral war."

Fourth, the ideological orthodoxy of radical advocates created intense internal conflicts within the movement, frustrating efforts to develop sound and politically acceptable amnesty proposals. Individuals who raised more moderate, pragmatic arguments were often subjected to public calumny from those who should have been their allies. The amnesty movement finally paid the price for years of intransigence when President Carter's military program came under attack in Congress. Legislation repudiating that program was passed, with only eleven dissenting votes. Outside of Carter's inner circle, just two voices urged a veto of this new legislation.*

The ideological grounds upon which amnesty was proposed invited counterarguments that could not be overcome. The movement's quarrel was with the government, not with Vietnam veterans, but anti-amnesty forces used the veterans as the basis for their moral case against amnesty. Victim was set against victim. Rather than seeing all of these men as casualties of Vietnam, the American people were asked to make a choice. Nixon told the country where its values should lie. Amnesty, he said, was "the most immoral thing I can think of. . . ."

> I can think of no greater insult to the memories of those who have fought and died, to . . . those who have served, and also to our POWs, to say to them that we are now going to provide amnesty for those who deserted the country.

Administration spokesmen openly ridiculed amnesty advocates like Congresswoman Bella Abzug, who contended that draft resisters and deserters were "the finest, most conscientious, most creative young people." Drawing as sharp a contrast as possible, Nixon aides labeled them as the very worst of their generation. Speechwriter Patrick Buchanan called them "malingerers, opportunists, criminals, and cowards," and Charles Colson echoed that they were "victims of their own character deficiencies." Spiro Agnew lumped them in with "malcon-

---

*The Washington *Post*, which had earlier approved of the legislation, belatedly editorialized against it. Father Theodore Hesburgh, President of Notre Dame, sent Carter a personal telegram recommending a veto.

tents, radicals, incendiaries, civil and uncivil disobedients, . . . yippies, hippies, yahoos, Black panthers, lions, and tigers—I would swap the whole damn zoo for a single platoon of the kind of young Americans I saw in Vietnam."

An American Legion spokesman confidently predicted that the nation would never decide that "those who violated the law have the superior moral position to the President, the Congress, and the men who served." He was right. Washington *Star* columnist Smith Hempstone pleaded that "it simply isn't so . . . that men who spent the war comfortably living off remittances from Mom and Pop in Toronto coffee houses are the cream of their generation. . . . They want America to accept their image of themselves and their version of history, and this no self-respecting nation can grant."

As the antiwar movement reconstituted itself into the amnesty lobby, supporters of the war formed their own antiamnesty organizations. The Young Americans for Freedom sponsored a nationwide "No Amnesty Campaign," but most of the effort came from the older generation— the Veterans of Foreign Wars, the American Legion, the POW-MIA lobby. The leader of the opposition was President Nixon, who viewed the issue as an opportunity to take the offensive against his liberal enemies. "Never, never will we grant amnesty," he said during his reelection campaign. "Until this war is over, until we get the POWs back, those who chose to desert their country . . . can live with their choice."

Chiding Democrats for their contrary views, Vice President Agnew invited them to "seek [their] future leaders in the deserters' dens of Canada and Sweden." "Amnesty, Acid, and Abortion" was a slogan used against George McGovern in 1972, just as "Rum, Romanism, and Rebellion" had helped Republicans beat Democrats in earlier times. Under pressure, McGovern retreated from his original call for a general amnesty to a much more limited position, requiring alternative service and excluding deserters altogether.

McGovern's defensiveness and the political vulnerability of the amnesty lobby's moral arguments were no match for Nixon's political acumen. In June 1972, a Harris poll found that the public opposed amnesty by a 3–2 margin. By the following March, that margin had grown to 3–1. As the Watergate scandal undermined his moral and political authority, neither Nixon nor his spokesmen said much more about amnesty. But even in the midst of Watergate, the amnesty community could not gain the upper hand.

Out of the unsuccessful effort of the 1972 campaign, however, ground was laid for a compromise approach later embodied in President Ford's clemency program. In 1971, a conservative Ohio doctor wrote Senator Robert Taft, Jr., suggesting that draft resisters be amnestied if they worked for four years on public service jobs. Taft believed the idea had political promise because it sidestepped the ideological arguments for and against amnesty, and he sponsored a bill patterned on the idea. At the time, there was a widespread recognition that any form of amnesty was premature until all American troops and prisoners-of-war had returned from Vietnam, and Taft's bill attracted little open support. President Nixon derided the idea of making a "junket in the Peace Corps" a substitute for punishment.

After America's disengagement in 1973, "clemency" became increasingly popular among moderates of both political parties. Several bills and resolutions were introduced in both houses of Congress proposing some form of clemency. Two former Nixon administration officials, Melvin Laird and Robert Froehlke, who had been respectively Secretary of Defense and Secretary of the Army, publicly called on the President to institute a compromise program.

The debate, however, remained divided between advocates of universal, unconditional amnesty, and those who insisted that nothing be done. With amnesty still entwined with arguments over the merits of the Vietnam war, most political leaders were reluctant to take a position on the issue.

Clemency, Not Amnesty

A few days after Gerald Ford became President in August 1974, his son Jack suggested that he begin his administration by declaring some sort of amnesty. Given the circumstances of his accession to the presidency, Ford was eager to reestablish public confidence in the fairness of government, and he liked his son's idea. He asked the White House staff to assemble all relevant policy papers prepared by the Nixon administration. Except for speeches, there was nothing but a Defense Department study of AWOL, useless as a policy guide. The new President thus had to rely on his instincts. A close friend of Melvin Laird, with whom he had served in Congress, Ford was attracted to the compromise "clemency" idea that Laird had been urging on his predecessor.

Rather than wait for official studies, the President announced his intentions immediately and left the details to be worked out later. To a surprised and antagonistic VFW convention, the same forum that had earlier cheered Spiro Agnew's tough antiamnesty statements, Ford called for "the restoration of the essential unity of Americans, within which honest differences of opinion do not descend to angry discord, and mutual problems are not polarized by excessive passion." Ford's appeal to moderation as a means of "binding the nation's wounds" drew a strong positive response from the public. For many, this was the finest hour of his presidency.

The President's speech and the new era it promised engendered a mixture of anticipation and skepticism among amnesty forces. They viewed the Ford initiative as one of great promise, but even greater risk. Their principal fear, born of years of distrust of the government, was that a clemency compromise would prove empty of meaning, leaving draft resisters and deserters to pursue existing remedies through normal government channels.

The spirit of reconciliation fostered by Ford's speech was swept away in the outrage over his surprise pardon of Richard Nixon in early September. When he announced the details of his clemency program a few days later, he drew an angry reaction from all sides. To conservatives, many of whom were disturbed by the Nixon pardon, Ford's clemency action added one mistake to another. To liberals, the clemency program was a political gesture, intended mainly to ease the public reaction to what looked like an unsavory deal between Nixon and his successor. To amnesty forces, the limited terms of Ford's clemency offer, contrasted with the leniency granted Nixon, seemed an outrageous double standard of justice: "For his very real and very serious crimes, Richard Nixon has received an unconditional amnesty—plus a posh pension. For their justified resistance to an illegal and immoral war, war resisters must still pay a penalty."

To the general public, however, the clemency program seemed a reasonable and attractive solution to the amnesty problem. As the newly created Presidential Clemency Board concluded in its final report a year later, "clemency, not amnesty" was the "course of moderation. . . . No program at all would have left old wounds festering. Unconditional amnesty would have created more ill-feeling than it would have eased." Ford's "limited, conditional, case-by-case clemency" offered "a reasoned middle ground."

The Washington *Post*, which later became critical of the Ford program, initially praised it as "a reasonable balance between the view that calls for complete amnesty and the view that calls for no amnesty or clemency at all." The Philadelphia *Bulletin* noted that "the fact that the hard-liners on each side of the amnesty issue dislike President Ford's proposal could be proof that it is a moderate and workable approach."

Unfortunately, this view of the Ford program as a fair compromise between continued punishment and unwarranted generosity was heavily influenced by the public's widespread ignorance about the way the government was currently enforcing the law against draft resisters and deserters. By the time Gerald Ford became President, lenient treatment for offenders was the rule, not the exception. In fact, the Ford program offered little or no improvement over remedies that were already available. As the mother of an exiled draft resister observed, "Since 1970, whenever the FBI came around, they said Kenny had three choices: the service, jail, or alternate service. Now they're offering the same thing, and they call it amnesty. So what is different?"

Under Ford's program, fugitive draft resisters could sign up with their local U.S. Attorneys, perform a maximum of twenty-four months of alternative service, and then have their charges dismissed. Draft counselors knew, however, that those who refused clemency and pursued their cases in court had about a 90 percent chance of getting charges dismissed without having to do alternative service, and about a 99 percent chance of avoiding prison.

The President invited military fugitives to appear at a special clemency processing center at the Fort Harrison Army base near Indianapolis. Once there, they received immediate Undesirable Discharges, thereby ending their fugitive status and any threat of court-martial and military prison. They could also earn Clemency Discharges by performing up to twenty-four months of alternative service. This brand-new discharge was given under "other-than-honorable" conditions, just like an Undesirable Discharge and, like the latter, it bestowed no veterans' benefits. By 1974, however, the military had virtually stopped court-martialing deserters. Deserters who turned down the clemency program were all but guaranteed quick Undesirable Discharges if they surrendered at lenient Army bases like Fort Dix and Fort Sill. In fact, deserters discharged outside the Ford program had a ten times greater chance of receiving a General or Honorable Discharge, entitling them to veterans' benefits; they also incurred no obligation to do alternative service. All they lost was the dubious opportunity to earn a Clemency Discharge.

Convicted draft resisters and discharged deserters could receive presidential pardons from the Clemency Board, conditioned on the performance of periods of alternative service that rarely exceeded six months. Most draft resisters were already eligible to apply to the U.S. pardon attorney for the same pardon without alternative service, and none of the handful who had earlier done so had been refused. Deserters were also offered Clemency Discharges via the Clemency Board. Outside the Ford program, almost all deserters were eligible to apply through normal military review procedures, where they stood about a one-in-three chance of getting upgraded to General or Honorable Discharges entitling them to veterans' benefits. The Clemency Board could not grant these remedies.

Outraged by the inadequacies of the Ford program, amnesty groups labeled it a "dangerous trap," a "cynical smokescreen," and "shamnesty." Many did what they called "repatriation counseling," helping thousands to take advantage of remedies inside or outside the clemency program. However, the rest of the amnesty community declared a formal boycott, publicly discouraging people from applying. They feared that high application figures would persuade the public that the program was a success, dooming future prospects for a more comprehensive amnesty.

Their fears had some basis in recent history. After World War II, Americans favored a general amnesty for draft resisters by a three-to-one margin, and Congress began considering legislation to grant them relief as a class. In response, President Truman appointed an amnesty board and asked it to review all cases individually. After a year's work, the board granted relief only to those whose offenses resulted from religious beliefs, accusing the rest of having "no respect for the law or the civil rights to which they might have been restored." But it also refused to pardon Jehovah's Witnesses, because "to do so would be to sanction an assertion by a citizen that he is above the law, that he makes his own law, and that he refuses to yield his opinion to that of organized society. . . ." The Truman board recommended less than 10 percent of its 15,805 cases for presidential pardons. When its work was done, the public and the Congress believed that every case had been fairly decided, and the issue was forgotten.

For his part, President Ford appeared quite willing to let his program run its course and be forgotten. Although he privately indicated his desire for a successful and generous program, he delegated near-total responsibility to Justice and Defense department officials and paid little attention to the program they devised. Neither they nor the White House staff ever personally supported the President's idea. They wished only to have a quick and quiet program that interfered as little as possible with their own interests.

After the program had been formulated, former Senator Charles Goodell, a personal and political friend of Ford's from their days together in the House of Representatives, was chosen to head the Clemency Board. Goodell had been a staunch critic of the Nixon administration's war policies, and the administration had publicly opposed his reelection because of his stand. His appointment appeared to signal a real desire on Ford's part to make the program work. Goodell believed he would be the spokesman for the entire program, exercising authority over all its phases on behalf of the President. When, however, he tried to assert this authority, even over matters pertaining only to the Clemency Board, the President did not support him, and the White House staff worked against him. Evidence that the program was headed for failure made little impression. "The program was a success the day it was announced," observed the junior White House aide charged with overseeing its operation, who saw no political advantage in trying to make it better. As one spokesman commented, the clemency program was "about as important as the spat over the President's swimming pool."

Ultimately, only 6 percent of the roughly 350,000 eligible persons ever applied to the program. This was more the result of widespread ignorance, distrust, and lack of interest than a consequence of the amnesty community's boycott. Surveys found that most of the ninety thousand eligible deserters with bad discharges never knew they could apply, thinking instead that the Ford program was just for fugitives in Canada. Others were disdainful of the meager benefits of the program, or resented the necessity of what Attorney General William Saxbe called "acts of contrition"—signing an oath of allegiance, cooperating with Selective Service, and doing alternative service work. As one draft resister commented, "They want me to shuffle and scrape and mumble, 'I'm sorry, folks, I shouldn't of done it—please forgive me,' all so Ford can feel good about letting Nixon off the hook. They can cram it."

Of the 21,500 who applied, just 8,000 eventually received the formal clemency offered by the program (see Figures 8 and 9). President Ford later said it was "tragic" that so few participated, and Board chairman Goodell called the program "a partial success, at best."

The major effect of the Ford initiative was the reinforcement of several of the myths that had long plagued the amnesty issue. The program was tailored to suit the public image of draft resisters and deserters as conscientious war objectors, who were supposedly being given a second chance to satisfy the requirements of CO status by doing alternative service. Above all, the Ford program reinforced the mistaken view that Selective Service, the Justice Department, and the Defense Department had enforced the law strictly and fairly throughout the Vietnam era. This was the natural consequence of their dominant roles in the planning and implementation of the program, roles given them despite their long-standing antagonistic relationships with draft resisters and deserters.

Selective Service was chosen to supervise alternative service, just as it had supervised similar work by conscientious objectors during the war. Many of its top officials despised the people they were supposed to help. But without the Ford program, according to one official of the Office of Management and Budget, "Selective Service might have been zero-budgeted right out of existence." As it was, supervising alternative service became the main task of an agency that was fast being phased out.

It was a singularly poor choice. Not only unwilling, Selective Service proved incapable of performing its task of finding and overseeing thirteen thousand alternative service jobs. Part of the problem was that many draft resisters could not forget the unfair treatment they had previously received from these very same officials. One exile signed up for the program and went home to San Diego, only to get immersed in a series of quarrels with Selective Service: "I came back to the U.S. because I thought the purpose of the President's program was reconciliation. I found, instead, that Selective Service officials used the program to retaliate against me. If I'd known what to expect, I would have stayed in Canada."

Officials in the Defense and Justice departments had a more tolerant disposition toward the program, if only because of their interest in trimming backlogs of fugitive cases. As one Pentagon planner recalled, "We all wanted to wash our hands of these people as quickly as possible."

The Defense Department accomplished this largely through what became known as the clemency loophole. Contrary to what the public believed, deserters were rarely court-martialed after 1970. Instead, they were quickly given administrative Undesirable Discharges and sent home (see Part IV). The clemency program continued this practice, with one new twist. Applicants had to sign promises to do alternative service, thereby risking possible prosecution if they dropped out.

Most deserters had no desire to perform this service. A few publicly declared their intention, prompting antiamnesty critics to insist that all dropouts be prosecuted. Defense officials were well aware that they lost jurisdiction to court-martial these men once they received Undesirable Discharges, and that the Justice Department had little hope and no intention of prosecuting them as civilians. Fearful of admitting openly that the clemency program was unenforceable, Defense Department

FIGURE 8: AMNESTY—CIVILIANS

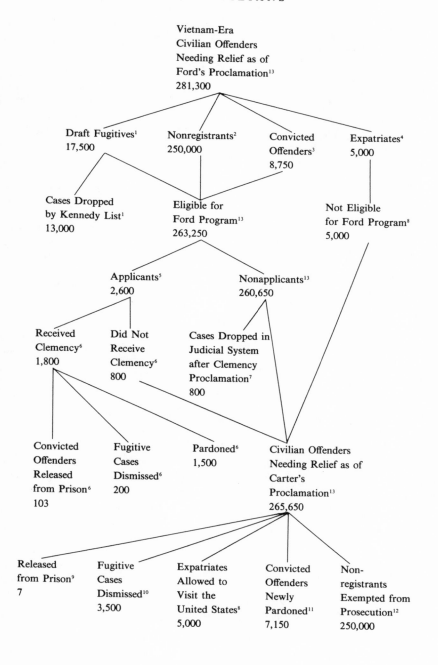

Vietnam-Era
Civilian Offenders
Needing Relief as of
Ford's Proclamation[13]
281,300

Draft Fugitives[1]
17,500

Nonregistrants[2]
250,000

Convicted
Offenders[3]
8,750

Expatriates[4]
5,000

Cases Dropped
by Kennedy List[1]
13,000

Eligible for
Ford Program[13]
263,250

Not Eligible
for Ford Program[8]
5,000

Applicants[5]
2,600

Nonapplicants[13]
260,650

Received
Clemency[6]
1,800

Did Not
Receive
Clemency[6]
800

Cases Dropped in
Judicial System
after Clemency
Proclamation[7]
800

Convicted
Offenders
Released
from Prison[6]
103

Fugitive
Cases
Dismissed[6]
200

Pardoned[6]
1,500

Civilian Offenders
Needing Relief as of
Carter's
Proclamation[13]
265,650

Released
from Prison[9]
7

Fugitive
Cases
Dismissed[10]
3,500

Expatriates
Allowed to
Visit the
United States[8]
5,000

Convicted
Offenders
Newly
Pardoned[11]
7,150

Non-
registrants
Exempted from
Prosecution[12]
250,000

FIGURE 9 : AMNESTY — MILITARY

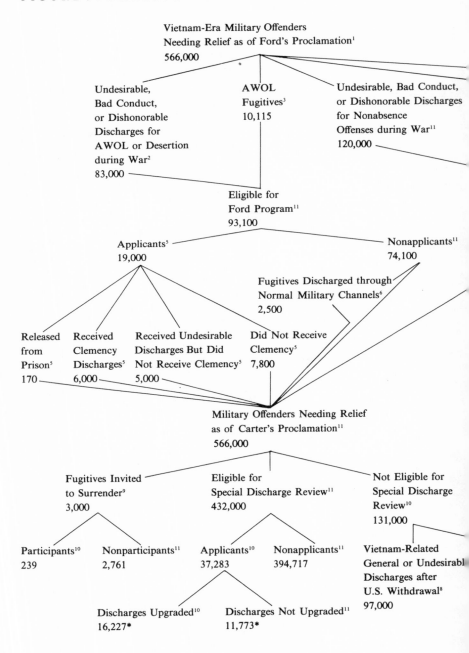

Vietnam-Era Military Offenders
Needing Relief as of Ford's Proclamation[1]
566,000

Undesirable,
Bad Conduct,
or Dishonorable
Discharges for
AWOL or Desertion
during War[2]
83,000

AWOL
Fugitives[3]
10,115

Undesirable, Bad Conduct,
or Dishonorable Discharges
for Nonabsence
Offenses during War[11]
120,000

Eligible for
Ford Program[11]
93,100

Applicants[5]
19,000

Nonapplicants[11]
74,100

Fugitives Discharged through
Normal Military Channels[6]
2,500

Released
from
Prison[5]
170

Received
Clemency
Discharges[5]
6,000

Received Undesirable
Discharges But Did
Not Receive Clemency[5]
5,000

Did Not Receive
Clemency[5]
7,800

Military Offenders Needing Relief
as of Carter's Proclamation[11]
566,000

Fugitives Invited
to Surrender[9]
3,000

Eligible for
Special Discharge Review[11]
432,000

Not Eligible for
Special Discharge
Review[10]
131,000

Participants[10]
239

Nonparticipants[11]
2,761

Applicants[10]
37,283

Nonapplicants[11]
394,717

Vietnam-Related
General or Undesirabl
Discharges after
U.S. Withdrawal[8]
97,000

Discharges Upgraded[10]
16,227*

Discharges Not Upgraded[11]
11,773*

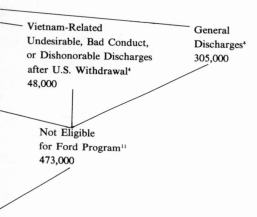

Vietnam-Related
Undesirable, Bad Conduct,
or Dishonorable Discharges
after U.S. Withdrawal[4]
48,000

General
Discharges[4]
305,000

Not Eligible
for Ford Program[11]
473,000

Court-Martial
Discharges[7]
34,000

*As of October 1977, approximately 9,000 cases remained to be processed.

General Counsel Martin Hoffman publicly warned applicants to perform alternative service or face prosecution for fraud. Military lawyers began giving applicants equivocal advice, like "Maybe there's a loophole, but the Department's policy is to prosecute people," or "It's a dangerous area; you be the jury and think about it."

Almost 90 percent of the fugitive deserters who applied for clemency never completed alternative service, and no one was ever prosecuted. However, some were intimidated by Hoffman's warning. John Walters, a deserter from Kansas, found an alternative service job working for his hometown government. After local veterans' groups intervened to get him fired, Walters was unable to find another job that met the standards of the program. Eventually, Selective Service officials convinced him to sign a statement declaring himself a clemency program dropout, and they told him that the statement would be forwarded to prosecutors. For months, Walters lived with the same day-to-day fear of arrest he had known for so many years as a deserter.

Don Kuzier leased his Winnipeg house and abandoned his one-man trucking business to find an alternative service job in Kalamazoo, Michigan, his old hometown. But because he was a deserter, no one offered him a job. Kuzier had to sell his truck to support his family, and his wife suffered a collapsed lung. Discouraged, the Kuziers moved back to Canada, but not into their own house. They had given a binding two-year lease to someone else.

Through the clemency program, the Defense Department cut its fugitive list by almost two-thirds. The Justice Department accomplished the same thing, also in a manner that avoided any serious inquiry into its record of enforcement. At the start of the clemency program, approximately 17,500 draft resisters still believed they faced prosecution. But when the first clemency applicant surrendered amidst press fanfare in San Francisco, the U.S. Attorney told him that his case had already been dropped. The Justice Department then released a list of only 6,200 men still wanted for draft offenses. Several weeks later, however, a number of persons not on this list were indicted by a Boston grand jury, and concern spread that the list was a trap.

Prompted by complaints from amnesty groups, Senator Edward Kennedy demanded a final, closed list of all persons still wanted for draft offenses. In January 1975, the Department produced what many called the "Kennedy list," with 4,522 names. Except for unidentified nonregistrants, everyone else was free of prosecution, including the overwhelming majority of Canadian exiles. Although expatriates who had accepted foreign citizenship were still excluded from returning to the United States, some thirteen thousand people received what amounted to unconditional amnesty.

Despite an official commitment from Washington that those not on the Kennedy list were now relieved of prosecution, some U.S. Attorneys began to file additional cases. They complained that they had not realized the lists were final and binding. In Oregon, the U.S. Attorney had distributed most of his files to defense attorneys to update their materials, and these cases were inadvertently left off the list he sent to Washington. One draft resister wrote a letter to his Virginia prosecutor, saying "fuck the clemency program." The prosecutor left his name off, believing he had no intention of applying for clemency. In Wisconsin, two unrelated draft resisters had identical first and last names. The state Selective Service director got their files mixed up, so the U.S. Attorney notified the wrong one that his name had been left off the Kennedy list. U.S. Attorneys across the country eventually produced more than eight hundred cases they claimed had been omitted by mistake. But Edward Levi, the new Attorney General, refused to add their names. The eight hundred received an inadvertent amnesty, but amnesty nonetheless.

Ironically, the alternative service loophole and the Kennedy list meant that those who benefited the most from President Ford's clemency program were not the ones who conscientiously earned clemency. The pardons and Clemency Discharges were, at best, symbolic measures of forgiveness, of little practical value to most recipients. General Donald Connally, commander of the clemency processing center at Fort Harrison, said that earning clemency was "like making up a grade from D to an A," but few agreed with him. Charles Goodell told a press conference at the end of the program that he would never advise anyone to work for two years to earn a Clemency Discharge.

Those who did try to earn clemency encountered constant difficulties. Qualifying jobs were hard to find, and those who found them were often subjected to intense local opposition. The Veterans Administration, despite the President's personal plea for cooperation, publicly refused to help clemency applicants find alternative service jobs. The Arizona state legislature passed a special resolution denying state employment to all persons granted clemency under the Ford program. In Palm Beach, Florida, a draft resister lost his job after complaints like the following from the mother of a soldier killed in Vietnam: "I lost a son and all I got was a flag. This man hid, and now he has a good-paying job."

Many of the problems in the design of the Ford program became apparent to officials responsible for implementing it, but they were powerless to make changes. Vernon Jordan, head of the National Urban League and a member of the Clemency Board, recalled how surprised he was when "the conventional image of the spoiled rich kid who ran away to Canada to beat the draft just didn't hold true." After reading case after case of poorly educated, low-income people, many of them Vietnam veterans, the Clemency Board recommended to the White House that the program be liberalized, making it of real value to those who merited relief. The Board wanted Clemency Discharges to be "neutral," not given under "other-than-honorable" conditions, and it wanted pardons to be accorded full respect by all federal agencies. The Clemency Board also wanted to give discharges under honorable conditions to veterans with good combat records, making them eligible for veterans' benefits.

These recommendations were either rejected or ignored by President Ford. Yet, even had they been implemented, they would have brought only marginal improvements in the program. More sweeping changes were never suggested, largely because of the Board's desire to preserve its fragile consensus. Many members feared that substantial modifications in the "earned clemency" concept would produce open dissension and embarrass the President.

Despite the Board's growing sense that the program was fundamentally flawed, only Vernon Jordan resigned in protest. Marine General Lewis Walt and three others, complaining that the Board had a pro-amnesty bias, wrote an angrily worded minority report. The majority stayed on, some for no purpose other than preventing the program from deteriorating further. At the end, many of them were discouraged. Like

Board member Joan Vinson, they found in retrospect that they had worked on "a totally hollow program." Through an elaborate case-by-case process, costing $10,000,000 and requiring a full-time staff of six hundred, the Clemency Board drew careful but essentially irrelevant distinctions among its fifteen thousand cases. It offered meaningless relief to people who needed far more.

The military lawyers at Fort Harrison also tried to liberalize the program after encountering deserters with "the goshawfulest stories we ever heard." Elvin McCoy had been in the service more than five years when his two brothers were killed, one in a car accident and the other in Vietnam. McCoy was wrongly denied discharge as a sole surviving son, and he went AWOL to return to his family. He qualified for better than an Undesirable Discharge under standard military policy. After seeing a number of cases like McCoy's, military lawyers eventually prevailed on the Fort Harrison commanding general to deal with meritorious applicants outside the framework of the formal clemency program and discharge them under his normal authority as commander. They could thereby receive General and Honorable Discharges, with full entitlement to veterans' benefits.

This alternative was much more time-consuming than the one-day clemency program, and few returning deserters were willing to stay the weeks or months it usually required. Paul Elias was addicted to heroin when he enlisted in the Army. He was qualified for a medical discharge and veterans' benefits, but only if he were willing to spend several weeks at Fort Harrison. Elias was undergoing methadone treatment in New York City, and no one could find a methadone source in Indianapolis. Rather than undergo withdrawal, he accepted an Undesirable Discharge and went home.

Just 1 percent of the 5,555 returning servicemen who passed through Fort Harrison endured the long waiting period and received better than an Undesirable Discharge. Military lawyers estimated that ten or twenty times as many could have been helped if every file had been carefully reviewed without delay. One official called the Fort Harrison clemency process an "in-by-nine, out-by-five dry cleaning operation," more efficient at discharging people than at giving them the relief they deserved.

Both the Fort Harrison staff and the Clemency Board issued comprehensive reports that described the applicants sympathetically. The Defense Department never publicly released the Fort Harrison report, which was critical of the leadership problems that contributed to many AWOLs. At the insistence of one Board member who was a former Selective Service official, the Clemency Board deleted from its report language sharply critical of the draft system. The White House later issued the Board's report in a way that minimized its public impact. When the Government Accounting Office conducted an inquiry into the clemency program, the White House claimed executive privilege and barred it from speaking with Clemency Board officials. As a result, the public gained no better understanding of the individuals who had committed draft or military offenses.

Despite its shortcomings and the constant criticisms from all sides, the Ford initiative did achieve its narrow political purpose of deflating the amnesty issue. A Gallup poll in August 1975, near the end of the program, showed that a majority of Americans supported conditional clemency and did not want it broadened. Most believed a fair offer had been extended, making it no fault of the President's if the resisters turned him down. Ford himself helped cultivate this view. When asked about his program, he said, "I think we gave them a good opportunity. I don't think we should go any further." This reinforced the widely held belief that non-participating draft resisters and deserters were selfish and uncompromising.

A new measure of scorn was now afforded the 97 percent of the draft resisters and deserters who never applied for clemency or who failed to complete alternative service. To a senior attorney in the Fort Harrison clemency program, they were "double deserters," who had twice demonstrated poor citizenship. One veteran with an Undesirable Discharge was about to be granted limited benefits by the Veterans Administration, but when the VA learned that he had been discharged by the Fort Harrison clemency program and had not done his assigned alternative service, it turned him down.

The end of the Ford program saw the collapse of much of the vitality of the amnesty movement. Many of the more visible exiles had solved their immediate legal problems through the Kennedy list, the Fort Harrison loophole, or the government's lenient discharge and prosecution policies. The long effort to achieve amnesty left others exhausted and dispirited. The American Civil Liberties Union ended its amnesty project for want of funds, depriving the movement of a major source of legal support and an important bridge to liberal opinion. Legislative efforts by Congressmen Robert Kastenmeier and Edward Koch succeeded in moving an amnesty bill past its first stages, but their efforts faltered more from lack of interest than from outspoken opposition.

The old arguments pro and con no longer excited the public. The radical members of the community combined amnesty with new lists of demands. The American Deserters Committee pressed for amnesty, "vigilance against U.S. aggression in the Middle East, and an end to the dictatorial government of the U.S. puppet regime in South Korea." The National Council on Universal, Unconditional Amnesty demanded amnesty, "a single type discharge for all veterans, jobs or income for all, and no more imperialist wars." On the other side, James Wagonseller of the American Legion repeated the argument that any further forgiveness was "a direct insult to the millions of Americans who served honorably during the Vietnam war and an even greater insult to those who died, were incapacitated, or are still missing in action."

A month before he left office, President Ford called Jane Hart after the death of her husband, Senator Philip Hart of Michigan, a close friend of Ford's and a leading proponent of amnesty. When Ford asked her if there was anything he could do, she told him there was—he could declare the amnesty that her husband had not lived to see. Hopes then grew that Ford might end his Presidency by declaring a general amnesty. Ford had considered this step before, after South Vietnam collapsed in the spring of 1975. But at the urging of his White House advisers, he rejected the idea. His election defeat removed the political constraints that had weighed heavily on his mind. The President had before him the example of Harry Truman, whom he liked to consider his spiritual mentor, and who had issued a Christmas pardon to peacetime deserters in his last month of office. Ford would thus relieve his successor of a major source of controversy, lift the amnesty issue from partisan politics, and accomplish his original goal of "binding the nation's wounds."

The President had also been urged by Charles Goodell to take several steps short of amnesty that would have benefited large numbers of people. Ford rejected all but one of Goodell's suggestions. Just before disbanding in September 1975, the Clemency Board had recommended that the President upgrade the discharges of five hundred Vietnam combat veterans, or at least make them eligible for medical benefits to care for their service-incurred injuries. President Ford had originally turned down this suggestion, and the Defense Department agreed only to give these cases priority treatment if the individuals applied to the discharge review boards. Fifteen months later, only eight applications had been reviewed, five of which were granted upgrades. In his last week as President, Ford ordered yet another case-by-case review of these combat veterans.

Blanket Pardons

In 1973, a year before President Ford launched his clemency program, the annual convention of the Association of the U.S. Army went on record opposing "blanket amnesty," but left the clear impression that pardons for draft resisters and deserters might be acceptable.

Despite the legal distinctions between "pardon" and "amnesty," there is little practical difference between the two. In an amnesty, it is the pardoning power of the Constitution that gives the President his authority to act. Certificates of pardon signed by the President are formal evidence of the relief directed to amnestied persons. Nonetheless, the terms assumed an important political and emotional significance in the Vietnam context. Amnesty came to connote relief for groups of persons whose violations were grounded in political or moral opposition to the government. An amnesty was said to reflect official recognition that the acts in question were not fundamentally criminal, and might be excused or even justified in the interests of political reconciliation. A pardon, by contrast, is directed to individuals. It does not distinguish between ordinary felons and those who acted out of political or moral conviction. Furthermore, the law traditionally requires that a pardon be accepted, and this acceptance is technically regarded as a personal acknowledgment of guilt. For these reasons, the amnesty movement never considered pardons to be acceptable for war resisters.

Mindful of the political importance of these emotion-laden terms, Jimmy Carter capitalized on the distinction drawn by the AUSA. Campaigning in Iowa two years later, he gave it a new twist. "Amnesty says what you did was right," he explained. "Pardon says whether what you did was right or wrong, you are forgiven for it." Legal scholars questioned his semantics, and the Republican vice-presidential candidate, Robert Dole, later looked vainly through his Webster's for the Carter definitions. An "amnesty," said his dictionary, is "a general pardon." Dole was right, but that did not detract from the political significance of Carter's formulation.

Carter had once opposed amnesty in any form, but he changed his mind apparently at the urging of his draft-age sons, one of whom had a General Discharge from the Navy for smoking marijuana. In what he later described as the "single hardest decision" of his campaign, Carter came to the conclusion that resisters, right or wrong, had suffered enough. He promised to grant them "blanket pardons" during his first week in office.

More than any other major political figure, Carter addressed amnesty not as a question of ideology, but as a matter of national reconciliation:

> I think it is time to get the Vietnamese war over with. I don't have any desire to punish anyone. I'd just like to tell the young folks who did defect to come back home with no requirement that you be punished or that you serve in some humanitarian capacity or anything. Just come back home, the whole thing's over.

But Carter's desire to "get the war over with" excluded a significant portion of those who needed help. More important than his distinction between "blanket amnesty" and "blanket pardons" was the line he drew between draft resisters and deserters. The latter, in his view, were less deserving.

Many of the early amnesty proposals, including Senator Taft's 1971 bill, had also excluded deserters. Senator Philip Hart once character-ized deserters as "guys who take off with the company cash," and most people perceived of them as common criminals. A Howard Johnson place mat, for example, warned diners that picking up hitchhikers was dangerous because many were AWOL soldiers.

It was not until Senator Edward Kennedy's amnesty hearings in 1972 that deserters began to be considered in the same terms as draft resis-ters. A number of witnesses argued strongly that deserters were the military equivalent of antiwar draft resisters, and stressed the fact that deserters more often came from disadvantaged backgrounds. The hear-ings had the important result of blending the two groups together in the public mind. During the next four years, few suggested that the two should be treated differently, and in this spirit President Ford's clem-ency program tried to deal with them comparably. Throughout the 1976 presidential campaign, Carter was the only candidate of either party who distinguished between them.

Carter's justification for a "blanket pardon," moreover, seemed to argue for more sympathy toward deserters, not less. In a conversation with the editors of the Washington *Post* in March 1976, he acknowl-edged the special seriousness with which he viewed desertion, but he also recognized the large measure of class injustice in the way America had fought the war:

> In the area of the country where I live, defecting from military service is almost unheard of. Most of the young people in my section of Georgia are quite poor. They didn't know where Sweden was, they didn't know how to get to Canada, they didn't have enough money to hide in college. They thought the war was wrong. They preferred to stay at home, but still they went to Vietnam. A substantial disproportion of them were black. They had never been recognized for their service to the country. They had often been despised, characterized as criminals, they were never heroes, and I feel a very great appreciation to them. They were extraordinarily heroic, serving their country in great danger even if they didn't have the appreciation of their fellow citizens and even if they felt the war was wrong. It's very difficult for me to equate what they did with what the young people did who left the country.

Yet Carter never acknowledged that many deserters were like the Georgians he described. As candidate and later as President, he persisted in drawing a sharp distinction between draft resisters and deserters.

During the Democratic Convention, amnesty forces, led by former peace activist Sam Brown, lobbied the platform committee for a plank that treated both groups equally. When the Carter forces held firm, they had to settle for a compromise that offered a "case-by-case review" for deserters. The language was vague enough to mean anything from including deserters in a nearly universal amnesty to excluding them from any special program. It committed Carter to nothing. "Candidly," admitted former Ohio Governor John Gilligan, chairman of the committee's foreign policy task force, "the question of covering desertion was so controversial that we walked away from it."

In one of the more emotional events of the convention, Ron Kovic, a severely crippled Vietnam veteran, gave a moving and powerful speech about amnesty in nominating Fritz Efaw, a fugitive draft resister, for Vice President. After attending the convention as an alternate delegate for overseas Americans, Efaw surrendered a few days later in Oklahoma. His case was dropped at the prosecutor's request because of draft board irregularities.

A few weeks later, Carter reaffirmed his plans to pardon draft resisters in a speech before the American Legion convention. Not surprisingly, the Legionnaires' reaction was strongly negative. Except for a passing exchange during his first televised debate with President Ford, Carter said little more during the campaign, and did not clarify his position on deserters. Ford never pressed him on the issue; the failures of his own clemency program left him vulnerable to counterattack, and his private polls showed that the American people had scant interest in the subject.

Two weeks after the election, President-elect Carter met with Father Theodore Hesburgh, president of the University of Notre Dame, and McGeorge Bundy, president of the Ford Foundation. They presented him with what they called a program of "reconciliation" and strongly urged that he change his mind about deserters. He promised to study the proposal, but warned them, "You know, I may not agree with you."

The amnesty movement knew this was probably its last opportunity. Its lobbyists showed a new sense of pragmatism, arguing less for public vindication than for meaningful relief for a half million or more individuals. Some even supported the idea of excluding deserters who fled from combat, the principal heroes of the early days of the movement. Much of this new-found pragmatism evaporated, however, when Charles Kirbo, Mr. Carter's closest confidant, invited leading advocates to a discussion of the issue. The group that went to see him included what one participant later called "a very unfortunate choice of people" —the mother of a well-known deserter who had fled to Sweden through the Soviet Union, a radical deserter-at-large who told Kirbo that any amnesty program should include billions of dollars in reparations to Vietnam, and other voices reminiscent of the radicalism of the 1960s. Their approach clashed with the old-fashioned patriotism of Kirbo and Carter.

The debate within Carter's inner circle split almost precisely on generational lines. The younger members of his staff suggested broad relief for deserters and other military offenders, while Carter's contemporaries—Kirbo, Defense Secretary-designate Harold Brown, and Attorney General-designate Griffin Bell—urged a more cautious approach.

As Carter's inauguration approached, news leaks suggested that the President-elect was changing his mind about deserters. In mid-December, Carter's transition staff released a statement that "substantial agreement" had been reached on a plan offering broad-based relief for 250,000 deserters and other military offenders, and Charles Kirbo commented that as many as 800,000 Vietnam-era veterans might get upgrades to Honorable Discharges. But this was not to happen.

On January 21, 1977, his first full day in office, the new President issued a "blanket pardon," offering total relief—in effect, unconditional amnesty—for draft resisters. Except for a handful who used "force or violence," 7,150 convicted draft offenders were pardoned,* and all of the 3,000 remaining fugitives had their cases dropped. The immigration

---

*The 1,600 convicted draft offenders previously pardoned by President Ford received nothing new from President Carter.

rules were eased to allow some five thousand expatriates to visit the United States. A quarter of a million nonregistrants were assured that they no longer faced prosecution upon discovery. In all, roughly 265,000 people were affected (see Figures 8 and 9). For deserters, Carter announced only that he had asked the Defense Department to study their situation.

Carter's program drew very little praise. *Pravda* hailed it as an official admission of American wrongdoing in Vietnam. Conservatives were furious, as Carter himself had predicted. Senator Barry Goldwater said it was "the most disgraceful thing a President has ever done." The chairman of the Republican National Committee called it "a slap in the face of all Americans and families who did their duty." "It's the saddest day in American history," complained the director of the VFW, "even sadder than Watergate and Vietnam itself." Veterans' groups in some parts of the country threatened to circulate blacklists of pardoned offenders among local employers.

The amnesty community had a mixed reaction to Carter's policy. Some spokesmen called it "hopeful" or a "first step." But others accused the President of a class bias, forgiving draft resisters but not the disproportionately black, low-income, and poorly educated military offenders. Many Vietnam veterans, some of whom opposed pardons for draft resisters, were particularly angered by the exclusion of servicemen, which they regarded as yet another example of the nation's insensitivity to the men who had served in uniform during the war. Yet most of the protests were feeble. As one pardoned draft resister said, "I'm sorry, but I'm happy." The heart had gone out of the movement. In Toronto, only two hundred of an expected four hundred attended what many regarded as the last amnesty conference. *Newsweek* called it "the last major battle by opponents of the Vietnam war." They feared their cause and their sacrifices would be forgotten.

For most draft resisters, Carter's pardons made very little difference, even though he offered them all the legal relief within his power. By 1977, few convicted draft resisters were any longer in prison or on probation. Nonregistrants were extremely unlikely to be found and punished. Exiles had established permanent homes outside the United States; they expected to visit their families now and then, but few had any intention of coming back permanently. In the first six months after Carter's announcement, just ninety-nine individuals asked the Justice Department for pardon certificates, and only 85 exiles returned permanently to the United States.

Meanwhile, the Defense Department conducted the deserter study requested by the President. The Carter administration was relying for advice here on some of the same Pentagon officials who had helped shape President Ford's clemency program. The first proposal submitted by the Defense Department was rejected by the White House as too stringent, and the plan finally adopted was a compromise between competing views within the administration.

In late March, the Defense Department announced a "Special Discharge Review Program" through which 432,000 veterans with Undesirable or Clemency Discharges were invited to apply for upgrades via existing discharge review boards. Those with Undesirable Discharges who had completed tours in Vietnam, had two years of good service, or had received Clemency Discharges under the Ford program were virtually guaranteed automatic relief. The boards were directed to "reexamine" other cases in a "spirit of compassion." Yet large categories of veterans were excluded. Those who had deserted from Southeast Asia were automatically barred, even though many of their offenses involved conscientious war resistance, combat fatigue, or other extenuating circumstances. The program also failed to cover the 22,000 individuals who were discharged by court-martial for offenses against military discipline, even though Defense Department officials acknowledge privately that their misconduct was generally no worse than that of the 130,000 who accepted Undesirable Discharges as plea bargains. In fact, many of the most conscientiously motivated individuals had refused to plea-bargain, maintained their innocence, and insisted on standing trial.

A fundamental weakness in the Carter program for military offenders was its requirement that eligible veterans apply within a six-month period. During the six and a half months of President Ford's program, only 15 percent of its ninety thousand eligible veterans with bad discharges had applied. The Ford program offered fewer benefits than Carter's, but its top officials believed that the low application level resulted mainly from ignorance, apathy, confusion, and distrust of the government—problems no less serious in 1977 than in 1974. Father Hesburgh and McGeorge Bundy had warned the President that any program requiring applications or imposing deadlines would help relatively few people. They further suggested that the President order a comprehensive file review at the military records center to assure that his program reach as many people as possible. However, Carter chose to follow the advice of Pentagon officials who rejected the Hesburgh-Bundy approach as an "administrative nightmare." Those same Defense Department officials forecast that only about 120,000 of the 432,000 eligible veterans would apply, and that roughly 70,000 would get upgrades. For them, and apparently for the President, those numbers were sufficient.

The Carter program required that fugitive deserters also apply in person—Defense Department officials rejected the idea of granting them Undesirable Discharges "in absentia." As before, fugitives could surrender at any military base and be virtually assured of an immediate administrative discharge, but many still feared they would be court-martialed and sent to prison. In contrast to the 1974 program, they stayed away in droves.

The Defense Department estimates proved wildly optimistic. The Carter program attracted a scant 9 percent of the 432,000 eligible veterans, far below the 19 percent proportion who had applied to the less generous Ford program. As of October 4, 1977, the date the program ended, the Defense Department had received only 37,283 applications. Of 28,000 cases processed, 16,000, or 60 percent, received upgrades.

The Defense Department had originally planned to spend $200,000 on a public information program to stimulate applications, but Congress prohibited any expenditures for advertising. Congressional opposition to Carter's program also persuaded many eligible veterans to follow the advice of pro-amnesty veteran's counselors, who warned that applying to the program might only compound their problems. Carter seemed content simply to announce his program and then let his policy fare as best it could without any further effort to enlist public support. Candidate Carter had spoken eloquently about the social inequities of the war, but President Carter said nothing. As it was, the public perceived Carter's military program more as an unfair windfall for deserters than as an effort to correct the injustices of the Vietnam era.

Working through Congress, conservative veterans' groups mounted an attack against the program. In the weeks before the President's inauguration they fostered a Senate resolution condemning any kind of amnesty policy. This was stymied only because the new President announced the pardons for draft resisters his first day in office. Then, in rapid succession, Congress enacted legislation which attempted to prohibit the use of funds for processing returning exiles, for issuing pardon certificates, and for the dropping of draft prosecutions. And to prove that politics does indeed make for strange bedfellows, Alan Cranston, a liberal Senator who had been sympathetic to the amnesty cause, joined with Strom Thurmond, a longtime opponent, in a particularly vindictive bill which denied veteran's benefits to those who had received upgrades under the special rules of the Carter program.

Arguing that the Vietnam war was no different from other wars, and that its veterans deserved no special treatment, the bill's supporters challenged the basic premise of the Carter program. Taking advantage of the administration's inept, halfhearted defense, legislators on the House and Senate Veterans Committees succeeded in moving the bill through both houses of Congress. The President pondered whether to sign the legislation for the full ten days constitutionally allotted him, and Secretary of Defense Harold Brown, Attorney General Griffin Bell, and top White House aides all urged him to veto it. Other Carter aides, however, had inadvertently committed the President to acceptance of the bill, in the mistaken belief that the somewhat less stringent Senate version had been adopted. Reluctant to renege on his commitment to House Speaker Tip O'Neill and concerned that a veto might not be sustained, President Carter ultimately decided to sign it. The distinction between draft-evaders and deserters he had drawn during the campaign was thus reaffirmed.

Carter offered more significant relief to more people at less taxpayers' expense than Ford. Unlike his predecessor, President Carter had full access to the facts about draft resisters and deserters when he constructed his program, he was personally and politically committed, and he enjoyed a far stronger mandate to effect a fair solution. Yet, his must stand as the greater disappointment. Ford's concept of "earned re-entry" may not have been a satisfactory approach, but it did reflect an understandable personal philosophy and an internally consistent response. Carter, by contrast, offered total amnesty for draft resisters but, by signing the Cranston-Thurmond bill, provided very little for their military counterparts, who deserved no less and needed far more than the civilians.

Both Presidents, however, must share equal responsibility for the government's failure to secure what draft resisters and deserters needed most—a change in the public's longstanding misconceptions about who they were and what they had done. Both Gerald Ford and Jimmy Carter failed to use the prestige of their office to change public attitudes and bring about a true national reconciliation.

The Next War

Throughout the amnesty debate, fear was often expressed that any measure of official forgiveness, no matter how limited, would undermine America's ability to fight future wars. When talk of amnesty spread through Congress in 1972, Congressman William Jennings Bryan Dorn of South Carolina warned his colleagues that "amnesty would be a severe blow to the defenses of our nation. It would be a step toward anarchy, chaos, and a breakdown of all discipline so necessary for the survival of our democratic institutions." Later, Congressman Sonny Montgomery of Mississippi led the opposition to President Carter's blanket pardons by warning that a future generation of draft-age men might refuse induction or desert from the military on the assumption, born of the Vietnam era, that they would be amnestied a few years later. Carter's own distinction between draft resisters and deserters reflected his concern about the military's ability to maintain discipline in future wartime situations. When Charles Kirbo met with amnesty advocates before Carter's decision, he asked them, "Well, what do we do when the next war comes?"

Throughout its two-hundred-year history, America has fought almost a dozen wars. Many of the conflicts were divisive, engendering considerable war resistance. Most were followed by some form of amnesty. The experience of each war left its imprint on the public. But the amnesties were quickly forgotten and had little, if any, bearing upon the nation's subsequent ability to mobilize troops. During the Vietnam war, draft resisters and deserters seldom broke the law with a view to history, confident that they, like Whiskey Rebellionists or Confederates, would eventually be amnestied. Years from now, when historians look back to the post-Vietnam amnesties, they will probably find them to have had little influence on resistance or evasion in subsequent military crises. It is hard to imagine future war resisters taking much solace in the official measure of relief that followed the years of anxiety, exile, and social disgrace of Vietnam-era offenders.

If the legacy of Vietnam should affect a future wartime mobilization, the reason will not be President Ford's clemency or President Carter's blanket pardons. If draft-age men are unwilling to serve, it will be less in hope of another amnesty than because of a fundamental skepticism about the government in time of military crisis. The Vietnam generation's experiences with the war—the antipathy to military service, the inequities of the draft, and the widespread belief that war resisters were right when the government was wrong—have shaken the nation's confidence that it can order young people to fight in anything short of an unquestioned national emergency.

Some view this as a blessing. One of the original goals of Vietnam resistance and the amnesty movement was to force legal and political acceptance of the individual's moral right to decide for himself whether to fight in any given war. According to a spokesman for the pacifist Mennonite Church,

> The United States government may wish to wage a major unpopular war requiring more personnel than the active armed services and the reserves can supply, a war which does not have the support of the American people and for which volunteers would not be forthcoming. . . . In a democratic system, however, the justification for fighting such a war seems dubious at best.

Thus would a form of pure democracy determine the nation's defense policy and prevent future Vietnams. This has some appeal in theory, especially for those who loathe the memory of Vietnam. But could America fight such a "democratic" war when its long-term security but not its immediate survival is at stake?

Despite court challenges to the Vietnam-era draft, it remains the law that one may not legally refuse to fight in a particular war, no matter how morally based the decision. The Supreme Court, in the 1971 *Gillette* decision, held that there is no constitutionally recognized principle of "selective conscientious objection." In the Court's view, such a principle is incompatible with the need of the country to defend itself.

The *Gillette* case may have denied the legal principle of selective objection, but Vietnam-era policies condoned the practice. A draft-age man could be selective, not as a matter of conscience, but as a matter of conscientious avoidance. Millions selected themselves out of the war by lawful avoidance, safe military service, or unlawful but unpunished evasion. Their conduct reflected the public's general distaste for coercion in a free society, a distaste that eventually led to the end of the draft.

In 1971, the same year as the *Gillette* decision, the Gates Commission reported to President Nixon that an all-volunteer force was desirable and feasible for the postwar period. The Gates report drew strong attack from an uncommon alliance of liberals and conservatives. The former, led by Senator Edward M. Kennedy, feared that the armed forces would become disproportionately poor and black and that a professional military would lose the leavening influence of civilian soldiers. Conservatives, led by Senator John Stennis, complained that an all-volunteer force would give the nation inadequate flexibility to meet an emergency. Notwithstanding these warnings, President Nixon and Defense Secretary Melvin Laird endorsed and later implemented the Gates Commission recommendations. When the all-volunteer force came into being in 1973, the principle of selective objection became national policy. In effect, each individual could selectively object simply by not volunteering for military service. Temporarily, at least, this resolved the tension between personal freedom and the needs of the government.

The all-volunteer force has also led to significant reforms that might not have happened in a conscripted army. The military has had to compete in the marketplace like any other employer, and it has quickly learned that increased pay and a reduced risk of combat are not enough. The memories of the earlier army—of makework tasks, poor leadership, and excessive discipline—are still fresh in the minds of nineteen-year-olds. "Today's youth," warned Peter Hauser in *America's Army,* "just will not join that sort of organization—at least not in the quality and quantity necessary to accomplish the Army's mission." So, to enlist men and retain them once they are trained, the military has tried to improve its image and, in particular, its treatment of recruits.

During the Vietnam era, volunteers were often promised the opportunity to learn new skills. But for too many, the only skill learned was combat. In the all-volunteer force, enlistment contracts have been made binding. Recruits now know what they are getting into and what is expected of them. If the government fails to deliver, or if recruits prove unqualified for the specialties they want, they can leave the service with Honorable Discharges.

The life of a soldier is far better than it was just a few years ago. Barracks have given way to dormitories. Longer haircuts, mustaches, and other expressions of individuality are permitted more widely than before. What soldiers used to call the "Mickey Mouse" aspect of military life has largely disappeared. Civilians have been hired for KP and the other kinds of menial labor that soldiers have always resented. There is increasing talk of a serviceman's union. Day-to-day relationships between officers and enlisted men have improved; drill sergeants, in particular, have become less abusive. New human relations programs have been devised to help soldiers with personal problems. "We're trying to approach men with a concept of mutual trust," commented General George Forsythe, coordinator of the Army's shift to a volunteer force. "A man old enough to fight and die is old enough to be trusted."

Some of the more far-reaching reforms have come in the area of discipline. The draft provided a cheap and apparently inexhaustible supply of manpower resources. If an individual did not perform well, he was punished, sent to the stockade, or put to demeaning and unproductive chores. It cost little to keep him around, and his punishment was thought to discourage others from misbehaving. Poor performers were kept in the service until their petty offenses led to major offenses, resulting in court-martial convictions and bad discharges. By contrast, every soldier in the all-volunteer force has become an expensive and scarce resource, and the military can ill afford to keep those who are unproductive. Since 1970, the annual cost per soldier has tripled. The cost of tolerating and punishing poor performers has been estimated to be about $1 billion a year. "Suddenly," said Roger Kelley, former assistant secretary of defense for manpower, "the armed forces have had to become efficient managers of people."

The military has begun to deal with poorly performing recruits the same way private sector employers do with poorly performing employees—by firing them, or by trying not to hire them in the first place. All branches of service have tried to be more selective in the hiring of marginally qualified young men with AFQT scores in Category IV. Compared to the Vietnam era, a much greater effort is made to screen out potential disciplinary problems, but a number of poorly educated, low-IQ recruits are still accepted. Otherwise, despite the presently high unemployment rate among nineteen-year-olds, enlistment quotas could not be filled.

An important change in the approach to discipline has come with the introduction of what some soldiers call the "I quit" or "you're fired" discharge. The initial training months are now regarded as a trial period. If the recruit or his commanding officer decides that the new soldier is not suited for military life, either can take the initiative to sever the military contract in a matter of days. The "trainee discharge" that follows is usually an Honorable and never worse than a General Discharge. This enables the services to dispose of potential disciplinary problems quickly. In some branches of the service, as many as 20 percent of new recruits are separated before the end of the initial training period. First-term servicemen who complete their training period but then begin to present disciplinary problems can be eliminated almost as easily under the "expeditious discharge" program. These discharges are similarly either Honorable or General, and they qualify an individual for veterans' benefits after six months of service.

In fiscal 1977, almost 30 percent of all new recruits failed to finish two years of service.

The AWOL soldier can still receive an Undesirable Discharge, but even this reflects the military's decriminalization of unauthorized absences. This lenient treatment began in the latter years of the war, gaining impetus when the loophole of the Ford clemency program guaranteed returning deserters automatic administrative discharges. Since the end of the Ford program, court-martial trials for absence offenders have become rare. In 1975 and early 1976, only one hundred deserters were sentenced to prison terms, almost all at Fort Gordon, Georgia. However, the sentences were commuted by the Pentagon shortly after the men arrived at Fort Leavenworth prison. Fort Gordon eventually complied with the prevailing policy of giving AWOL soldiers nothing worse than immediate Undesirable Discharges. Today, the military looks at AWOL as a problem more of management than of discipline, and even the official terminology has changed. Soldiers who go AWOL are no longer "deserters"; they are "absentees."

The changing military attitudes have also had a retroactive impact on veterans of earlier times. Post-discharge review procedures have been liberalized in recent years, making it easier for veterans with bad discharges to have them upgraded to General or Honorable. President Carter's special discharge review program for Vietnam-era veterans was in some respects a codification of existing policies, but it also reflected a continuing liberalizing attitude toward veterans with bad discharges from all eras. The military has established a number of regional discharge review boards, enabling applicants to pursue their cases without making long and expensive trips to Washington. Under pressure of a lawsuit, the boards have agreed to issue detailed reasons for each decision. This should improve the consistency of decisions and may reduce the wide disparity among branches of service and individual commanders who make original discharge decisions.

The changes in discharge review are partly the result of a proliferation of veteran counseling organizations. Staffed by Vietnam veterans and the remnants of the draft-counseling community, some two hundred organizations have been established since the war. The result has been a dramatic increase in the number of veterans applying to discharge review boards. At the Army board alone, the number of monthly cases has increased tenfold in the last several years. Even before the announcement of the Carter program, discharge review boards were expecting as many as fifteen thousand applicants annually. By 1977, their backlogs had grown to seven thousand cases, straining the review process to the breaking point. But success rates have been higher than ever before, ranging from 29 percent at the Army board to 49 percent at the Air Force board. Applicants who appear in person and have experienced counselors do even better, with an upgrade rate approaching 50 percent. During Carter's discharge review program for deserters, 80 percent of the eligible applicants were upgraded.

Continued public criticism of the military's discharge system, reinforced by the rapid increase in the numbers of veterans seeking upgrades, has increased the pressure on the services to reform the current five-tiered system. Throughout the armed forces, there is a growing awareness of the long-term social and economic costs of less-than-Honorable discharges, especially those imposed administratively without the due process safeguards of court-martial trials. Yet the military has continued to resist this most basic of reforms.

The progress made by the post-Vietnam military is partly the product of the war and partly the product of the all-volunteer force that followed it. But the future of the nonconscript army is hardly secure. Enlistment quotas have not been reached without accepting more high school drop-outs. But retention of these drop-outs has become a serious problem, with more than 50 percent of them failing to complete their initial three-year enlistment. An anticipated drop in the number of eligible eighteen- and nineteen-year-olds will aggravate the problem in the 1980s. Manpower officials are pleased with the positive attitude of recent recruits, but they complain of a growing difficulty in attracting men with special talents and high aptitudes—the same men who once could be lured into noncombat assignments by the threat of induction. The all-volunteer force has not been as predominantly black and low-income as many had feared, but it still does not represent a true cross-section of American youth.

The commitment to the all-volunteer force has never been universal. Many defense leaders question whether it will ultimately prove feasible even in peacetime. The economic arguments in favor of a draft are regaining popularity. Questions are also asked whether an all-volunteer system can provide the necessary troops to meet a military emergency of more than a few months. Under the current "total force" concept, the reserves are seen as the necessary backup to the active duty force in the event of a crisis. But with the end of the draft, there has been difficulty in attracting reservists, and the deterioration of reserve strength is expected to grow more severe in the coming years. William Brehm, formerly assistant secretary of defense for manpower and reserve affairs, testified to Congress that today's active forces could supply less than half of the combat troops that a major ground war in Europe would require. Even if the President activated all combat-trained reserves, Brehm believed that there still would be a shortage of 250,000 combat troops. The 1976 Defense Manpower Commission likewise warned that "in the event of sudden major hostilities, our volunteer forces would be weakened by casualties without adequate loss replacements. In time they would be unable to conduct sustained operations, and would be annihilated."

Theoretically, at least, the anticipated shortage could be solved through the marketplace by increasing combat enlistment bonuses beyond their $1,000–$2,500 peacetime levels. However, bonuses might have to reach extraordinary levels in time of war. The underlying dilemma about defense manpower policy has not been solved; it has only been postponed.

Whatever the fate of the all-volunteer force during peacetime or limited conflict, there is widespread acknowledgment that a prolonged conflict would require a return to a draft. It remains to be seen how many of the recent military reforms would survive conscription. Binding discharge contracts, trainee and expeditious discharges, and leniency toward absentees might all become casualties of a reversion to a conscript army, especially during hostilities.

The public attitude is certain to dictate the success or failure of any future draft system. The social and political environment of a future crisis cannot be predicted. It is possible that the next draft-age generation will exhibit the same eagerness to serve and willingness to sacrifice that characterized World War II. Avoiders, evaders, and professional draft counselors may be held in disrepute by their peers. Draft boards, prosecutors, and judges may enforce the law strictly and effectively.

But the next set of parents and national leaders will come from the Vietnam generation, almost half of whom thought they were treated unjustly by Selective Service or the armed forces. According to the Notre Dame survey, four of five lost respect for the government as a result of what happened to them or their friends. No one can say what effect this will have on the nation's long-term defense posture, but there will be an impact. World War II conditioned the responses of the older generation toward Vietnam; Vietnam will likewise affect the younger generation's response to future wars. Part of this conditioning will be political, affecting the kinds of declared or undeclared wars the nation is willing to fight. Another part will be personal, affecting the individual's willingness to serve—or have his children serve—in time of need.

Over the next twenty years, the 53 million men and women of the Vietnam generation will have their own children come of age. Family discussions in the 1990s will seldom recall national sacrifice, a dedicated response to the call to arms, or the generosity of a grateful nation toward those who served in its name. Millions of draft-age youths will know that their fathers were avoiders, war resisters, or disillusioned veterans. This is not the stuff upon which to build an ethic of unquestioning patriotism.

The offspring of the Vietnam generation may inherit or even magnify the skeptical values of their parents. As one advocate of amnesty warned, a generation of disillusioned parents will produce sons and daughters who "will question the actions of the military before they get involved," and they may do so earlier and to a greater extent than their fathers did during Vietnam.

When the nation's youth are next called upon to fight, the ultimate legacy of Vietnam may be a widespread attitude that the draft and the armed forces are not to be trusted. Isolationist and pacifist sentiments may be strong, prompting a revival of the resistance and draft-counseling network. A renewed guerrilla war against the draft might have greater success in paralyzing draft boards, jamming the courts, and destroying discipline in the armed forces. The whole system of conscription might break down, and the United States might not be able to raise an army.

At present, little thought has been given to the obstacles confronting a return to the draft. Since 1975, draft-age men have not been required to register with Selective Service and draft boards have been disbanded. All that is left of the Selective Service system is a small caretaker staff, much of whose time is spent disposing of old records. Nonetheless, present contingency plans assume that an immediate registration would enable the drafting of 100,000 men within four months and a half million by the eighth month, through a system nearly identical to the one abandoned in 1972. These plans are predicated on the successful mass registrations of World Wars I and II. World War I registration began seventeen days after the enactment of a conscription law, and 475,000 men were drafted within six months. The World War II draft registered 16,500,000 men within thirty days, and mass inductions began just one month later. But history offers little assurance, given the fresh memory of Vietnam and the residue of the antidraft movement.

In the Vietnam era, just 1 percent of all draft-age men failed to register, and another 1 percent refused induction. Still, the draft barely survived the challenge. In the next war, if 10 percent or even 5 percent of all draft-age persons do not register, there might indeed be a "snowballing" effect like the one the Resistance movement tried, unsuccessfully, to catalyze in the late sixties. That prospect is a very real threat. In early 1976, Selective Service announced plans for a one-day mass registration of eighteen-year-olds, and draft resistance groups quickly organized a boycott. The plan was canceled, ostensibly for budget reasons; had it been carried out, the combined effect of the boycott and public apathy might well have produced an alarmingly low turnout.

The effective functioning of a post-Vietnam draft hinges on a number of other optimistic assumptions: the overnight mobilization of a draft structure that is presently nonexistent, the fair application of laws and regulations by draft boards whose Vietnam-era performance did not withstand judicial scrutiny, swift and certain criminal enforcement by a judicial system that dismissed more than 90 percent of all Vietnam-related cases, and the absence of a concerted resistance effort by pacifist groups who oppose conscription as a matter of principle. Most important, it requires a reversal of the present antipathy toward the idea of a draft. "Going back to the draft would upset the whole country," conceded Byron Pepitone, Director of Selective Service during the Ford administration. "The mothers of America have learned to like the past four years."

Unless the nation wants to gamble its security on these optimistic assumptions, it has to develop reasonable, publicly acceptable plans for coping with a military crisis. At the same time, it must design manpower and enforcement policies which avoid the social inequities, disrupted lives, and permanent stigmas of the Vietnam era.

The all-volunteer force may be the nation's choice. If so, the high cost of emergency mobilization has to be acknowledged in advance, along with the risk that low-income youths may do a disproportionate share of the fighting. Alternatively, all draft-age youths could be ordered to perform two years of civilian or military service, the minimum time the armed forces consider necessary for a useful military tour. Jobs would have to be created for eight million young men and women, the great bulk of them in the civilian economy. The cost would be staggering. Americans would also have to accept what many consider the dangerously totalitarian notion that the government has the right to demand involuntary civilian service of its citizens. The problem of conscientious objection would still exist, and rules would have to be developed for determining who fights and who stays at the homefront.

Selective conscription, modeled after the Vietnam-era lottery, is the third alternative. However, the experience of Vietnam suggests that any system with status-based deferments and exemptions would again encourage manipulative behavior, legal challenges, and social inequities unless all subjective decision-making were eliminated. As long as anyone can contrive to flunk a physical exam or persuade a draft board that he—or she—is a conscientious objector, the draft system would be vulnerable to abuse and legal challenge. Yet if incapacitated persons and conscientious objectors are pressed into military service, thousands of draft offenses would occur.

In any system of limited conscription, the issue of selective objection has to be faced and resolved. As one possibility, anyone unwilling or unable to perform military service might be permitted to excuse himself at his own initiative, without having to demonstrate his sincerity. This would be similar to the CO provision in the West German draft law. New York Congressman Jonathan Bingham has proposed a scheme whereby selective CO's would have to declare themselves before becoming subject to a draft lottery. In doing so, they would commit themselves to alternative service regardless of their lottery numbers. In effect, this would build on the Vietnam-era precedent of offering noncombat assignments to draft-age men who enlisted for three or four years in the Navy, Air Force, or Coast Guard. But unlike the Vietnam era, anyone could become a selective objector, regardless of his background, education, or social status.

Reconciling personal freedom with national security will never be easy in America's democratic society. It is part of the legacy of Vietnam that the nation may find itself unprepared in a future military crisis.

VII | LEGACIES

Half a decade has passed since the last American troops left Vietnam. The debate about the war has moved from the newspapers to the history books. Former Johnson administration officials who helped shape the nation's Vietnam policy are now sharing power in the Carter administration with a number of activists who opposed that policy. With a collective sigh of relief, the nation has closed a tragic chapter of its history.

The 26,800,000 men of the Vietnam generation are preoccupied with building careers, raising families, and making their way in American life. But their experience with the war can never be erased. Few can forget the decisions, compromises, and sacrifices they had to make. Nor can they forget what happened to their friends and peers who fared perhaps better, perhaps worse than they. The war may fade in everyone else's mind, but not in theirs. In *We Are All POW's,* Vietnam veteran Gary Wood was asked by his co-author, convicted draft resister Chuck Noell, whether America would ever "work through" Vietnam. His answer: "No. The rest of society will pretend it never happened. Or they'll pretend that it isn't important. And our generation will go on reliving Vietnam until it dies off."

Combat veterans, especially, cannot forget. While others stayed home, they were uprooted from their loved ones, subjected to the rigors of military training, and sent to fight for a cause that had little meaning for many of them. Most were lucky and returned without wounds or bad discharges. But there were few parades, ceremonies, or even notes in their local newspapers. They came home, that was all.

They are the orphans of the war. To some, they represent a defeated army, losers of a war that could have been won. One veteran recalled getting in a fistfight with a Legionnaire who blamed him and his buddies for the loss of Vietnam: "I fought just as well as he did, maybe better. Guys like him always talked a lot about how great the war was, and how everybody should support it, but deep down they had no respect for grunts like me who had to fight it."

To others, they are the criminals of My Lai, killers of women and children, the spreaders of defoliants, napalm, and cluster bombs. A Chicano from Los Angeles found that "everyone I talked to was negative. 'What is it like to kill? How does it feel?' Questions like that. A lot of it was just well-founded curiosity, I think, but a lot of it was twisting it in you. It was like—hey—you're really a loser." An Ohio veteran, militantly antiwar himself, was shamed and ridiculed whenever he wore his army uniform around town: "People just look down on you. They treat you altogether different when you're in uniform. I went up to the campus to see my girl, and I got called pig and murderer and all kinds of things just because I was in uniform."

Vietnam veterans have learned through bitter experience that military service did not gain them personal honor or a headstart in life. Their time in the military taught them few useful skills. All too many had serious problems finding jobs when they returned and, even now, unemployment remains disproportionately high among disabled, minority, and younger veterans. As Michael Marks explained:

> Stuck with the stigma of being a Vietnam vet, I couldn't get a job for a long time. TV commercials were begging business people to hire Vietnam vets, but where in the hell was a job for *me?* Sure, I made it back, unscathed by combat wounds, alcoholism, or drug addiction. But my personal pride was at an all-time low.

Their peers are years ahead of them in building careers and families. Understandably, many veterans resent those who saw the war only from living rooms. One recalled getting a letter from a college-educated friend:

"Harry," he wrote, "maybe we're doing a terrible thing, trying to destroy a whole way of life, trying to impose Catholicism and Americanism on Asia. Think about it, Harry." Think about it? I never answered him, the son of a bitch. Here he was, deferred as a schoolteacher, and me getting shot at. What did Asian culture mean to me? What about my men, some of whom were still in Vietnam and might never come home alive? Here I was, sitting among draft dodgers and flag-waving sons of bitches, none of whom took the trouble to go and fight for the country they say they love so much, and all a bit drunk and holding their girls' tits, and my men, my buddies, far away, abandoned, left to decay in a place that didn't exist for me anymore.

Another recalled his anger at coming home to an antiwar demonstration:

I ran into a "Resist the Draft" rally on the street. At first I smiled; kids at it again, just a fad. Then I started gettin' sore. About how I had to go and they could stay out. My Negro buddy didn't like the war, but he went in too. I just stood there and got sore at those spoiled rich kids tellin' people to "resist the draft." What about us poor people? For every guy who resists the draft, one of us gotta go, and he gets sent out into the boonies to get his backside shot at. One of their signs read, "We've Already Given Enough." And I thought, "What *have* they given?"

Paul Starr interviewed hundreds of veterans for *The Discarded Army*, his book about post-Vietnam adjustment problems. Starrr found "they feel overwhelmingly that people who were not in Vietnam have no right to judge them, that such judgments are a luxury of those who stayed at home and had nothing to do with the situations they confronted."

As Starr noted, combat veterans rarely feel guilty for doing what they did—"they believe they were much more sinned against than sinning." But they also feel little pride in having done the fighting for others. When they are called heroes, it is usually for a cause other than their own—as an argument for opposing amnesty, for example. What the

Vietnam veteran wants, and what he has not gotten, is understanding. As psychologist Dr. Peter Bourne commented, "It is not so important that he be treated as a hero, but that some recognition be given to the experiences and suffering he has endured."

Just as the American people have forgotten the Vietnam veteran, so too have they forgotten that every member of the generation is, in a very real sense, a veteran of Vietnam. Ron Bitzer, a former combat infantryman who is now a veterans' counselor, laments that "the American people seldom realize that Vietnam veterans and deserters are very similar; sometimes, in fact, they are one and the same. If people really cared about any of us, they would care about all of us." Bitzer's "all of us" includes the entire generation, not just the relative few who saw combat or paid a price for breaking the law.

Except for the few who considered military service an honor and privilege, and except for the lucky ones who saw fate pass them by, every draft-age man had to choose from among a number of unpleasant choices. The alternatives—combat, avoidance in or out of service, evasion, desertion, or exile—each involved the possibility of sacrifice, punishment, or moral guilt. This was a difficult decision for a young man to make.

In the late 1960s, Eddie Correia, Jim Fallows, and John Foote each had the opportunity to escape the draft by means of a physical exemption. Correia knew from childhood that he would be disqualified, no matter what he did. Fallows was in excellent health, but won an exemption by exploiting the system. Foote turned down a near-certain disqualification to become an infantry officer in Vietnam. Here are their accounts:

Eddie Correia

The war. My generation called it then (and now) simply The War. To our parents it was the "war in Vietnam"—the latest in a series of wars they and the nation had to endure. While the honor of serving in this war might not be so honorable, and the heroes of this war not so acclaimed, it was to them a war much like other wars. But to my generation, it was more a political and personal phenomenon than an effort to defend our country.

Vietnam, at least for three or four years, hovered over my life and the lives of those around me. It was the source of scores of discussions about the folly of our involvement and the focus of shared views about how drastically wrong political leaders could be. It was, I believe, the strongest force driving young people to distrust their leaders and to destroy what they felt was worst about American life.

The war was the center of heated arguments between us and our parents and their contemporaries. I remember speaking to a men's civic club about American involvement. Those men, who, on other days, were proud and supportive of us, seemed to despise me that day. Their frustration and anger poured over me. These arguments across the age and experience barrier were to be repeated many times, and I believe some scars remain. In our desperate efforts to convince each other, we almost always failed and almost always felt some bitterness.

I, as most others, I think, passed through a period of reflection and confusion—first about the rightness of the war, then about the meaning of fighting in it. I, as many others, came to doubt the war more and more strongly until the conviction became an emotional one.

But in the most crucial way of all, the war passed me by. I always knew I would not have to serve in Vietnam. I have a handicap, a mark of childhood polio. It left one leg smaller and weaker—not enough to make me inactive, but more than enough to make a physical exemption certain. I know now this handicap was, in one important sense, a luxury. My lottery number, 83, was low enough so I would have been drafted had I not been exempted. As the lottery was based on chance, so was my physical disability. In my case, chance spared me the dilemma faced by millions of others. That dilemma—the critical choice whether to serve if drafted—was confronted by many of my friends. Some of them were terrified.

One of my closest and most sensitive friends chronically wrestled with the prospects of prison or flight to Canada. His fears were very real. He believed he would be in Canada all his life, or, if he went to prison, his life would be destroyed. He once told me he feared he would be homosexually raped in prison, and he felt he should prepare himself psychologically. Although he was the most conscientious of objectors, his religious beliefs did not fit the Selective Service's standards. I believe he would not have fought in the war, and I believe some of his fears would have come true. As with many of us in the white middle class, however, he won his reprieve. After long and, it seemed, desperate efforts, he got a physical exemption. When he received this news, it was a time of rejoicing for him, for me, and for everyone who knew him.

Would I have gone to Vietnam if I had been forced to make the choice? Going would have meant fighting in a war I hated and, perhaps, killing others under circumstances I believed were inhuman. Going would have meant betraying myself by failing the first important moral test I created for my life. Going would have meant risking death for nothing.

Yet I do not know. Resisting would have led to prison or a life in another country. It would have meant imposing a grief on my family from which they never fully would have recovered. Resisting would have meant destroying a career I hoped (and expected) to be a successful and satisfying one. It would have meant creating a suspicion in myself that I was a coward.

Most choices in life, I believe, lend themselves to weighing one course against the other. The war seemed to present alternatives that were so bleak, so empty, and so destructive than any rational decision-making was pointless. I do not know what I would have done. That I was not forced to choose caused me some guilt and, I believe, caused my friends some unspoken resentment.

I am sure, however, I cannot judge what any of my friends did or what any of the millions of my contemporaries I will never know chose for themselves. I am simply thankful I did not have to decide. And I am thankful the war is over.

Jim Fallows

In the fall of 1969, I was beginning my final year in college. As the months went by, the rock on which I had unthinkingly anchored my hopes—the certainty that the war in Vietnam would be over before I could possibly fight—began to crumble. It shattered altogether on Thanksgiving weekend when, while riding back to Boston from a visit with my relatives, I heard that the draft lottery had been held, and my birth date had come up number 45. I recognized for the first time that, inflexibly, I must either be drafted or consciously find a way to prevent it.

In the atmosphere of that time, each possible choice came equipped with barbs. To answer the call was unthinkable, not only because, in my heart, I was desperately afraid of being killed, but also because, among my friends, it was axiomatic that one should not be "complicit" in the immoral war effort.

Draft resistance, the course chosen by a few noble heroes of the movement, meant going to prison or leaving the country. With much the same intensity with which I wanted to stay alive, I did not want those things either. What I wanted was to go to graduate school, to get married, and to enjoy those bright prospects I had been taught that life owed me.

I learned quickly enough that there was only one way to get what I wanted. A physical deferment would restore things to the happy state I had known during four undergraduate years. . . .

Although, on the doctor's advice, I made a halfhearted try at fainting spells, my only real possibility was beating the height and weight regulations. My normal weight was close to the cutoff point for an "underweight" disqualification, and, with a diligence born of panic, I made sure I would have a margin. On the morning of the draft physical I weighed 120 pounds. . . .

I stepped on the scales at the very beginning of the examination. Desperate at seeing the orderly write down 122 pounds, I hopped back on and made sure that he lowered it to 120. I walked in a trance through the rest of the examination until the final meeting with the fatherly physician who rules on marginal cases such as mine. I stood there in socks and underwear, arms wrapped around me in the chilly building. I knew as I looked at the doctor's face that he understood exactly what I was doing.

"Have you ever contemplated suicide?" he asked after he finished looking over my chart. My eyes darted up to his. "Oh, suicide—yes, I've been feeling very unstable and unreliable recently." He looked at me, staring until I returned my eyes to the ground. He wrote "unqualified" on my folder, turned on his heel, and left. I was overcome by a wave of relief, which for the first time revealed to me how great my terror had been, and by the beginning of the sense of shame that remains with me to this day.

It was, initially, a generalized shame at having gotten away with my deception, but it came into sharper focus later in the day. Even as the last of the Cambridge contingent was throwing its urine and deliberately failing its color blindness tests, buses from the next board began to arrive. These bore the boys from Chelsea, thick, dark-haired young men, the white proles of Boston.

Most of them were younger than us, since they had just left high school, and it had clearly never occurred to them that there might be a way around the draft. They walked through the examination lines like so many cattle off to slaughter. . . .

We returned to Cambridge that afternoon, not in government buses but as free individuals, liberated and victorious. The talk was high-spirited, but there was something close to the surface that none of us wanted to mention. We knew now who would be killed. . . .

On either side of the class divide, the war has left feelings that can easily shade over into mistrust and hostility. Among those who went to war, there is a residual resentment, the natural result of a cool look at who ended up paying what price. On the part of those who were spared, there is a residual guilt, often so deeply buried that it surfaces only in unnaturally vehement denials that there is anything to feel guilty about.

In a land of supposed opportunity, the comfortable hate to see the poor. Beneath all the explanations about self-help and just deserts, there remains the vein of empathy and guilt. Among the bright people of my generation, those who have made a cult of their high-mindedness, the sight of legless veterans and the memories of the Navy Yard must also touch that vein. They remind us that there was little character in the choices we made.

John Foote

I come from a conservative southern background, growing up extraordinarily conscious of the Civil War. When younger I could recite the order of march into the major battles of the war, and the names of the great generals were second nature to me. Viewed from the distance of a hundred years, it all seemed so incredibly romantic. Even the Second World War seemed somehow to have been reinforcement for the notions of duty, honor, and country. This romanticization of war, and the view of it as a time of anonymity and individual elevation through feats of arms, affected my whole perception of military service.

Both my parents, though not particularly warlike, were strong believers in the duty to serve and the honor that was associated with honorable service. They rarely spoke of Vietnam, or even of my impending service, in other than immediate terms (fear for my life), but my father once told me that if I chose not to serve, I should do so in the knowledge that his home would no longer be open to me. I never believed him, for such things would have been out of character, but the statement had an impact on me. He had served honorably in World War II, and is a reasonable man who believes himself a patriot.

My college life gave incredible reinforcement to my earlier training. Louisiana State University, an island of near-timeless beauty, was a remarkably womblike environment during the late 1960s. For most of my time there, Vietnam was nothing. It did not exist. Of course, my classmates and I were as aware as anyone who could watch the national news that things were getting progressively worse there, but none of us believed that this meant anything to us.

Like death, war was something that happened to someone else.

I cannot say with any certainty that I ever felt any serious "moral" reservations about the war, but I was troubled by it. I thought deeply about it, but I was totally unable to find any personally acceptable reason for refusal to serve. Although it galls me to acknowledge the shallowness of my sentiment, my opposition to military service was largely based on my personal distaste for leaving my girl friend of those days, and truncating my education, just as my antiwar feelings were principally a concern for the effectiveness of American policy: it was not "moral" revulsion.

I graduated from LSU in 1968, just as the draft calls were on the steady rise, and a friend of mine learned that he and I were at the top of the list. I would not be able to make it through my first year at law school. In July of that summer, I was summoned for my preinduction physical, and the war became a real part of my world. I was extremely bitter about the seeming helplessness with which I faced the draft.

It was around this time that I discovered that an allergy to bee stings was a surefire way to avoid induction, and I had a documentable case. It was clear now that I had an easy out, but despite the fact that I could now avoid service without danger, I began to wonder about the choice of doing *that,* just as much as I had wondered about the choice of refusing service.

Although still very much embittered that these forces beyond my control were moving at me, I began to see Vietnam as the preeminent historical experience of my lifetime, certainly of my youth. Wrongly or rightly, Vietnam had to be faced. And it seemed to me then that there were only three ways to face it honorably: go to war, go to jail, or go to Canada. I accepted that one's participation in the event could take the form of fighting the war or fighting against it. It was not necessary that one join up; it was fully enough to show the courage to fight against the war, and to take the consequence of one's actions. All other methods of legally avoiding service were somehow tainted, cowardly. They were to miss a participation, demanded of all, in this overwhelming historical event. War was, I knew it then and still believe it to be, a life-changing experience.

In the summer of 1968 my draft notice arrived. Although I went into the Army, I did not do it without remaining qualms. Ultimately, however, I was still unable to find any personally acceptable, principled reason to refuse service. Therefore, I believed that my only choice was to go to the guts of the matter and serve in the infantry: the quintessential military experience. But in the end, my time as an infantry officer in Vietnam was undistinguished. My services were marked by boredom more than bravery, and when it was over, I think I was half pleased, half not.

I suppose after all this reflection, and in the wake of personal criticism from those who refused to go, I do not believe my choice to serve was wrong. Indeed I believe that honorable service is an honorable thing and not to be derogated. But since I know the torment that went through my own mind in coming to my choice, I can appreciate and even admire the courage (if not the response) of those who made affirmative decisions different from my own.

(John Foote later became a top official in President Ford's clemency program, and a strong amnesty advocate. A close friend of Foote's at LSU, Blake Jones, was also allergic to bee stings. But unlike Foote, Jones saw a doctor, documented his case, and secured an exemption. After graduating from law school, he became one of the South's best draft counselors, never losing a case.)

The members of the Vietnam generation are now in their late twenties and thirties. Vietnam was and always will be their war, just as World War II belonged to their parents, and World War I to their grandparents. The war stories of older generations—stories about mustard gas, Guadalcanal, or the liberation of little French towns—have no meaning for those who came of age during Vietnam. Like Eddie Correia, Jim Fallows, and John Foote, these 27 million men have their own stories, but they are seldom told with pride. Their battles were with the police, their narrow escapes involved draft boards and courts, and the enemy was the government. Some feel guilty, others lucky. Many have a faint sense of disquiet from having been touched but not really touched, from having left the fighting and dying to others.

The war affected them in complex ways, but it engendered a strong sense of kinship. Vietnam was a crisis that they all faced—whether in the barracks, on the campus, or in the streets. Unlike other Americans, most members of the Vietnam generation are reluctant to judge a man by his personal response to the war. They know that the labels—loser, coward, evader, deserter—are part of the tragedy of Vietnam.

NOTES

In the following pages we set forth the citations of the material we have used from secondary sources. With a few exceptions, we have not cited anecdotes and quotes gathered in interviews. Textual and figure notes are presented separately.

I | THE VIETNAM GENERATION

The estimate of 500 Vietnam casualties for the "Kennedy generation" is derived from official Defense Department casualty statistics. The cost of the war is estimated from Department of Defense statistics cited in the *Congressional Quarterly* of January 27, 1973, p. 148. George Will's quote is from his column in the Washington *Post* of January 13, 1977. The Manchester quote is from *The Glory and the Dream*, p. 287. The breakdown of Vietnam casualties is from Emerson, *Winners and Losers*, p. 58, and Pilisuk, "The Legacy of the Vietnam Veteran," in the *Journal of Social Issues*, vol. 31, p. 9. The high-school survey is taken from Bachman and Jennings, "The Impact of Military Experience," in the *Journal of Social Issues*, vol. 31, p. 149. The Harris survey data is referred to in Helmer, *Bringing the War Home*, p. 92. The Glassman comment appears in the *Congressional Record* of March 23, 1976, p. 4023. James Fallows is the source of the *Harvard Crimson* story and the Rhodes scholar's comment, both of which appear in his article "What Did You Do in the Class War, Daddy," in the October 1975 issue of the *Washington Monthly*. The University of Michigan student is quoted in "The Draft: The Unjust vs. the Unwilling," *Newsweek*, April 11, 1966. The Delaware defense worker is quoted in Sanders, *The Draft and the Vietnam War*, p. 116. Kingman Brewster is quoted by Harry Marmion in *Selective Service: Conflict and Compromise*, p. 19. The doctor draft is described in Selective Service's *Semi-Annual Report* of January 1971, p. 6. The Fiedler comment appears in his article "Who Really Died in Vietnam," in the *Saturday Review* of November 18, 1972. The Marshall quote comes from Tax, *The Draft*, p. 64. Racial inequity data is from Little, *Selective Service and American Society*, p. 149, and Starr, *The Discarded Army*, p. 187.

The 1965–66 study of college draftees is from Davis and Dolbeare, *Little Groups of*

Neighbors, p. 12. The O'Konski survey is from Strickland, *Championship Debater's Complete Sourcebook,* p. 64. The Harvard experiences in World War II and Vietnam are from Fallows' *Washington Monthly* article. The comparative likelihood of Vietnam service by educational level is from Defense Department MARDAC data. The Long Island and other surveys on combat deaths are cited in Useem, *Conscription, Protest, and Social Conflict,* p. 108. The Badillo and Curry study, "Social Incidence of Vietnam Casualties," is published in volume 2 of *Armed Forces and Society,* May 1976, p. 397.

General Lewis Hershey contributed in a personal interview the fact that the Rockefeller brothers and other notables of class and wealth volunteered early in World War II. The quotes from Thurmond and Brophy come from their testimony in the 1972 Senate Selective Service and Amnesty Hearings, pp. 181, 241, and 319. The Nixon quote comes from Carl Rogers' written statement in the 1974 House Amnesty Hearings, p. 729. The Eddie Slovik quote is taken from William Huie, *The Execution of Private Slovik,* quoted in Hayes, *American Deserters in Sweden,* p. 50. The resister's quote about everyone being an evader is taken from William Wick's testimony before the 1974 House Amnesty Hearings, p. 648. Mrs. Diliberti is quoted in "Parents Personify the Amnesty Appeal," *Newsday,* March 31, 1974.

II | A V O I D E R S

Channeling

The Milligan case comes from the March 1, 1976 issue of *The New Yorker.* Hershey's channeling quotes come from his 1965 memorandum "On Manpower Channeling," reprinted in the December 1966 issue of *Ramparts,* and from Davis and Dolbeare, *Little Groups of Neighbors,* pp. 21–22, 154. Hershey's "administrative or financial challenge" quote is from Chapman, *The Wrong Man in Uniform—Our Unfair and Obsolete Draft and How We Can Replace It,* p. 11, and his "selfish individual" quote from O'Sullivan and Meckler, *The Draft and Its Enemies,* p. 242. The military character of the Selective Service staff is described in Wamsley, *Selective Service and a Changing America,* pp. 73 and 99.

The Confederate and Union drafts are explained in Liston, *Greeting,* pp. 30–31; Miller, *Why the Draft: The Case for a Volunteer Army,* pp. 132–37; and William Wick's testimony in the 1974 House Amnesty Hearings, pp. 641–43. The World War I draft is described in Liston, pp. 36–40; Morris, *Why Draft Repeal?* p. 25; and the government report "War Department Policy with Reference to the Disposal of Draft Deserters," August 1920. The Wilson quote comes from O'Sullivan and Meckler, p. 128. The World War II situation is described in Ginzburg, *The Lost Divisions,* p. 36; and Marmion, *Selective Service: Conflict and Compromise,* p. 37. The worrisome postwar quotes are from Dr. M. H. Trytten, director of the Office of Scientific Personnel, National Academy of Science, and Betty Vetter, executive secretary of the Scientific Manpower Commission, quoted in Willenz, *Dialogue on the Draft,* pp. 46 and 54. The postwar draft and the accompanying quotes are described in O'Sullivan, p. 196; Gerhardt, *The Draft and Public Policy,* pp. 116, 154, 233, and 269–70; and Willenz, pp. 53–54 and 71.

The Vietnam-era draft exam is described in Sanders, *The Draft and the Vietnam War,* p. 38; and Little, *Selective Service and American Society,* pp. 46–47. Hershey's "mathematical" quote is from Chapman, p. 19; his "reclassification" quote from William Wick's testimony in the 1974 House Amnesty Hearings, p. 644; and his "bastard" quote from O'Sullivan, p. 213. The "accordion," "putting something over," "Boy Scouts," "trolley," and "slot" quotes are from Little, pp. 87, 92, and 98. His "all over my back" and "can't muddle around" quotes come from a personal interview. The Ann Arbor case is from Williams, *The New Exiles,* p. 17, and the Rudd case from Suttler, *IV-F: A Guide to Draft Exemption,* p. 101. The post-lottery jump in the physical rejection rate is described in Selective Service's *Semi-Annual Report* of January 1975, p. 80. The administrative details underlying the lottery loophole are discussed in Selective Service's *Semi-Annual Report* of July 1971, pp. 54–55. Curtis Tarr's testimony is in the 1972 Senate Selective Service and Amnesty Hearings, p. 370. The Truman's death escape is described in Selective Service's *Semi-Annual Report* of July 1972, p. 63.

Artful Dodgers

The 7% jump in college enrollments is calculated from a comparison of nationwide enrollment trends from 1965 to 1972 with straight-line increments from 1964 to 1973. The data come from the Commerce Department's *Statistical Abstract of the United States* (1973), Table 203, p. 130. The Emory prank is described in Sanders, p. 86; the business school survey in Tax, *The Draft,* p. 64; and the New York City teacher glut in Gaylin, *In the Service of Their Country,* p. 269. The Hershey "PhDs" quote comes from a personal interview. The Hamilton case comes from Chapman, p. 13, and Eisenhower's "babying out" quote from O'Sullivan, p. 215. The nationwide rise in marriage rates is described in Useem, *Conscription, Protest, and Social Conflict,* p. 101, and Canby, *Military Manpower Procurement,* p. 40. Colonel Smith's quote is from Strickland, *Championship Debater's Complete Sourcebook,* p. 67.

The *One Third of a Nation* report refers to the report of the 1963 President's Task Force on Manpower Conservation, p. 25. The .22 rifle case comes from William Wick's testimony in the 1974 House Amnesty Hearings. Draft Board #100 is described in Tatum and Tuchinsky, *Guide to the Draft,* p. 35; *Amex-Canada* magazine, vol. 2, no. 7, p. 10; and the May 16, 1966 issue of *Newsweek.*

Aid and Comfort

The O'Konski quote comes from the December 9, 1966, issue of *Life.* The Luci Johnson, proud mother, and "rotten, stinking war" quotes are all from Sanders, pp. 15, 61, and 76–77. The braking systems quote is from Little, p. 86; the presidential commission quote from Davis and Dolbeare, pp. 82–83; and the doctor quote from Suttler, p. 4. The Seeger case is cited as *U.S.* v. *Seeger,* 380 U.S. 163 (1965).

The Smith and Los Angeles prosecutor quotes are from Frank Slatinshek's testimony in the 1970 House Armed Services Hearings, p. 12839. Draft counseling sites are described in Schiller and LeBlanc, *Exiled,* pp. 78–109. The "sit down and think" quote is from "If War Is Hell," Central Committee for Conscientious Objectors (CCCO) Booklet No. 6, May 1972. Prepping at the Jane Addams Center is described in Miller, p. 32. The Denver draft board quote is from O'Sullivan, p. 224, and the *Newsweek* quote from the November 1, 1975 issue. Alternative service dropout statistics are from Selective Service's *Semi-Annual Report* of January 1975, p. 82.

The Peard, "investigating hippies," medical counselor, IV-F fraud, and "acting crazy" quotes are from Suttler, pp. 4, 12, 66–67, and 74. The "draft immunization" quote is from Lynd, *We Won't Go,* p. 96. The Caplan quote comes from *Newsweek,* November 9, 1970, and the NATO data from Strickland, p. 121. The "chronically injured athlete" quote is from Marmion, p. 6; the "dental cop-out" quote from John Wheeler's testimony in the 1970 House Armed Services Hearings, p. 12504; and the homosexual fakery quote from Sanders, p. 86. The homosexual bluff case comes from Chapman, p. 190, and the Chicago activist case from Ferber and Lynd, *The Resistance,* p. 63. The racial statistics for physical exam rejections come from Little, p. 144. The Bourne quote is from a personal interview, and the "pinch the wrong foot" quote from Thomas Elias' testimony in the 1970 House Armed Services Hearings, p. 12502.

Safety in Service

The New York Jets case comes from the December 3, 1965 *New York Times.* All other football cases (except the Detroit Lions case) are from the December 9, 1966 issue of *Life,* pp. 44–47. The National Guard racial statistics come from Walton, *The Tarnished Shield,* p. 157, and the college graduate statistics from the 1976 Defense Manpower Commission's *Report to the President,* p. 159. The Defense Department's comment about National Guard riot control and the 1968 callup are described in the June 5, 1971 *National Journal,* pp. 1212–13. The draft motivation for National Guard and reserves enlistment is discussed in Walton, pp. 180–81; Hauser, *America's Army in Crisis,* p. 155; and Cortright, *Soldiers in Revolt,* p. 8.

The noncombat specialty assignment rates for the Spanish-American War, World War II, and the Vietnam war come from Glick, *Soldiers, Scholars, and Society,* p. 42. The noncombat specialty survey is from the Opinion Research Corporation's "Reaction of 17–21 Year Olds to Military Service," p. xix. The "don't enlist to fight" quote, the risk of death for draftees versus enlistees, and the description of computerized assignments come from Glass, "Defense Report," in the August 15, 1970 *National Journal.* The draft-motivated college-graduate statistic is from Helmer, *Bringing the War Home,* p. 340 (citing a 1968 Defense Department survey). The death-risk statistics are taken from Canby, *Military Manpower Procurement,* pp. 64–65. The Air Force recruiter quote is from *Amex-Canada*, vol. 2, no. 5, p. 27; the "no Viet Cong submarines" quote from the April 11, 1966 issue of *Newsweek;* and the "Action Army" quote from Barnes, *Pawns,* p. 71.

The West Point combat volunteers are described in Sanders, p. 119. The counseling manual quote comes from Rivkin, *GI Rights and Army Justice,* p. 54. The data on CO approvals come from Cortright, pp. 15–17; General Leo Benade's testimony in the 1974 House Amnesty Hearings, p. 545; and CCCO "News Notes" for Autumn 1975, p. 6. The court-imposed CO standards are described in Polner, *No Victory Parades,* pp. 95–97. The Pacific Counseling Service activities are discussed in Cortright, p. 17. The "Getting Out" pamphlet was published by the CCCO.

The cases of the fourteen-year veteran, the deliberate wounds, and the sergeant who refused antimalaria pills are from Polner, *No Victory Parades,* pp. 69 and 115. The Oberstrom case is from *Amex,* vol. 2, no. 1, p. 21, and the Patterson case from "This Suit Doesn't Fit, Sarge," a CCCO pamphlet. The risks facing combat troops are extrapolated from the data in Figure 3. The "search-and-evade" quote is taken from Walton, p. 237, and the $350 bounty case is from Linden, "The Demoralization of an Army," in the January 8, 1972 *Saturday Review.* The "CYA" quote comes from Hauser, p. 102; the firebase reenlistment study from Williams, pp. 267–68; and the "million-dollar wound" quote from Woodstone, *Up Against the War,* p. 158.

III | E V A D E R S

The Resistance

The Mario Savio quote comes from Ferber and Lynd, *The Resistance,* p. 277. The quote from the St. Louis pact of joint resistance is from Lynd, *We Won't Go,* p. 146. Staughton Lynd's target of 100,000 acts of resistance was first printed in the April 1967 edition of *Liberation* magazine. The "Call to Resist Illegitimate Authority" is cited in Woodstone, *Up Against the War,* p. 58. William Sessions' quote came from his testimony in the 1970 House Armed Services Hearings, p. 12852. The O'Brien case is cited as *U.S.* v. *O'Brien,* 391 U.S. 367 (1968). The antiwar civil liberties cases decided contrary to O'Brien include *Tinker* v. *Des Moines School District,* 393 U.S. 503 (1969); *Schacht* v. *U.S.,* 398 U.S. 58 (1970); *Cohen* v. *California,* 403 U.S. 15 (1971); *Smith* v. *Goguen,* 415 U.S. 566 (1974), and *Spence* v. *Washington,* 418 U.S. 405 (1974). The Catonsville Nine account comes from Ferber and Lynd, p. 202. and Sessions' testimony in the 1970 House Armed Services Hearings, p. 12842. The other draft board raids are from O'Sullivan and Meckler, *The Draft and Its Enemies,* p. 227; *Amex-Canada,* vol. 4, no. 3, p. 9; and Ferber and Lynd, p. 33. The other references to the resistance and antidraft activities are taken from Useem, *Conscription, Protest, and Social Conflict,* pp. 7, 54–55, 60–62, and 165–67.

Surveys and anecdotes about individual threats of draft defiance come from O'Sullivan and Meckler, p. 225; Ferber and Lynd, pp. 93 and 286; and Williams, *The New Exiles,* pp. 33 and 37. The Seeger case is cited as *U.S.* v. *Seeger,* 380 U.S. 163 (1965). The lawyer's handbook with four hundred defenses was *The Selective Service and Military Guide for Attorneys,* published by Curry First. The "fine-tooth comb" quote was by Sessions in his testimony before the 1970 House Armed Services Hearings, p. 12873. The discussion about Selective Service's delinquency practice is partly taken from Williams, p. 31, and Ferber and Lynd, p. 280.

Breakdown

The comment about being "laughed out of court in New York" was from Michael Kennedy, quoted in the June 1, 1970 *National Observer.* The San Francisco dismissals for out-of-district draft board members emanated from *U.S.* v. *Machado,* 306 F.Supp. 995 (ND Cal. 1969). The antiwar activist sent to prison for challenging the "imperialist" system had his conviction sustained in *Harris* v. *U.S.,* 412 F.2d 384 (9th Cir. 1969). The case of the Washington, D.C. draft resister who forum-shopped in San Francisco is cited in Frank Slatinshek's testimony at the 1970 House Armed Services Hearings, p. 12839. The statistics about San Francisco declinations and dismissals come from a table submitted by the Justice Department to the 1970 House Armed Services Hearings, pp. 12858–60. San Francisco U. S. Attorney James Browning is quoted in the June 1, 1970 *National Observer.* General Hershey's "call Ramsey" quote comes from a personal interview. Curtis Tarr's "splendid support" statement comes from the 1970 House Armed Services Hearings, p. 12480, and his "most difficult problems" statement comes from the Selective Service System's January 1972 *Semi-Annual Report,* p. 41. The William Sessions quote is taken from his testimony before the 1970 House Armed Services Hearings, pp. 12871–72. Congress' expediting of Selective Service cases came through 50 U.S.C. App. 462.

The three landmark cases are *Gutknecht* v. *U.S.,* 396 U.S. 295 (1970); *Welsh* v. *U.S.,* 398 U.S. 333 (1970); and *Mulloy* v. *U.S.,* 398 U.S. 410 (1970). The Cassius Clay (Muhammad Ali) case is cited as *Clay* v. *U.S.,* 403 U.S. 698 (1971). The principal retroactivity cases are *U.S.* v. *Fargnoli,* 458 F.2d 1237 (1st Cir. 1972), and *Andre* v. *Resor,* 313 F.Supp. 957 (N.D. Cal. 1970). All sentencing statistics come from the various annual reports of the Administrative Office of the United States Courts. Five-dollar fines and one-day probations were ordered in a number of cases, but the one-hour probation came in *U.S.* v. *Feliciano Grafals,* 309 F.Supp. 1292 (DPR 1970). Chuck Noell's quote from *We Are All POW's* comes from p. 77. All statistics about 1967–70 declinations and dismissals are from the Justice Department's table in the 1970 House Armed Services Hearings, pp. 12858–60. The juror who could not ignore the war was quoted in *Brotsky,* "The Trial of a Conscientious Objector," a chapter in *The Relevant Lawyers,* edited by Ann Fagan Ginger and the Seattle juror was quoted in *Amex,* vol. 3, no. 7, p. 41.

The Ones Who Got Away

The Morton case is drawn from *Imus* v. *U.S.*, 447 F.2d 1008 (10th Cir. 1973). The "forget it" quote comes from Thomas Elias' testimony before the 1970 House Armed Services Hearings, p. 12499. The Jones story comes from Lynn, *How to Stay Out of the Army*, p. 102. Nonregistration conviction data is extrapolated from the Presidential Clemency Board's survey of civilian applicants, described in Chapter 3 and Appendix C of its final report. The Gutknecht quote comes from *Check Out the Odds*, a 1971 manual he coauthored through the Twin Cities Resistance. The Ford Foundation account of nonregistrants is taken from its 1974 report on amnesty, "Veterans, Deserters, and Draft-Evaders—The Vietnam Decade," p. 44. The Walker case is described in *Check Out the Odds*. The Minnesota survey of nonregistrants was conducted by the state selective service office, with findings published in the 1972 Senate Selective Service and Amnesty Hearings, p. 378.

The two-million nonregistrant estimate was made by former Attorney General Ramsey Clark, quoted in Richard Lyons, "Full Amnesty Apparently Has a Long Way to Go," in the January 25, 1976 *New York Times*. The "fools coming to our door" quote is from Woodstone, p. 73. The Census Bureau's undercounting of young men is explained in its publication "Evaluation and Research Program: Estimates of Coverage of Population by Sex, Race, and Age" (1975), pp. 29–30. The Hooton case comes from Gutknecht, *Check Out the Odds*. Data pertaining to the Justice Department's prosecution of nonregistrants come from Assistant Attorney General Henry Peterson's testimony before the 1974 House Amnesty Hearings, p. 37. The nonregistrant statute of limitations decisions are *Toussie* v. *U.S.*, 397 U.S. 112 (1970), and *U.S.* v. *Richardson*, 514 F.2d 105 (3d. Cir. 1975).

William Sessions' quote is from his testimony before the 1970 House Armed Services Hearings, pp. 12871–72. Statistics on declinations and dismissals in nondraft cases are taken from the Census Bureau's 1973 *Statistical Abstract of the United States*, p. 152. Curtis Tarr's contention was made on p. 44 of Selective Service's July 1972 *Semi-Annual Report*. Robert Mardian and Walter Morse made their contentions before hearings of the Senate Judiciary Committee, Subcommittee on Courts and Civil Liberties (1972), pp. 164 and 204. Stuart Loory's quote comes from his book *Defeated: Inside America's Military Machine*, p. 246. The *New York Times* survey was reported on April 16, 1971, and described in the 1972 Senate Selective Service and Amnesty Hearings, p. 464. The capitulating draft resister is quoted in Lynn, p. 111. The "our job is to prosecute draft dodgers" quote is from Judson Bowles, head of the Criminal Division's Selective Service unit, recounted in Woodstone, p. 65. The Justice Department's twelve-month sample of reasons for case closings is described in a letter from Kevin Maroney to Senator Edward Kennedy, reprinted in the Senate Subcommittee Report, p. 395. An additional analysis of dropped cases was made by John Schultz in his testimony before the 1975 House Presidential Clemency Program Hearings, pp. 96–97.

The Wheels of Justice

The Horn, orthodontist, Black, Ramirez, Johnson, Jackson, Blass, Allen, Wilson, Eckhart, Taliaferro, Greene, Craig, Daley, Hare Krishna, heroin addict, post office examinee, and disappointed law student cases all come from the Presidential Clemency Board's final report—cases 3–5, 3–13, 3–22, 3–7, 3–29, 3–33, 4–7, 3–37, 3–15, 4–6, 3–3, 3–4, 3–31, 3–36, 3–50, 3–52, 3–54, and 3–53, respectively. Data about the characteristics of convicted draft offenders are also taken from Chapter 3 and Appendix C of the Clemency Board's report. The Young Republican case comes from William Sessions' testimony in the 1970 House Armed Services Hearings, p. 12843. The FBI discovery of draft evasion organizations are described in "The Draft: The Unjust Versus the Unwilling," an article in the April 11, 1966 edition of *Newsweek*. The corrupt local board member story is from the "Draft Counselor's Handbook" of the Philadelphia-based Central Committee for Conscientious Objectors (CCCO). The Sisson case is cited as *U.S.* v. *Sisson,* 399 U.S. 267 (1970).

The Walker and Peters cases come from Polner, *When Can I Come Home?* pp. 165 and 116–17. The Lavelle case came from Lynd, pp. 100–103; the Wagler case from Gaylin, *In the Service of Their Country,* p. 274; the Jenkins and premature baby cases from Woodstone, pp. 39–40 and 58; the Tucker case from an oral presentation before the February 26, 1976 ad hoc Amnesty Day hearings in the United States Senate (unpublished); the James case in the April 17, 1974 New York *Post;* the Buford case in Willard Gaylin's testimony before the 1972 Senate Selective Service and Amnesty Hearings, p. 296; and the Halsted case in Sanders, *The Draft and the Vietnam War,* p. 81. The Justice Department's treatment of Muslims is described in a letter from J. Oscar Smith, quoted in Lynd, p. 233. The Clay (Muhammad Ali) quote also comes from Lynd, pp. 230–34. Sentencing statistics are taken from the annual reports of the Administrative Office of the U.S. Courts. The "threaten society," "opposed to conscription," "sacrifice to their principles," General Hershey, and Brooklyn judge quotes all come from "Sentencing Selective Service Violators: A Judicial Wheel of Fortune," *Columbia Journal of Law and Social Problems,* vol. 5, no. 2 (1969), pp. 190, 189, 175, and 174. The "Decline and Fall" quote is from O'Sullivan and Meckler. Kevin Maroney's quote comes from his testimony before the 1972 Senate Selective Service and Amnesty Hearings, p. 276.

The encouraging words about prison life come from Tatum and Tuchinsky, *Guide to the Draft,* p. 266, and from the Friends Peace Committee pamphlet quoted in the December 9, 1966 *Life* magazine. The "I am lonely," "who'd ever thought," "friends ask us," "massive mill wheels," and "duck the bullets" quotes all come from Lynd, pp. 107, 114, 52, 59, and 64, respectively. The Vincent McGee quote comes from his testimony before the 1972 Senate Selective Service and Amnesty Hearings, p. 342. The "jolly good felon" and "Antigone" quotes are from Chuck Noell in *We Are All POW's,* a book he coauthored with Gary Wood, pp. 266 and 32. The Morris and Jones cases and all other quotes from incarcerated draft resisters come from Gaylin, pp. 36, 59, 68, 84, 123, 129, 154, 157, 182, 212, 239, 274–75, 278, and 284.

IV | DESERTERS

Over the Hill

The description of desertion by the Senate Armed Services Committee is from the 1968 Senate report, *Treatment of Deserters from Military Service,* March 11, 1969, pp. 7–8. The reference to World War II deserters sentenced to death is from Barnes, *Pawns,* p. 280. The 100-troop disciplinary breakdown is from Cortright, *Soldiers in Revolt,* pp. 24–25. The Mason, Meaks, Morehead, and Nolan cases are taken from the final report of the Presidential Clemency Board, cases 3–81, 3–75, 3–74, and 4–31. The Gilman case is from Hayes, *American Deserters in Sweden,* p. 93. The Saunder case is from *Amex-Canada* magazine, vol. 2, no. 7, p. 9. The Gruening quote is from the 1974 House Amnesty Hearings, pp. 221–22. The references to Civil War deserters is from the Clemency Board's final report, p. 366. The data about World War II deserters are from Helmer, *Bringing the War Home,* p. 38, and originate in the clerk's office of the U.S. Army Judiciary. The figures for Vietnam-era courts-martial for desertion to avoid hazardous duty are from data supplied by the Court of Military Appeals, interviews with the U.S. Army Judiciary, and the Clemency Board's final report. The references to the difficulty of deserting in Vietnam are from Emerick, *War Resisters in Canada,* p. 161, and *Amex,* vol. 3, no. 4, p. 27. The estimate of deserters in "AWOL alley" is from *Amex,* vol. 4, No. 3, p. 39. The Hansen case is from Emerick, pp. 76–77.

The McAllen quote is from the 1972 Senate Selective Service and Amnesty Hearings, p. 338. The quote about the California missile base comes from Emerick, p. 86. The estimate of military families below the poverty level is derived from figures in the *Congressional Quarterly,* April 3, 1970, p. 931. The Steiger quote comes from Stuart Loory, *Defeated,* pp. 191–192. The number of congressional complaints is from hearings by the Special Subcommittee on Recruiting and Retention of the House Armed Services Committee, 92d Congress, p. 8117, quoted by Cortright, p. 23. The quote from the Ford clemency program comes from the Defense Department Joint Report to the Service Secretaries, p. IV-2, and the Clemency Board statistic appears on p. 127 of its report. The Smith and Watson cases are from Sherrill, *Military Justice Is to Justice as Military Music Is to Music,* pp. 30–31. The composite deserter is derived from data in the Clemency Board report and Bell and Houston, *The Vietnam Era Deserter,* a 1976 report for the Army Research Institute. The official AWOL film is described in Barnes, pp. 105–6. The official comparison of AWOL during the Korean and Vietnam wars is from the testimony of General Leo Benade, Deputy Assistant Secretary of Defense, in the 1974 House Amnesty Hearings, p. 540. The Vietnam deserter figures are from Cortright, p. 13. The frequency of absence offenses and their manpower equivalents are derived from data in the Senate Armed Services Committee report, pp. 24–25.

The Bottom Third

Much of the discussion in this chapter is based on Starr, *The Discarded Army*, pp. 185–97, and Barnes, pp. 66–68 and 258–59 (Matts case). The Peters case is from the Clemency Board report, case 3–62. The reference to Ginzburg's findings on high-school dropouts is from his *Patterns of Performance*, pp. 113–14. The discussion of pre-Vietnam military standards is from Gerhardt, *The Draft and Public Policy*, p. 220, and the Citizens Advisory Panel on Military Manpower Procurement, Report to the House Armed Services Committee, February 28, 1967, p. 9. The 1965 survey on black motivation for enlisting is from Little, *Selective Service and American Society*, p. 148. The Moynihan quotes are taken from Morris, *Why Draft Repeal?* p. 110, and Starr, p. 186. The General Nickerson and *Army Times* quotes are also from Starr, pp. 185 and 191–92. The Grant case is from Sherrill, p. 25. The Polner quote is from pp. 80–81 of his book *No Victory Parades*. The characteristics of Project 100,000 men are taken from Barnes, pp. 66–68; the Clemency Board report, Chapter 3; and Bell and Houston, *The Vietnam Era Deserter*, a 1976 Army Research Institute report. The 1964 study of Category IV military assignments is from Cortright, p. 195. Disciplinary problems of Category IV troops are from Sherrill, pp. 219–22; Clemency Board data; and 1972 House Defense Appropriations Hearings, p. 582. Data on post-Vietnam levels of Category IV are from Roger Kelley. The quote from Colonel Hays is from Tax, *The Draft*, p. 15.

Kooks, Heads, Brothers

Much of the material in this chapter comes from Haynes Johnson and George Wilson's *Army in Anguish*. The quotations that begin the chapter are from p. 116; the Froehlke quote is from p. 154; the references by the employee at the Vietnam rehabilitation center are from pp. 26–27; the quotes about black attitudes by the battalion commander and at the counseling session in Germany appear at pp. 37–38 and 48–49; and the quote about black views of military justice as white racism is from p. 47.

The general's description of Vietnam-era soldiers as "kooks" is from Finn, *Conscience and Command*, p. 15. The Cortright quote, the data on daily heroin usage in Vietnam in 1971, the discussion of drug treatment programs, and the references to the Black Caucus and NAACP racial survey are all from Cortright, pp. 31, 156, 174–75, and 207–13. The quote from Ward Just and the rest of that paragraph are taken from his book *Military Men*, p. 73. The data on marijuana usage are from a report of the Human Relations Research Organization, "Survey of Drug Abuse," pp. 72–78. The Harris survey is from Helmer, p. 190. The quote from the drug counselor comes from an article by Linden in the *Saturday Review* of January 8, 1972. The costs of marijuana and the statistics on drug enforcement in Vietnam are from the report of Army Judge Advocate General George Prugh, *Law at War*, pp. 106–7. The figures on pot smoking in 1967 and 1971 and the study of the demographics of addicts are from Helmer, pp. 75 and 87. The paragraph on alcoholism is from Loory, p. 204. The 1972 data on the usage and cost of heroin in Vietnam and the U.S. are from the *Congressional Quarterly* of January 22, 1972, pp. 145–46. The data on the Laird drug discharge upgrade program is from Glass, "Defense Report," in the *National Journal* of August 8, 1970, p. 1776. General Kerwin's quote comes from 1972 House Defense Appropriations Hearings, p. 571.

The pejorative description of black soldiers is from Glick, *Soldiers, Scholars and Society,* pp. 28–29. The 1971 Department of Defense racial survey is cited in the *Congressional Quarterly,* September 18, 1971 at p. 1943. The Urban League reference is from the testimony of Ronald Brown at the 1974 House Amnesty Hearings, pp. 411–12. The references to the Defense Department *Task Force Report on Military Justice* are from vol. I, p. 32, and vol. II, p. 14.

Vietnam and Back

The "tore the fabric" quote is from General Walter Kerwin in his testimony during the 1972 House Defense Appropriations Hearings, p. 554. The survey of attitudes toward the war is from Starr, *The Discarded Army,* p. 23, and the Polner quote appears on p. 36 of *No Victory Parades.* The Pacek story appears in *We Are All POW's* by Chuck Noell and Gary Wood, pp. 24–25. The material on prosecutions for antiwar activity is from Polner, pp. 98, 105–12. The Chadwick, Hodgkins, Dantlee, Cutter, Rainwater, McKuen, Jollie, Stokes, and Barajian cases are all taken from the Clemency Board final report, cases 3-78, 3-77, 3-92, 4-37, 3-83, 3-89, 3-93, 3-91, 4-70, and 7, respectively.

The statistics on fragging between 1969 and 1971 and the example of the general's parade are from Johnson and Wilson, pp. 92, 110–11. The raid on the officers' club and the quote that follows are taken from Linden's article in the *Saturday Review* of January 8, 1972. The story of the company that refused to retrieve the documents is from Hauser, *America's Army in Crisis,* p. 99. The Starr quote appears on p. 28 and the Emerick quote on pp. 161–62 of their respective books. The Cannille and Rathbone stories are from Barnes, p. 258, and Williams, *The New Exiles,* pp. 296–97 and 304. The Johnson story is from Killmer, *They Can't Go Home Again,* p. 81. The Lee story is from an article by Austin Scott, "Deserters Live Openly in the U.S.," in the Washington *Post* of October 12, 1974. The Johnson-Wilson quote appears on p. 73 of their book. The quote about military deserters processed under the Ford program is from the Defense Department *Report to the Service Secretaries,* p. IV-4. The Barnes quote appears on p. 124 of his book.

Canceling Them Out

The Shoup story is related in Sherrill, pp. 218–19. The 1971 study is *Leadership and Situational Factors Related to AWOL,* by McCubbin, U.S. Army CTF, Ft. Riley, Kansas, p. ii. The Westmoreland quote is cited in Johnson and Wilson, p. 81, and the Kerwin quote is from the 1972 House Defense Appropriations Hearings on Department of Defense Appropriations, p. 603. The references to young officers' attitudes toward the war is from Johnson and Wilson, pp. 119–20. General Berg's "cancel . . . out" quote is from the 1968 Senate Deserter Hearings, p. 66. The summary history of the military discharge system is from Admiral John Finneran's testimony of November 5, 1975, before the House Armed Services Committee (unpublished). The defense of the characterized discharge system was made by General Leo Benade, quoted in Frederick Smalkin's "Administrative Separations: The Old Order Changeth," Department of Army pamphlet 27–50–17. The reference to the deterrent effect of bad discharges is from the 1971 McCubbin study, p. 26. The quote from the *Report of the Task Force on Military Justice* appears at p. 33 of Vol. II. Leo Benade's explanation of the SPN system is from the 1974 House Amnesty Hearings, p. 542. The list of SPNs is reprinted in the *ACLU Practice Manual on Discharge Upgrading* by Addlestone and Hewman, p. 293. The quote by the Macy's representative is from Congressman John Downey's testimony at the 1975 House Armed Services Hearings. The veteran's story that follows is from testimony at the 1974 House Amnesty Hearings, p. 289. The figures on the disparity of discharges are from the *Task Force Report,* p. 355.

The Banks, Dodson, Sanders, Barnes, and Cook cases are taken from the Clemency Board report, cases 3–114, 3–121, 4–36, 3–116, and 3–117, respectively. The Duke case is from Loory, p. 200. Data pertaining to employer discrimination against veterans with bad discharges are from the Clemency Board report, p. 403. The NCO's gripe is from Johnson and Wilson, pp. 131–33. The observation on the difficulty of trials in Vietnam is from *Law at War,* p. 198. The statistics on Army Chapter 10 discharges are from the Department of Defense Office of Manpower and Reserve Affairs, reprinted in Baskir and Strauss, *Reconciliation After Vietnam,* p. 123. The Army warning against excessive use of Chapter 10's is from a *New York Times* story of September 10, 1972, quoted in *Amex,* vol. 3, No. 6, p. 40. The quote about undesirable discharges is from Fred Halstead, *GI's Speak Out,* a CCCO reprint, pp. 46–47. The story of the two GIs from Sweden comes from "Guide for the AWOL GI," a CCCO pamphlet. The comparison between undesirable discharges and punitive discharges is derived from unpublished Clemency Board statistics.

V | EXILES

On the Run

The flight of 80,000 Tories is described in Duscha, "Amnesty," in the December 24, 1972, *New York Times Magazine,* p. 15. Descriptions of the Udall and Agnew nephews are presented in *Amex-Canada* magazine, vol. 2, no. 6, p. 25, and vol. 2, no. 3, p. 20. Data about the proportion of draft and military offenders who took flight come from Chapter 3 of the Presidential Clemency Board's final report. The "self-retired veterans" quote comes from *Amex,* vol. 3, no. 4, p. 37. The listing of the positions of trust held by fugitive deserters comes from the Fort Harrison *Report to the Service Secretaries* (on the implementation of Presidential Proclamation 4313), p. VII-w.

The $25 bounty for captured deserters is described in Franks, *Waiting Out a War*, p. 214. The Berkeley City Council's asylum policy is mentioned in Loory, *The Defeated*, p. 250. The Seattle steelworker case comes from Fialka, Washington *Star*, Oct. 6, 1974; the oil wildcatter case from Scott, Washington *Post*, Oct. 12, 1974; and the termite case from Woodstone, *Up Against the War*, p. 80. The Santa Claus case, "little Canada," and the government's prosecution of those who "enticed" desertion are discussed in *Amex*, vol. 2, no. 2, p. 8; vol. 3, no. 7, p. 49; and vol. 2, no. 4, p. 25. The San Francisco "GI Help" program is described in Ferber and Lynd, *The Resistance*, pp. 231–32. The "deserter inducement programs" quote comes from Major Donald Kennedy's testimony at the 1968 Senate Military Deserters hearings.

Taking Exile

The capsule descriptions of Brazil, Haiti, and Venezuela come from Schiller and Leblanc, *Exiled*, pp. 11–15. The "brain drain" comment comes from a Canadian immigration official quoted in Woodstone, p. 92. The Mitchell Sharp quote is from *Amex*, vol. 1, no. 7, p. 8. The "frontier" and "big beautiful jail" quotes come from Lynd, *We Won't Go*, pp. 115–19. The Danielson, Csikor, Peters, and Swedish hijacking cases are all from *Amex*, vol. 5, no. 6; vol. 2, no. 2, p. 14; vol. 2, no. 2, p. 14; and vol. 2, no. 9, p. 14. Canadian immigration rules are described in Harrop Freeman's testimony before the 1972 Senate Selective Service and Amnesty Hearings, pp. 452–55, and Tatum and Tuchinsky, *Guide to the Draft*, p. 239. The "checking into a hotel" quote comes from "Amnesty for War Exiles," *Newsweek*, Jan. 17, 1972. The advertisement for Canadian women is described in *Amex*, vol. 2, no. 8, p. 29. The number of illegal immigrants amnestied in 1972 comes from an oral report from the Canadian Embassy in Washington, D.C.

The account of draft-avoiding Swedes, the story of the one-way SAS passenger, the Dodson case, the quotes from Swedish officials, and the description of welfare benefits for newly arriving exiles in Sweden are all from Hayes, *American Deserters in Sweden*, pp. 41–42, 100, and 141. The "live like human beings," "Al Capone," and "partying" quotes come from Whitmore, *Memphis-Nam-Sweden*, p. 169. The exile delegation to Denmark is described in Franks, p. 151. The accusation that Sweden was "subsidizing" desertion comes from the 1968 Senate *Treatment of Deserters* Report, p. 12.

Richard Nixon's "those few hundreds" quote is taken from the 1974 House Amnesty Hearings, p. 729, and the 100,000 estimate comes from materials submitted by the Amnesty Committee of the Center for Pursuit of Peace in the 1974 House Amnesty Hearings, p. 622. The triple-exile (Israeli volunteer) story comes from "Amnesty Plan —Story of Two Local Men," Ann Arbor *News*, August 17, 1975. Holland's subsidy for draft resisters, Australian and Vietnamese exiles in Canada, the "Bobby Kennedy" quote, the violent radical quote, the Puerto Rican accused murderer case, the antiwar editors in Canada, and the *Life* magazine case all come from *Amex:* vol. 2, no. 4, p. 13; vol. 2, no. 5, p. 23; vol. 2, no. 8, p. 5; vol. 2, no. 6, p. 17; vol. 3, no. 6, p. 53; and vol. 2, no. 3, p. 29. The four deserter categories are described in Loh, "An Analysis of Amnesty,"

Journal of Social Issues, vol. 31 (1975), p. 158. The Brooks case and the fact that one-third of all exiles qualified for deferments come from Emerick, *War Resisters in Canada,* pp. 72 and 81. The Britt and Sheehan cases are from Williams, *The New Exiles,* p. 337. The Brophy quote is taken from the 1972 Senate Selective Service and Amnesty Hearings, p. 319. The fact that half of all deserters never asked for help before leaving is from Bell and Houston, *The Vietnam Era Deserter,* a report of the Army Research Institute, July 1976.

American-Canadians and American-Swedes

The "runaway slave" quote, the vitriolic family letter, the "brand new kind of immigrant" quote, the Toronto *Daily Star* editorial, the *McQueen* and *Explosion* episodes, the "pigs" quote, the Toronto *Telegram* editorials, the Dow chemical demonstration, the "vicious whispered lobbying" quote, and the "draft dodger chauvinism" quote all come from *Amex:* vol. 2, no. 7, p. 13; vol. 2, no. 3, p. 27; vol. 2, no. 7, p. 7; vol. 2, no. 7, p. 6; vol. 2, no. 2, p. 23; vol. 2, no. 4, p. 25; vol. 2, no. 9, p. 5; vol. 2, no. 6, p. 14; vol. 2, no. 2, p. 5; and vol. 2, no. 9, p. 6. The Levine quote comes from Levine, "American Exiles in Canada: A Social and Psychological Follow Up," *Psychiatric Opinion,* November 1974, p. 24. The descriptions of vagabond life, Swedish antiwar sentiment, Swedish headlines, magazine quotes, and fast cars and unleashed dogs come from Franks, pp. 104 and 163–72. The facts about criminal activity and deportation come from Pat Buchanan, "The Facts on Exiles," *New York Times,* February 20, 1973 (quoting William Leth, Swedish Director of Immigration). The "stay cool" quote is from Whitmore, p. 185. The five suicides are described in Hayes, p. 190; Franks, p. 188; and *Amex,* vol. 2, no. 6, p. 24, and vol. 2, no. 9, p. 26.

Coming Home

The "American Dream" quote comes from Noell and Wood, *We Are All POW's,* p. 43. The Molotov-cocktails discussion and "rebellion against authority" quote are in Taylor, "Draft Dodgers in Canada," *The Reporter,* May 2, 1968. The cancellation of the Nixon trip, the story of the Blaine siege, the "Ho Chi Minh Trail," the Poirrot case, and the Kallen and First letters are from *Amex:* vol. 3, no. 4, p. 13; vol. 6, no. 6, p. 12; vol. 3, no. 6, p. 38; vol. 3, no. 5, p. 4; vol. 3, no. 7, p. 4. The Brasile case is from "Amnesty for War Exiles," *Newsweek,* Jan. 17, 1972. Operation CHAOS is described in the 1976 Senate report, *Intelligence Activities and the Rights of Americans,* pp. 99–102. The Brown case is described in Franks, pp. 57–58, and the Lovett case in Whitmore, p. 144. American embassy activities in Sweden, the China deserter case, the fate of the 20 exiled deserters, the $15 fine, the Inouye quote, the Fitt quote, and the fact that only 2 of the 20 returning exiles were sent to Vietnam are all from the 1968 Senate Military Deserters hearings, testimony from Alfred Fitt (Defense Department), Frederick Smith (State Department), and Commander Carlton Wilgus (Navy), pp. 5, 26, 41, and 65. The critical reaction to the Brown case comes from the 1968 Senate *Treatment of Deserters* Report, p. 19. The fact that fewer than 150 former exiles went to military prison comes from the 1971 House Administrative Discharges Hearings, p. 5872. The discharges *in absentia* are described in a written submission from General Leo Benade in the 1972 Senate Selective Service and Amnesty Hearings, p. 385. The Tatum quote comes from Tatum and Tuchinsky, p. 233. The calculation that 13,000 cases were dropped comes from a survey of about 3,000 telephone inquiries received by the clemency information center in the weeks following the list's release. The "tears of rage" quote is from John Schultz's testimony before the House Subcommittee on Courts and Civil Liberties, p. 205. The immigration statute barring reentry of aliens who avoided military service is U.S.C. App. 1182(a) (22). The "Man, it'll weight you down" quote is from Hayes, p. 43.

Morality and Mythology

The Australian amnesty experience is from "The Australian Clemency Program" by Wil Ebel in Appendix G of the Clemency Board's Final Report, pp. 379 ff. Tom Hayden's call for amnesty and the exiles' responses are from *Amex-Canada*, vol. 2, no. 4, p. 10, and vol. 2, no. 5, p. 3. The Swedish exile's observation is quoted in Hayes, *American Deserters in Sweden*, p. 46. The 1972 *Amex* proamnesty quote is from vol. 3, no. 4, pp. 44–45. The "moral point" quote is from former Oregon Congressman Charles Porter, who headed a group called "Amnesty Now," quoted in *Newsweek* of January 17, 1972. The "powerful tool" quote is from Shank, "Amnesty: Remembering the Past" in *Win* magazine, November 13, 1975. The "principled fight" *Amex* quote is from vol. 5, no. 3. The activist's quote on the larger significance of amnesty is from *Amex*, vol. 3, no. 6, p. 5. The "centrist core" quote is from William Yolton's testimony in the 1974 House Amnesty Hearings, p. 717. Mary McGrory's observation is from her column of March 12, 1974. The Agnew comments are from his remarks at a VFW congressional dinner of March 6, 1973; a VFW national convention on August 25, 1972; a Lincoln's Day dinner quoted in *Amex*, vol. 3, no. 7, p. 23; and a statement of February 10, 1970, cited in Lifton, *Home from the War*, pp. 369–71. Richard Nixon's "most immoral thing" quote and Agnew's "malcontents" quote are from Lifton, *Home from the War*, pp. 369–71. Bella Abzug's and Charles Colson's remarks are from the March 11, 1973 issue of the Baltimore *Sun*, and Pat Buchanan's comments from "The Facts on Exiles" in the February 20, 1973 *New York Times*. The Legion spokesman is John Geiger, former national commander, testifying at the 1972 Senate Selective Service and Amnesty Hearings, p. 242. Hempstone's column is from the Washington *Star* of March 20, 1974. The origins of Senator Taft's bill are described in the May 5, 1972 *Saturday Review*. Nixon's comment on the "Peace Corps junket" is quoted in the 1974 House Amnesty Hearings, p. 697. Froehlke's position is documented in his testimony before the 1974 House Amnesty Hearings, p. 371, and Laird's position in a letter to VFW Commander Ray Soden, reprinted in the 1974 House Amnesty Hearings, p. 339.

Clemency, Not Amnesty

Information regarding the formulation and operation of the final clemency program is largely based on the personal observations of the authors; the Clemency Board final report; the report to the service secretaries of the (Defense Department) Joint Alternative Service Board (April 11, 1975); the *After Action Report* by the Office of the Army Deputy Chief of Staff for Personnel (October, 1975); the hearings by the 1974 House Presidential Clemency Program Hearings and Report; and the General Accounting Office's 1977 report on the clemency program.

President Ford's speech to the VFW Chicago convention outlining his intentions on clemency was on August 19, 1974. On September 16, 1974, he sent a message to the VFW national commander further explaining his program. The "very serious crimes" quote is from the November 1974 issue of *Amex*. The excerpts from the Clemency Board report appear on page 1. The *Post* and *Bulletin* comments appear in their editorials of September 18, 1974. The comment by the draft resister's mother is from *Newsweek,* September 30, 1974. The material on the Truman board comes from its final report, reprinted in the 1974 Senate Clemency Program Practices and Procedures Hearings on p. 255, and from Harrop Freeman's "Amnesty Now," a CCCO pamphlet. The survey on knowledge of eligibility for the program is described in the Clemency Board's final report, pp. 20–23. Attorney General Saxbe's comment is cited in an article by Robert Seeley, "No Amnesty," a CCCO pamphlet. The draft resister's criticism of the program is from Noell and Woods, *We Are All POW's,* p. 10. President Ford's observation on the results of his program was made to a group of Durham, New Hampshire, students on February 8, 1975. Chairman Goodell's observations were made at his press conference of January 15, 1976. The San Diego exile's comments are from a letter to a 1975 issue of *Playboy* magazine. Hoffman's warning is from his news conference of October 3, 1974, reprinted in the *New York Times* of October 7, 1974. The Walters case was related in Senate Ad Hoc Amnesty Day Hearings, February 26, 1975. The surrendering draft exile's experiences appeared in *Newsweek,* September 30, 1974. The Arizona resolution is number 2004, filed April 10, 1975. The Palm Beach story is related in Noell and Woods, p. 79.

Vernon Jordan's comment was published in "Amnesty Still an Issue," an Urban League column reprinted by the National Council for Universal, Unconditional Amnesty. The estimate of the overall cost of the Clemency Board was disclosed in an interview with an official of the Office of Management and Budget. The White House claim of executive privilege on the GAO inquiry is alluded to in the GAO report, p. 2. The Gallup poll results are reprinted in the Clemency Board report, p. 389. President Ford's remark on his program came in an interview in *Newsweek,* October 4, 1976. The new demands of the amnesty groups are from *Amex,* vol. 5, no. 3, 1974. James Wagonseller's comment appears in the *Congressional Quarterly,* September 20, 1974. President

Ford's exchange with Jane Hart and his later clemency order are related in the Washington *Post* of December 29, 1976, and January 19, 1977.

Blanket Pardons

The resolution of the AUSA was reported in the *Army Times* article "Clemency Board Seen as King," September 25, 1974. The "amnesty" versus "pardon" debate is best explained in the Supreme Court case of *Burdick* v. *U.S.*, 236 U.S. 79 (1915), and the *New Republic* of June 26, 1976. Carter's Iowa remarks are reprinted in a March, 1976 compilation of campaign statements issued by his campaign office. His "get the Vietnamese war over with" and "defecting from military service" statements are reprinted in the Washington *Post* editorial of January 9, 1977. The Hart quote and Howard Johnson's place mat are described in "The Truth about Deserters," a CCCO pamphlet. The inclusion of deserters in the amnesty issue was discussed in the testimony of Amherst professor Henry Steele Commager at the 1972 Senate Selective Service and Amnesty Hearings, p. 182. Carter's discussion with the *Post* editors is included in that paper's editorial of January 9, 1977. The debate at the Democratic Platform Committee is summarized in the *New Republic,* June 26, 1976. Carter's promise of a blanket pardon came in his American Legion speech of August 24, 1976, and Dole's reply came at the same forum on the following day. Reactions to Carter's early intentions are described in the *New York Times* of August 26, 1976.

The preinauguration report that Carter would include military offenders appeared in the *New York Times* of December 17, 1976. *Pravda*'s comment was reported on CBS radio on January 30, 1977. The reactions of Goldwater, the Republican National Committee, the VFW, and the amnesty community are quoted in the *New York Times* of January 22, 1977, the Washington *Post* of February 3, 1977, and the January 31, 1977 issue of *Newsweek.* The tally of pardon certificate requests comes from the U.S. pardon attorney's office, and the tally of returning exiles from the Immigration and Naturalization Service. All other tallies come from the Washington *Post* of October 5, 1977.

The Next War

Congressman Dorn's remark is quoted in the *Congressional Quarterly,* October 14, 1972, p. 2663, and Congressman Montgomery's in the *Congressional Record* of January 11, 1977, p. 11268. Kirbo's comment was related by a participant at the meeting. The Mennonite position is in a written statement submitted to the 1972 Senate Selective Service and Amnesty Hearings, p. 102. The Gillette case is cited as *Gillette* v. *U.S.,* 401 U.S. 437 (1971). The Gates report is formally known as the *Report of the President's Commission on an All-Volunteer Armed Force,* February 20, 1971. The Hauser quote is from his book *America's Army in Crisis,* pp. 158–59.

The costs of separating modern-day soldiers were estimated by Roger Kelley, former assistant secretary of defense for manpower. Category IV information is from the Commission's Defense Manpower report, p. 159, and Dr. William King's February 1977 report to the Senate Armed Services Committee, "Achieving America's Goals: Rational Service or the All-Volunteer Armed Force?" pp. 15 and 25. Information about the operation of the discharge review boards was obtained through interviews with Defense Department officials. Future manpower levels, current black representation in the volunteer army, and reserve problems are described in the Defense Manpower Commission's report, pp. 160 and 387, and "Achieving America's Goals," pp. 18 and 23. The Commission's "sudden major hostilities" quote comes from p. 427 of its report. Brehm's observation appears in the 1976 House Selective Service System Hearings, pp. 2 and 169. The Vietnam generation's attitudes about the draft and military are taken from the Notre Dame survey. The plans for the 1976 registration and Byron Pepitone's comment on the impact of a return to the draft are from personal interviews. Current contingency plans for emergency mobilization and the account of World War I and II registration campaigns are taken from the testimony of Byron Pepitone and Congressman Robert Drinan before the 1976 House Armed Services Hearings, pp. 28 and 104. The Bingham plan is described in his testimony in the 1970 House Armed Services Hearings, p. 12763. The figures for high school drop-outs come from a Department of Defense press release of November 15, 1977.

VII | LEGACIES

The Noell quote is from p. 82 of *We Are All POW's,* which he coauthored with Gary Wood. The Chicano's comment is from the Washington *Post* of January 23, 1977, and the Ohio veteran's is from Johnson and Wilson, *Army in Anguish,* p. 117. The "Harry" and "Resist the Draft" quotes are from Polner, *No Victory Parades,* pp. 77 and 29. The quotes from Starr and Bourne appear in Starr, *The Discarded Army,* pp. 33 and 35. Correia's and Foote's recollections are from personal communications with the authors; Fallows' story originally appeared at greater length in his article "What Did You Do in the Class War, Daddy," in the *Washington Monthly* of October 1975, and has been excerpted with his permission.

Figure 1: Vietnam Generation

¹The Vietnam generation is defined to include anyone who was of draft-eligible age during the Vietnam war. Draft-eligible age is defined as 19, the age at which induction was possible, and up to (but not including) 26, the age at which induction was no longer a threat to anyone other than medical specialists. Specifically, those who were ages 23 through 38 on June 30, 1977, are considered part of the Vietnam generation. It should be noted that 18-year-olds did fight in Vietnam, but because of the phased pullout of American troops during 1972 and 1973, it is unlikely that more than a very few were to be part of the Vietnam generation as defined here. A much larger number of older

military personnel served in Vietnam, and they are excluded from the statistics wherever possible.

[2]These base statistics come from data in the *Statistical Abstract of the United States* (1973), Table 35, p. 31. To the base figures in the *Statistical Abstract* must be added 1.15%, to include those who died before the census was taken. According to the Census Bureau's "Estimates of Coverage of Population by Sex, Race, and Age: Demographic Analysis" (February 1974), the 1970 census undercounted the 16–31 male population by 860,000–960,000 and the 16–31 female population by about half that amount. To account for this underenumeration problem, the "men" and "women" tallies are augmented by 900,000 and 450,000, respectively.

[3]This is an error factor that cannot be accounted for elsewhere. Some of the statistics shown in these charts are quite precise, while others are extrapolations from a limited amount of clear evidence. The fact that the error factor shown here is small (0.5%) does not mean that all other statistics are nearly correct; it simply means that if one statistic is too high, another must be too low.

[4]Historical data are included from July 1, 1960, assuming that the average individual was drafted during his twenty-first year in the early 1960s. From July 1, 1964, through July 1, 1973, 1,773,000 were drafted. The others were drafted before then, some serving during the Vietnam war. *Selected Manpower Statistics,* DOD-OASD (Comptroller), May 1975, pp. 51–54.

[5]See Figure 3.

[6]See Figure 6.

[7]See *Selected Manpower Statistics,* p. 108, and *Statistical Abstract of the United States* (1973), Table 447, p. 275. National Guard and reserves computations assume 19-year-old enlistments, so historical data from July 1, 1959, are used.

[8]See Figure 2.

[9]See Figure 4.

[10]See Figure 8.

[11]No comprehensive data of any kind can enumerate nonregistrants. Most efforts to measure them have used census data, but the analysis is very unconvincing. Many— perhaps most—of the individuals who never registered for the draft are the same ones who are never counted by the census. The only alternative to analyzing aggregate statistics is to sample. A sample of 1,586 males of formerly draft-eligible age was surveyed in Washington, D.C., South Bend, and Ann Arbor; roughly one-fourth of the respondents were blacks or members of other minority groups. That sample found a number of nonregistrants, distributed racially as follows:

white	0.6%
black	3.9%
other	1.7%

When these percentages are applied to overall racial data for the United States, it appears that the numbers of nonregistrants, by racial group, are as follows:

white   130,000
black   110,000
other   10,000

It should be noted that the questionnaires of nonregistrants were carefully scrutinized to assure the authenticity of the response (e.g., to screen out cases of individuals who never registered for the draft because they enlisted at a young age, or draft-ineligible aliens who were not required to register). For base racial data, see *Statistical Abstract of the United States* (1973), Table 32, p. 30.

[12]Similar data about unreported draft offenses were obtained through these questionnaires. Five such individuals were found, all of them white. Two had destroyed their draft cards, two had refused induction, and one had failed to perform alternative service as a condition of conscientious objection. This enables an estimate of 110,000 unreported draft offenders to be derived. See *ibid.* for base data.

[13]See *Selected Manpower Statistics.* The number has been derived by extrapolation and comparison with other military manpower data in that same volume. It appears that roughly 190,000 served during the Vietnam era and 60,000 before the Vietnam era. These numbers are inexact, because separate enlistment and discharge data could not be found for each year of the period.

[14]These official statistics were obtained from Women's Affairs Division of the Department of Defense Public Affairs Office.

[15]At the Clemency Board, approximately 0.1% of all applicants with bad discharges were women. At the Ft. Harrison (DOD) clemency program, 0.14% were women. These proportions indicate that women may have received about 500 of the 563,000 less-than-Honorable discharges of the Vietnam era.

[16]All of these are derivative, calculated by adding or subtracting all other displayed statistics from the appropriate base statistics.

Figure 2: Civilian Avoiders

[1]The Vietnam generation is defined here to include individuals aged 19 to 34 on June 30, 1973, yet the last persons to face induction were those who turned 20 during the 1972 calendar year. Although the 3,020,000 persons who turned 19 after January 1, 1972, could have joined the military and gone to Vietnam, possibly spurred by draft pressure, none would have been drafted. Apparently, 165,000 guardsmen and reservists and 310,000 active duty personnel belonged to this age group. The remainder, 2,545,-000, avoided military service because of their young age. See *Statistical Abstract of the United States* (1973), Table 81, p. 59, and *Selected Manpower Statistics,* pp. 38 and 108.

²This assumes that 21 was the average age of induction throughout the era. Accidents accounted for most of these deaths. For base data, see *Statistical Abstract of the United States* (1973), Table 81, p. 59.

³This tally was derived through computations based upon the statistics in the *Semi-Annual Reports* of the Director of Selective Service throughout the lottery years (1970–1972). Table 4 in each issue lists the total number of registrants, and enables a number of calculations to be made. When one subtracts the number overage or underage, presently or formerly in military service, deferred or exempted for any reason, unclassified, or in a holding classification, one can determine the number of I-A registrants vulnerable to the draft. For example, in 1970 there were 1,175,000 such individuals. In 1970, the lottery cutoff was 195, so one can conclude that those with higher numbers—47% of all those in the eligible pool—were not drafted because of their high lottery numbers. Comparable analysis was done for each year, based upon its lottery cutoff.

⁴The number of individuals with vulnerable lottery numbers (125 and below) who were benefited by this loophole cannot be exactly ascertained, but one measure is available. Using the same analysis described in note 3, one can trace the impact of the draft on all persons with I-A status on December 31, 1971. Only 153,000 were drafted in 1971 out of 1,132,000 persons with vulnerable lottery numbers who were classified I-A. After one accounts for unsuccessful induction attempts, active appeals, and draft-induced enlistments (which can be estimated as the same proportion of draft calls in 1971 as in 1969, 1970, and 1972), 633,000 individuals escaped the draft for no accountable reason. They were the apparent beneficiaries of the "lottery loophole."

⁵*Semi-Annual Report of the Director of Selective Service,* January–June 1973, App. 8 (p. 52) and App. 13 (p. 55). The tally shown includes rejections from July 1, 1960, through June 30, 1973; this assumes that the typical individual is examined during his twenty-first year. Age statistics are not widely available, but see *ibid.,* p. 54. The tally also assumes that IV-F and I-Y exemptions, once given, are not rescinded. They could be rescinded, but this was very rarely done during the Vietnam war. The rejections at the induction station usually involved volunteers who had never taken preinduction physical exams, but some individuals failed their induction physicals after having passed their preinduction physicals.

⁶Year-by-year breakdowns of the reasons for disqualification were not available, but good cross-sectional data existed for July–December of 1969 in the *Semi-Annual Report of the Director of Selective Service,* July–December, 1969, Table 5, p. 19. Data for the 1950–69 period is available in the same table, but it would include too much extraneous data. With a 46% preinduction rejection rate and a 19% induction rejection rate, 1969 was close enough to the mean for the Vietnam era to give some validity to its cross-sectional data. See the appendices cited in note 1.

⁷A "moral" defect includes evidence of prior association with subversive organizations, substantial criminal record, prior discharge from the military under other than

honorable conditions, or related reasons making an individual "not qualified for administrative reason(s)." *Ibid.,* p. 19.

[8]Assuming that the typical individual received the exemption during his twenty-first year, data from July 1, 1960 through June 30, 1973 are used for I-O classifications. *Semi-Annual Report of the Director of Selective Service,* January–June, 1975, App. 27, p. 82.

[9]Conscientious objectors were classified I-O and then reclassified I-W if they began performing alternative service. Selective Service data indicate that 59% of all conscientious objectors completed alternative service. To account for two years of alternative service, data from July 1, 1963 through June 30, 1976 are used (including the 124 individuals still doing alternative service on the latter date). *Semi-Annual Report of the Director of Selective Service,* January–June, 1975, App. 27, p. 82.

[10]It is very difficult to ascertain how many individuals failed to complete an obligation of alternative service. Before 1970, it must be assumed that all conscientious objectors had an obligation to perform alternative service, because all would have otherwise been inducted (aside from the occasional case of incipient hardship or physical defect which would warrant reclassification). After the draft lottery, many conscientious objectors did not have to perform alternative service because of high lottery numbers. An eight-month sample of 110,000 conscientious objectors with lottery numbers indicated that 43% of them had lottery numbers sufficiently high to free them from an alternative service obligation. *Semi-Annual Report of the Director of Selective Service,* January–June, 1971, p. 58. This percentage did not vary much between 1969 (when the cutoff number was 195) and 1970 (when the cutoff was 125). Assuming this same percentage for all conscientious objectors from January 1970 through June 1973, one can estimate that 29,300 individuals did not have to perform alternative service. As a consequence, it appears that some 46,000 were not certified as having fulfilled their apparent obligations. No other statistics can be found that bear upon this question. It should be noted that some local boards may simply have failed to reclassify individuals as I-W upon their completion of alternative service—but enough case examples of non-performance exist to suggest that many thousands may not have fulfilled this obligation.

[11]According to Clemency Board statistics, 13.4% of its civilian applicants had been convicted of failing to complete alternative service. Applying this percentage to the 8,750 convicted draft offenders shown in Figure 4, one gets the result shown. No statistics are available to indicate how many Selective Service complaints to the Department of Justice about nonperforming conscientious objectors did not result in convictions.

[12]Graduate student deferments were available only to students who had completed at least one year of graduate school by the end of the 1966–67 school year. In order for a graduate student deferment to be a means of escape from the draft, it was usually necessary to have one for three years (to take an individual beyond—or very close to —the age of 26). The statistic presented here assumes that the only male students who could have enjoyed this escape valve without later having to shift to other deferments

were those who completed law school between 1965 and 1969 or received Ph.D.s between 1965 and 1970. Excluding women, 69,000 law degrees and 115,000 Ph.D.s were issued during those years. See "Legal Education: A Time of Change," *American Bar Association Journal*, Volume 62, March 1967, and the *Statistical Abstract of the United States* (1973), Department of Commerce, Tables 217–18, pp. 136–37.

[13]Millions of men used college deferments to postpone their confrontations with the draft, but the only individuals who permanently escaped the draft through college deferments were students who entered college in the fall of 1969 and 1970 (the classes of 1973 and 1974) who did not have high lottery numbers or any other exemptions. Selective Service records indicate that a surprisingly small number had student deferments in December of 1972, the last month of the lottery. *Semi-Annual Report of the Director of Selective Service*, July–December, 1972, Table 1, p. 20.

[14]Prior to 1972, ministry students were accorded ministerial exemptions; thereafter, they received ministry student deferments. (See note 16 for the means of calculating their numbers.)

[15]The number of elected officials deferred from the draft to serve in state or national office fluctuated very little during the latter years of the war, indicating that the same 85 individuals may have benefited from this deferment throughout the war.

[16]To understand these occupational deferment calculations (and the alien and hardship calculations, notes 17 and 20), two points must be recognized. First, if an individual had a deferment or an exemption at age 26, he was almost never reclassified or removed from the rolls by his draft board until he reached age 35. (This was also true for those who received physical, mental, psychiatric, or moral exemptions.) Second, after June 30, 1970, draft boards began reclassifying individuals with high lottery numbers as I-H (holding classification), regardless of their earlier classifications. As a consequence, June 30, 1970, data is the most useful for calculating deferment or exemption totals. Also, on April 23, 1970, President Nixon issued an executive order preventing new occupational and dependency deferments—but the old ones still could be kept.

One can make an accurate estimate of the number of Vietnam generation individuals who avoided the draft through occupational deferments by subtracting the June 30, 1960, total from the June 30, 1970, total. This assumes that the typical occupational deferment was granted during the registrant's twenty-first year. Many individuals were granted occupational deferments only to lose them later, so the deferment did not provide them with an escape mechanism, but they would not be included in the above calculation unless they lost their deferments after June 30, 1970. Given the arrival of the lottery and the 1971 reconstitution of draft boards (which added to Selective Service's administrative burdens), it is unlikely that more than a few thousand occupational deferments were taken away after that date. For the official statistics, see the *Annual Report of the Director of Selective Service*, 1961, and the *Semi-Annual Report* for July–December, 1970, p. 7.

[17]This statistic reflects the difference between the alien exemptions on June 30, 1971 and on June 30, 1960. After mid-1970, aliens and most other registrants with high lottery numbers were reclassified I-H and could not be traced. The number of exempt aliens

might have exceeded 13,000, as some may have come to the United States, escaped the draft, and returned to their native country. See the *Annual Report of the Director of Selective Service*, 1959 and 1961, and the *Semi-Annual Report* for January–June 1970, Table 1, p. 18.

[18]The number of sole surviving sons exempted from the draft except during a congressionally declared war can be determined only for the years 1972–73, when a separate IV-G exemption was created for them. Before September 28, 1971, they were included with veterans of military service in class IV-A. The 1972–73 statistic may exclude some sole surviving sons with high lottery numbers who could have been reclassified I-H after June 30, 1970. For the most recent statistic, see the *Semi-Annual Report of the Director of Selective Service*, Table 1, p. 20.

[19]American citizens who were overseas on their eighteenth birthday and did not have a home address in the United States (e.g., were overseas military dependents), were exempt from induction from 1962 through July 1971, as long as they remained outside the United States. The exact size of this exempt group over time cannot be ascertained, but the overseas registrant draft board ("Draft Board 100" in Washington, D.C.) had 27,000 registrants in 1970. After the special exemption was removed, overseas registrants could apply for other deferments and exemptions, as well. The 20,000 statistic is a minimum tally, reflecting only the 10% who would have turned 26 between 1970 and 1971 and the 67% who would have had high lottery numbers once the exemption expired.

[20]Like the occupational deferment and alien statistics (notes 16 and 17), the hardship and dependency statistic is derived by subtracting June 30, 1970, data from June 30, 1960, data. Like occupational deferments (note 16), hardship deferments were often taken away; if so, they would not be included in the calculation shown here. Dependency deferments were almost never taken away, although they were granted with diminished frequency as the war years progressed. There is no data available to identify how many of these deferments were for hardship (economic deprivation, sole means of support) and how many were for dependency (marriage, fatherhood). After April 23, 1970, no new dependency deferments were given.

[21]All of these are derivative, calculated by adding or subtracting other displayed statistics from the appropriate base statistics.

Figure 3: Military Avoiders

[1]*Selected Manpower Statistics*, DOD-OASD (Comptroller), May 1975, pp. 39, 46, 61, and 108. The statistic is modified here to exclude women, persons of the wrong age, and persons who did not serve in the Vietnam era (as defined in these charts). Some of the era modifications resulted from estimates given by the DOD Directorate for Information, Operations, and Control, to enable the inclusion of July 1964 discharges and the exclusion of July–December 1973 accessions. Since these charts pertain to the male Vietnam generation only, most statistics shown here are smaller than total manpower statistics.

For example, the actual Vietnam-era military manpower total is about 10,300,000, (including reserves). Where applicable, the comparable total statistics are included below.

[2]*Ibid.*, p. 39, 46, and 61 (overall total: 9,025,000). As in note 1, some era modifications had to be made.

[3]*Ibid.*, pp. 39 and 61 (overall totals: 3,400,000 in Southeast Asia; 2,600,000 in Vietnam). It is assumed here that military personnel over 26 in 1964 served in Southeast Asia and Vietnam in percentages comparable to their overall proportion in the armed forces.

[4]*Selected Manpower Statistics,* p. 108. The tally covers July 1, 1964 through June 30, 1973.

[5]Binkin, *U.S. Reserve Forces,* pp. 80–81.

[6]No combat/noncombat statistics are available to cover the entire war period. In the Notre Dame survey, 75% of all Vietnam veterans answered "yes" to the question "Did you ever engage in combat in Vietnam?" The only other statistic available (Ambrose and Barber, *The Military and American Society,* p. 195) indicates that only 25% were in combat situations at any one time, without taking account of assignment rotations. That finding was made in 1967, early in the war.

[7]All casualty statistics come from *Selected Manpower Statistics,* p. 62. This includes 492 wounded in Vietnam before 1964, most of whom would have been part of the Vietnam generation as here defined. An unknown percentage of casualties was suffered by those in noncombat situations (e.g., from mortar or rocket attacks). Defense Department casualty statistics indicate that 90% of all deaths were suffered by men under 30, so—given some margin of error—it is assumed that about 90% of all injuries were suffered by the Vietnam generation.

[8]This includes 46,163 killed in action (*ibid.*, p. 62) and 10,081 who died of disease, accidents, and other nonhostile causes. Hearings before the Subcommittee on Courts, Civil Liberties, and the Administration of Justice (93d Cong., 2d Sess.), p. 340 (letter from Melvin Laird to Commander Soden). The 46,163 figure includes 120 killed before 1964, most of whom would have been part of the Vietnam generation, as here defined. Ninety percent of these 56,000 deaths, or a total of 51,000, are assumed to involve the Vietnam generation. See note 7.

[9]All of these are derivative, calculated by adding or subtracting other displayed statistics to or from the appropriate base statistics.

Figure 4: Evaders

[1]Henry Peterson, statement to Hearings before the House Subcommittee on Courts, Civil Liberties and the Administration of Justice (1974), p. 36. This statistic includes 25,382 complaints filed in the 1963 and 1964 fiscal years, assuming a two-year lag time

between violation and conviction. All but a very small fraction of these earlier defendants would have been of Vietnam-generation age—and, since draft offenses are typically considered continuing offenses by the courts, by mid-1964 they stood charged with draft offenses.

[2]"Federal Offenders in U.S. District Courts," Historical Offense Table 10: "Disposition of Defendants Charged with Violation of Selective Service Act," obtained from the Administrative Office of the U.S. Courts. Some recent (FY 1975) cases were added to these base statistics.

[3]These estimates resulted from personal conversations with Assistant U.S. Attorneys who prosecuted cases in New York City, Philadelphia, Richmond, Detroit, Milwaukee, Dallas, Los Angeles, and San Francisco. Conversations with prosecutors in Concord (N.H.), Boston, Pittsburgh, Madison (Wis.), Nashville, New Orleans, and Portland (Ore.) corroborated this overall range of responses, although they preferred not to make percentage estimates. While these estimates are imprecise, it should be noted that no jurisdiction—nor the Department of Justice, nor Selective Service—kept tallies on this question.

	Defective Cases	Acceptance of Induction	Number of Cases Dropped Between 1967 and 1970	Number of Apparently Defective Cases
New York City	25 %	75 %	5,688	1,422
Philadelphia	50	50	1,862	931
Richmond	50	50	885	443
Detroit	40	60	2,128	851
Milwaukee	90	10	359	323
Dallas	30	70	1,310	393
Los Angeles	80	20	11,884	9,507
San Francisco	60	40	3,584	2,150
			27,700	16,020

[4]The 47% failure rate at preinduction physical exams was the national average for FY 1967–73. Assistant U.S. Attorneys and draft counselors confirm that about half failed the exam as a way to avoid prosecution.

[5]Approximately 48% of military personnel on active duty went to Vietnam during the 1968–71 period when these individuals would have most often been in the service. See "Profile of DOD First-Term Enlisted Personnel Separated from Active Service During 1970 and 1971," DOD (M&RA), February 1972, Table 2.

[6]Extrapolations from the Presidential Clemency Board Survey of 472 civilian applicants, as described in Appendix C of the Board's final report. The sample included 12 convicted draft offenders who served in the military. Eight went to Vietnam (one of whom deserted in a combat situation), and 4 received bad discharges.

[7]Sentencing statistics are from "Federal Offenders in U.S. District Courts" data. Prison time data are extrapolated from the findings of the Clemency Board's survey of 472 civilian applicants, described in App. C of its final report. The sentences and the actual time served in prison do not correspond exactly, although—as the data indicate—the relationship is close.

[8]In January 1975, the Justice Department published the "Kennedy List" of 4,522 known fugitives; aside from nonregistrants, these were the only draft resisters who still faced charges.

[9]This is derivative, calculated by adding or subtracting other displayed statistics from the appropriate base statistics.

Figure 5: Military Offenders

[1]See Figure 3.

[2]Statistics from the Department of Defense (Office of Manpower and Reserve Affairs), November 15, 1976. Statistics are available only for FY 1967–73, so FY 1965–66 data is extrapolated from 1967 data. Also, Marine Corps data for FY 1967–69 is extrapolated from the average rate for the rest of the period. The exact numbers are calculated as 1,522,000 and 563,000, rounded here to reflect their inaccuracy. The latter statistic bears no direct relation to the number of less-than-Honorable discharges, which, by coincidence, is also 563,000.

[3]This includes 541,800 General, Undesirable, Bad Conduct, or Dishonorable Discharges given from July 1, 1964, through June 30, 1974. Discharges prior to July 1, 1974, are presumed to have been Vietnam-related, as they usually involved servicemen inducted or enlisted before the end of the war. It also includes 21,600 "Chapter 10" discharges given from July 1, 1974 through June 30, 1975, since the overwhelming majority of those cases involved AWOL or some other Vietnam-related behavior.

[4]This is, at best, a rough estimate based upon the Defense Department's belief that AWOL offenders accounted for about 83,000 of the 204,000 servicemen given Undesir-

able, Bad Conduct, or Dishonorable Discharges within the window period of the Ford clemency program. See Figure 9.

[5]This figure is also a rough estimate, based on information which the Defense Department gave the Presidential Clemency Board. That agency reported that approximately one-third of the 34,000 Bad Conduct and Dishonorable Discharges were for civilian-type crimes.

[6]Extrapolations from the Presidential Clemency Board's survey of 1,009 military applicants, described in Appendix C of the Board's final report.

[7]This data was supplied by the clerks of the U.S. Army, Navy, and Marine Corps judiciaries. The data include only court-martial convictions for this offense, and do not include Air Force cases (for which no data is available).

[8]All of these are derivative, calculated by adding or subtracting other displayed statistics to or from the appropriate base statistics.

Figure 6: Military Punishments

[1]See Figure 3.

[2]This tally includes all General, Undesirable, Bad Conduct, and Dishonorable Discharges for the period July 1, 1964, through June 30, 1974. Discharges "for the good of the service" are also included through June 30, 1975. See *Selected Manpower Statistics,* DOD-OASD (Comptroller), May 1975.

[3]An unpublished Defense Department analysis of MARDAC data indicates that the ratio of General Discharges to Honorable Discharges with bad "spins" is about 10:7; this suggests that about 200,000 veterans fall in the latter category.

[4]See note 2.

[5]No sampling has ever been published, but Defense Department officials involved in the Ford clemency program reported that approximately one-third of all punitive discharges were for civilian-type crimes. Almost all of the rest were for absence offenses.

[6]These are extrapolations based on the Clemency Board's survey of 1,009 military applicants, described in Appendix C of its final report.

[7]All of these are derivative, calculated by adding or subtracting other displayed statistics to or from the appropriate base statistics.

Figure 7: Exiles

[1]See Figure 5.

[2]See Figure 4.

[3]Statistics from the Ford clemency program suggest that only about 12% of all deserters and 15% of all draft resisters ever took flight. However, the circumstances of those

surveys indicate that the true proportion of fugitive deserters was somewhat higher. The best way of reconstructing the fugitive population is to identify the number who went to Canada and use that as a basis for extrapolation. In Tables 17 and 18 of Baskir and Strauss, *Reconciliation After Vietnam,* pp. 135–36, Canadian immigration data is juxtaposed to estimate a total of 30,000 American exiles in Canada. (Note two errata in Table 18: 6,605 should read 1,473, and 17,614 should read 12,482.) Of that total, 20,000 are thought to have been landed, and 10,000 nonlanded (illegal).

Ford clemency program data, reinforced by the observations of knowledgeable persons, suggest that the ratio of Canadian-based exiles to other exiles to fugitives in the American underground was about 3:1:1. This projection—which is very inexact—indicates that about 50,000 persons were fugitives, 40,000 in exile and 10,000 remaining in the United States. These same sources indicate about a 3:2 ratio of draft resisters to deserters. See *Reconciliation After Vietnam,* pp. 75, 89–90, and 119; the Clemency Board's final report, Chapter 3 and Appendix C; and Bell and Houston's report for the U.S. Army Research Institute, *The Vietnam Era Deserter* (1976).

[4]In September of 1972, the Swedish government tallied 660 American exiles in that country, 71% of whom were deserters. Informed persons consider that tally somewhat low, as it excludes illegal immigrants, deserters who were not American citizens, and a small number of post-1972 arrivals. One thousand seems a reasonable approximation. See *Amex-Canada* magazine, vol. 3, no. 5, p. 7.

[5]According to a 1971 Defense Department survey, almost identical proportions of deserters were in Mexico and Sweden. See *Amex,* vol. 3, no. 7, p. 50.

[6]These tallies were extrapolated from unpublished data obtained in the Clemency Board's survey of 472 civilian and 1,009 military applicants. See Appendix C of the Board's final report.

[7]This includes 1,000 applicants to the Clemency Board, 500 to the Defense Department phase, and 500 to the Justice Department phase. All are extrapolations from available data. See note 3.

[8]Prior to Carter's pardons, the available evidence suggests that there were 3,000 draft fugitives, 3,000 military fugitives (Vietnam-era only), and 5,000 expatriates. The overwhelming majority of these 11,000 persons were in exile. See Baskir and Strauss, *Reconciliation After Vietnam,* pp. 75–80 and 88–90. The number of expatriates was calculated through annual Canadian citizenship statistics provided by the Canadian embassy.

[9]All of these are derivative, calculated by adding or subtracting other displayed statistics from the appropriate base statistics.

Figure 8: Amnesty—Civilians

[1]These figures can be calculated from the findings of an *ad hoc* survey of more than 3,000 telephone inquiries received by civilian counselors after the release of the 4,522-

name Kennedy list. This survey learned that 85% of those not on the Kennedy list were also not on the 6,200-name list previously released by the Justice Department. This indicated that more than 11,000 individuals not on either list still thought that they faced prosecution—and that 13,000 had their cases permanently dropped with the release of the Kennedy list. See the *Military Law Reporter*, Nov.–Dec. 1974, 2 MLR 1083.

[2]See Figure 1.

[3]See Figure 4.

[4]These were individuals who could not reenter the United States even though no charges were brought against them. For a precise calculation, based on annual Canadian immigration statistics, see *Reconciliation After Vietnam*, Table 19, p. 137.

[5]See the Presidential Clemency Board's final report, p. xiii.

[6]These are composite statistics combining the Clemency Board and Justice Department phases of the Ford program. See *Reconciliation After Vietnam*, Chapter 3 and Table 21, pp. 27–48 and 139.

[7]Of the 4,522 individuals on the Kennedy list, 736 applied for clemency, about 3,000 remained fugitives, and an estimated 800 had their cases dropped by U.S. attorneys or dismissed by federal judges. No precise records were kept, so this estimate was based on conversations with defense counsel and prosecutors.

[8]See Note 4.

[9]This was an actual count taken at the time of President Carter's announcement.

[10]This included the 3,000 fugitives at large and the 538 applicants to the Justice Department phase of the Ford program who had not yet completed alternative service.

[11]This included the 8,750 convicted offenders, less the 1,600 pardoned through the Ford program. The latter were also pardoned by Carter, but received nothing new of any legal consequence.

[12]See Note 2.

[13]All of these are derivative, calculated by adding or subtracting other displayed statistics to or from the appropriate base statistics.

Figure 9: Amnesty—Military

[1]See Figure 6.

[2]This statistic is based upon informal but official estimates provided by the Defense Department to the Presidential Clemency Board. An insignificant percentage of these cases involved women or overage men. The Defense Department claimed that 83,000 men had AWOL-related discharges during the Vietnam era. Most were charged with AWOL (absence without official leave), but almost all had been administratively classified as deserters for being absent more than thirty days. See the Presidential Clemency Board's final report, Chapter 3 and Appendix C.

[3]This was the final count issued by the Defense Department in the fall of 1974. *Ibid.*, p. xiii.

[4]These tallies include all bad discharges through June 30, 1974, which are presumed to include draftees and draft-era enlistees, and all Undesirable Discharges "for the good of the service" through June 30, 1975, which are presumed to include Vietnam-era absentees. See *Selected Manpower Statistics,* DOD-OASD (Comptroller), May 1975.

[5]These are composite statistics combining the Clemency Board and Justice Department phases of the Ford program. See *Reconciliation After Vietnam,* Chapter 3 and Table 21, pp. 27–48 and 139.

[6]About 850 fugitives were discharged through normal channels during the Ford program, and another 1,650 in the eighteen months prior to Carter's inauguration.

[7]See Figure 6.

[8]See Note 4. Of this tally, approximately half are General Discharges.

[9]*Reconciliation After Vietnam,* pp. 88–90. Of the 10,115 fugitives at the start of the Ford program, 5,555 surrendered through that program, and about 2,500 surrendered through normal military channels. See note 6.

[10]Washington *Post,* October 5, 1977.

[11]All of these are derivative, calculated by adding or subtracting other displayed statistics to or from the appropriate base statistics.

BIBLIOGRAPHY

THE VIETNAM-ERA DRAFT

"Bald Case in Point: Pro Football's Magic Immunity," *Life*, lxi, December 9, 1966.

Canby, Steven L., *Military Manpower Procurement*, Rand Corporation Study. Lexington, Mass.: Lexington Books, 1972.

Chapman, Bruce K., *The Wrong Man in Uniform: Our Unfair and Obsolete Draft and How We Can Replace It*, New York: Trident Press, 1967.

Davis, James W., and Kenneth M. Dolbeare, *Little Groups of Neighbors: The Selective Service System*, Chicago: Markham Publishing, 1968.

Defense Manpower: The Keystone of National Security, Report to the President and the Congress by the Defense Manpower Commission, April 1976.

Draft Counselor's Newsletter, CCCO, San Francisco, California.

"The Draft: The Unjust vs. the Unwilling," *Newsweek*, lxvii, April 11, 1966.

Fallows, James, "What Did You Do in the Class War, Daddy," *Washington Monthly*, October 1975.

Gerhardt, Roger W., ed., *The Draft and Public Policy*, Columbus: Ohio State University Press, 1971.

In Pursuit of Equity: Who Serves When Not All Serve? Report of the National Advisory Commission on Selective Service, February 1967.

Kendall, David, and Leonard Ross, *The Lottery and the Draft: Where Do I Stand?* New York, Evanston, and London: Harper & Row, 1970.

Legal Aspects of Selective Service, Selective Service System, January 1, 1973.

Leinwand, Gerald, *The Draft*, New York: Pocket Books, 1970.

Little, Roger W., ed., *Selective Service and American Society*, New York: Russell Sage Foundation: 1969.

Lynn, Conrad J., *How to Stay Out of the Army: A Guide to Your Rights Under the Draft Law*, 2d ed., rev., New York and London: Grove Press, 1967.

Manchester, William, *The Glory and the Dream*, New York: Bantam Press, 1975.

Marmion, Harry A., *Selective Service: Conflict and Compromise*, New York: John Wiley & Sons, 1968.

Miller, James, III, et al., *Why the Draft: The Case for a Volunteer Army*, Baltimore: Penguin Books, 1966.

Morris, Mark, *Why Draft Repeal?* National Peace Literature Service, Philadelphia: American Friends Committee, 1970.

Notre Dame survey of 1,586 young men in Washington, D.C., South Bend, Indiana, and Ann Arbor, Michigan, who were of draft age during the Vietnam war.

One Third of a Nation, Report of the President's Task Force on Manpower Conservation, Washington: Government Printing Office, 1964.

O'Sullivan, John, and Alan M. Meckler, eds., *The Draft and Its Enemies: A Documentary History*, Urbana: University of Illinois Press, 1974.

Reeves, Thomas, and Karl Hess, *The End of the Draft*, New York: Random House, 1970.

"Riots, Songs, and Fishbowls, The Hullabaloo Is Old Hat to Mr. Hershey: America's Mr. Draft," *Life*, lix, August 20, 1965.

Sanders, Jacquin, *The Draft and the Vietnam War*, New York: Walker, 1966.

Selective Service Law Reporter, The Public Law Education Institute.

Semi-Annual Reports of the Director of Selective Service, Government Printing Office, 1965–1975.

Shapiro, Andrew O., and John M. Striker, *Mastering the Draft: A Comprehensive Guide for Solving Draft Problems*, Boston: Little, Brown and Company, 1970.

Strickland, Glenn W., *The Championship Debater's Complete Sourcebook on the Draft and Its Alternatives*, Inglewood, Colo.: Championship Debate Enterprises, 1968.

Suttler, David, *IV-F: A Guide to Draft Exemption*, New York: Grove Press, 1970.

Tatum, Arlo, and Joseph Tuchinsky, *Guide to the Draft*, Boston: Beacon Press, 1968.

Tax, Sol, ed., *The Draft: A Handbook of Facts and Alternatives*, Chicago: University of Chicago Press, 1967.

Wamsley, Gary L., *Selective Service and a Changing America*, Columbus, O.: Charles E. Merrill Publishing Co., 1969.

Willenz, June A., ed., *Dialogue on the Draft*, Report of the National Conference on the Draft, American Veterans Committee, Washington, D.C., 1966.

CIVILIAN OFFENDERS

"A Youth's Reason for Spurning the Draft—A Judge's Answer," *U.S. News and World Report,* June 8, 1970.

Brotsky, Allan, "Trial of a Conscientious Objector," pp. 98–115 in *The Relevant Lawyers,* edited by Ann Fagan Ginger, New York: Simon and Schuster, 1972.

Clemency Board survey of 472 convicted civilian offenders.

Collier, Peter, "The Unilateral Withdrawal of Private Weise," *Ramparts,* February 1970.

"The Demonstrators: Why? How Many?" *Newsweek,* lxvi, November 1, 1965.

"Ducking the Draft and Dodging the Cameras: Fathers and Sons Face Charges," *Life,* lix, April 15, 1966.

"Evading the Draft, Who, How and Why," *Life,* lxi, December 9, 1966.

Federal Offenders in United States District Courts, Administrative Office of the United States Courts, annual Selective Service violation statistics.

Ferber, Michael, and Staughton Lynd, *The Resistance,* Boston: Beacon Press, 1971.

Gaylin, Willard, *In the Service of Their Country,* New York: Grosset & Dunlap: 1970.

Gooding, Richard, "An Exile in My Own Country," *Look,* February 24, 1970.

Gutknecht, David, Peggy Naas, Scott Sanovik, and Dave Wood, *Check Out the Odds,* Minneapolis: Twin Cities Resistance, 1971.

Lynd, Alice, *We Won't Go,* Boston: Beacon Press, 1968.

Peacemaker magazine, Ernest Bromley, publisher, Cincinnati, Ohio.

Rohr, John A., *Prophets Without Honor: Public Policy and the Selective Conscientious Objector,* New York: Abingdon Press, 1971.

"Sentencing Selective Service Violators: A Judicial Wheel of Fortune," *Columbia Law Journal,* vol. 5, no. 2, August 1969.

Statistical Abstract of the United States, U.S. Department of Commerce, 1973.

Useem, Michael, *Conscription, Protest, and Social Conflict: The Life and Death of a Draft Resistance Movement,* New York: John Wiley & Sons, 1973.

THE VIETNAM-ERA MILITARY

Ambrose, Stephen E., and James A. Barber, Jr., eds., *The Military and American Society,* New York: Free Press, 1972.

Analysis of Casualties by Learning Abilities, U.S. Department of the Army, Personnel Office, June 28, 1968.

Bachman, Jerald G., and John D. Blair, *Soldiers, Sailors, and Civilians: The Military Mind and the All-Volunteer Force,* Ann Arbor: Institute of Social Research, University of Michigan, 1975.

Barnes, Peter, *Pawns,* New York: Warner Paperback Library, 1971.

Binkin, Martin, *U.S. Reserve Forces: The Problem of the Weekend Warrior,* Washington, D.C.: Brookings Institution, 1974.

Binkin, Martin, and John Johnston, *All Volunteer Armed Forces: Progress, Problems, and Prospects,* report prepared for the Senate Armed Services Committee, June 1, 1973.

Code of Federal Regulations: Pensions, Bonuses, and Veterans' Relief, Office of the Federal Register.

Cortright, David, *Soldiers in Revolt: The American Military Today,* New York: Anchor Press/Doubleday, 1975.

Emerson, Gloria, *Winners and Losers: American Stories—Battles, Retreats, Gains, Losses, and Ruins from a Long War,* New York: Random House, 1976.

Fiedler, Leslie, "Who Really Died in Vietnam?" *Saturday Review,* November 18, 1972.

Glass, Andrew, "Defense Report/Draftees Shoulder Burden of Fighting and Dying in Vietnam," *National Journal,* August 15, 1970.

Glick, Edward B., *Soldiers, Scholars and Society: The Social Impact of the American Military,* Palisades, Calif.: Goodyear Publishing, 1971.

Gray, J. Glenn, *The Warriors: Reflections on Men in Battle,* New York: Harcourt Brace, 1958.

Halstead, Fred, *GI's Speak Out Against the War,* New York: Pathfinder Press, 1970.

Hauser, William L., *America's Army in Crisis,* Baltimore: Johns Hopkins University Press, 1973.

Helmer, John, *Bringing the War Home: The American Soldier Before Vietnam and After,* New York: Free Press, 1974.

Hersh, Seymour, "The Decline and Near Fall of the U.S. Army," *Saturday Review,* November 18, 1972.

Janowitz, Morris, *The New Military,* New York: Russell Sage Foundation, 1971.

Johnson, Haynes, and George Wilson, *Army in Anguish,* New York: Pocket Books, 1971.

Just, Ward, *Military Men,* New York: Avon, 1970.

King, Edward L., *The Death of the Army: A Pre-Mortem,* New York: Saturday Review Press, 1972.

Lane, Mark, *Conversations with Americans,* New York: Simon and Schuster, 1970.

Lifton, Robert Jay, *Home from the War,* New York: Touchstone Books, Simon and Schuster, 1973.

Liston, Robert A., *Greeting: You Are Hereby Ordered for Induction,* New York: McGraw-Hill, 1970.

Loory, Stuart H., *Defeated: Inside America's Military Machine,* New York: Random House, 1973.

Mantell, David, and Mark Pilisuk, "Soldiers in and after Vietnam," *Journal of Social Issues,* vol. 31, no. 4, 1975.

Marginal Man and Military Service, Department of the Army, December 1965.

Moskos, Charles C., *The American Enlisted Man: The Rank and File in Today's Military,* New York: Russell Sage Foundation, 1970.

Polner, Murray, *No Victory Parades: The Return of the Vietnam Veteran,* New York: Holt, Rinehart & Winston, 1971.

Rideau, Wilbert, "Veterans Incarcerated," *Penthouse* magazine, April 1976.

Selected Manpower Statistics, Department of Defense, Office of the Comptroller.

Starr, Paul, *The Discarded Army: Veterans After Vietnam,* New York: Charterhouse, 1973.

Tauber, Peter, *The Sunshine Soldiers,* New York: Simon and Schuster, 1971.

The Vietnam Veteran in Contemporary Society, materials collected by Department of Medicine and Surgery, Veterans Administration, Washington, D.C., May 1972.

Walton, George, *The Tarnished Shield: A Report on Today's Army,* New York: Dodd, Mead, 1973.

Waterhouse, Carry G., and Marianne G. Wizard, *Turning the Guns Around: Notes on the GI Movement,* New York: Praeger Publishers, 1971.

MILITARY OFFENDERS

Bell, D. Bruce, and Thomas J. Houston, *The Vietnam Era Deserter: Characteristics of Unconvicted Army Deserters Participating in the Presidential Clemency Program,* U.S. Army Research Institute for the Behavioral and Social Sciences, July 1976.

Boulanger, Raymond P., "The Undesirable Veteran," *Commonweal,* September 21, 1973.

Clemency Board Survey of 1,009 discharged military offenders.

Ginzburg, Eli, *Breakdown and Recovery,* New York: Columbia University Press, 1950.

Ginzburg, Eli, *The Lost Divisions,* New York: Columbia University Press, 1950.

Ginzburg, Eli, *Patterns of Performance,* New York: Columbia University Press, 1950.

Lang, David, "AWOL," *The New Yorker,* October 21, 1972.

Linden, Eugene, "The Demoralization of an Army: Fragging and Other Withdrawal Symptoms," *Saturday Review,* January 8, 1972.

McCubbin, Hamilton I., et al., *Leadership and Situational Factors Related to AWOL: A Research Report,* U.S. Army Correctional Training Facility, Fort Riley, Kansas, 1971.

Musil, Robert K., "The Truth about Deserters," *The Nation,* April 16, 1973.

Shoultz, James C., Jr., MPC Commander, "Literature Review: Research on Military Offenders," *The AWOL Soldier: A Challenge to Leadership,* vol. 4, U.S. Army Correctional Training Facility, Fort Riley.

Treatment of Deserters from Military Service, Report of the Committee on Armed Services, U.S. Senate, March 11, 1969, 91st Cong., 1st Sess.

Woodstone, Norma Sue, *Up Against the War,* New York: Tower Publications, 1970.

MILITARY DISCIPLINE

Addlestone, David F., and Susan H. Hewman, *ACLU Practice Manual on Military Discharge Upgrading,* Military Rights Project of the ACLU Project on Amnesty, 1975.

Effron, Andrew, "Punishment of Enlisted Personnel Outside the UCMJ: A Statutory and Equal Protection Analysis of Military Discharge Policies," *Harvard Civil Liberties Law Review,* vol. 9, no. 2, March 1974.

Finn, James, *Conscience and Command,* New York: Random House, 1971.

Jones, Bradley, "The Gravity of Administrative Discharges: A Legal and Empirical Evaluation," *Military Law Review,* vol. 59, Winter 1973.

Military Law Reporter, Public Law Education Institute, Washington, D.C.

Moger, Homer E., Jr., *Justice and the Military,* Public Law Education Institute, 1972.

Prugh, George S., Major General, *Law at War,* Vietnam Studies, 1964–1973, Department of the Army, Washington, D.C., 1975.

Report of the Special Civilian Committee for the Study of the United States Army Confinement System, Department of Defense, 1970.

Report of the Task Force on the Administration of Military Justice, Department of Defense, 4 volumes, November 1, 1972.

Rivkin, Robert, *GI Rights and Army Justice: The Draftee's Guide to Military Life and Law,* New York: Grove Press, 1970.

Rogers, Capt. Richard M., "The USCMA and the Involuntary Volunteer: *United States v. Catlow,*" *The Army Lawyer,* July 1974.

The Search for Military Justice, Report of the NAACP Inquiry into the Problems of the Negro Servicemen in West Germany, 1971.

Sherman, Edward F., "The Civilianization of Military Law," in *With Justice for Some,* Bruce Wasserster and Mark J. Green, eds., Boston: Beacon Press, 1970.

Sherrill, Robert, *Military Justice Is to Justice As Military Music Is to Music,* New York: Harper & Row, 1970.

Willenz, June, *A Report on the Human Rights of the Man in Uniform,* American Veterans Committee, 1968.

EXILES AND EXPATRIATES

Alsop, Stewart, "The Need to Hate," *Newsweek,* July 27, 1970.

Amex-Canada, assorted volumes.

Annual Canadian citizenship and immigration statistics.

Emerick, Kenneth, *War Resisters in Canada,* Knox, Pa.: Knox Free Press, 1972.

Fleming, Karl, "America's Sad Young Exiles," *Newsweek,* February 15, 1971.

Franks, Lucinda, *Waiting Out a War,* New York: Coward, McCann, and Geoghegan, 1974.

Hayes, Thomas Lee, *American Deserters in Sweden,* New York: Associated Press, 1971.

Jones, Douglas, and David Raish, "American Deserters and Draft Evaders: Exile, Punishment, or Amnesty," *Harvard International Law Journal,* vol. 13, no. 1, Winter 1972.

Killmer, Richard, et al., *They Can't Go Home Again,* Philadelphia: United Church Press, 1971.

Levine, Saul V., M.D., "American Exiles in Canada: A Social and Psychological Follow-up," *Psychiatric Opinion,* vol. 11, November 1974.

Levine, Saul V., M.D., "Draft Dodgers: Coping with Stress, Adapting to Exile," *American Journal of Orthopsychiatry,* 42(3), April 1972.

Noell, Chuck, and Gary Wood, *We are All POW's,* Philadelphia: Fortress Press, 1975.

Polner, Murray, *When Can I Come Home? A Debate on Amnesty for Exiles, Anti-War Prisoners, and Others,* Garden City, N.Y.: Anchor Books, 1972.

Schiller, Lisa, and Joe LeBlanc, *Exiled,* undated pamphlet published by the Philadelphia Resistance.

Whitmore, Terry, *Memphis-Nam-Sweden,* New York: Doubleday, 1971.

Williams, Roger Neville, *The New Exiles: American War Resisters in Canada,* New York: Liveright Publishers, 1971.

THE AMNESTY DEBATE

Alexander, Shana, "Amnesty, Agony and Responsibility," *Newsweek*, March 19, 1973.

"Amnesty for the War Exiles?" *Newsweek*, January 17, 1972.

"Amnesty for Whom, and How Much," *The National Observer*, March 11, 1972.

Baskir, Lawrence M., and William A. Strauss, *Reconciliation After Vietnam*, South Bend, Ind.: University of Notre Dame Press, 1977.

Commager, Henry Steele, "The Case for Amnesty," *The New York Review of Books*, April 6, 1972.

Duscha, Julius, "Should There Be Amnesty for the War Resister?" *New York Times Magazine*, December 24, 1972.

Finn, James, "The Amnesty Issue," *Commonweal*, November 3, 1972.

Reston, James, Jr., "Reconciliation, Not Retribution—Universal Amnesty," *The New Republic*, February 5, 1972.

"Veterans, Deserters and Draft-Evaders—The Vietnam Decade," New York: Ford Foundation Issue Paper, 1974.

Wyatt, Michael K., "Making the Case for Congressional Amnesty," *The New Republic*, June 10, 1972.

PRESIDENT FORD'S CLEMENCY PROGRAM

After Action Report, Department of Defense, Implementation of President's Clemency Program, prepared by Office of the Deputy Chief of Staff for Personnel, Department of the Army, October 1975, 2 volumes.

Cowlishaw, Patrick R., "The Conditional Presidential Pardon," *Stanford Law Review*, November 1975.

"Limited Program, Limited Response," *Time*, September 30, 1974.

Maxfield, David M., "Clemency Program: Should It Be Extended?" *Congressional Quarterly*, September 20, 1975.

"Outlook for Amnesty," *Newsweek*, September 2, 1974.

Pearman, William A., "An Analysis of the Impact of Clemency Discharges on Recipients' Employment Opportunities," in *Report to the President*, Presidential Clemency Board, p. 403.

Reeves, Richard, *A Ford, Not a Lincoln,* New York and London: Harcourt Brace Jovanovich, 1975.

Report to the President, Presidential Clemency Board, GPO, 1975.

Report to the Service Secretaries by the Joint Alternative Service Board in Support of Presidential Proclamation 4313, Department of Defense, 1975.

CONGRESSIONAL HEARINGS AND REPORTS

90th Congress: Senate Armed Services: Amending and Extending the Draft Laws; April 12–19, 1967.

———: Senate Armed Services: Military Deserters; May 21 and 22, 1968.

91st Congress: House Armed Services Special Subcommittee on the Draft: To Amend Military Selective Service Act of 1967; September 30, 1969.

———: Senate Judiciary Subcommittee on Administrative Practice and Procedures: The Selective Service: Its Operation, Practices and Procedures; October–November, 1969.

———: House Armed Services Special Subcommittee on the Draft: Review of the Administration and Operation of the Draft Law; July 23, 1970.

———: House Armed Services Committee: Hearings and Special Reports on Subjects Affecting the Naval and Military Establishments; 1970.

92d Congress: House Armed Services: Hearings on H.R. 523, Administrative Discharges; June 2–8 and July 7, 1971.

———: House Appropriation Subcommittee: Department of Defense Appropriations for 1972—Morale and Discipline in the Army; September 23, 1971.

———: Senate Judiciary Subcommittee on Administrative Practice and Procedures: Selective Service and Amnesty; February 28–March 1, 1972.

———: Senate Subcommittee on Drug Abuse in the Military: Drug Abuse in the Military; February 29, 1972.

———: Senate Armed Services Subcommittee on the Volunteer Armed Force and Selective Service: Volunteer Armed Forces and Selective Service; March 10 and 13, 1972.

93d Congress: House Judiciary Subcommittee on Courts, Civil Liberties, and the Administration of Justice: Amnesty; March 8, 11, and 13, 1974.

———: Senate Judiciary Subcommittee on Administrative Practice and Procedures: Clemency Program Practices and Procedures; December 18 and 19, 1974.

94th Congress: House Judiciary Subcommittee on Courts, Civil Liberties, and the Administration of Justice: The Presidential Clemency Program; April 14, 17, and 18, 1975.

————: House Judiciary Subcommittee on Courts, Civil Liberties, and the Administration of Justice: report on the Presidential Clemency Program; August 1975.

————: Senate Committee to Study Governmental Operations With Respect to Intelligence Activities, *Intelligence Activities and the Rights of Americans;* April 1976.

95th Congress: King, William, "Achieving America's Goals: Rational Service or the All-Volunteer Armed Force?" report to the Senate Armed Services Committee, February 1977.

————: Senate Committee on Veterans' Affairs: "Eligibility for Veterans' Benefits Pursuant to Vietnam Era Discharge Upgrading," Report to accompany S. 1307, June 28, 1977.

INDEX

A NOTE ON THE TYPE

The text of this book was set via computer-driven cathode ray tube, called TIMES ROMAN, designed by STANLEY MORISON for *The Times* (London), and first introduced by that newspaper in 1932.

Among typographers and designers of the twentieth century, Stanley Morison has been a strong forming influence, as typographical adviser to the English Monotype Corporation, as a director of two distinguished English publishing houses, and as a writer of sensibility, erudition, and keen practical sense.

In 1930 Morison wrote: "Type design moves at the pace of the most conservative reader. The good designer, therefore realizes that, for a new fount to be successful, it has to be so good that only a very few recognise its novelty. If readers do not notice the consummate reticence and rare dicipline of a new type, it is probably a good letter." It is now generally recognized that in the creation of *Times Roman* Morison successfully met the qualifications of this theoretical doctrine.

Composed, printed and bound by The Haddon Craftsmen Inc., Scranton, Pennsylvania.

Design by Margaret M. Wagner